Guide to the

SPACE AGE

Guide to the

SPACE AGE

compiled and edited by

C. W. BESSERER

HAZEL C. BESSERER

PRENTICE-HALL, INC.
Englewood Cliffs, N. J., 1959

47,840
Sept. 1964

PREFACE

WITHIN the span of a few short years, space technology with its related fields of missilery and rocketry has become a sophisticated industry with a widespread interest not only to those individuals directly involved but to the general public as a whole.

As has been proved in the past, when a new technical area has come into being, or when there has been a combination of previously used technical disciplines with new technical developments, it inevitably becomes necessary to evolve a vocabulary to enhance the always complicated problem of communication; old terms either take on new meanings or they are placed in use by different groups to whom the meaning and usage is new and strange. Such is the case in the fields of missiles, rockets, and space flight.

So universal has the requirement for a language of space and weapon technology become, that within recent years many companies directly involved in the business have disseminated privately compiled "glossaries of terms" in an effort to acquaint individuals with the current terminology. Inevitably there follows divergence in the definitions of many terms.

In addition to use by technical and supporting personnel directly involved in the industry, the "jargon" has been adopted by newspapers, broadcasters, and telecasters in disseminating news, with resulting confusion of the public who, in general, lack the basic technical training and general knowledge for interpretation of what they read and hear.

Thus the purpose of this volume is twofold: (1) An effort at the standardization of the specialized language for all those areas generally associated with missiles and rockets (i.e., propulsion, guidance, control, aerodynamics, structures, electronics, meteorology, atmosphere, etc.); and (2) presentation of the language in a form easily understood by both technical and lay persons. Terms are definitive, authentic (hopefully), and as broad in scope as is permissible within the bounds of security. To the end of obtaining the broadest translations possible, every known and available source of information pertinent to the field(s) has been researched for inclusion of terms herein.

Toward improved and broadened standardization, the editors will welcome suggestions for additional terms, more precise and better definitions, and corrections to existing items.

Grateful appreciation is acknowledged to those companies and individuals, listed separately, for permission to extrapolate and utilize material; and to the Department of Defense for security review.

CARL W. BESSERER
HAZEL C. BESSERER
Los Angeles, California

SOURCES

We are extremely grateful to the following publications used as references and as source material. No attempt has been made to indicate the individual source of a definition. Many are extracted verbatim, but more have received substantial editing and rewriting; in a number of cases definitions from different sources have been combined. The editors take full responsibility for errors, inaccuracies, and omissions.

Particular attention is called to the following publications from which considerably more detail may be obtained. These sources were used liberally to provide the broad foundation of the Guide:

Missile Engineering Handbook, C. W. Besserer. D. Van Nostrand Co., Inc., 1958.
International Dictionary of Physics and Electronics, The; D. Van Nostrand Co., Inc., 1956.
The Space Encyclopedia, M. T. Bizony (ed.). E. P. Dutton and Co., Inc., 1958.
The United States Air Force Dictionary, W. A. Heflin (ed.). D. Van Nostrand Co., Inc., 1956.
Pictorial Microwave Dictionary, Victor J. Young and Meredith W. Jones. John R. Rider Publisher, Inc., 1956.

In addition, the following sources were used to a varying degree. All are considered authentic and authoritative.

Aircraft and Missile Manufacturing. Chilton Publishing Co.
Aircraft and Missile Propulsion, M. J. Zucrow. John Wiley and Sons, Inc., 1958.
Aircraft Gas Turbine Data Book. General Electric Corp., 1954.
Aircraft Gyroscopic Flight Instruments. Sperry Gyroscope Co., 1956.
Aircraft Materials and Processes, 5th ed., G. F. Titterton. Pitman Publishing Co., 1956.
Air Force Missile Test Center, Air Research and Development Command. Prepared and published by the Office of Information Services and Visual Presentations Branch, DCS/Comptroller.
ARDC Model Atmosphere, The. Air Force Cambridge Research Center, 1956.
Astronautics. Published by the American Rocket Society.
Aviation Age. Conover-Mast Publishing Co.
Aviation Week. McGraw-Hill Publishing Co.
Control Engineering. McGraw-Hill Publishing Co.
Control Engineer's Handbook, John G. Truxal (ed.). McGraw-Hill Book Co., Inc., 1958.
Delay Lines. ESC Corporation.
Design News. Rogers Publishing Co.
Dictionary of Astronomy and Astronautics, Armand Spitz and Frank Gaynor. Philosophical Library, Inc., 1959.
Dictionary of Electronic Terms, A, H. L. Van Velzer (ed.). Allied Radio Corp., 1953.
Dynamical Analogies, H. F. Olson. D. Van Nostrand and Co., Inc., 1958.
Dynamics of Machinery, J. B. Hartman. McGraw-Hill Book Co., Inc., 1956.

Electrical Manufacturing. Gage Publishing Co.

Electronics Design. Hayden Publishing Co.

Elements of Electronics, H. V. Hickey and W. M. Villines. McGraw-Hill Book Co., Inc., 1955.

Engineering Supersonic Aerodynamics, E. A. Bonney. McGraw-Hill Book Co., Inc., 1950.

Engineering and Technical Handbook, Donald C. McNeese and Albert L. Hoag. Prentice-Hall, Inc., 1957.

Engineer's Ramjet Primer, The. Curtiss-Wright Corp., Wright Aeronautical Division.

Exterior Ballistics of Rockets. Davis, Follin, and Blitzer. D. Van Nostrand Co., Inc., 1958.

Fundamentals of Aircraft Structures, M. V. Barton. Prentice-Hall, Inc., 1948.

Flight. 1957.

Gas Dynamics, A. B. Cambel and B. H. Jennings. McGraw-Hill Book Co., Inc., 1958.

Glossary of Guided Missile Terms. The Martin Co., Denver, Colorado, Oct., 1957.

Glossary of Operational Terms. Western Development Division/The Ramo-Wooldridge Corp., Los Angeles, Calif.

Glossary of Terms in Nuclear Science and Technology, ASA N1.1-1957. National Academy of Sciences. Published by the American Society of Mechanical Engineers, 1958.

Handbook of Chemistry and Physics. Chemical Rubber Co.

Handbook of Rockets and Guided Missiles, The, Norman J. Baurman. Perastadion Press, 1957.

Handbook of Space Flight, W. Proel and N. J. Bowman. Perastadion Press, 1950.

Handbook of Supersonic Aerodynamics. Department of the Navy, Bureau of Ordnance.

High Speed Aeronautics, A. Ferri, N. J. Hoff, and P. A. Libby. Brooklyn Polytechnic Institute, 1955.

Internal Constitution of the Earth, B. Gutenberg. Dover Press, 1951.

Introduction to the Theory of Error, Yardley Beers. Addison-Wesley Publishing Co., Inc., 1957.

I-T-E Circuit Breaker Co.

Jet Engine Manual, E. Mangham and A. Peace. Newnes, 1955.

Jet Propulsion. American Rocket Society.

"Key Guide to Outer Space," This Week Magazine, Joseph M. Chamberlain. Rand McNally & Co. and United Newspapers Magazine Corp., 1958.

Machine Design. Penton Publishing Co.

Materials and Methods, Materials in Design Engineering. Reinhold Publishing Corp.

Mechanical Engineering. Published by the American Society of Mechanical Engineers.

Mechanical Vibrations, 3rd ed., J. P. Den Hartog. McGraw-Hill Book Co., Inc., 1947.

Missiles and Rockets. American Aviation Publications.

Pocket Data for Rocket Engines. Bell Aircraft Corporation.

Principles of Guided Missile Design, Grayson Merrill (ed.). D. Van Nostrand Co., Inc.
  Vol. I: *Guidance,* A. S. Locke, 1955.
  Vol. II: *Aerodynamics, Propulsion, Structures and Design Practice,* E. A. Bonney, M. J. Zucrow, and C. W. Besserer, 1956.
  Vol. III: *Operations Research, Armament, Launching,* G. Merrill, H. Goldberg, and R. H. Helmholz, 1956.
  Vol. V: *Space Flight,* K. A. Ehricke.

Principles of Radar, J. F. Reintjes and G. T. Coate. McGraw-Hill Book Co., Inc., 1956.

Proceedings of the Conference on High-Speed Aeronautics, A. Ferri, N. J. Hoff, P. A. Libby (eds.). Brooklyn Polytechnic Institute, 1955.

Proceedings of the Third National Symposium on Reliability and Quality Control in Electronics. Sponsored by IRE, RETMA, AIEE, ASQC, Jan., 1957.

Product Engineering. McGraw-Hill Publishing Co., Inc.

Radar Pocket Book, R. S. H. Boulding. D. Van Nostrand Publishing Co., Inc., 1955.

Reference Data for Radio Engineers, 4th ed. International Telephone and Telegraph Corp., 1956.

Rocket Propulsion Elements, 2nd ed., George P. Sutton. John Wiley and Sons, Inc., 1957.

Solid Propellant Rockets, A. J. Zaehringer. American Rocket Co., 1955.

Space Weapons, Air Force Magazine. Published by the Air Force Association, March, 1958.

Specialties Handbook. Specialties, Inc.

Supersonic Inlet Diffusers and Introduction to Internal Aerodynamics, Dr. Rudolf Herman. Minneapolis-Honeywell Regulator Co., 1956.

Telemetry Standards. Inter-Range Instrumentation Group; White Sands Proving Grounds.

Theory and Application of FM/FM Telemetry, The. Bendix-Pacific Division, Bendix Aviation Corp., 1958.

Transistor Electronics, David Dewitt and Arthur L. Rossoff. McGraw-Hill Book Co., Inc., 1957.

Turbojet Fundamentals, Howard L. Morgan. McGraw-Hill Book Co., Inc., 1958.

U.S. Missile Market, The. Prepared and published by the Industrial Market Development Committee, Domestic Trade Department, Los Angeles Chamber of Commerce, March, 1958.

Vibration and Shock Isolation, Charles E. Crede. John Wiley and Sons, Inc., 1951.

HOW TO USE THE GUIDE

1. The material contained herein falls roughly into the following categories:
   (a) Basic technical terms directly related to the art (e.g., escape velocity; impedance matching; shock wave; etc.).
   (b) Terms in standard use, but peculiar to the fields of missiles, rockets, and space flight (e.g., mass ratio; beam rider; specific impulse; orbit; cislunar space; etc.).
   (c) Common and standard abbreviations and acronyms (e.g., SSM; PFRT; DEW; AFMTC; LOX; etc.).
   (d) Vernacular (or slang) of the trade (e.g., bird; beast; cookie-cutter; fizz-pot; five-by-five; crossing the trough; etc.).
   (e) Names and descriptions (within the limits of security) of missiles, rockets, and space satellites, probes, and ships (e.g., ATLAS; TALOS; MINUTEMAN; AEROBEE HI; SPUTNIK; EXPLORER; X-15).

2. In no case has any attempt been made to classify words as to parts of speech with the one exception that on occasion the word "to" is used to broaden the meaning of a word as a verb. Emphasis within the book is on standardization of definition rather than on the manner in which a word is used.

3. All terms have been listed in true and exact alphabetical order regardless of basic subject matter (e.g., antimissile missile will be listed in section *A* under "anti"; ballistic missile will be listed in section *B* under "ballistic"; contraorbit missile will be listed in section *C* under "contra").

4. However, for those prone to look for items under a "common" or "subject matter" name (e.g., missile) and to aid in discovering quickly the scope of a particular type term, there will be found throughout the book a broad system of cross indexing to direct the attention to a more extensive and complete definition. For example, directly following the definition for the basic term "missile" will be an entry which reads:

   missile. *Types of, see* antimissile–; ballistic–; contraorbit–; guided–; guided ballistic–; etc.

5. Abbreviations are interspersed in true alphabetical sequence with standard definitions. Where an abbreviation has an explanatory definition the reader is directed to the full term as follows:

   SAM. Surface-to-Air Missile (q.v.).

   The definition will then be given in alphabetical sequence as follows:

   surface-to-air missile.

6. The instruction (q.v.) will appear frequently within the context of a definition. This has reference to the item immediately preceding, and is indicative of an explanatory reference for the term used. For example:

abortive failure. A failure (q.v.) that judgment and experience indicate could result in a catastrophic failure (q.v.) of the entire weapon system.

In cases of this kind, those interested in pursuing a definition would then refer to definitions listed: *failure* and *catastrophic failure*. The abbreviation (q.q.v.) refers the reader to all the preceding related terms.

7. Quite frequently one term will have several meanings, in which case each meaning will be listed in numerical order: (1); (2); etc. Where one term has a specific meaning in a particular field, the definition will be classified thus: (1) In electronics, etc.; (2) In meteorology, etc.

8. Figures are inserted, in general, near the primary definition. However, the same figure number is used to illustrate a number of terms; hence, frequent direction to a figure located elsewhere (e.g., out of alphabetical sequence) in the book will be found.

Guide to the

SPACE AGE

A

A. Angstrom unit (q.v.).

AAM. Air-to-Air Missile (q.v.); a model designation (q.v.).

AAM-N-2. Navy Bureau of Aeronautics designation for the air-to-air guided missile termed SPARROW I (q.v.).

AAM-N-3. Military designation for the air-to-air guided missile termed SPARROW II (q.v.).

AAM-N-4. Navy Bureau of Aeronautics designation for the air-to-air guided missile termed SPARROW III (q.v.).

AAM-N-7. Navy designation for the air-to-air missile termed SIDEWINDER (q.v.).

abampere. A unit of electric measurement.

$$1 \text{ abampere} = 10 \text{ amp} = 2.998 \times 10^{10} \text{ statamp}$$

abcoulomb. A unit of electrical quantity measurement.

$$1 \text{ abcoulomb} = 0.00278 \text{ amp-hr} = 10 \text{ coulombs} = 2.998 \times 10^{10} \text{ stat-coulombs}$$

$$1 \text{ abcoulomb/sq cm} = 10 \text{ coulomb/sq cm}$$

aberration. The apparent shift forward of the light from the stars due to rotation of the Earth in its orbit. For those stars at right angles to the direction of the Earth's travel the maximum effect is 20.5 sec of arc.

abfarad. A unit of electrical capacity measurement.

$$1 \text{ abfarad} = 10^9 \text{ farads} = 10^{15} \text{ microfarads} = 8.988 \times 10^{20} \text{ statfarads}$$

abhenry. A unit of electrical inductance measurement.

$$1 \text{ abhenry} = 10^{-9} \text{ henry} = 0.001 \text{ microhenry} = 10^{-6} \text{ millihenry} = 1.113 \times 10^{-21} \text{ stathenry}$$

ABL. Allegany Ballistics Laboratory, Cumberland, Maryland. Solid propellant rocket development laboratories. Owned by Hercules Powder Co.

ablating nose cone. A reentry body (q.v.) of a ballistic missile (q.v.) which depends on controlled erosion of the nose cone to accomplish heat removal to permit reentry without performance degradation. *See* ablation.

ablation. A technique used in reentry bodies (q.v.) to absorb heat by removal of mass from the surface. A mass transfer method of surviving very large heat fluxes.

ABMA. Army Ballistic Missile Agency, Redstone, Alabama.

abohm. A unit of electrical resistance measurement.

$$1 \text{ abohm} = 10^{-15} \text{ megohm} = 0.001 \text{ microhm} = 10^{-9} \text{ ohm} = 1.113 \times 10^{-21} \text{ statohm}$$

abort (aborted). (Vernacular) Discontinuance of test.

abortion. (1) A kill (q.v.) which prevents enemy targets from proceeding with their tactical mission. (2) An unplanned termination of a missile mission.

abortive failure. A failure (q.v.) that judgment and experience indicate could result in a catastrophic failure (q.v.) of the entire weapon system (q.v.).

abort, weather. *See* weather abort.

absolute altimeter. An altimeter (q.v.) that registers the absolute altitude of an aircraft. It usually works on the principle of measuring the time for transmission and return of radio-frequency energy.

absolute altitude. Altitude with respect to the average surface of the Earth as differentiated from altitude with respect to sea level. Sometimes referred to as *geometric altitude*.

absolute angle of attack. The acute angle between the chord of an airfoil or of a body at any instant in flight and the chord of that airfoil or body at zero lift.

absolute ceiling. The maximum altitude above sea level at which an airborne missile can maintain horizontal flight in a standard atmosphere.

absolute delay. The time interval between the transmission of two synchronized radio or radar signals.

absolute error. An error expressed in dimensional numbers (e.g., a velocity error in ft/sec).

absolute humidity. The mass of water vapor present per unit volume of space; i.e., the density of water vapor, usually expressed in *grams per cubic meter* or *grains per cubic foot;* the actual amount, by weight, of water vapor in a given volume of space. Also termed *vapor concentration.*

absolute pressure. Pressure measured with zero equal to a perfect vacuum.

absolute pressure pickup. In telemetry, an end instrument which compares an unknown source of pressure with respect to zero pressure and translates this information into an analog quantity (e.g., change of inductance or resistance).

absolute temperature. A temperature expressed in terms of a scale beginning at absolute zero (q.v.). When Centigrade degrees are used, the scale is converted to the Kelvin scale (°K); when Fahrenheit degrees are used, the scale is converted to the Rankine scale (°R).
A degree Kelvin equals a degree Centigrade in range, therefore:

absolute temperature °K = °Centigrade temperature + 273.16

A degree Rankine equals a degree Fahrenheit in range, therefore:

absolute temperature °R = °Fahrenheit + 459.7

See also temperature conversion equations.

absolute velocity. The highest velocity theoretically attainable by any means whatsoever; i.e., the velocity of light (186,284 mi/sec).

absolute weapon. A theoretical weapon having the ultimate in destructive power.

absolute zero. The temperature at which all thermal motion or heat action ceases. This temperature is approximately −273.16°C or −459.7°F.

absorption. (1) The process whereby the kinetic energy of a particle is reduced while traversing a body. This loss of kinetic energy (of corpuscular radiation) is also referred to as *moderation, slowing,* or *stopping.* (2) The process whereby some or all of the energy of electromagnetic radiation is transferred to the body on which it is incident or which it traverses.

absorption spectra. Spectra which consist of dark lines, dark bands or a dark continuum placed over or above a bright background. They are caused by the absorption of light by a substance placed in front of a bright source. (e.g., the dark lines of the solar spectrum are pro-

duced by radiation from the deeper layers being absorbed in the cooler, outermost layers of the Sun). *See* spectroscopy.

abvolt. A unit of electromotive force measurement.

1 abvolt = 0.01 microvolt = 10^{-5} millivolt
= 3.336×10^{-11} statvolt = 10^{-8} volt

Ac. Acceptance number (q.v.).

AC. (1). Associated Contractor. (2). Alternating current.

acceleration. The time rate of change of velocity in either speed or direction.

longitudinal acceleration: forward and aft acceleration. Acceleration applied forward is positive.

lateral acceleration: angular acceleration about the yaw axis. Looking down the yaw axis, positive acceleration is clockwise.

vertical (normal) acceleration: angular acceleration about the pitch axis. From the left side of a vehicle, positive acceleration is clockwise.

roll acceleration: angular acceleration about the longitudinal axis. Looking forward, positive acceleration is clockwise.

See also physical units and constants.

acceleration. *Types of, see* amplitude–; Coriolis–; error–; lateral–; linear–; longitudinal–; net–; normal–; phantom–; roll–; vertical–.

acceleration blowout. Inadvertent loss of combustion in a turbojet engine incident to an attempted acceleration and overrich fuel mixture. Does not normally apply to engines using an acceleration control. Also termed *rich extinction; flameout.*

acceleration feedback. A sensing system in which acceleration of a body (e.g., missile) rather than velocity or position is used as a reference or signal source for a control system. May be used to eliminate effects of body bending or to maintain angles of attack at predetermined values.

acceleration of a body. Toward an attracting planet:

$$g = g_0 \frac{r_0^2}{r^2}$$

where g_0 = gravity at the surface; r_0 = radius of the planet; r = radius to point in question.

acceleration spectral density. A measure of the energy distribution in a complex wave.

$$ASD = \frac{g^2}{f} \quad \text{and} \quad g = \sqrt{\frac{1}{2} \Sigma A}$$

where ASD = intensity for 1 cycle of bandwidth; f = bandwidth, cps; g = root mean square gravity; A = max. amplitude of acceleration for each frequency in the bandwidth.

Also termed *power spectral density* (q.v.).

acceleration switching valve. A transfer valve in which the spool velocity is proportional to the error signal. The valve operates as a perfect integrator in a switching mode and controls actuator acceleration by means of modulation of the electronic multivibrator dwell time.

accelerator. In nuclear science, a device for imparting large kinetic energy to charged particles, such as electrons, protons, deuterons, and helium ions. Common types of accelerators are the *cyclotron, synchrotron, synchro-cyclotron, betatron, linear accelerator,* and *Van de Graaf electrostatic accelerator. See also* linear accelerator; mass accelerator.

accelerometer. A device used to measure acceleration, which, when integrated, will yield velocities or displacements (depending on the particular sensing elements and related networks). Accelerometers may sense angular or linear accelerations and usually have a high natural frequency.

accelerometer. *Types of, see* integrating–; pendulous gyroscope–; stopped–.

accelerometer matching. A method of aligning two remote reference systems (e.g., stabilized platforms) by comparing the outputs of identically oriented accelerometers while the two systems are experiencing the same motions.

acceptable environmental range test. Tests to determine the range of the environmental conditions in which an equipment can function properly.

acceptable quality level (AQL). A nominal value expressed in terms of per cent defective or defects per hundred units specified for a given group of defects of a product. It is a measure of quality or the fraction defective which will be accepted some preassigned percentage of the time, by a sampling plan. *Note:* Sampling plans may be indexed by other points on the curve, such as lot tolerance fraction defective. *See* operating characteristic curve for acceptance sampling plan (OC curve).

acceptable reliability level (ARL). The required level of reliability for a part, system, device, etc. It may be expressed in a variety of terms (e.g., number of failures allowable in 1000 hours of operating life).

acceptance number. The largest number of defectives (or defects) in the sample or samples under consideration that will not prevent the acceptance of the inspection lot.

acceptance tests. Factory tests made to establish degree of conformance to a specification to determine whether a component, system, missile, etc., should be accepted by the buyer.

accessory. A supplementary device, used in conjunction with an item of equipment or a system, contributing to the effectiveness thereof without extending or varying the basic function of the equipment (e.g., recording camera attachment, emergency power supply).

accessory power supply (APS). A self-powered device used to supply electrical and/or hydraulic power to accessory or other auxiliary equipment carried in a missile or aircraft. The same as *auxiliary power supply* (APS); *auxiliary power unit* (APU); or *accessory power unit* (APU).

accidental jamming. Jamming (q.v.) due to transmission by friendly equipment.

acclimatization. The functional and structural adjustments of the body when subjected to a change in climatic environment.

accumulator. (1) A reservoir that supplies a fluid under pressure when needed; short for "fuel accumulator" or "hydraulic accumulator." (2) In computer applications, a device which stores a number and which, on receipt of another number, adds it to the number already stored and then stores the sum.

accumulator, fuel. *See* fuel accumulator.

accuracy, control. *See* control accuracy.

accuracy in measurement. The degree of correctness with which a method of measuring yields the "true" value of a measured quantity. It is usually expressed in terms of error, the units being those of the measured quantity or the ratio (or per cent) of the error to the full scale or to the actual value (e.g., 1000 miles ±1 mile or ±0.1%).

acoustical capacitance. In an acoustical (sound) system, the potential energy associated with compression of a gas (increasing with gas compression and decreasing with expansion). The capacitance opposes a change in applied pressure. Analogous to compliance in a mechanical system and capacitance in an electrical system.

acoustical impedance. In an acoustical (sound) system, the value of the impedance of a portion of a concentrated system is obtained by multiplying the flux (volume velocity × area) and the pressure difference driving that portion. Analogous to impedance in electrical and mechanical systems.

acoustical inertance. In an acoustical (sound) system, the inertial energy, the acoustical element which opposes a change in volume current. Analogous to inductance in an electrical system and moment of inertia in a mechanical system.

acoustical reactance. In an acoustical (sound) system, a part (imaginary) of the characteristic acoustical impedance. Analogous to the reactance of an electrical system.

acoustical resistance. In an acoustical (sound) system, that part of the impedance responsible for dissipation of energy. Analogous to electrical resistance.

acoustical system. A system adapted for the transmission of sound and consisting of one or all of the following acoustical elements: acoustical resistance, inertance, capacitance (q.q.v.).

acoustic speed. The speed at which sound waves and small pressure disturbances are propagated in a fluid. Sonic speed (q.v.):

$$a = \sqrt{K/\rho}$$

where K = bulk modulus of a fluid, lb/sq ft; ρ = density, slug/ft.

acoustic velocity. *See* acoustic speed; sonic speed.

acoustomotive pressure. Sound pressure (q.v.).

acquisition radar. A radar used for early warning and identification of targets at long range. The range and position data are in turn passed on to fire control radars or to missile guidance radars.

acquisition, target. *See* target acquisition.

action. *Types of, see* derivative–; rate–.

action time. In solid rocket usage, the period of engine operation beginning when some percentage of thrust is reached and lasting until some other value is reached during decay (frequently taken as the burning period from the time 90% of average thrust is attained to the time during decay corresponding to 90% of average thrust).

activation. (1) Pertaining to preparation of equipment, such as a control section, for service use. *Reactivation* usually includes depreservation, reassembly (where required), and testing, to insure good operation in service. (2) In facilities usage, the time at which the facility can be utilized for its intended purpose (e.g., a launching stand can accept a missile for test).

activator. *Types of, see* engine hydraulic–; inertial–.

active filter. In electronics, a filter used for smoothing data. The time delay and/or phase lag introduced by such a low pass filter (q.v.) is cancelled by use of an identical "reciprocal" filter in the feedback circuit of the associated amplifier.

active electronic countermeasures. Electronic countermeasures (q.v.) involving actions of a nature such that their employment is detectable by the enemy.

active homing guidance. A system of homing guidance (q.v.) wherein the source for illuminating the target and the receiver are carried within the missile, as contrasted to the system which reacts to signals generated by a separate system not carried in the missile.

active jamming. The intentional, deliberate radiation or reradiation of electromagnetic energy with the object of impairing the use of a specific band of frequencies.

actual range. The horizontal distance that a vehicle travels from the moment of release until the moment of impact.

actuating signal ratio. The frequency response of the actuating signal for a control system to the reference input. Under linear conditions, this ratio is expressed:

$$\frac{E}{R} = \frac{1}{1 + GH}$$

where G = gain; H = feedback.

actuating system. One that supplies energy for the operation of mechanisms or equipments. Actuating systems include electrical, hydraulic, pneumatic, mechanical, and other methods of applying energy.

adaptation kit. The device needed to install and service a special component or system (e.g., warhead) in a missile, particularly where modernization or adaptation of an improved model is required. It includes structural fittings, fuze, safety and arming mechanism, test circuitry, etc.

adapter. Any device designed to adapt an object or objects to a particular fitting or use, e.g., a threaded bushing used to adapt a fuze to a projectile, or a fitting for an electric receptacle for use with a special plug.

adapter. *Types of, see* air–; launcher–; VHF homing–.

ADC. Air Defense Command.

ADCC. Air Defense Control Center.

Adcock antenna. A vertical antenna, transmitting only vertically polarized waves with low-angle radiation. Five Adcock antennas are utilized in an Adcock radio-range (q.v.) station, four for transmission of radio-range signals, and one for voice transmission or for signal transmission to a radio compass.

Adcock radio range. A radio range using Adcock antennas. The four-range transmitting antennas of an Adcock radio range are situated at the four corners of a square. A fifth antenna is located at the center of the square, utilizing a separate transmitter from the other four. Thus the Adcock radio range is a "simultaneous" type radio range; i.e., it can transmit radio-range signals and voice communications at the same time. Two of the antennas in an Adcock radio range transmit in code the letter "A," and the other two the letter "N," making four quadrants in this type of range, the northernmost and southernmost quadrants always being "N-quadrants," with the "A-quadrants" lying in easterly and westerly directions, alternating with the "N-quadrants." A graphic representation of the pattern of this type of radio range resembles a four-leaf clover. An "A-quadrant" or an "N-quadrant" is recognized by the signal appropriate to it. However, as each quadrant overlaps the quadrant adjacent to it, there are thus created four bisignal zones and four equisignal zones. Each bisignal zone has either the "A" or "N" signal predominating on each side of the equisignal zone, which is created where the two signals merge, and which is approximately 3° wide. The merging of the two signals in the equisignal zone produces a steady hum. A vehicle is on its course or "on the beam" when it is following any of the four equisignal zones radiating out from the radio-range station. The Adcock radio range is similar to the loop-type radio range (q.v.). Adcock ranges are designated in radio facility charts as *RA* (range, Adcock) for full-power ranges, *MRA* for medium power ranges.

ADDC. Air Defense Direction Center.

adder. In computing applications, a device which can form the sum of two or more numbers or quantities.

address. In computer applications, an expression, usually numerical, which designates a particular location in a storage or memory device, or other source or destination information.

adiabat. One of a series of diagonally parallel lines on an adiabatic chart (q.v.) showing graphically the cooling that takes place when a thermally insulated parcel of dry air rises vertically, or the heating that takes place when a parcel descends. Also termed an *adiabatic path*.

adiabat. *Types of, see* moist–; pseudoadiabat.

adiabatic change. A change in the temperature of the air or other gas due alone to a change in the pressure on the air or gas.

adiabatic chart. A diagram containing a series of diagonally parallel lines, termed *adiabats* or *adiabatic paths*, showing graphically the cooling which theoretically takes place in a series of thermally insulated parcels of ascending dry air, or the heating which theoretically takes place in a series of so insulated parcels of descending dry air.

adiabatic efficiency. The degree to which a change in state of a gas approaches an adiabatic (no change in energy) process.

ADIZ. Air Defense Identification Zone.

adjustable. Of a missile component, subject to being set or fixed in two or more positions. (An *adjustable* surface differs from a *movable* surface in that, once adjusted to a particular purpose, it is firm as though fixed.)

admittance. The reciprocal of impedance (q.v.).

admittance, indicial. *See* indicial admittance.

advection. A horizontal movement of air in the atmosphere.

advection fog. (1) A fog formed by the horizontal movement of air over a surface colder or warmer than the air. (2) A fog formed in one place and transported to another by a horizontal air movement.

ADW. Air Defense Warning.

ADWKP. Air Defense Warning Key Point.

AEC. Atomic Energy Commission.

AEDC. Arnold Engineering Development Center, Tullahoma, Tennessee. An Air Force installation, providing facilities for static testing and evaluating supersonic aircraft, guided missiles, and engines.

AEDD. Air Engineering Development Center.

Aeria. An ochre-colored "desert" region on Mars.

aeroballistic missile. A missile launched on a ballistic course with mid-course at altitudes and speeds which permit aerodynamic lift. *See* boost glide vehicle.

AEROBEE. Research rocket for atmospheric sounding. Army Signal Corps designation: XASR-SC-2. Used also by the Air Force and the Navy.

Length: 19 ft; diameter: 15 in.; weight of payload: 150 lb; range: 70 miles. Simple in design; contains no guiding equipment of any kind and depends entirely on arrow stability. A liquid propellant rocket, it is launched with the aid of a solid propellant booster from a 140-ft launching tower which can be tilted off vertical. The instrument-carrying compartments are sealed off and maintained at constant pressure during flight.

Prime Contractor: Aerojet-General Corp. Engine: Aerojet.

AEROBEE HI. Research rocket for atmospheric sounding. Air Force designation: AGUL-0113C. Navy designation: XRV-N-13.

An advanced version of the AEROBEE rocket. It is slightly larger than AEROBEE and can carry a payload of 200 lb to about 130 miles, or smaller loads to nearly 200 miles.

Prime Contractor: Aerojet-General Corp. Engine: Aerojet.

aerodynamic balanced surface. A control surface that is balanced when acted upon by aerodynamic forces.

aerodynamic center. A point on a cross section of a wing or rotor blade, through which the forces of drag and lift are acting, and about which the pitching moment coefficient is practically constant.

aerodynamic coefficients. A system of nondimensional coefficients used in aerodynamics. The system permits extrapolation of model data to full-scale designs, development of aids, etc.

Lift coeff. $C_L = L/qS$

Drag coeff. $C_D = D/qS$

Nussealt No. $= hD/k$

Reynolds No. $= \rho V L/\mu$

Prandtl No. $= c_p\mu/k$

Stanton No. $= k/c_p\mu = 1/Pr$

Moment coeff. $C_M = M/qS$

Force coeff. $C_F = F/qS$

where L = lift; D = drag; M = moment; F = force; q = dynamic pressure $- \frac{1}{2}\rho V^2$; S = a characteristic surface area; h = heat transfer coeff. Btu/sec/ft²/°F; r = temperature recovery factor; k = ratio of specific heats; ρ = density, slug/ft; μ = viscosity, slugs/ft sec; c_p = specific heat at constant pressure; V = velocity of gas-stream, ft/sec; L = characteristic length.

aerodynamic control. A control surface. So called because of the local aerodynamic forces created by its use.

aerodynamic damping. Resistance to motion of a missile caused by aerodynamic forces acting on the aerodynamic surfaces at a distance from the center of gravity incident to the pitching motion of the missile. The component of lateral velocity of such a surface, in combination with the velocity due to forward speed of the missile, produces an angle of attack which, in itself, provides a restoring moment.

aerodynamic drag. The retarding force acting on a body moving through air. At low speeds the air flow past a moving object is *streamline*, i.e., the layers of air near the body slip smoothly over one another; at high speeds turbulence sets in and the air eddies past the object. Various factors combine to give the total air resistance: skin form, interference, and wave drag.

aerodynamic forces and moments. The aerodynamic effects experienced by a missile in flight. They are functions of ambient atmospheric pressure, flight MACH number, and missile size and may be described by the following general relations:

Force $\quad F = C_F \cdot \frac{1}{2}\gamma\, pM^2S = C_FqS$

Moment $\quad m = C_m \cdot \frac{1}{2}\gamma\, pM^2Sd = C_mqSd$

where C_F and C_m = dimensionless coefficients; γ = ratio of specific heats for air = 1.40; $q = \frac{1}{2}\rho V^2$ = dynamic pressure; p = ambient pressure, lb/ft²; M = MACH number; S = representative area (usually wing planform or body cross section) ft²; d = representative linear dimension (usually wing mean aerodynamic chord or body diameter) ft.

aerodynamic heating. The structural heating caused by energy absorption from air at stagnation temperatures at the surface of the skin.

$$T_{\text{skin}} = T_0(1 + 0.18M^2)$$
$$T_0 = \text{initial temperature, °R}$$
$$M = \text{MACH number}$$

aerodynamic lifting surfaces. Missile surfaces which produce normal forces to overcome gravity or to execute a maneuver. For supersonic applications generally, of either the *double wedge, modified double wedge* (having a flat section for a certain portion of the chord length), or *biconvex* cross-sectional profile. The latter has a slight advantage in minimum drag and higher cross-sectional strength in addition to absence of sharp corners which affect flow conditions over the surface. The biconvex section also provides larger wedge angles at the leading and trailing edges, thus improving stiffness (and, hence, resistance to chordwise twisting moments) characteristics. Shock detachment, however, will occur at slightly lower angles of attack because of this increased leading-edge angle. The wedge sections have the advantage of simplicity of manufacture, particularly in solid (not built-up) sections.

aerodynamic loads. Those forces and moments which are produced solely by aerodynamic forces on the airframe.

aerodynamic report. A document covering the available detailed aerodynamic information pertinent to the design and operation of a missile. Data in this report are obtained from the results of theoretical calculations, wind tunnel and ballistic range tests, and, where possible, results of flight tests which may be available at the time the report is written and which apply to the design. The report contains the results of all analytical work carried out in obtaining the stability and control characteristics, that is, the stability derivatives and coefficients in terms of lists of these slopes and constants for various flight conditions. The overall aerodynamic operating characteristics of the design are shown. Such a report is usually broken down into divisions covering (a) the missile external aerodynamic characteristics; (b) the engine characteristics (in the case of ramjets or turbojets, but not with rockets); and (c) the overall performance characteristics.

aerodynamics. The branch of dynamics which treats of the motion of the air and other gases and of the forces acting on bodies in motion through air or on fixed bodies in a current of air (or other gases).

aerodynamic test vehicle. A flight test article designed specifically to obtain aerodynamic data. Most commonly used during the development phase of a missile program.

aerodynamic tolerances. Parametric boundaries which have adverse effects if exceeded. They include: (a) shape and thickness of wing and tail leading edges, principally as they affect drag; (b) thickness and shape of wing and tail trailing edge as they affect drag and hinge moments and, to a lesser extent, maximum lift characteristics; (c) wing and tail cross-sectional design, that is, camber, fairness, and smoothness of external surfaces, joints, and surface characteristics as they affect drag and hinge moments; (d) wing and tail planform tolerances as they affect lift and hinge moments; (e) leading edge radius of the diffuser inlet or "cookie cutter" (with a ramjet or turbojet inlet type of design) as it affects drag; (f) mating of the body sections affecting the angular alignment of the centerline of the two sections which, in turn, affects steering bias (trim) and aerodynamic loads; (g) mismating of adjoining body sections allowing portions of the aft section to protrude into the airstream or to lie below the surface with respect to the continuation of contour (and flow) from the forward surface; (h) alignment of aerodynamic surfaces with respect to each other and with respect to the body centerline as they affect steering roll bias, and aerodynamic loads.

aerodynamic turbine. A closed-cycle turbine (q.v.).

aerodyne. Any vehicle that derives its lift in flight chiefly from aerodynamic forces.

aeroelastic effects. Structural deformations due to aerodynamic forces. The magnitude of aeroelastic effects for any particular airframe configuration at a particular flight condition will depend on (a) the dynamic pressure, q; (b) the trim conditions (which are in turn affected by cg location and MACH number; (c) structural rigidity; and (d) normal acceleration. Aeroelastic effects are predominantly influenced by variations in dynamic pressure and may be expected to be most serious at low altitude and high MACH number.

aeroelasticity. The study of vehicle structures in which the interaction of elastic deformations in structural elements and the aerodynamic loadings upon these elements are used in structural design and in evaluating stability and control.

aerology. That branch of meteorology concerned with the study of the free air as noted by the use of such instruments as kites, balloons, and clouds.

aeromedical. Of or pertaining to aviation medicine as applied to diseases incident to flight in the atmosphere as distinguished from flight in or into space.

aeronautics. The science dealing with flight and travel. Sometimes arbitrarily assumed to include the regime from sea level to 200 kilometers (approximately 124 miles). *See* astronautics, cosmonautics.

aeropause. A layer in the upper atmosphere that marks the limit beyond which man has not yet penetrated. *See* altitude barrier.

aeropulse. A propulsive jet device producing thrust intermittently from intake of air, as distinct from water as in the hydropulse. *See* pulse-jet.

AEROSOUND. A variation of the AEROBEE (q.v.) sounding rocket.

Launched from an airplane in a vertical attitude. It has raised a 20-lb payload to more than 100 miles altitude using two stages.

aerospace. The regime in which airborne vehicles, ballistic missiles, space vehicles, satellites, and similar devices operate. It includes the atmospheric envelope and the space above.

aerostatics. A branch of physics concerned with the equilibrium of solid bodies immersed in gaseous fluids and with the equilibrium of gaseous fluids.

aerothermochemistry. The science of gas dynamics of a continuum, including consideration of fluid motion, thermal and chemical effects. Sometimes termed *aerothermodynamics.*

aero-thermodynamic-duct. Athodyd. *See* ramjet.

AEW. Airborne Early Warning. *See* airborne early warning radar.

AFAC. Air Force Armament Center; Eglin Air Force Base, Valparaiso, Florida.

AFC. Automatic Frequency Control (q.v.).

AFCRC. Air Force Cambridge Research Center; Laurence G. Hanscom Field, Bedford, Massachusetts. Conducts fundamental and applied research in electronics, geophysics, radiochemistry, and radio-biology for military applications.

AFFTC. Air Force Flight Test Center; Edwards Air Force Base, Edwards, California. Primary testing of new aircraft. Formerly Edwards Air Force Base.

AFMDC. Air Force Missile Development Center; Holloman Air Force Base, Alamagordo, New Mexico. Tests rockets and short range guided missiles, and does electronic and upper atmosphere research. Installations include: (a) several launching complexes; (b) 35,000-ft rocket sled track; (c) short deceleration track; (d) tracking stations; (e) rocket test stands (one having a million-pound thrust capacity).

AFMTC. Air Force Missile Test Center; Atlantic Missile Range, Cocoa, Florida. The ARDC long range test facility established to conduct tests on and launch guided missiles, controlled targets, drones, satellites, lunar and other probes for the Air Force, Army, and Navy. The range consists of the following stations: (1) Canaveral AAFB (launching site); (2) Jupiter AAFB; (3) Grand Bahama AAFB (152 nm); (4) Eleuthera AAFB (290 nm); (5) San Salvador AAFB (414 nm); (6) Mayaguana AAFB (544 nm); (7) Grand Turk AAFB (660 nm); (8) Dominican Republic AAFB (830 nm); (9) Mayaguez AAFB (955 nm); (10) St. Lucia AAFB (1400 nm); (11) Fern. De Noronha AAFB (3585 nm); (12) Ascension AAFB (4400 nm). Station 12 is at a range of about 4400 nautical miles, but tests can be conducted to a range of 5000 nautical miles.

AFOSR. Air Force Office of Scientific Research, Washington, D.C.

AFPO. Air Force Procurement Officer.

AFPR. Air Force Plant Representative.

AFPTRC. Air Force Personnel and Training Research Center; Lackland Air Force Base; San Antonio, Texas. Tests devices, methods, procedures, and policies for the selection, classification, assignment, and training of Air Force individuals, teams, and organizations.

AFSWC. Air Force Special Weapons Center; Kirtland Air Force Base, Albuquerque, New Mexico. Studies, designs, develops, and tests the best combinations of aircraft and nuclear weapons.

AFSWP. Air Force Special Weapons Project.

aft. At, near, or toward the rear of a vehicle or section of a vehicle.

afterburner. An auxiliary combustion chamber within, or attached to, the tailpipe of certain jet engines, in which hot unused oxygen of exhaust gases from fuel already burned is used to burn additional fuel and thus augment the temperature and density of the exhaust gases as they leave the tailpipe.

afterburning. (1) The characteristic of certain rocket motors to burn irregularly for some time after the main burning and thrust have ceased. (2) The process of fuel injection and combustion in the exhaust jet of a turbojet engine (after the turbine). (Reheating, tailpipe burning, post combustion, augmentation.)

A-G. Aerojet-General Corporation; Azusa, California.

AGARD. Advisory Group for Aeronautical Research and Development. An agency of NATO.

AGC. Automatic Gain Control (q.v.).

age hardening. A process of hardening an alloy by aging at room temperature or elevated temperatures which occurs only in alloys which are supersaturated solid solutions. The aging process, which increases hardness and strength while usually decreasing ductility, is associated with the precipitation of one or more phases which may or may not produce recognizable particles. Also termed *precipitation hardening.*

agent. *Types of, see* damage–; destructive–; fuze–.

AGM. Air-to-Ground Missile (q.v.); a model designation (q.v.).

agonic line. *See* isogonic line.

AGUL-0113C. Air Force designation for the research atmospheric sounding rocket termed AEROBEE HI (q.v.).

AI. Air Intercept radar (q.v.).

AIA. Aircraft Industries Association.

aided tracking. A system for tracking a moving object in azimuth, elevation, or range (or any combination of these) by means of a semiautomatic radar tracking mechanism. (The tracking mechanism requires some manual control.)

AIGS. All-Inertial Guidance System.

aim-bias. The error between the aiming point and the center of the dispersion area of missile trajectories.

aiming point. The theoretical impact point at which a missile is aimed.

air. *Types of, see* free–; polar–; polar continental–.

air adapter. A part in a centrifugal-flow jet engine that receives the air from the diffuser, increases the air pressure, and leads the air to a combustion chamber.

air bearing gyroscope. One in which the sensitive element is supported on a gas (i.e., air) to reduce the output axis torque.

airborne commutator. Commutator switch (q.v.).

airborne early warning radar. An early warning radar set or system especially designed to be carried by aircraft, the radar signals being relayed from the aircraft to surface stations. Especially used as a part of the radar network used for early warning of approaching enemy aircraft.

airborne gate. An electronic device that maintains information pulse width within prescribed specifications.

airborne guidance system. *See* onboard guidance system.

airborne instrumentation. The complete measuring, transmitting, and receiving apparatus that is part of, and flies with, a missile.

airborne interception radar. A kind of specially designed radar normally carried by interceptors for locating hostile aircraft. Frequently a part of the fire control system.

air breakup. Destruction of a high-altitude or reentry research vehicle by aerodynamic forces on its reentry into the atmosphere; on certain research vehicles done to reduce the impact velocity and to aid in the recovery of records and instruments.

air-breathing engine. An engine that uses or takes in air from the outside to oxidize its fuel,

(e.g., turbojet engine, ramjet engine). Distinguish from a rocket motor or rocket engine.

air-breathing jet. A generic term for engines that operate by taking in air and ejecting it as a high-speed jet.

airburst. (1) An explosion in the air; a bomb explosion above the surface, as distinguished from an explosion on contact with the surface or after penetration. (2) The explosion of a nuclear weapon in the air, above land or water, at a height greater than the maximum radius of the fireball.

airburst fuze. Any fuze designed to set off an explosion in mid-air (e.g., proximity fuze, time fuze).

aircraft, pilotless. *See* pilotless aircraft.

aircraft rocket. A rocket missile specially designed to be carried by, and launched from, an airplane.

aircraft rocket launcher. A device attached to an aircraft for holding and launching offensive aircraft rockets.

aircraft rocket launcher. *Types of, see* displacement–; drop–; full automatic–; post–; rail–; semiautomatic–; tree–; tubular–.

air defense system. A weapon system whose mission is to defend a target complex from air attack; usually includes an early warning radar and ground observer network, interceptors, surface-to-air guided missiles, rockets, and conventional AA guns.

air density. The ratio of the mass of air to its volume, expressed as its weight per unit of volume (e.g., kilograms per cubic meter).

airfoil. A surface or body, especially designed to obtain a reaction (e.g., lift) from the air through which it moves.

airfoil. *Types of, see* biconvex (section)–; double wedge (section)–; laminar flow–; modified double wedge (section)–.

airfoil section. A cross section of an airfoil, taken at right angles to its longitudinal axis at any given point.

airframe. The assembled principal structural and aerodynamic components of a vehicle, less propulsion system, control and guidance equipments, and payload. The airframe usually includes only the primary structure, that is, the space frame on which is mounted equipment.

airglow. Radiation arising in the upper atmosphere from recombination of dissociated molecules and ionized molecules and atoms after they have been affected by solar radiation. In the daytime it keeps the sky light even at heights of fifty miles, while at night it limits photographic exposures at astronomical observatories. Perfect blackness of the sky is not obtained even when the moon is not in the night sky. Some of the remaining light (about one-sixth) comes from the stars and nebulae, and from interplanetary materials reflecting the solar rays. But a large proportion of the total arises within the Earth's atmosphere itself. During the daytime the solar rays dissociate molecules and ionize atoms in the upper atmosphere. At night the energy absorbed by these processes is released, and some of it appears as visible light, thus giving rise to the airglow. Airglow limits the faintest objects which can be photographed from terrestrial observatories, and this can be overcome only by establishing observatories beyond the atmosphere.

air intercept radar (AI). An interceptor-borne radar which normally permits search for, acquisition and tracking of, a target, and control of an air-to-air or air-to-ground guided missile.

air-launched. A rocket, missile, or space vehicle launched, or designed to be launched, from an aircraft in flight.

air logistics. That part of logistics (q.v.) that maintains the Air Force, as distinguished from the logistics provided the other military services.

air mass. A large body of air within the atmosphere having approximately uniform temperature and moisture characteristics throughout in a horizontal direction. An air mass derives its original properties from the surface over which it forms. A *polar air mass* is formed in a cold northern region; a *tropical air mass* is formed in a region in or near the tropics.

air mass fog. Any fog occurring in an air mass, in which the principal factor for formation is cooling of the air to its dew point (q.v.), caused by advection (q.v.), or by radiation, or both.

air-mass thunderstorm. Any thunderstorm occurring within an air mass, as distinguished from a *frontal thunderstorm* (q.v.).

air materiel area (AMA). (1) Any one of the several areas of the U.S. set up by the Air Materiel Command for expediting Air Force maintenance and the supply of Air Force organizations and installations within those areas. (2) The organization that operates any of these areas under the Air Materiel Command, comparable in echelon to a numbered Air Force. Air materiel areas operate in a western zone and an eastern zone.

Air Materiel Command (AMC). A major command of the Air Force that provides logistic support to the United States Air Force. The Air Materiel Command's mission of logistic support includes (a) contracting; (b) procurement and industrial planning; (c) supply and maintenance.

air mile. A nautical mile (q.v.) by air.

air pocket. (Vernacular) An airspace characterized by strong current flow which, when entered or encountered by a vehicle, causes it suddenly to rise or drop.

air pressure fuze. A barometric fuze (q.v.).

air pressure, static. *See* static air pressure.

Air Proving Ground Command (APGC). A command of the Air Force whose work is related to that of ARDC in that it determines the operational suitability of aircraft, materiel, and equipment used or proposed for use by the Air Force, except for atomic weapons and their specialized equipment.

air resistance. *See* aerodynamic drag.

air sounding. The action of measuring or determining atmospheric pressure, humidity, etc., by means of instruments carried or sent aloft; a measurement, graph, or record resulting from this action.

air specific impulse. A figure of merit for a jet engine expressed as pounds of thrust per pound of fuel consumed each second; the ratio of the critical stream thrust (at $M = 1$) to the air mass flow.

$$I_{sp} = \frac{1}{g}(V_j - V) = \frac{V_j}{g}(1 - \mathbf{V})$$

where $\mathbf{V} = V/V_j$; $V_j =$ exhaust velocity; $V =$ vehicle velocity; $g =$ acceleration of gravity.

airspeed boom (pitot boom). A pole extending from a wing into the airflow, in which instruments are located for measuring air pressures used to compute speed. Used especially in flight-testing.

airspeed, equivalent. *See* equivalent airspeed.

airspeed head. Any instrument or device, usually a pitot-static tube, mounted on a missile for receiving the static and dynamic pressures of the air used to compute speed.

air surveillance. A surveillance (q.v.) conducted above ground with a standard L-band radar having a surface range of about 180 miles against large targets.

air target material. Those materials (e.g., photographs, charts, mosaics, intelligence digests, radar navigation guides, weather reports, etc.) prepared for the planning, training, or conduct of operations against one or more specific targets.

air-to-air missile (AAM). A guided missile which can be launched from one aircraft against another. Passive or active guidance may be used. Usually named for birds (e.g., FALCON, SPARROW). *See* guided missile; model designation.

air-to-ground missile (AGM). A guided missile with or without a propulsion system which can be launched from an aircraft against a surface target. Categories include air-to-ground and air-to-underwater types. Types include: BULL PUP, HOUND DOG, RASCAL. *See* guided missile; model designation.

air-to-surface missile (ASM). *See* air-to-ground missile; guided missile; model designation.

air vector. In air navigation, a vector representing the true heading and true airspeed of an aircraft, and forming a part of the wind triangle.

air warfare system. The integrated total of weapon and support systems and operational support equipment peculiar to or employed in the performance of a designation mission of a major operational command. There are three air warfare systems: *strategic, defense,* and *tactical.*

AJ11-6. Designation for the Air Force version of the research atmospheric sounding rocket AEROBEE HI (q.v.).

AJ11-18. Designation for the Navy version of the research atmospheric sounding rocket AEROBEE HI (q.v.).

A-kill. *See* kill.

Alaska time. *See* standard time.

albedo. The fraction of the total incident sunlight which is reflected back in all directions by a planet, satellite, or asteroid, or any part of their surfaces. Albedos observed astronomically may be compared with those of known substances measured in the laboratory, and can give valuable clues as to the nature of the surfaces of the celestial body. Some typical albedos are:

Moon	0.07
Mars	0.15
Venus	0.59
Asteroids	0.1 (approx.)

ALBM. Air-launched ballistic missile, WS138A. Objective is to extend usefulness of B-47, B-52, and B-58 aircraft by providing an increased range for the missiles carried by the aircraft. Systems Engineering and Prime Contractor: Douglas Aircraft Co.

alcu. Altocumulus cloud (q.v.).

align. In radio and electronics, the process of lining up or adjusting of two or more resonant circuits, so they will give satisfactory response to a given frequency.

alignment station. A ground-based structure housing the equipment required to align an inertially guided missile to its proper azimuth (q.v.). It provides proper coordinate data and reference axes for the gyroscope stabilized platform (q.v.).

allowable flutter speed. A speed above maximum expected operation speed at which flutter (q.v.) may occur. (Good practice indicates that flutter speed should exceed maximum operation speed by at least 25 per cent.)

allowable stress. If a member is so designed that the maximum stress, as calculated for the expected conditions of service, is less than some certain value, the member will have a proper margin of security against damage or failure. This certain value is the allowable stress, of the kind, and for the material and conditions of service, in question. The allowable stress is less than the damaging stress, to allow for non-uniformity of material and inaccuracy of stress analysis. The margin between the allowable stress and the damaging stress may be reduced in proportion to the certainty with which the conditions of service are known, the intrinsic reliability of the material, the accuracy with which the stress produced by the loading can be calculated, and the degree to which failure is unattended by danger or loss.

allways fuze. An impact fuze designed to function regardless of the direction in which it makes contact with the target.

Alpha 57-1. A code system established for identifying Earth satellites and components. Alpha 57-1 is the Russian SPUTNIK I rocket vehicle, Alpha 57-2 the SPUTNIK satellite body, and Alpha 57-3 the protective nose cone designation. See Table 6, page 245.

Alpha 58-1. The official code identification for EXPLORER (q.v.), the first Earth satellite to be launched successfully in 1958. See Table 6, page 245.

alphabet. *Types of, see* Greek–; ICAO phonetic–; military phonetic–.

ALPHA DRACO. An aeroballistic test vehicle designed, fabricated, and tested by MacDonnell Aircraft.

alpha gain. For transistors, the ratio of the change in collector current to the change in emitter current with collector and base voltages held constant; designated by the symbol α.

alpha hinge. A drag hinge.

alpha particle. A helium nucleus consisting of two protons and two neutrons, with a double positive charge. The alpha particle has great ionizing power but very little penetrating power and is dangerous to living tissue.

altigraph. An altimeter (q.v.) that records its readings on a graph.

altimeter. An instrument for indicating altitude above or below a given datum point, usually the ground or sea level. The most common form is based on the variation of atmospheric pressure with altitude; others are radio and radar.

altimeter. *Types of, see* absolute–; pressure–; pulsed–; radar–.

altimeter-calibration standard pressure. An altitude-pressure table computed from the NACA standard atmosphere, and used in calibrating aeronautic instruments.

altitude. *Types of, see* absolute–; angular–; arming–; base–; bombing–; celestial–; circle of equal–; critical–; density–; design–; equivalent–; high–; medium–; pressure–; simulated–; tabulated–; true–.

altitude barrier. (1) The upper limit in the atmosphere beyond which the oxygen supply is insufficient for power plants using oxygen, or the air is too thin to react upon the surfaces of a vehicle. (2) The aeropause (q.v.).

altitude circle. Any circle on the celestial sphere parallel to the celestial horizon.

altitude correction. An altimeter (q.v.) correction made for a non-standard atmosphere.

altitude (max.) for rocket propelled missiles. The maximum altitude attainable by a vertically fired rocket:

$$h_p = g(I_{sp})^2 \left[\frac{(\log N)^2}{2} - \frac{1}{A} \left(\log N - \frac{N-1}{N} \right) \right]$$

where g = acceleration of gravity, ft/sec^2; I_{sp} = specific impulse, sec; N = loaded weight/empty weight = W_0/W_e; $A = F/W_0$ = initial acceleration; F = thrust.

altitude intercept. A celestial intercept (q.v.).

altitude, relative distances (arbitrary scale).

Minimum altitude	0 to 2000 ft above the surface
Low altitude	2000 to 5000 ft above the surface
Medium altitude	5000 to 13,500 ft above the surface
High altitude	13,500 to 18,000 ft above the surface
Maximum altitude	from 18,000 ft upward

altocumulus cloud. In meteorology, a billowed cloud of small cumuli (*see* cumulus) which generally forms in layers. It is composed of water droplets, although it may lie either above or below the freezing level. It is a middle-level cloud. Altocumulus clouds cast shadows and range in color from pure white to nearly black. In general, they are whitish with darker shadows. "Mackerel sky" is an appropriate description for many altocumulus bands.

altostratus cloud. In meteorology, a translucent to opaque cloud composed of water droplets through thin layers of which the Sun or Moon might appear as seen on a ground-glass screen. It is a middle-level cloud in contrast to the high cirrus forms, but may lie either above or below the freezing level. Very frequently, the top part of a layer of altostratus is a cirrus-type cloud, although this is not observable from below. Altostratus clouds following cirrus and cirrostratus are an almost certain indication that a cyclonic disturbance is approaching.

aluminum borohydride [Al(BH$_4$)$_3$]. A liquid rocket propellant *fuel*. See Table 3, page 157.

AM. Amplitude Modulation (q.v.).

AMATC. Air Materiel Armament Test Center.

ambient fuze. A type of proximity fuze (q.v.) which is not activated as a consequence of actual determination of target presence but by measurement of a parameter associated with the environment in which the target is normally found.

AMC. Air Materiel Command (q.v.); Wright-Patterson Air Force Base; Dayton, Ohio.

American Rocket Society (ARS). Founded in 1930 as the "American Interplanetary Society"; has devoted itself to the development of propulsion methods and more recently to the science of guided missiles and space flight problems. ARS publishes *Jet Propulsion* and *Astronautics*.

AMF. American Machine and Foundry Company.

amine-boranes (R$_3$NBH$_3$). High energy liquid or solid rocket propellant *fuels*. A boron derivative.

ammonia (NH$_3$). A liquid rocket propellant *fuel*. See Table 3, page 157.

ammonium nitrate (NH$_4$NO$_3$). A solid rocket propellant inorganic *oxidizer* with 20% available oxygen. Very inexpensive and readily available. See Table 5, page 214.

ammonium perchlorate (NH$_4$ClO$_4$). A solid rocket propellant *oxidizer* with 25% available oxygen. See Table 5, page 214.

AMPCO. Associated Missile Products Company; a division of Marquardt Aircraft Co.

ampere. The unit of the rate of flow of an electric current. A current of one ampere, when passed through a solution of silver nitrate in water, deposits silver at the rate of 0.001118 gram per sec. An ampere is equal to the flow of a quantity of electricity sufficient to transfer one coulomb of charge per sec.

> 1 ampere = 0.1 abampere = 2.998 × 10⁹ stat-amperes
> 1 ampere-hour = 360 abcoulombs = 3600 coulombs = 0.0373 faraday = 1.080 × 10¹³ statcoulombs
> 1 ampere/sq cm = 0.1 abampere/sq cm = 2.998 × 10⁹ statamperes/sq cm = 6.452 amperes/sq in.
> 1 ampere/sq in. = 0.0155 abampere/sq cm = 0.155 ampere/sq cm = 4.647 × 10⁸ statamperes/sq cm

amplidyne. A rotary magnetic or dynamo-electric amplifying device frequently used in servomechanism and control applications because of its high power gain. A single-stage device with a high degree of positive feedback.

amplification factor. (1) The ratio of the output to the input of any device whose purpose is to amplify a signal or power source. (2) The ratio between the response of an object flexibly supported by a structure which is subjected to a force applied over a short period of time (e.g., to a shock) and the response the object would have if the same force were applied very slowly. Response may be measured in terms of *force, load, displacement, acceleration,* or other convenient units. Amplification is greatest when the duration of the force application corresponds to the resonant frequency of the object.

amplifier. A device for increasing the power or strength of anything (e.g., that of a radio signal).

amplifier. *Types of, see* autopilot–; buffer–; compensated–; control–; information–; linear–; logarithmic–; paraphase–; push-pull–; quantum-mechanical–; vacuum tube–; video–.

amplitude. A measure of the magnitude of maximum deviation from a "rest condition." Amplitude may be expressed either in a positive or a negative direction for force, displacement, velocity, or acceleration. For sinusoidal motion the amplitudes are one-half the peak-to-peak values. (1) In mechanics, the extent of a vibration. (2) In electricity, the maximum variation of departure from the average of an alternating

current. (3) In electronics, the greatest value of an alternating radio wave (or the like) in one direction, measured from zero.

amplitude. *Types of, see* double–; peak-to-peak–.

amplitude acceleration. Amplitude expressed in terms of the acceleration inherent in the change of direction of motion of a particle vibrating at a given amplitude and frequency. For a sinusoidal motion, this relation is:

$$a = A(2\pi)^2 f^2$$

where a = acceleration, distance-time units; A = amplitude, linear units; f = frequency, cps.

Dividing both sides of the equation by the acceleration of gravity, the acceleration in g's is approximated by:

$$g = 0.1 \frac{A}{2} f^2$$

if the amplitude is measured in inches.

amplitude distortion. *See* harmonic distortion.

amplitude-modulated transmitter. A transmitter which transmits an amplitude-modulated wave. In most amplitude-modulated transmitters, the carrier frequency is stabilized.

amplitude modulation (AM). A method of modulating a radio-frequency carrier by causing the amplitude of the carrier to vary above and below its quiescent value in accordance with the audio or other signal to be transmitted. The frequency of the carrier remains constant.

AMR. Atlantic Missile Range (q.v.).

AMS. Army Map Service.

AMTI. Airborne Moving Target Indicator.

AN. Army-Navy.

ANA. Army-Navy-Aeronautical.

anabatic wind. In meteorology, a wind blowing uphill. In general, anabatic winds refer to winds originating in connection with surface heating, such as a breeze blowing up a valley when the Sun warms the ground. *See also* winds.

analog. The representation of one system in terms of the characteristics of another (e.g., electrical circuits can be used to represent mechanical or acoustical systems).

analog computer. An electronic calculating machine in which quantities and relationships are represented by continuously variable physical quantities such that approximate solutions can be obtained readily. In an analog computer quantities are represented without explicit use of language.

analogy. *Types of, see* dynamical–; mobility–.

analysis. *Types of, see* data–; frequency response–.

analyzer. *Types of, see* differential–; subcarrier–.

ANC. Army-Navy-Commercial.

ancillary equipment. An equipment of a guided missile not directly employed in its operation, but necessary for logistic support, preparation for flight, or assessment of target damage (e.g., test equipment, vehicle transport).

anechoic test chamber. A test chamber for subjecting equipment to an acoustical environment which is echo free. Sometimes termed a *free-field room* or *chamber*.

anelasticity. In general, any deviation from the ideal behavior postulated by classical elasticity theory (where the strain is proportional to the applied stress and follows instantaneously upon its application). The term is applied particularly to those phenomena associated with the damping of elastic waves in solids. Numerous causes are known for these effects, such as thermal diffusion, motion of grain boundaries, diffusion of twin boundaries, atomic solution diffusion, etc. The damping associated with a given process depends strongly on the frequency of the elastic wave. Also termed *internal friction*.

anemometer. An instrument for measuring the speed of wind or other airstream.

aneroid. A disc-shaped metallic capsule from which all the air has been evacuated, which expresses its sensitivity to changes in atmospheric pressure by expanding and contracting.

angel. (Vernacular) (1) A type of confusion reflector (q.v.). (2) A measure of altitude equivalent to 1000 ft.

angle. *Types of, see* burble–; critical–; deflection–; free-flight–; flight path–; Greenwich hour–; hour–; intercept lead–; lead–; local hour–; MACH–; missile lead–; nozzle cant–; reference–; sidereal hour–; solar–; squint–; tilt–.

angle of attack. (1) The acute angle between the chord of an airfoil and a line representing the undisturbed relative airflow. Sometimes termed *angle of incidence*. (2) Any other acute angle between two reference lines designating the cant of an airfoil relative to oncoming air.

angle of attack. *Types of, see* absolute–; critical–; effective–; induced–; zero-lift–.

angle of attack for infinite aspect ratio. In aerodynamics, an assumed angle of attack at which a given airfoil would produce a specified amount of lift if the airfoil were of infinite span, the angle being formed by the chord of the airfoil and a line representing the relative direction of the undisturbed airflow.

angle of fire. An indication of antenna direction or of a missile launcher.

angle of incidence. (1) The angle of an aerodynamic control surface setting. (2) In electronics, the angle between the direction of an electromagnetic wave and a line perpendicular to a reflecting surface struck by the wave.

angle of pitch. The acute angle between the longitudinal axis of a vehicle and its line of travel, looked at from the side.

angle of roll. The acute angle between the lateral axis of a vehicle and the horizontal. The angle is positive when the port tip is higher than the starboard tip.

angle of yaw. The acute angle between the longitudinal axis of a vehicle and its line of travel, looked at from above. It is positive when the vehicle travels to the right.

Ångstrom unit (Å). A unit of length equal to one ten-thousandth of a micron, or one hundred-millionth of a centimeter. Used to express lengths of extremely short waves. *See* metric system.

$$1 \text{ Ångstrom unit} = 10^{-8} \text{ cm} = 3.937 \times 10^{-9} \text{ in.} = 10^{-10} \text{ meter} = 100 \text{ micromicrons} = 0.0001 \text{ micron} = 10^{-7} \text{ mm} = 0.1 \text{ millimicron}$$

angular altitude. A measure in degrees of a given object above the horizon, taken from a given or assumed point of observation, and expressed by the angle between the horizontal and the observer's line of sight. The angular altitude of a celestial body is measured by the arc of a vertical circle between the body and the celestial horizon, ranging from zero through ninety degrees.

angular momentum. A quantity which is defined for any body which is rotating or traveling in a curved path, around some axis; it is the product of the mass of the body and the rate of its rotation. *See* conservation of angular momentum.

angular motion. The motion of a body about a fixed axis, measured by the rate of change in the angle between two lines perpendicular to the axis, one fixed in space, the other in the moving body.

angular position pickup. An end instrument which translates variations in angular position into an analog quantity (e.g., change of inductance or resistance).

angular velocity. The rate of change of the direction of a moving point as measured from a point at rest. All points on a rotating disc have the same angular velocity about the center, but their speed of motion increases with increasing distance from the center.

aniline ($C_6H_5NH_2$). A liquid rocket propellant *fuel.* See Table 3, page 157.

anisoelastic. *See* nonisoelastic effects.

AN nomenclature system. A joint Army-Navy-Air Force code system set up for designating certain communication and electronic equipment (e.g., AN/APN-7: airborne radar navigational aid. A responder beacon; AN/FPS-1: ground, fixed radar search. A long range, early warning radar). The prefix AN does not imply that a particular piece of equipment is used by *all* the services, but merely that the designation was assigned under the AN nomenclature system.

anode. In electronics, the radio tube electrode to which the main electron stream flows. It is commonly termed the *plate,* and is usually placed at high positive potential with respect to the cathode. It is usually identified on diagrams by the letter P.

anode, keep-alive. *See* keep-alive anode.

anodized coating. A process used for coating aluminum and aluminum alloys. Used for corrosion resistance provided by the aluminum hydroxide surface. The surface is soft and must be treated with a coat of primer before handling. Anodizing is *not* a plating process. The coating is applied by a chromic acid oxidation process.

anomalistic year. The time between two successive passages of the Earth through perihelion (q.v.).

anomalous elasticity. Property of a material in which the stress-strain curve does not fit an easily derivable mathematical expression.

anomaly. *Types of, see* gravitational–; pressure–; propagation–.

Antarctic Circle. The parallel of latitude 66° 33′ South. It is the limit of the area in the Southern Hemisphere within which the Sun does not set at mid-summer.

antenna. In electronics, a conductor linked to a radio transmitter for radiating, or to a receiver for intercepting radio waves. The size and shape of an antenna or *aerial* depend on the frequencies for which it is intended, on its directional properties, and on the reflectors and waveguides with which it may be linked.

antenna. *Types of, see* Adcock–; array of arrays–; broad beam–; cheese–; cosecant-squared–; Coulmer array–; dipole–; directional–; dish–; gain–; helix–; horn–; image–; isotropic–; J antenna; L antenna; loop–; notch–; omnidirectional–; sense–; spiral–; unidirectional–.

antenna array. A term used to designate two or more antennas coupled together for the purpose of obtaining directional effects.

antenna array. *Types of, see* aperture of–; broadside–; binomial–; closed space–; continuous linear–; end-fire–; linear–.

antenna bandwidth. In electronics, the range of frequencies within which the performance of an antenna, in respect to some characteristic, conforms to a specified standard.

antenna cross talk. In electronics, a measure of undesired power transfer through space from one antenna to another. Numerically, antenna cross talk is the ratio of the power received by one antenna to the power transmitted by the other, usually expressed in decibels.

antenna, effective height. The effective antenna height, h, is found from the following relationship:

$$h = 0.287 \frac{\epsilon d}{\omega I}$$

where h = effective height, ft; ϵ = measured field of intensity in microvolts per ft; d = distance in miles from antenna to point of ϵ measurement; ω = angular frequency in kiloradians per sec; I = antenna current in amperes at point of energization.

antenna gain. In electronics, a measure of the directivity of the antenna field patterns as compared to a standard dipole antenna (q.v.); the ratio of the power that must be supplied to the standard antenna to deliver a certain field strength in the desired direction, to the power that must be supplied to the directional antenna (q.v.) to obtain the same strength in the same direction.

$$G = \frac{4\pi A}{\lambda^2}$$

where A = antenna area; λ = wavelength.

antenna lens. A lens often placed in front of another radiator such as a dipole (q.v.) or horn (q.v.) to satisfy high directivity requirements. In much the same manner as an optical lens focuses light waves, these microwave lenses focus the high-frequency energy into a sharp beam.

antenna multiplex coupler. In telemetering, a mixing device used to combine the FM outputs of several telemetering packages into one composite FM signal. The signal is applied to the telemetering antennas for transmission to ground equipment.

antenna pattern. In electronics, a diagrammatic representation of the radiation field from an antenna, usually in terms of loci representing equal power levels. The radiation characteristics vary inversely as the square of the distance and depend on direction from the source.

antenna power gain. In electronics, in a given direction, 4π times the ratio of the radiation intensity in that direction to the total power delivered to the antenna.

antiaircraft missile. A guided missile launched from the surface against an airborne target.

anticlastic curvature. The curve or change of shape, due to the Poisson effect (q.v.), of a thin sheet of material when compression loaded on the edge.

anticyclonic wind. *See* winds.

antidisturbance fuze. A fuze designed to be so sensitive after being armed as to detonate with the slightest disturbance.

antigravity. An effect upon masses (e.g., rocket vehicles and human bodies) by which some still-to-be-discovered energy field would cancel or reduce the gravitational attraction of Earth.

antimissile missile. A defensive weapon system (q.v.), including detection, tracking, and calculation of the extended trajectory of incoming missiles, and launching of a guided missile to destroy an attacking missile.

antinode. In a vibrating system, a surface composed of particles which have larger amplitudes (q.v.) than nearby particles.

antipodal bomber. (1) A special type of boost-glide bomber (q.v.) that lands at the antipode of its launching point, the place on the globe diametrically opposite, after dropping the bombs from a point on its out-of-the-atmosphere trajectory. (2) A plan for using a rocket-propelled bomber to obtain a range of 15,000 miles was proposed by Eugene Sanger and Irene Bredt in 1942. The plane would be launched from a sled on a 1.8 mile long track, using solid propellant boosters which would give it a velocity of 1650 fps before main motor took over. It would ricochet off the upper atmosphere layers by means of having it enter denser layers at too steep an angle and too high a velocity. Oxygen and gasoline fuel would be used for main motor with a thrust rating of 225,000 lb for 8 minutes.

antitransmitter-receiver. A device used in microwave radar to permit utilization of the same antenna for transmitting and receiving.

antitriptic wind. *See* winds.

anvil cloud. The anvil-shaped top part of a well-developed cumulonimbus cloud (q.v.).

A/P. Autopilot. *See* automatic pilot.

APDA. Auxiliary Pump Drive Assembly (q.v.).

aperture-gain-wavelength relation (of an antenna). The fundamental relation for the maximum gain G_o, the area of the aperture A, and the wavelength λ:

$$G_o = \frac{4\pi A K_o}{\lambda^2}$$

The dimensionless factor K_o is equal to 1 if the excitation is uniform in phase and intensity over the whole aperture; in actual antennas K_o often is as large as 0.6 or 0.7 and is rarely less than 0.5.

aperture of the antenna array. That portion of a plane surface near the antenna, perpendicular to the maximum direction of radiation, through which the major portion of the radiation passes.

APGC. Air Proving Ground Command (q.v.); Eglin Air Force Base, Valparaiso, Florida. Does development and testing of Air Force weapons and armament equipment.

aphelion. The point of orbit farthest from the Sun when the Sun is being orbited (i.e., the primary). *See* apogee.

APL/JHU. Applied Physics Laboratory/The Johns Hopkins University; Silver Spring, Maryland. Developers of the VT Fuze (q.v.), the MK 61 gun director, the Bumblebee project missiles [e.g., TERRIER, TALOS (q.q.v.)], and other Navy Bureau of Ordnance projects.

Applied Science Corporation of Princeton (ASCOP). A commercial producer of data acquisition and reduction equipment.

apogee. The highest point of a ballistic missile trajectory (q.v.); more precisely for an elliptical orbit (q.v.), the point of intersection of the trajectory and its semi-major axis. The term is borrowed from celestial mechanics, where it refers to that point in the orbit of any celestial body which is at the greatest distance from the center of the Earth. *Apogee* is the opposite of *perigee* (q.v.). Note that the apogee is a *point*, not a *distance*. See Fig. 27, page 293.

apparent horizon. The horizon (q.v.) formed by the apparent meeting of the Earth and sky as observed from any point.

apparent precession. The relative angular movement of the spinning axis of a gyroscope (q.v.) in relation to a line on the Earth, resulting from the rotation of the Earth and the property of the gyroscope to maintain its spinning axis in the same direction.

apparent time. A reckoning of time as measured by the apparent motion of the Sun about the Earth. Apparent time differs from mean time (q.v.) in that it results in days of unequal length.

applied research. Research aimed at a specific application of scientific laws, principles, and phenomena. In contrast to basic research (q.v.), the prospect of practical application of the results is a primary motive for applied research. Frequently even the methods to be used are clear before work is begun.

approach apron. In missilery, a concrete apron adjoining the missile erection area that provides a solid support surface for transtainers and other ground handling equipment.

approach, ground-controlled. *See* ground-controlled approach.

APS. Accessory Power Supply (q.v.).

APU. (1) Auxiliary Power Unit (q.v.). (2) Accessory Power Supply (q.v.).

AQ. Aircraft Quality. Denoting highest quality of workmanship.

AQL. Acceptable Quality Level (q.v.).

Arabia. An ochre-colored "desert" region on Mars.

ARCON. Research sounding rocket. Navy cognizance.

Solid fuel propellant, no booster used. Payload: 40 lb to 70 miles maximum altitude.

Prime Contractor: Atlantic Research Corp.

ARCUS. Single stage research rocket. Navy cognizance.

Weight: 72 lb; length: 6 ft; diameter: 4½ in. Used for meteorology studies. Parachute recovery of a 12-lb payload from 200,000 ft.

Prime Contractor: Atlantic Research Corp.

ARDC. Air Research and Development Command; Andrews Air Force Base, Maryland. Has ten research, development, and testing centers.

area. (1) The surface of anything; the measure of its extent. In special meanings an extent or space on the Earth. (2) The scope or extent of something intangible, as the "area of responsibility," the "area of study," or the "area of power."

area. *Types of, see* air materiel–; dispersion–; echo–; effective–; equivalent flat plate–; field assembly–; high pressure–; impact–; launch base–; low pressure–; moment of area; port reduction of area; reference–; restricted–; target–; target profile–.

area ratio. The ratio of one surface area to another (e.g., the ratio between the chamber area and the throat area of a rocket nozzle).

area rule concept. A concept of aircraft design based on the notion that interference drag (q.v.) at transonic speed (q.v.) depends almost entirely on the distribution of the aircraft's total cross-sectional area along the direction of flight. Drag (q.v.) at transonic speed decreases in proportion to how closely the cross-sectional area resembles a theoretical optimum body shape. To obtain minimum transonic drag, the designer reworks the shape of a given vehicle to achieve a distribution approximating the ideal shape.

ARGO E-5 (Project Jason). Five stage test vehicles fired in conjunction with the ARGUS project (q.v.) nuclear firings to obtain measurements at about 30 nautical miles altitude. 50 lb payload.

> 1st stage—HONEST JOHN (q.v.)
> 2nd stage—NIKE (q.v.) sustainer engines
> 3rd stage—NIKE sustainer engines
> 4th stage—RECRUIT (q.v.)
> 5th stage—T-55 rocket

ARGO D-5—vehicle with 50 lb payload to 1000 miles.

ARGO D-8—vehicle with 50 lb payload to 2000 miles.

ARGUS project. Project to fire a nuclear warhead at approximately 300 miles altitude. Launched by the X-17 test vehicle (q.v.).

ARINC. *A*eronautics *R*adio, *I*ncorporated.

arithmetic unit. That part of a computer which performs arithmetic operations as contrasted to the storage or program elements.

ARL. Acceptable Reliability Level (q.v.).

ARMA. American Bosch-Arma Corporation.

armament system. Those components used to produce and control the damage effects of a missile: fuze, safety and arming mechanism, and warhead (q.q.v.).

armed. That condition of the safety and arming mechanism (q.v.) which permits warhead detonation by fuze action.

arming. (1) The act of completing the firing signal transfer path through the "S and A" (safety and arming mechanism, q.v.). (2) The process of changing a fuze (q.v.) or a warhead (q.v.) from a safe condition to a state of readiness for initiation.

arming altitude. (1) The altitude at which a warhead is armed, dictated by the combined effects of several extreme conditions: the maximum desired burst height for an incoming missile. (2) The highest target elevation expected for a surface-to-air- missile.

arming signal. An electrical signal for arming the warhead.

arming system. *See* safety and arming mechanism.

armor. (1) Any physical protective covering, such as sheet metal, used on vehicles against projectiles or fragments. (2) In a weapon system, that component that gives protection to the vehicle or the weapon on its way to the target.

armor. *Types of, see* face-hardened–; homogeneous–.

Army hot day. A day with an arbitrarily selected set of conditions considered to be average for the summer months in the United States. It is used chiefly in connection with engine-cooling problems. Sometimes termed *Army summer day*. At sea level, Army hot day temperature is considered to be 38°C (100.4°F).

ARPA. Advanced Research Projects Agency, the division of the Department of Defense responsible for space exploration.

array. *Types of, see* antenna–; broadside–; colinear–; end fire–; linear–; –of arrays antenna.

array function. In electronics, the result of combining the element functions of a group of similar elements by multiplying the element function of a single antenna by an array function to provide the radiation pattern of the group. The group may then be treated as a single source of radiation.

array of arrays antenna. A number of similar antenna arrays (q.v.) each having a moderate amount of directivity which may be arrayed to form an array of arrays.

ARS. *See* SENTRY.

ARS. American Rocket Society (q.v.).

artificial gravity. The centrifugal force which may be used to simulate gravity in manned rockets and space stations.

artificial horizon. (1) A line on a flight indicator which lies within the horizontal plane, about which the pitching and banking movements of an aircraft may be shown. (2) A flight indicator. (3) A bubble horizon (q.v.).

artificial satellite. Any one of the man-made objects placed in orbit around the Earth (e.g., SPUTNIK, EXPLORER, VANGUARD (q.q.v.).

artillery mil. *See* mil.

ascension, right. *See* right ascension.

ascent, free. *See* free ascent.

ascent path. (1) The flight path leading from the surface of a celestial body into an orbit (q.v.) in space. (2) The powered flight portion of a ballistic missile (q.v.) trajectory (q.v.) plus that portion of the trajectory up to apogee (q.v.).

ASCOP. Applied Science Corporation of Princeton (q.v.).

A-scope. A radarscope that presents the target range by a vertical deflection of the time base, or, in certain modified versions, by a horizontal deflection.

ASESA. Armed Services Electro Standards Committee.

ASETC. Armed Services Electron Tube Committee.

ASG. Aeronautical Standards Group.

ashen light. The name given to the faint luminosity of the night hemisphere of Venus, when that planet appears as a crescent.

ASI. Amended Shipping Instructions.

Askania phototheodolite. A type of cine-theodolite manufactured by the Askania Regulator Company. *See* theodolite. Used for field instrumentation for guided missile flights.

ASM. Air-to-Surface Missile. *See* air-to-ground missile, model designation.

ASM-N-4 and ASM-N-5. Designation of the production version of the air-to-surface and air-to-underwater missile termed DOVE (q.v.).

ASM-N-7. Navy Bureau of Aeronautics designation for air-to-surface missile termed BULL PUP (q.v.).

ASP. (Atmospheric Sounding Project). Sounding rocket for research purposes. Navy cognizance.

Solid propellant rocket engine; single stage rocket with telemetry head, missile body, motor case, fin and aft skirt assembly. Monorail launcher.

Prime Contractor: Cooper Development Corp. Engine: Grand Central Rocket Co.

aspect indicator. An instrument used in missiles and rockets to measure the position of the axis of the missile relative to its line of advance. It usually consists of a pivoted system of vanes which register deflection by the air-stream electrically, and beyond the atmosphere gyroscopes (q.v.) provide fixed directions in space against which any tilt or tumbling of the missile may be measured.

aspect ratio. (1) In winged missiles, the ratio of the square of the span to the total area of an airfoil. (2) In wingless missiles, the ratio of body diameter to its mean length. (3) In television, the numerical ratio of frame width to frame height nominally standardized as four units horizontally to three units vertically.

ASROC. Ship-to-underwater torpedo missile. Navy Bureau of Ordnance cognizance.

Described as a solid propellant rocket-boosted torpedo that is fired through the air for a considerable range, then enters the water where an electric-powered torpedo is directed by a homing device to the target. Designed for the destruction of surface vehicles.

Prime Contractor: Minneapolis-Honeywell Regulator Co.

assembly (or subassembly). A group of component parts, commonly mounted, which may be subject to a disassembly, and which is not capable of performing a complete operation by itself (e.g., assemblies when they are an integral part of a component). An IF strip, a terminal board with component parts attached, a gyroscope, a fuel meter, a tail fin, and an antenna are examples of assemblies.

assembly. *Types of, see* auxiliary pump drive–; booster–; pump drive–; tail–; thrust chamber–.

assisted take off. The action of a vehicle's taking off with an added boost from a rocket motor or other device. *See* Jato; Rato.

associate contractor. A contractor to a military service responsible for developing and producing a portion of the equipment that is essential to a complete weapon system (q.v.). A system used primarily by the Air Force Ballistic Missile Division.

associated failure. A failure (q.v.) which results from the failure of another interdependent equipment. A failure which judgment and experience indicate would not have occurred if failure of an associated equipment had not occurred.

asteroid (astron). A starlike body, especially one of the numerous small planets, nearly all of whose orbits lie between Mars and Jupiter. Also termed *planetoid* (q.v.) and *minor planet.*

ASTIA. Armed Services Technical Information Agency; Dayton, Ohio. A source for classified documents if need-to-know (q.v.) is established.

astrionics. The science of electronics as employed in astronautics (q.v.).

astrogation. Navigation in space.

astrolabe. An instrument for measuring the altitude of celestial bodies. It is a circular disc marked off in degrees along its rim and fitted with a movable arm carrying sights through which the star is viewed. When in use, it is held suspended in a vertical plane. It is now entirely replaced by the *sextant,* but its name has been adopted for a modern instrument which gives very exact measurements on firm ground.

astron. *See* asteroid.

astronautics. The science dealing with space flight and space travel (q.q.v.). Sometimes arbitrarily assumed to commence at an altitude of 200 kilometers (about 124 miles). *See* aeronautics, cosmonautics.

astronomical distance. Distance expressed in the astronomical unit (AU), the light year, the parsec, and in terms of parallax.

		Miles (millions)	*Astronomical Units, AU*	*Light Years*
1 AU	=	92.9	1	8 light min
1 light yr	=	5,880,000	63,300	1
1 parsec	=	19,150,000	206,000	3.26

astronomical twilight. That period of twilight that occurs, for computation purposes, when the Sun is between the horizon and a point about 18 degrees below the horizon, the latter measured at the middle of the Sun. In a restrictive sense, when the middle of the Sun is between 12 and 18 degrees below the horizon.

astronomical unit (AU). The mean distance of the Earth from the Sun. It is used as a unit for measuring and expressing the distances within the solar system and among the nearer stars, and is equal to 92,907,000 miles according to the most recent determination. Since a larger unit of distance, the *parsec* (q.v.), is based on the astronomical unit, it is most desirable that its value should be accurately known. The best results so far have been obtained from parallax (q.v.) measurements made on those asteroids (q.v.) that pass within the Earth's orbit around the Sun; artificial satellites will make further refinements possible.

astrophysics. The physics of astronomical bodies, including the study of stellar light, energy sources, constitution of celestial bodies, etc.

asymptote. A (usually straight) line which approaches nearer and nearer to a line without ever touching it.

ATC. Air Training Command.

athodyd. *Aero-thermodynamic-duct;* a ramjet (q.v.).

ATI. Air Technical Intelligence.

ATIC. Air Technical Intelligence Center.

Atlantic Missile Range (AMR). The Air Force-operated missile test range. Formerly AFMTC (q.v.).

ATLANTIS. An Intercontinental Ballistic Missile, submarine-launched; proposed by the Navy as a follow-on project to the Intermediate Range Ballistic Missile POLARIS (q.v.).

ATLAS. Surface-to-surface, 1½ stage Intercontinental Ballistic Missile. Air Force designation: WS107A-1, and for the missile, SM-65.

Length: approximately 80 ft; body diameter: 10 ft; launching weight: more than 200,000 lb; design range: 5500 miles. Liquid rocket engines: two 150,000-lb booster engines, one 60,000-lb thrust sustainer and two 1000-lb Vernier engines. Propellants are LOX/RP-1. All thrust chambers are fired on the ground and all have gimbal mountings. Vernier engines are used for roll control and velocity adjustment.

Systems Engineering Contractor: Space Technology Laboratories. Prime Contractor: Convair; division of General Dynamics Corp. Airframe and control system: Convair. Engines: Rocketdyne, North American Aviation, Inc. Guidance system: radar: General Electric Co.—inertial: American Bosch-Arma Corp. Nose cone: General Electric Co.

ATLAS ABLE. A 3-stage satellite/space probe launching vehicle consisting of an ATLAS (q.v.) booster and the same upper stages as the THOR ABLE (q.v.).

ATLAS HUSTLER. A satellite launching vehicle consisting of an ATLAS (q.v.) first stage and a Bell Hustler liquid engine for the second stage. Capable of orbiting about 3,000 lb at 300 miles altitude. The configuration used in the Lockheed 117L communication satellite program.

ATLAS satellite (Project Score). On 18 December, 1958, an NASA (q.v.) sponsored project, under the direction of the Air Force, put an ATLAS missile with a 150 lb payload (but less the staged booster engines) into orbit for the purpose of conducting a number of communications relay experiments. Apogee (q.v.) was 625 miles and perigee (q.v.) was 118 miles. Total orbited weight was approximately 8700 lbs. Velocity attained was about 17,000 mph. It apparently burned up on 21 January 1959, thirty-four days after launching. Radio transmission ceased on 31 December 1958. See Table 6, page 245.

atmosphere. The gaseous envelope which surrounds the Earth. It is arbitrarily subdivided with increasing altitude into: the *troposphere* (q.v.), 0 to 10 miles; the *stratosphere* (q.v.), 10 to 20 miles; the *chemosphere* (q.v.), 20 to 50 miles; the *ionosphere* (q.v.), 50 to 250 miles; and the *mesosphere* (q.v.), from about 250 miles and into space. See Fig. 1.

atmosphere. *Types of, see* altimeter-calibration standard–; effective–; ICAO–; interplanetary–; lower–; model–; one atmosphere; physiological–; rarefied–; sensible–; standard–; standard international–; standard U.S.–; stellar–; upper–.

atmosphere. A unit of measurement. *See* one atmosphere.

1 atmosphere = 76 cm of mercury at 0°C
           = 33.899 ft of water at 39.2°F
           = 29.921 in. of mercury at 32°F
           = 2116.2 lb/sq ft = 14.696 lb/sq in.

atmosphere of the Earth. A thin envelope of gases surrounding the Earth. Its approximate composition by volume is: nitrogen, 78%; oxygen, 21%; argon, 0.94%; helium, 0.0004%; and minute traces of other rare gases. In addition, there are varying amounts of water vapor.

The weight of the atmosphere creates a pressure at sea level of about 14.7 lb per sq in. (= 1 atmosphere or 760 mm of mercury).

atmospheric attenuation. (1) Reduction in the intensity of the manifestations of a nuclear detonation (nuclear thermal radiation and air blast) caused by the Earth's atmosphere. (2) The attenuation (q.v.) of electromagnetic radiation (q.v.).

atmospheric attenuation computation. Computation in which the attenuation by haze obeys Beer's exponential law:

$$I_\lambda = I_{o\lambda}\, e^{-\alpha\lambda X}$$

where $I_{o\lambda}$ = incident intensity of radiation at wavelength λ; I_λ = intensity transmitted at wavelength λ; α_λ = attenuation coefficient due to scattering by the haze; X = length of the optical path.

atmospheric braking. The deliberate maneuver of applying atmospheric drag to decelerate a satellite or space vehicle for landing upon a planet that has a *usable* atmosphere; it can be accomplished by entering at a nearly flat, gradual trajectory (q.v.) or by making a series of passes through the atmosphere.

atmospheric circulation. The circulation of air in the atmosphere. The structure of this circulation is vast and complicated, and is sometimes classified as *primary* or *planetary circulation*, *secondary circulation*, and *tertiary circulation*. *Primary circulation* occurs on a planetary scale

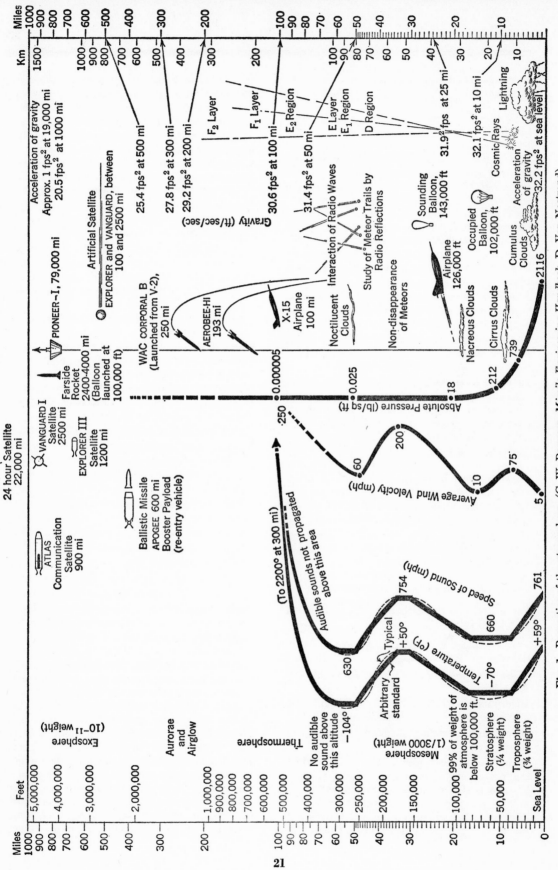

Fig. 1. Properties of the atmosphere. (C. W. Besserer, *Missile Engineering Handbook*, D. Van Nostrand)

21

and results from a gain in heat in the equatorial regions coupled with a net loss of heat by radiation in the higher latitudes, the heat energy being transferred from the equator to the poles by actual movement of air. Because of the Earth's rotation and because of the effects of land and sea, this circulation is deflected and rendered complex with resultant semipermanent centers of action. The heated air rises at the equator, moves toward the poles as the anti-trade winds, settles to the Earth, and returns to the equator in the northeast and southeast trade winds, except that part of the subsiding anti-trade winds escapes toward the poles at high levels, from where they return to the equator as polar easterlies.

Secondary circulation embraces smaller wind systems, such as the monsoons, tropical and extratropical cyclones, and anticyclones.

Tertiary circulation comprises numerous variable winds, thunderstorm winds, land and sea breezes, etc.

atmospheric control. Any device or system designed to operate movable aerodynamic control surfaces (q.v.) to direct a guided missile in atmosphere dense enough for such control to be effective; the control provided by such a device.

atmospheric drizzle. An atmospheric condition wherein numerous very small liquid droplets whose diameter is less than 0.5 mm and whose rate of fall is usually less than 3 mm per sec. Normally the drops appear to float downward.

atmospheric pressure. The pressure upon a body in the atmosphere due to the weight of air above it. For altitudes up to the isothermal layer (35,300 ft):

$$P = P_{sl}\left(1 - \frac{h}{145,366}\right) 5.255$$

For altitudes in the isothermal layer (35,500 ft to 105,000 ft):

$$\log_{10}\frac{P_{sl}}{P} = \frac{h}{48,211} - 0.09759$$

where P = pressure at altitude; P_{sl} = pressure at sea level.

atmospheric refraction. Refraction of light from a celestial body by the atmosphere.

atmospheric sounding diagram. An adiabatic chart (q.v.).

atom. The smallest part of an element which can participate in ordinary chemical changes. The atoms of a given element are unvarying in average mass, but are different in such mass from atoms of all other elements. *Chemically,* the smallest electrically neutral constituent part of an element that can take part in a chemical reaction. *Physically,* a positively charged nucleus surrounded by a compensating number of negative electrons in various orbits.

atomic clock. A *very* accurate source of frequency (or time) which depends upon the invariant nuclear resonance of certain elements (e.g., caesium), when subjected to an RF electromagnetic field. Accuracies of one part in 10 million are achievable.

atomic device. Any device that makes use of nuclear fissionable, radioactive material, especially an atomic bomb, shell, or other atomic missile.

atomic fission. The breaking down of a large, heavy atom with the liberation of energy in the form of heat and gamma radiation, freeing of atomic particles, and creation of new elements from the larger fragments.

atomic fusion. The joining of two small atomic nuclei to form one larger one, generally with liberation of appreciable energy. When this reaction involves extremely high temperatures (in the million-degree range), it is generally known as a *thermonuclear reaction* (q.v.).

atomic number. The number of excess positive charges on an atomic nucleus. The essential feature which distinguishes one element from another and which determines the position of the element in the periodic table.

atomic pile. A nuclear reactor (q.v.).

atomic power. The power (energy) released by a nuclear or thermonuclear reaction (q.q.v.).

atomic radiation. The radiation or radioactivity which results from the decomposition of a nuclear fissionable, radioactive material, or from the fusion of atomic nuclei.

atomic reactor. A device designed to maintain a controlled nuclear chain reaction.

atomic weight. The weighted mean of the masses of the neutral atoms of an element expressed in atomic weight units. Unless otherwise specified it refers to a naturally occurring form of the element. The atomic weight unit (awu) is exactly one-sixteenth of the weighted mean of the masses of the neutral atoms of oxygen of isotropic composition found in fresh lake or rain water: 1 awu = 1.600×10^{-24} gm = 1.000272 amu. The experimentally determined ratio of the atomic weight unit to the atomic mass unit is termed the *atomic mass conversion factor.* The value of this factor is uncertain in the seventh significant figure because of variations in the isotropic composition of oxygen from different natural sources. In the future its value, and hence that of the atomic weight unit, may be rendered exact by definition.

atomization. The breaking down of fuel into minute particles as it is forced into the cylinder of an engine under extreme pressure.

ATR. AntiTransmitter-Receiver (q.v.).

ATRAN. Automatic Terrain Recognition And Navigation system (q.v.).

ATRC. Air Training Command; Scott Air Force Base, Belleville, Illinois.

attached shock. In supersonic aerodynamics, the flow conditions occurring when the shock wave (q.v.) created at the leading edge (q.v.) of a body is attached to or has its vertex on the body. For contrast, see detached shock; swallowed shock.

attack, feint. See feint attack.

attained bandwidth. (Attained total deviation). The actual band of frequencies used by a given oscillator-pickup combination with full-range input stimulus.

attenuation. (1) The loss of effectiveness of an emission because of the distance an electromagnetic wave (q.v.) travels. It is caused by absorption due to molecular resonance. The attenuation ratio of received-to-transmitted power is:

$$\frac{P_r}{P_t} = \frac{G_t A_r}{4\pi D^2}$$

where G_t = transmitting radiator gain; A_r = receiver cross section; D = distance traveled. (2) The difference in amplitude between the input and output pulses when a network is terminated in its characteristic resistance. Expressed in db as:

$$\text{atten. (db)} = 20 \log_{10} \frac{E_0}{E_1}$$

where E_0 = output voltage; E_1 = input voltage.

attenuation. Types of, see atmospheric–; flame–; inverse square law–.

attenuator. (1) A device designed to cause a loss in energy in a transmission system without introducing appreciable distortion in the desired frequencies. (2) A resistive network for reducing amplitude of an electrical signal without appreciable phase or frequency distortion.

attitude. The position of a missile as determined by the inclination of its axes to some frame of reference. If not otherwise specified, this frame of reference is fixed to the Earth. Attitude is defined by the following terms: roll, pitch, and yaw (q.q.v.).

attitude. Types of, see horizontal–; lateral–; longitudinal–; missile–; vertical–.

attitude control. A system which aligns a missile to a desired flight path.

attitude control system. See automatic pilot.

attitude jets. Fixed or movable gas nozzles on a rocket, missile, or satellite operated continuously or intermittently to change the attitude or position either in the atmosphere (q.v.) or in space (q.v.). Sometimes termed steering jets, attitude-control jets, or roll, pitch, and yaw jets.

attribute. A characteristic or property which can be appraised only in terms of whether it does or does not exist.

attribute, method of. See method of attribute.

attrition. Destructive military action which denies the enemy the use of his resources and materials; a gradual reduction in numbers, usually owing to enemy action.

audio. Pertaining to frequencies of audible sound waves between about 20 and 20,000 cps.

audio frequency. Any frequency that affects the human ear, ranging between 15 and 20,000 vibrations per sec, the most audible being between 500 and 4000 per sec.

audio subcarrier. A subcarrier whose frequency lies within the audible range, usually between 30 cps and 1500 cps. Compare with subcarrier (q.v.).

augmentation, thrust. See thrust augmentation.

augmented launch station. A launch station with facilities for launching two or more missiles.

augmented thrust ratio. The ratio of thrust obtained by a turbojet with its afterburner operating to that without. It may be expressed mathematically as:

$$\frac{F_a}{F} = \frac{V_{ja} - V}{V_j - V} = \frac{\sqrt{(T_{6a}/T_6)} - v}{1 - v}$$

where V_{ja} = exhaust velocity with afterburning; V_j = exhaust velocity without afterburning; V = vehicle velocity; T_{6a} = temperature of exhaust gases with afterburning, °R; T_6 = temperature of exhaust gases at exit without afterburning, °R; v = ratio of V/V_j.

augmenter. In a jet engine, a duct usually enclosing the exhaust jet behind the nozzle exit section to provide increased thrust. See afterburning.

AUM. Air-to-Underwater Missile (see air-to-ground missile); a model designation (q.v.).

AUM-N-2. Production version of the Navy air-to-surface, air-to-underwater missile termed PETREL (q.v.).

aural null. A condition of minimum or no aural signal being received over a radio-receiving set using a directional antenna (q.v.). With a loop-type directional antenna (q.v.) aural null occurs when the plane of the loop is at right angles to the direction of the transmitted signal.

aural radio range. A radio range (e.g., the loop-type radio range) in which the on-course signal is an aural signal only.

aural-type VHF range. A very high frequency aural-type range (*see* aural radio range).

aurora. Commonly known as the *northern and southern lights;* a high-altitude airglow (q.v.) caused by solar particles, predominantly protons, moving as charged particles in the Earth's magnetic field and interacting with the Earth's atmosphere.

autocollimator. A device by which a lens makes diverging light from a slit parallel, and then after the parallel light has passed through a prism to a mirror and been reflected back through the prism, the same lens brings the light to a focus at an exit slit.

auto-igniting propellant. Any propellant (q.v.) that ignites spontaneously at room temperature. A synonym for *hypergolic propellant* (q.v.).

automatic celestial navigation. *See* celestial navigation, star tracking.

automatic control system. Any operable combination of one or more automatic controls connected in closed loops (q.v.) with one or more processes.

automatic frequency control (AFC). A circuit which generates a low frequency correction to maintain the intermediate frequency at its correct value (performed by frequency-modulating the local oscillator at an audio rate to provide a carrier).

automatic gain control (AGC). A means of accomplishing regulation of the magnitude of the output signal level of a (usually electronic) system.

automatic master sequencer system. Equipment used for automatic countdown (q.v.) operations.

automatic pilot (A/P). An automatic control device for keeping a missile in level flight and on a set course or for executing desired maneuvers. Sometimes termed *gyropilot, mechanical pilot, robot pilot, autopilot, control system.*

automatic search jammer. An intercept receiver and jamming transmitting system that automatically searches for and jams enemy signals of specific radiation characteristics.

automatic stability. The stability (q.v.) of a vehicle maintained by such mechanical devices as an automatic pilot (q.v.) which operates the control surfaces (q.v.) automatically.

automatic terrain recognition and navigation system (ATRAN). A map-matching system for missile navigation developed by Goodyear. One version uses a tape or film recording of terrain covered in the flight and previously obtained by reconnaissance from radar or camera coverage. A continuous comparison of desired position with actual position is made to provide appropriate corrections.

automatic tracking. Tracking in which a servomechanism (q.v.) keeps the radar beam trained on the target, by locking the servomechanism to the echo signal from the target.

automation. The technique of improving human productivity in the processing of materials, energy, and information by utilizing in various degrees elements of self-control and of automatically executed product programming.

autopilot (A/P). Automatic pilot (q.v.).

autopilot amplifier. A device which receives signals from the outputs of the gyroscope reference system and rate gyroscopes (q.v.), and converts the signals to a form usable for guidance by the actuator assemblies.

Autosyn. *Auto*matically *syn*chronous. A Bendix Aviation Corporation trade name for a synchro (q.v.).

autotrack. *See* radar lockon.

autumnal equinox. (1) The point where the Sun appears to cross the celestial equator from north to south. (2) The time of this crossing when day and night are of equal length. The *autumnal equinox* occurs about 21 September. Contrast with *vernal equinox* (q.v.). *See also* equinox.

auxiliary booster. An additional energy-producing device used for initiating a warhead and needed for a large bursting charge which would otherwise not be properly detonated by a booster alone.

auxiliary power unit (APU). A separate prime mover used to supply electrical, hydraulic, or other power to a vehicle or system. Power take-offs from primary engines are not in this category.

auxiliary pump drive assembly (APDA). In rockets, a mechanical assembly consisting of a turbine and pumps. The turbine is driven by gases from a gas generator (q.v.), and the pumps provide the propellant flow to the gas generator. *See* boot-strap.

auxiliary system. One that serves as an aid or adjunct to the basic or primary systems of a missile in the performance of its mission. Auxiliary systems include such items as self-destruction, jettisoning, cooling, and pressurization systems.

available time. Usable time (q.v.) minus preventive maintenance time.

average error. Mean absolute error (q.v.).

average load. (1) A qualitative term used in the design of shipping containers to denote an item (or items) of low or moderate density, which, when packed directly into a shipping container, provides non-shifting support at several points on each face of the container. (2) More often, the arithmetical average of a load on a missile over a complete loading cycle.

average unit stress. *See* unit stress.

aviation gasoline ($C_{8,5}H_{18}$). A liquid rocket propellant *fuel*. See Table 3, page 157.

avionics. *Avi*ation electr*onics*. A coined term describing the field of airborne electronics and associated control systems.

AWS. Air Weather Service.

axial compressor. A compressor employing many stages, each consisting of a rotor and a stator member. The rotor adds kinetic energy to the air-stream in an axial direction, and the stator converts this kinetic energy into pressure energy. The outlet velocity of the air is usually equal to that at the inlet.

axial flow jet engine. A jet engine in which the flow of air is along the longitudinal axis of the engine; a turbojet engine that utilizes an axial flow compressor (q.v.).

axis. A straight line, real or imaginary, that passes through a body and about which the body may, or actually does, revolve. An aircraft is considered to have three mutually perpendicular axes, each passing through the center of gravity. The *longitudinal axis*, sometimes termed the *x-axis*, runs lengthwise in the plane of symmetry from fore to aft; the *lateral axis*, sometimes termed the *y-axis*, runs from side to side; the *vertical axis*, sometimes termed the *z-axis*, runs in the plane of symmetry from the back to belly.

axis. *Types of, see* celestial–; elastic–; hinge–; horizontal–; lateral–; spinning–; vertical–; *x*-axis; *y*-axis; *z*-axis; zenith-nadir–.

axis of precession. In a gyroscope (q.v.) or gyroscopic body, any axis perpendicular to the spinning axis, about which precession may take place. The axis of precession follows a line between the point at which force is applied and the spinning axis.

azel scope. A radarscope constructed to show both azimuth and elevation.

azimuth. A direction expressed as a horizontal angle usually in degrees or mils (q.v.) and measured clockwise from north. Azimuth may be true azimuth (q.v.) or magnetic azimuth, depending upon which north is used. *See* zero azimuth.

azimuthal equidistant chart. A modification of the polar gnomonic chart (q.v.) in which the parallels of latitude increase uniformly in radius so that the latitude scale is constant.

azimuth ballistic correction. A ballistic correction made in azimuth.

AZUSA. A guidance or range instrumentation system using directive antennas and phase comparison techniques for angle determination and multichannel subcarriers for range (distance) measurements by means of time delay. Equipment includes an elaborate ground antenna array, a transmitting and receiving station, and a missile-borne transponder. The system was developed by Convair, a division of General Dynamics Corporation. It is a CW polar system used to provide position and velocity in space. Range is limited to radio line-of-sight. Range estimate: MK I, 200 nm; MK II, 400 nm.

B

backfit. A modification of a missile or other equipment to incorporate changes made in later production of a similar piece of equipment. Backfitting may be done in the factory or field.

background. In radar, an object or objects, especially on the Earth's surface, that produce signals on a radar screen but are of no particular interest as a target; background returns.

background research. An aspect of basic research (q.v.) considered to provide a foundation for subsequent research. It usually involves systematic observation, collection, and organization of facts to provide adequate data upon which to project the analysis and experimentation required for the discovery or testing of new facts, principles, or hypotheses.

background return. In electronics, an echo from an object other than the target, appearing on a radar screen. *See* clutter.

backlash. In servo applications, the dead space or unwanted movement in a control system or any of its elements incident to imperfect fabrication.

backout. Reversing the countdown (q.v.) sequence because of the failure of an element in a missile or its support equipment. The most serious task during complete blackout is removal of liquid propellants from the missile tanks.

back-scattering. (1) In electronics, the radiation of unwanted energy to the rear of a radar antenna. (2) In nucleonics, the deflection of particles or of radiation by scattering processes through angles greater than 90° with respect to the original direction of motion. (3) In chemistry, the process of scattering or reflecting into the sensitive volume of a measuring instrument radioactive radiations originally having no positive component of motion in that direction. It is dependent on the nature of the mounting material, the sample, the type and energy of the radiations, and the particular geometrical arrangement. (4) The scattering of radiation in a generally backward direction.

backscratcher. (Vernacular) An umbilical connection to a missile—usually of the flush type.

backup item. In research and development programming, an additional item under development to perform the general functions of another item under development. The item may be secondary to an identified primary item or a parallel development to enhance the probability of success in performing the general function.

backward wave oscillator. A local oscillator employing a special vacuum tube in which oscillatory currents are produced by bunching electrons as they flow from cathode to anode. An oscillatory electromagnetic field is used to bunch the electrons. (Used in radar sets, signal generators, countermeasure receivers, etc.)

balance. (1) The stability achieved by a vehicle when the forces of drag, thrust, lift, and gravity are acting upon it so as to produce steady flight without roll, yaw, or pitch. (2) Any weight used for counterbalancing to eliminate flutter.

balance area. The area on a balanced control surface that lies forward of the hinge line. The purpose of the balance area is to reduce the hinge moment necessary to move the control surface.

balanced low pass filter. A low pass filter (q.v.) designed to be used with a balanced line.

balanced modulation. A system of adding sound to radio wave transmission whereby only the sidebands are transmitted, the carrier being eliminated.

balanced surface. A balanced aileron, rudder, or the like. A surface may be balanced for static conditions or for conditions where aerodynamic forces act upon it (dynamic conditions). *See also* aerodynamic balanced surface.

balancer. *See* dynetric balancer.

ballast tube. A resistance element sealed in a tube, usually in a hydrogen atmosphere, used as a series component of a circuit to maintain the current constant. This is accomplished by designing the ballast tube so the resistance increases and decreases rapidly with corresponding changes of current through it.

ballistic camera. A camera used to photograph

high velocity phenomena. Usually fixed in position with continuously open shutters or with very high frame speed so that successive images at precise times are available for study.

ballistic case. Any shell or casing given efficient ballistic characteristics, used to enclose explosive elements for delivery on a target; any bomb, shell, or rocket case.

ballistic coefficient (W/C_DA). A ratio used as an index of performance of nose cones or other bodies entering the atmosphere; the ratio of weight to drag. W = weight; C_D = drag coefficient; A = characteristic area.

ballistic condition. Any one of the conditions affecting the motion and behavior of a projectile in flight. Ballistic conditions may include velocity, weight, size, and shape of missile, rotation of the Earth, density of the air, etc.

ballistic curve. The curve described by the actual path of a rocket or missile (after its fuel is cut off) as determined by the ballistic conditions, i.e., by the velocity due to the propulsive force, by gravity, wind, temperature, etc.

ballistic density. A theoretical constant density of the atmosphere that would have the same effect on a missile in flight as the varying densities actually encountered.

ballistic efficiency. (1) The efficiency of a missile in overcoming air resistance, gravity, and other ballistic conditions. (2) The external efficiency of a rocket or other jet engine of a missile. *See* external efficiency.

ballistic guided missile. A ballistic missile (q.v.) which is guided during the powered portion of the trajectory (q.v.) and utilizes a free ballistic path during a portion of its flight.

ballistic lead. The correction or allowance for wind effects and gravity made when computing a lead angle.

ballistic missile. Any missile guided especially in the upward part of its trajectory, but becoming a free-falling body in the latter stages of its flight through the atmosphere. Such a missile contains guiding devices, such as preset mechanisms, but is distinguished from a guided missile (q.v.) in that it becomes a free-falling body, subject to ballistic reactions as it descends through the atmosphere. Currently, the term has a strong connotation of a missile designed to travel outside, or in the outer reaches of, the atmosphere before plunging to its target.

ballistic missile early warning system (BMEWS). That part of the anti-Intercontinental Ballistic Missile program associated with the long range radar elements.

ballistic missile, fleet. *See* fleet ballistic missile.

ballistic pendulum. An instrument used for measuring the horizontal velocity component of a projectile. In its usual form it consists of a simple pendulum of mass M, and of natural frequency f. A projectile of mass m, moving with a velocity V strikes the bob and is imbedded in it. The maximum excursion X of the bob is then measured. Assuming that $M \gg m$ and that little damping is present, it may be shown by application of conservation laws that

$$B = \frac{2\pi f \times M}{m}$$

ballistics. The science that deals with the motion of projectiles. *Interior ballistics* deals with the propulsion of the projectile, and *exterior ballistics* with the path it follows when it is not guided.

ballistics. *Types of, see* exterior–; interior–; internal–; penetration–; terminal–.

ballistic temperature. A theoretical constant temperature that would have the same effect on a missile in flight as the varying temperatures actually encountered.

ballistic trajectory. The trajectory of a body when its energy is less than one-half escape energy. It is a missile trajectory which follows a symmetrical path from launch to impact. The powered flight portion is followed by a "pure" ballistic or an elliptical trajectory to reentry. See Fig. 27, page 293.

ballistic wave. An audible disturbance caused by the compression of air ahead of a projectile or missile in flight.

ballistic wind (ballwin). A theoretical or assumed constant wind that would have the same effect on a missile, or on a bomb, from the point of its departure to its target as the varying winds actually encountered.

ballistic wind, differential. See differential ballistic wind.

ballistite. A colloidal propellant composed of nitroglycerin and nitrocellulose formed with the aid of a solvent; invented by Alfred Nobel in 1888.

balloon tanks. Propellant or fuel tanks which depend on internal pressure to stabilize the tank walls to provide a compressive load-carrying capability.

ballwin. Ballistic wind (q.v.).

balum. A piece of wire of any specified length, used in connection with a VHF antenna lead-in.

balun. (*balance-un*balance) Precision-wound auto-transformer for adapting from balanced to unbalanced lines. Used to prevent mismatch losses in electrical systems.

band. In electronics, a given segment of the electromagnetic spectrum, i.e., a range of frequencies within two definite limits. See Fig. 8, page 105.

band. *Types of, see* broadband, C-band; dead–; guard–; K-band; L-band; luminous–; pass band (of a filter); P-band; Q-band; S-band; telemeter–; twilight–; V-band; X-band; zodiacal–.

band-elimination filter. Two or more tuned circuits adjusted to highly attenuate a band of frequencies within predetermined upper and lower frequency limits. The graphical result (selectivity curve) is ideally an approximation of a square wave which has the required width.

band-pass filter. A network (electrical, mechanical, or acoustical) which passes a band of frequencies between two particular frequencies. The geometrical *mean* is equal to the geometric *mid-frequency* of the pass band.

band-rejection filter. A network (electrical, mechanical, or acoustical) which rejects a band of frequencies between two particular frequencies. The geometrical *mean* is equal to the geometrical *mid-frequency* of the reject band.

bandwidth. In electronics, the difference expressed in cps between the lowest and highest effective frequencies for a given frequency-limited system at which a desired fraction of the maximum output is obtained (usually determined by the half-power points in the frequency spectrum of the device); may refer to a tuned circuit, modulated radio signal, servo-mechanism, radio station channel assignment, etc.

bandwidth. *Types of, see* antenna, attained–; design–; discriminator–; filter–; maximum system–; noise–; receiver–.

bang-bang control. A control method wherein the corrective control applied to a missile is always applied to the full extent of possible servo motion. The frequency and dwell may vary.

banner cloud. A cloud floating from a tall mountain peak and suggesting a banner. It may be caused by reduced atmospheric pressure on the leeward side of the peak or may consist wholly or in part of drifting snow.

bar. In aerodynamics, a unit of atmospheric pressure equal to the pressure of one million dynes per sq cm. (The bar is equal to 29.5306 in. of mercury at 32°F at 45° latitude.)

1 bar = 0.98692 atmosphere = 10^6 dynes/sq cm = 10,197 kg/sq m = 2089 lb/sq ft = 14.50 lb/sq in.

BAR. Bureau of Aeronautics Representative.

barn. In nuclear applications, a unit of area equal to 10^{-24} cm². Cross sections per atom are customarily measured in *barns*.

baro. Abbreviation for barometer (q.v.).

barogram. A graphic record showing variations in atmospheric pressure.

barograph. A barometer that imprints a continuous record of atmospheric pressure on a graph. Also termed a *barometrograph*.

barometer. An instrument for measuring the atmospheric pressure.

barometric fuel control. A device that maintains the correct flow of fuel to a missile engine by adjusting to atmospheric pressure at different altitudes, as well as to impact pressure.

barometric fuze. A device similar to an aneroid-type altimeter used to perform certain program steps in the arming and detonation of an explosive device.

baroport. An opening on an aerodynamic surface where the effects of velocity on local air pressure introduce the least uncertainty in predicted altitude versus pressure relationships.

baroswitch. A pressure-sensitive device which provides a signal to a circuit.

barrage jamming. The simultaneous jamming (q.v.) of a number of adjacent channels or frequencies.

barrier. *Types of, see* altitude–; sonic–; sound, thermodynamic–; transonic–.

barycenter. (1) The center of gravity of the Earth-Moon system. (2) The center of gravity of any set of revolving masses.

base. *Types of, see* cloud–; hard–; soft–; support–; time–.

base altitude. An altitude maintained during a given flight, especially on the flight to the target.

base complex. In Air Force terminology, an air base for support of Air Force units consisting of landing strips and all components or related facilities for which the Air Force has operating responsibility, together with interior lines of communication and the minimum surrounding area required for local security. *See* hard base; launch base area; soft base.

base hardness. A description of the degree to which a missile facility installation is protected against enemy inflicted damage.

base line. In electronics, a flowing line on a radar screen representing the track covered by a radar scanner (q.v.). Echoes from reflecting objects appear as pronounced irregularities in the line.

base of trajectory. A straight line between the two ends of a trajectory (q.v.). See Fig. 27, page 293.

base pressure. The pressure at the rear or base of a missile. The *base pressure* has a large negative value with reference to the free stream pressure, thereby creating considerable drag, especially if the base is large. (The presence of a jet at the rear of a missile will decrease the effective base area as long as the jet is in operation.)

base support equipment (BSE). That portion of the unit mission equipment (q.v.) for tactical operation units which permits the establishment of *base-type* functions necessary to support a tactical mission.

base surge. The concentrated wave or cloud of mist or dust which shoots out from the foundation of the column caused by an underwater or underground nuclear explosion.

basic dry rating. The thrust at sea level of a jet engine not using water injection.

basic frequency. That frequency of a periodic quantity which is considered to be the most important. In a driven system, it is generally the driving frequency, while in most periodic waves it would correspond to the *fundamental* frequency.

basic load. In stress analysis, the load on a structural member or part of a missile in a condition of static equilibrium. When a specific basic load is meant, the particular condition of equilibrium must be indicated.

basic research. The theoretical or experimental study directed toward the increase of knowledge. It may result in the discovery of new scientific phenomena, principles, techniques, or significant data which add to the store of scientific knowledge. Immediate practical application is not necessarily a direct objective. This research is often done in phases, or by different people, each working on a part of the total effort, in which case any part of the activity is considered basic research. It involves continuous reappraisal of fact and hypothesis.

basic weight. The engine or missile weight that includes all fixed operating equipment, fixed furnishings, trapped fuel and oil.

battery. *Types of, see* primary–; reserve–; secondary–; thermal–.

battleship design. A term used to describe a very heavy structure simulating an airborne article and having certain characteristics to permit special tests.

battleship tanks. Heavily constructed, full-scale models of propellant tanks for testing flow and movement of propellants in order to derive final configuration of missile tanks.

battle short. An electrical circuit safety technique in which appropriate fusing is provided for test and checkout, but is shorted out for ultimate use conditions.

baud. A unit of signaling speed. The speed in bauds is the number of code elements transmitted per second.

bay. The space between two bulkheads or other structural partitions.

BAZOOKA. A light-weight rocket launcher developed by the U.S. principally for use against tanks.

BDA. Bomb Damage Assessment.

BDM. Bomber defense missile. Air Force cognizance.

Design adapted from HAWK (q.v.). Missile to be fired by bombers against attacking fighters.

Prime Contractor: General Electric Co., Special Products Division.

BDS. Bomb Damage Survey.

beacon. A device which serves as a signal for use as a guidance or warning aid. Radar beacons (q.v.) aid the radar set in locating and identifying special targets which may be difficult or impossible to sense otherwise.

beacon. *Types of, see* cone marker–; DME ground–; equisignal–; nondirectional–; radar splasher–; tracker–; Z marker–.

beacon antenna. *See* omnidirectional antenna.

beacon presentation. A radarscope presentation resulting from radio-frequency waves sent out by a radar beacon (q.v.).

beaconry. The science of using a beacon as a guidance or warning aid.

beam. A stream of radio or radar pulses or waves; the steady hum in an equisignal zone.

beam. *Types of, see* cosecant-squared–; electron–; fan–; pencil–; radar–; split–; variable elevation–.

beam capture. In a radar beam rider guidance (q.v.) system, the act of placing a missile in the radar beam so as to use coded guidance signals. Particularly applicable for those trajectories in which the missile is not tracked from launch

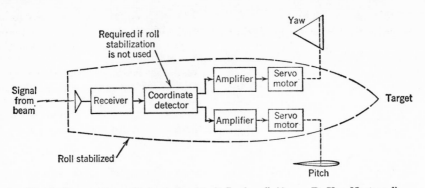

Fig. 2. Beam rider guided missile. (A. S. Locke, *Guidance*, D. Van Nostrand)

but depends on firing the missile through the beam to effect capture. See Fig. 27, page 293.

beam jitter. A small oscillatory, angular movement induced into the radar antenna array, and consequently into the radar beam. This movement is caused by: (a) the necessity of having to develop an error signal, when in automatic tracking, before the antenna will change its position; or (b) the circuitry being made intentionally "tight" to obtain plus and minus errors rather than only lagging errors; or (c) gear play in the radar tracking head.

beam loading. In electronics, energy loss from a cavity due to the coupling of the cavity to an electron beam.

beam rider (beam riding system). A guidance system in which the missile is directed along a line (often the line of sight, q.v.) between the beam source and the target no matter whether corrective control commands are generated automatically within the missile (*true beam rider*) or at a control point on the ground and transmitted to the missile (*command system*). See beam rider guidance. See Fig. 2, and Fig. 27, page 293.

beam rider guidance. A system for guiding missiles in which the vehicle rides along a beam (usually a radar beam) to its target. The beam along which the missile travels may be either movable or fixed; in the former case control is exercised over the missile in flight by moving the beam. See Fig. 2.

beamwidth. The angular separation in azimuth (q.v.) between the two directions to the right and to the left of the center of the beam, at which the power gain is one-half that at the center. Beamwidth may be measured also in elevation, in the vertical plane, or in an enclosed plane. See half power; side lobe.

beamwidth error. An error or distortion pre-

sented on a radarscope which is caused by the width of the scanning beam causing the target to appear wider than it actually is, or by covering two targets in a single sweep, thus making them appear as one target.

bearing. Relative position or direction with respect to a point and line of reference in a horizontal plane. It is often identified with azimuth (q.v.).

beast. (Vernacular) A missile.

beat frequency. When two signals of different frequencies are applied to a nonlinear circuit, they will combine, or beat together, and give, among other components, one which has a frequency equal to the difference of the two applied frequencies. This difference frequency is known as the *beat frequency*.

beat frequency oscillator (BFO). A device from which a single audio frequency (q.v.) is obtained by combining and rectifying two higher frequencies.

beats. Periodic variations in amplitude, which may be described as a superposition of disturbances having different frequencies.

beat, zero. See zero beat.

Beaufort Wind Scale. An arbitrary scale of wind velocities.

Code Number	Wind Velocity (mph)	Description
0	0-1	Calm
1	1-3	Light air
2	4-7	Light breeze
3	8-12	Gentle breeze
4	13-18	Moderate breeze
5	19-24	Fresh breeze
6	25-31	Strong breeze
7	32-38	Moderate gale
8	39-46	Fresh gale
9	47-54	Strong gale
10	55-63	Whole gale
11	64-75	Storm
12	Over 75	Hurricane

beavertail. A fan-shaped radar beam, wide in the horizontal plane and narrow in the vertical plane.

beeper. (Vernacular) An individual who directs an unmanned aircraft or missile by remote control.

behavior. *Types of, see* dynamic–; static–.

Belgium block course. An environmental test facility for evaluating the transportation environment. The course is a specially prepared road bed having varying degrees of roughness, waviness, and other controlled characteristics over which wheeled equipment is moved at varying speeds to study the effect of transportation shock and vibration.

bell nozzle. *See* Prandtl nozzle.

belt, high-temperature. *See* high-temperature belt.

belt, Van Allen. *See* Van Allen belt.

bending stress. The stress received by an object subjected to both tensile and compressive forces.

beneficial occupancy date (BOD). That date when buildings and/or other construction are completed to a point which would permit occupancy by a unit organization and installation team for the purpose of installing unit equipment and special and/or fixed equipment that is not included as installed equipment. Operational use is possible as soon as unit and special equipment are in place.

Bernoulli's theorem (binomial distribution). The theorem that if the chance of an event occurring upon a single trial is p, and if a number of independent trials are made, the probability P that the ratio of the number of successes n to the number of trials N differs from p by less than any pre-assigned quantity, however small, can be made as near certain as may be desired by making the number of trials sufficiently large. The theorem may be restated: "If the probability of an event is p, and if an infinity of trials are made, the proportion of successes is sure to be p."

$$P_n = \frac{p^n(1-p)^{N-n}N!}{n!(N-n)}$$

Beta 57-1. According to the International Geophysical Year code system used for identifying Earth satellites, this is the Russian-launched SPUTNIK II satellite and attached rocket launching vehicle (which was not separated from the rocket). See Table 6, page 245.

Beta 58. According to the International Geophysical Year code system used for identifying Earth satellites, this is the American VANGUARD

I (q.v.). It was launched by the Navy on March 17, 1958, and the 3.25-lb payload is expected to orbit for more than 200 years. See Table 6, page 245.

beta gain. For transistors, the ratio of the change in collector current to the change in base current with collector plus emitter voltages held constant; designated by the symbol β and related to α by the equation:

$$\beta = \frac{\alpha}{1-\alpha}$$

beta particles. Charged particles emitted from a nucleus and having a mass and charge equal in magnitude to those of the electron. Sometimes termed *high-speed electrons*. They are dangerous to living tissues.

BETTY (MK90). Navy development. An offshoot of LULU, the MK90 is a nuclear depth charge which can be launched from ships as well as aircraft.

BFO. Beat Frequency Oscillator (q.v.).

bias. The direct-current voltage between two elements of a vacuum tube; grid bias.

bias. *Types of, see* fixed–; grid–.

Bickford fuse. A central core of black powder surrounded by a protective shield; also known as *miner's fuse* or *safety fuse*. It burns at a rate of about 1 ft/min and is used for communicating fire.

biconvex (section) airfoil. An aerodynamic surface whose cross section is formed by a double circular arc. The wave drag is:

$$C_{D_w} = \frac{5.33r^2}{\sqrt{M^2-1}}$$

where r = ratio of maximum thickness to chord of the cross-sectional shape; M = MACH number.

bifurcated layer. The E layer of ions in the ionosphere (q.v.) which sometimes splits into two layers about nine miles apart.

BIG BROTHER. *See* SENTRY.

billow cloud. A cloud composed of nearly equally spaced parallel bands of thick cloud, usually having clear sky intervening between the bands. Also termed a *wave cloud* or *windrow cloud*.

binary code. A process or means of identifying the digits in a binary system (e.g., pulses varying in duration or spacing).

binary digit. A choice between two equiprobable events; the number of elements or marks used to represent each discrete quantity or value in a set of measurements, thereby determining the accuracy of representation (e.g., 10 bits would allow a quantity to be measured or represented to an accuracy of one part in $2^{10} = 1024$).

binary number system. A number system which uses two symbols (usually denoted by "0" and "1") and which has two as its radix, as opposed to the decimal system which uses ten symbols (denoted "0, 1, . . . , 9") and has ten as its radix. *See* radix.

binary pulse code modulation. Pulse code modulation (q.v.) in which the code for each element of information consists of one of two distinct kinds or values, such as pulses and spaces.

binary star (multiple star). A star consisting of two component stars which revolve about their common center of gravity. A *multiple star* is a system of more than two components.

binomial antenna array. A type of broadside antenna (q.v.) in which the radiation pattern will contain a single lobe (or two lobes if the pattern is bidirectional). All of the antennas are fed in the same phase, they are uniformly spaced at half-wavelength intervals, and the relative current amplitudes in various elements in the array follow the numbers of the binomial expansion.

binomial distribution. *See* Bernoulli's theorem.

bioastronautics. That field which covers the study of the effect of space environment on man; commonly termed *space medicine*.

bi-propellant. (1) A rocket propellant consisting of two unmixed chemicals fed to the combustion chamber separately [e.g., oxidizer (LOX) and fuel (RP-1)]. Contrast with *monopropellant* and *multipropellant* (q.q.v.). (2) A solid rocket propellant combination in which several propellant compositions are used to provide tailored thrust-time characteristics. The propellants are not mixed but are cast separately to the desired configuration within the same container.

bird. (Vernacular) A missile.

bird cage. (Vernacular) A directional gyroscope (q.v.).

BIRD DOG. *See* GENIE.

bird dog. (Vernacular) A radio direction-finder (q.v.).

bistatic radar. A system of two radars used for early warning. It provides good time resolution, but poor position accuracy and a ghost target at the third intersection of the beams are disadvantages.

bit. *B*inary dig*it* (q.v.).

B-kill. *See* kill.

BL. Butt Line (q.v.).

black body. An object that absorbs all of the radiation falling on it, neither reflecting nor transmitting any of the radiation.

black box. (1) A term used loosely to refer to any sub-component that is equipped with "connects" and "disconnects" so that it can be readily inserted or removed from a specified place in a larger system (e.g., the complete missile, or some major subdivision) without benefit of knowledge of its detailed internal structure. (2) A term pertaining either to the functional transformation that acts upon a specified input to give a particular output, or to the apparatus for accomplishing this transformation (without regard to the detailed circuitry used).

black fog. A fog containing a large amount of soot, as may occur over large industrial cities.

blank. To cut off the beam in a cathode-ray tube (q.v.).

blanket release system. A device for removal of insulation coverings from a missile immediately before firing. The covers are used to maintain the low temperature of the loaded cryogenic propellants and thus minimize boiloff.

blast. The brief and rapid increase in air pressure resulting from the detonation of any explosive matter.

blast chamber. (Vernacular) A combustion chamber.

blast cluster warhead. Composed of a number of sub-warheads, or sub-missiles (q.v.), each of which is a missile equipped with a full complement of armament.

blast deflector. A large curved metal plate used to deflect rocket exhaust gases from a test stand.

blast furnace. (Vernacular) A missile engine.

blastoff. (Vernacular) In astronautics, the take-off of a manned rocket.

blast pressure. The impact pressure of the air set in motion by an explosion.

blast warhead. A warhead (q.v.) designed primarily to convert its latent energy to a center of high pressure which is propagated away from the original warhead position. It damages targets by subjecting the target surface or structure to extreme pressure.

blast wave. The air wave set in motion by an explosion.

blip. The figure presented on the oscilloscope (q.v.) of a radar caused by the echo from the target. Also termed *pip*.

blip-scan ratio. In electronics, the ratio between a single recognizable blip (q.v.) on a radarscope and the number of scans necessary to produce it (varies with range, antenna tilt, target aspect, wind, etc.).

BLO. Butt Line Zero.

block diagram. A line drawing used to describe the functional interrelationship among the components of a system.

blockhouse. A building, usually heavily reinforced and near a launch site (q.v.), that houses the electronic equipment and controls for countdown (q.v.) and firing of a missile, together with auxiliary apparatus & personnel.

blocking capacitor or condenser. Any condenser used in a radio circuit to block the flow of direct current while allowing alternating current signals to pass.

blocking oscillator. An electrical circuit used to generate very narrow pulses of electrical energy. Two types are used: (a) *free running*—determines its own repetition rate and thus may be used as a master oscillator; (b) *driven*—used to convert broad trigger pulses into sharp, short pulses (approx. 1 microsecond duration).

blooming. (Vernacular) The expansion and distortion of the target spot on the face of a cathode ray tube (q.v.).

blow. (Vernacular) (1) Blowout or flameout (q.v.); (2) An explosive failure.

blow down. In firings (q.v.), simulated missile thrust engine system operation with noncombustible fuel combinations.

blower. A motor drive fan used for equipment ventilation.

blowoff. Separation of an instrument section or "package" from the remainder of the rocket vehicle by application of explosive force, to permit retrieval of instruments after they have collected the required information.

blowout, acceleration. *See* acceleration blowout.

blowout disc. A mechanism consisting generally of a thin metal diaphragm, used in a solid rocket (q.v.) as a safety measure against excess gas pressure in the combustion chamber or in any pressure vessel for relief of overpressure.

BLUE GOOSE. *See* GOOSE.

blue phone line. A party line telephone system which provides a link between personnel involved in the countdown (q.v.) procedure. All conversations over this system are automatically tape recorded.

BMC. Ballistic Missile Center, Air Materiel Command; Inglewood, California. Formerly BMO (q.v.).

BMD. Ballistic Missile Division, Air Research and Development Command (ARDC); Inglewood, California. Formerly designated WDD.

BMEWS. Ballistic Missile Early Warning System (q.v.).

BMO. Ballistic Missile Office, Air Materiel Command; Inglewood, California. Changed to Ballistic Missile Center (BMC) in 1958.

BMTS program. Ballistic Missile Test Systems. A program to provide a standardized test bed for ballistic missile test systems. Reliable missiles with established performance and high payload capability are planned to be used [e.g., THOR, ATLAS (q.q.v.)].

BOA. Broad Ocean Area.

board. *Types of, see* plotting–; Research and Development–.

boattail. The section of a missile body where the diameter is continually decreasing toward the rear. The principal purpose of a boattail is to reduce the overall aerodynamic drag of a missile airframe by reducing the base drag.

bobbing. (Vernacular) The fluctuation of the target spot on a radarscope.

BOD. Beneficial Occupancy Date (q.v.).

Bode chart. (or diagram) A plot of phase versus frequency or gain versus frequency to describe the frequency response characteristics of an amplifier, servo, or other device.

Bode's law. A numerical relationship for plotting the distances of the planets. Take the numbers 0, 3, 6, 12, 24, 48, 96, 192, and 384, each of which (apart from the first two) is double its predecessor. Add 4 to each. Taking the Earth's distance from the Sun as 10, this second series gives the distances of the other planets as follows:

Planet	Distance by Bode's Law	Actual Distance
Mercury	4	3.9
Venus	7	7.2
Earth	10	10
Mars	16	15.2
Ceres	28	27.7
Jupiter	52	52.0
Saturn	100	95.4
Uranus	196	191.8
Neptune	—	300.7
Pluto	388	394.6

The law breaks down for Neptune, and the Bode distance corresponds much more closely to that of Pluto; but when the law was announced, Uranus, Neptune, and Pluto were unknown. Nor was there a known planet corresponding to the distance 28, and the discovery of Ceres, the largest of the asteroids, was regarded as an extra verification of the rule. It is still uncertain whether Bode's law is fundamental, or is due purely to chance.

body. *Types of, see* gray–; reentry–.

body hardware. The fittings and parts connected to an airframe. They are usually part of the airframe assembly.

body lift. Aerodynamic lift on a fuselage or missile body resulting from an angle of attack (q.v.) of the body.

body mounted gyroscope. A gyroscope (q.v.) mounted directly on the airframe (q.v.), thereby using the airframe as a reference in lieu of a stabilized platform (q.v.).

bogey weight. A system or group weight established as a target at the start of a design. (It is usually fixed by the weight group and is periodically adjusted as a program progresses.) Also termed *target weight.*

boil-off. The vapor loss from any volatile liquid (e.g., liquid oxygen); particularly when stored in a missile ready for flight.

BOLD ORION. Air-to-surface ballistic missile study program. Air Force designation was WS 199; succeeded by WS 138A.

Two-stage solid propellant rocket with a 1000-mile range. Bomber launched.

Martin Co. and Lockheed Missile System Division worked on the study. *See* WS 199 B and C.

bolide. A fireball or bright meteor which explodes in the course of its flight through the atmosphere. *See* meteor.

bolometer. (1) A very sensitive type of metallic resistance thermometer, used for measurements of thermal radiation. *See* infrared detector. (2) In electronics, a small resistive element capable of dissipating microwave power, and using the heat so developed to effect a change in its resistance, thus serving as an indicator; commonly used as a detector in low- and medium-level power measurement.

bolometric magnitude. If a bolometer (q.v.) is joined to a spectroscope, the distribution of energy radiated in the infrared region of the spectrum of the source can be measured. From this, and by an application of the Stefan-Boltzman law (q.v.), a star's total emission of energy may be calculated. According to this quantity, a star is given a *bolometric magnitude,* and the scale has been arbitrarily adjusted so that for the Sun the *visual magnitude* is equal to the bolometric magnitude. For nearly all other stars, the bolometric magnitude is *less* than the visual magnitude; i.e., a *greater* part of their total

radiated energy lies outside the visible range than in the case of the Sun.

BOMARC. Surface-to-air interceptor missile. Air Force designation: IM-99. The name is derived from the early joint effort of *BO*eing and *M*ichigan *A*eronautical *R*esearch *C*enter.

Length: 47 ft 4 in.; span: 18 ft 2 in.; body diameter: 38 in.; launching weight: 15,000 lb; cruising speed: MACH 2.7; ultimate range: over 250 miles. Liquid propellant boost engine with gimbal-mounted chamber and twin Marquardt RJ 3 ramjets for cruise propulsion. IM-99B has a speed of approximately MACH 4 and operating altitude of 100,000 ft and uses a Thiokol solid propellant booster.

Prime Contractor: Boeing Airplane Co. Airframe: Boeing. Ramjet engines: Marquardt Aircraft Co. Rocket engine: Aerojet-General Corp. Guidance system (radar and active homing): Westinghouse Electric Corp.

bomb. *Types of, see* glide–; nominal–.

bomb damage assessment. *See* indirect bomb damage assessment.

bomber. *Types of, see* antipodal–; boost-glide–; skip-glide–.

bombing altitude, relative distances. According to the *Dictionary of U.S. Military Terms for Joint Usage:*

minimum	below 900 ft above the surface
low	between 900 and 8,000 ft above the surface
medium	between 8,000 and 15,000 ft above the surface
high	over 15,000 ft above the surface

bonding. A system of connections or contacts which insures that the metal parts of a vehicle form a continuous electrical unit, thus preventing the arcing of static electricity, and to provide a continuous ground plane.

boom. *Types of, see* airspeed–; nose cone–; sonic–.

boost. A descriptive term that defines the use of rocket propulsion, either solid or liquid propellant types, during initial climb, liftoff, and the first phase of propelled flight.

BOOSTED DEACON. A solid propellant high altitude rocket using the DEACON (q.v.) military rocket which forms part of the ROCKOON (q.v.) together with an AEROBEE (q.v.) type of booster and tower launching. BOOSTED DEACONS were used during the International Geophysical Year to explore the upper atmosphere up to 60 miles. The DEACON rocket is 16 ft in length and 8 in. in body diameter and weighs 200 lb. Its rocket motor gives a thrust of 5,700 lb for 3.5 sec.

booster. (1) In the launching system, an auxiliary propulsion system which travels with the missile and which may or may not separate from the missile when its impulse has been delivered. *See* booster rocket. A booster system may contain or consist of one or more units. *See* Jato. (2) In warheads, a high-explosive element sufficiently sensitive to be actuated by small explosive elements in a fuze and powerful enough to cause detonation of the main explosive charge.

booster. *Types of, see* auxiliary–; frangible–; warhead–.

booster assembly. The structure which is used with some missile types to support one or more Jatos (q.v.), transmit thrust to the missile, and orient the thrust line with respect to the center of gravity of the combination.

booster bottle. (Vernacular) A rocket used for a jet-assisted takeoff (q.v.).

booster impact area. The area, down range and along the line of flight, where booster rockets (q.v.) strike the surface of the Earth after having been detached from a missile at staging (q.v.) or end of boost phase.

booster rocket. A separate rocket added to a missile for the purpose of providing initial velocity. Boosters are used to attain speeds required for initiation of ramjet engine (q.v.) operation, provide rapid accelerations, assist in takeoff, etc. The initial stage of any two (or more) stage missiles (q.v.) is termed the *booster* (q.v.).

boost-glide vehicle. A vehicle, with wings or similar aerodynamic surfaces, which is propelled upward by rocket engines in the manner of a satellite or ICBM (q.v.) into the outer fringes of the atmosphere to glide or skip-glide on the atmosphere (comparable with a stone skipping over water) for long distances while completing its mission. *See* skip-glide vehicle.

boot-strap operation. In liquid rocket engine usage, a regenerative process used for starting. A portion of the turbopump output is fed back to the gas generator (q.v.) which causes an increase in energy available for driving the turbopump; which, in turn, delivers a greater quantity of propellants to the gas generator. The cycle terminates when rated system performance has been attained.

boranes. Rocket propellants based on compounds of boron and hydrogen. Specific impulses up to about 270 sec may be realized.

boresighting. (1) The process by which the axis of a radar, launcher, or gun bore and the line-of-sight of a sighting device are made parallel or made to converge on a point. (2) In electronics, the alignment of a radar beam with a fixed target to obtain initial settings.

boresight tower. A tower on which there are mounted a visual target and an electrical target (an antenna fed from a signal generator); these targets are used for the parallel alignment of the electrical axis of a receiving antenna and the optical axis of a telescope mounted on the antenna.

BOTLO. Navy *B*ureau of *O*rdnance *T*echnical *L*iaison *O*fficer.

bottle. *See* Rato bottle.

bounce. (Vernacular) In electronics, the fluctuation in magnitude of target echoes on a radarscope.

boundary conditions. Those known relations in a given physical problem which allow selection of the proper solution of one or more differential equations (e.g., when the variables of a problem are *distances*, the boundary conditions may well take the form of numbers which represent the value of the variable at some outer boundary of the space under consideration; when a variable of a problem is *time*, part of the boundary conditions may be the initial and final values of the unknowns).

boundary layer. In aerodynamics, the thin region of nearly static fluid (e.g., air) near the surface over which the fluid stream is moving.

boundary layer. *Types of, see* laminar–; turbulent–.

boundary layer control. The design or control of airfoils and certain airfoil attachments to reduce or remove undesirable aerodynamic effects (e.g., parasitic drag, q.v.) caused by the boundary layer.

bound vortex. In aerodynamics, a hypothetical vortex circulating around the center-of-pressure line of an airfoil (a simplification of the actual aerodynamic forces acting on a wing; used for mathematical purposes).

Bowen-Knapp camera. A very high speed, strip film, ballistic camera used for missile flight test documentation.

box. *Types of, see* black–; brain–; echo–; nozzle–.

brachistochronic problem. In space navigation, the problem associated with the minimum time required to reach a given point in space.

brain box. (Vernacular) A device, especially an electronic device, used to control a mechanism.

brains. (Vernacular) A guidance system.

braking. *See* atmospheric braking.

braking ellipses. In astronautics, the path used to retard the speed of a reentry body (q.v.) upon entering the Earth's (or other) atmosphere without the use of propulsion forces. The atmosphere is grazed with successively deeper penetrations on each ellipse (q.v.) and with a return to higher altitude to permit cooling outside the sensible atmosphere (q.v.). Eventually the speed is reduced to a sufficient extent to permit conventional landings. Sometimes termed *braking orbit*.

braking rocket. In astronautics, the rocket tubes installed in the tail assembly of a jet-propelled craft or vehicle. Upon a tail-first descent for landing, braking rockets are fired in order to slow the vehicle down sufficiently to accomplish a safe, smooth landing.

breadboard. An assembly of parts and/or components to test the feasibility of a proposed design. Usually is not packaged for "end use."

break. (1) A fault in an electrical circuit. (2) A type of presentation of a reflected pulse on a radarscope, appearing as a line perpendicular to the base line. (3) In communications, to interrupt a received transmission in a circuit in order to send signals to the transmitting station on the same circuit.

breakdown voltage. (1) The voltage at which an insulator or dielectric ruptures. (2) The voltage at which ionization and conduction take place in a gas or vapor.

breakthrough. (1) A penetration of the defenses of an enemy. (2) Any sudden success in scientific or technological advancement that opens the way to a new area.

breeder reactor. *See* breeding.

breeding. The process whereby a fissionable species is utilized as a source of neutrons to produce more nuclei of its own kind than are used up. This is the function of a *breeder reactor*.

breeze. *See* valley breeze.

bremsstrahlung. In atomic physics, an X-radiation caused by the collision of an atomic nucleus with an atomic particle such as a beta particle (q.v.).

brennschluss. Burnout. The termination of combustion in a rocket.

bridge. *See* resistance bridge.

briefing. A brief explanation; the instructions or lecture given before the flight of a vehicle regarding procedures to be followed, weather conditions, target, or any other subject pertinent to a flight or test.

brisance. The shattering effect of an explosion on materials.

British thermal unit (Btu). A unit of heat measurement. The quantity of heat required to increase the temperature of one pound of water one degree Fahrenheit at atmospheric pressure. *See also* mean British thermal unit.

$$1 \quad Btu = 251.98 \quad calories = 777.97 \quad ft\text{-}lb = 0.0003929 \quad hphr = 1054 \quad joules = 0.0002930 \quad kwhr = 0.2930 \quad watt\text{-}hr = 1054.8 \ watt\text{-}sec$$

$$1 \ Btu/min = 777.97 \ ft\text{-}lb/min = 0.02358 \ hp = 17.580 \ watts$$

$$1 \ Btu/sec = 1.415 \ hp = 1.0548 \ kw$$

$$1 \ Btu/sq \ ft/min = 0.1221 \ watt/sq \ in.$$

broadband. In electronics, a band having a wide range of frequencies.

broad beam antenna. In radar, an antenna that sends out a broad search beam.

broadside antenna array. Parallel antenna elements with currents in phase combined to form a broadside array (q.v.), so named because the direction of maximum radiation is broadside to the plane containing the antennas. The resulting radiation pattern has circular symmetry about the line of antennas as an axis.

broadside array. In electronics, an antenna array having its direction of maximum radiation perpendicular to the line or plane of the array.

bromine pentafluoride (BrF$_5$). A liquid rocket propellant *oxidizer*. See Table 3, page 157.

B-scope. A radarscope which presents the range of a target by a vertical displacement of the target signal on the face of the scope, and the bearing by a horizontal displacement.

BSE. Base Support Equipment (q.v.).

BTL. Bell Telephone Laboratories; Whippany, New Jersey.

Btu. British thermal unit (q.v.).

BTV. (Obsolete) Battleship test vehicle. Originally an 18-in. diameter ramjet test vehicle built to survive a rugged environment. A test article in the Bumblebee Project (q.v.) series.

BuAer. Department of the Navy; *Bu*reau of *Aer*onautics.

bubble horizon. (1) A circle on the celestial sphere parallel to the celestial horizon (q.v.), formed by the intersection of the sphere with the plane of the sensible horizon as established by a bubble sextant. (2) The plane established by a bubble sextant, termed the *sensible horizon* (q.v.).

bucket. (Vernacular) One of the blades or vanes attached to the turbine wheel in a jet engine or to the wheel of a gyroscope (q.v.).

buffer. (1) An isolating circuit used to avoid reaction of a driven circuit on the corresponding driving circuit. (2) A storage device used to compensate for a difference in rate of flow of information, or time of occurrence of events when transmitting information from one device to another.

buffer amplifier. One or more stages of RF amplification used in a transmitter to build up the control crystal frequency to an appropriate level before modulation. This is to prevent feedback of undesired frequencies to the crystal.

buffer condenser. Any condenser connected in an electronic circuit for the purpose of reducing peak or surge voltage amplitude to protect other parts in the same or following circuits.

buffer stage. An amplifier stage used to prevent feedback of energy from a power stage to a preceding stage.

buffeting. Irregular oscillations of a surface or body when aerodynamic turbulence is encountered, especially under conditions of compressibility.

buffeting limit. The limit to which buffeting may be sustained without materiel failure.

bug. (Vernacular) A defect in a vehicle, piece of equipment, organization, procedure, etc.

bulk density. In liquid rocket usage, an important parameter in establishing the efficiency of a propellant from the point of view of energy available on a density basis. The product $I_{sp} \times$ bulk density is used as an index.

$$\text{bulk density, } d = \frac{\text{unit weight}}{\text{unit volume}}$$

bulk modulus. The measure of the change in volume of a material due to the application of pressure.

$$M_B = -\frac{\Delta p}{\Delta V / V}$$

where Δp = increase in pressure; ΔV = decrease in volume; V = original volume.

BULL DOG. Air-to-surface missile. Navy Bureau of Aeronautics cognizance.

A larger and improved version of the BULL PUP (q.v.); range: 25,000 to 30,000 ft; speed: MACH 2.

Prime Contractor: The Martin Co., Orlando, Florida.

BULL GOOSE. *See* GOOSE.

BULL PUP. Air-to-surface missile. Navy Bureau of Aeronautics designation: ASM-N-7. A variant is expected to be used by the Air Force (WHITE LANCE). A predecessor of BULL DOG (q.v.).

Length: 11 ft; body diameter: 12 in.; wing span: 37 in.; launching weight: 600 lb; flight speed: MACH 1.8; maximum slant range: 15,000 ft. Solid propellant rocket engine. Command/optical guidance system.

Prime Contractor: The Martin Co., Orlando, Florida. Airframe: Martin. Engine: Aerojet-General Corp. Guidance system: Republic Aviation Corp.

Bumblebee Project. A project sponsored by the Navy Department, Bureau of Ordnance under the Section T arrangement and technically directed by the Applied Physics Laboratory/The Johns Hopkins University. A missile program which has led to the development of TALOS, TERRIER, TARTAR, TRITON (q.q.v.).

bumper. *See* meteor bumper.

BUMPER. Research rocket. The German V-2 was mated with the WAC-CORPORAL (q.v.) to test staging of missiles (in early days of rocket development) to heights as far as the ionosphere (q.v.).

BUMPER-WAC. A high-altitude research vehicle built by the General Electric Co. consisting of a modified German V-2 rocket used as a booster for an American WAC-CORPORAL (q.v.). This was the first successful two-step rocket and achieved a record altitude of 244 miles in 1949. In all, eight BUMPERS were launched, and some were programmed to follow almost horizontal trajectories in studies for the development of long-range weapons.

bump method. In aerodynamics, a method of testing vehicle models at supersonic speeds when the free-stream speed is subsonic (q.v.), by mounting the model on a bump in the wall of a wind tunnel.

BuOrd. Department of the Navy; *Bu*reau of *Ord*nance.

burble. Separation in the boundary layer (q.v.) of air about a stream-lined body, resulting in divergent velocities and pressures, especially over the upper surface of an airfoil. Causes loss of lift and increase of drag.

burble angle. A critical angle of attack (q.v.) for an airfoil.

burble, compressibility. *See* compressibility burble.

burble point. A point reached in an increasing angle of attack (q.v.) at which burble begins.

burner. (1) A combustion chamber, or can, in a jet engine. (2) A fuel-injection nozzle in the combustion chamber of a jet engine.

burner. *Types of, see* afterburner; end burner; oil burner; tailpipe.

burner basket. (Vernacular) An inner liner of a jet engine.

burner drag. Total internal drag due to the presence of a missile's propulsive system; usually includes the drag forces on the igniter, flame holders, diffuser wall, combustion chamber wall, etc.

burner ring. In a turbojet engine, a ring consisting of the fuel manifold together with the fuel nozzle for each combustion chamber.

burning. *Types of, see* afterburning; neutral–; outside–; progressive–; regressive–; resonant–; rough–.

burning rate. In solid propellant rockets, the rapidity with which the propellant burns. Usually it is linear and bears a relation to the chamber pressure as follows:

$$r_0 = a_2 p_c^n \frac{\dot{w}}{A_p \gamma_p}$$

where r_0 = linear burning rate, in./sec; p_c = combustion pressure, lb/sq in. abs.; n, a_2 = constants which must be determined by experiment. n is usually between 0.4 and 0.85; a is usually between 0.05 and 0.002; A_p = propellant burning surface, sq in.; γ_p = specific weight of propellant, lb/cu in.; $\dot{w}$ = propellant weight flow, lb/sec.

burning rate. *Types of, see* erosive–; linear–.

burning time, effective. *See* effective burning time.

burnout. The termination of combustion in a rocket; brennschluss (q.v.).

burnout point. The point on a missile trajectory (q.v.) at which the fuel supply of a specified rocket engine (booster, sustainer, or vernier) is cut off thus causing cessation of thrust.

burnout velocity. The velocity of a rocket, rocket-powered aircraft, or rocket-powered projectile when fuel combustion terminates.

In gravitationless, drag-free space, the velocity for vertical flight is:

$$V = V_j \log_e \frac{M_0}{M_0 - M_p}$$

In vertical flight, with gravity:

$$V = V_j \log_e \frac{M_0}{M_0 - M_p} - \bar{g}t$$

where V_j = exhaust velocity; M_0 = mass of rocket at takeoff; M_p = mass of rocket propellant; $\bar{g}$ = average acceleration of gravity; t = powered flight time.

See Fig. 27, page 293.

burnout weight. The weight of a missile at the time usable fuel supply is exhausted, but including any residual, unusable fuel.

burn-up. In astronautics, vaporization of an artificial satellite (q.v.) or other rocket by areodynamic heating in the Earth's atmosphere. *See also* orbital decay.

burst. (1) In missilery, the explosion of a warhead (q.v.). (2) In rocketry, the rupture of a solid propellant rocket case incident to excessive combustion pressure. (3) In rocketry, the rupture of a liquid propellant rocket tankage. (4) More generally, the rupture of any pressure vessel.

burst. *Types of, see* airburst–; deep water–; optimum height of–; surface–; underground–; underwater–.

bus bar. A metallic conductor used to carry a large current or used to make a common connection between several circuits.

BuShips. Department of the Navy; Bureau of Ships.

butt line. A longitudinal reference plane which is parallel to and includes the plane connecting the top and bottom points of a missile. The butt line number (inches) is negative to the left of butt line O and positive to the right of butt line O.

butyl mercaptan. A liquid rocket propellant *fuel*. See Table 3, page 157.

BuYdsDcks. Department of the Navy; Bureau of Yards and Docks.

buyer. In contractual terminology, the *unofficial* representative of an Air Force Procuring Contracting Officer (q.v.), whose authority is limited by the Procuring Contracting Officer. A buyer is not empowered to commit the Government unless so authorized by proper authority.

Buys-Ballot's law. In meteorology, a natural law that if an observer in the Northern Hemisphere stands with his back to the wind, the area of lower barometric pressure is on his left. *See* Coriolis force.

buzz. A noise set up by the vibrations of a control surface. Synonymous with *diffuser buzz* and *dither* (q.q.v.).

bypass condenser. A condenser used to provide a low impedance (q.v.) for radio or audio signals around a resistor or between a circuit terminal and ground.

bypass engine. A gas-turbine reaction propulsion engine, incorporating an air bypass duct, to provide high thrust without excessive jet stream velocities and giving low specific fuel consumption.

C

C*. Characteristic velocity (q.v.).

C$_L$. Lift coefficient (q.v.).

CAA. Civil Aeronautics Administration.

cabinet. *Types of, see* controlled temperature–; discriminator–.

CAFB. Cooke Air Force Base; SAC training and operational base; renamed Vandenberg Air Force Base, October, 1958.

cage. To lock the *gyroscope* (q.v.) of a gyro-controlled *instrument* in a fixed position with reference to its case.

CAJUN. Research rocket. It combines a NIKE (q.v.) booster with a DEACON (q.v.); replaced the ROCKOON (q.v.). During the International Geophysical Year, 65 CAJUNS were fired.

CAL. Cornell Aeronautical Laboratory; Buffalo, New York.

calculated risk. A risk of known proportions considered to be present if a given action is undertaken, but one deliberately accepted if alternative actions are believed inadequate for attaining the objective, or believed to involve greater risks.

caliber. (1) The outside diameter of a projectile. (2) In missiles, the maximum diameter of the body.

calibration. The process of determining the response characteristics of a device by measuring its output while an accurately known input is applied. It may also include adjustment of the device to minimize operational errors.

calibration. *Types of, see* discriminator–; end instrument–; inflight–; preflight system–; system–; radar–.

calibration curve. A curve which provides specific data concerning the operation of one specific piece of equipment. The curve is made by actually operating the equipment and recording the characteristics.

calibration timer. An airborne component of a telemetering system that supplies reference signals for the ground instrumentation equipment.

calibrator. *See* resistance calibrator.

calorie. *See* gram calorie.

calorimeter. *See* water calorimeter.

camber. The curve of an airfoil section from the leading edge to the trailing edge. Camber, which may be of the upper surface line, the lower surface line, or the mean line between them, is usually expressed as the ratio of the length of the curved line to the length of the straight line between the edges. *See also* lower camber.

camera. *Types of, see* ballistic–; Bowen-Knapp–; CZR-1–; Fastax–; IGOR–; Mitchell–; trimetrogen–.

Canard configuration. A type of airframe in which the control surfaces are small and well forward of the cg, while the main lifting surfaces are rigidly attached in the aft region of the body. Lift is obtained by increasing the angle of attack of the body-wing combination by means of the forward control surfaces.

can combustor. A type of ramjet or turbojet engine combustor resembling a conically shaped, perforated "can." It usually has a separate assembly for the pilot stage and is characterized by a wide operating range. See Fig. 15, page 227.

candle. A unit of luminous intensity equal approximately to the luminous intensity of a ⅞-inch sperm candle burning at 120 grains an hour.

canister. A protective container for housing a missile system, subsystem, or component, usually a pressurized cylindrical can.

cannibalization. A maintenance, modification, or repair method in which the required parts are removed from a similar missile or assembly for installation on another. Sometimes used in lieu of formal spare parts provisioning.

canted nozzle. A scheme used in solid rocket metal parts design to permit directing the thrust vector at a desired angle to the axis of the cant. (Nozzle cant angles are usually limited to a maximum of 30° and more typically to 15° because of loss in impulse and local heating problems.)

canted rotatable nozzle. *See* rotatable nozzle.

capability. *Types of, see* operational–; quick reaction–; ultimate operational–.

capacitance. In electricity, a term applied to the capacity of a condenser to hold an electrostatic charge, to the property of a circuit that opposes change in voltage, or to the ratio of a charge in a conductor to its potential.

capacitance. *Types of, see* acoustical–; electrical–.

capacitor. A device for adding capacitance (q.v.) to a circuit; a condenser.

capacitor. *Types of, see* blocking–; padding–.

captive firing. Test-firing of a complete missile where all or any part of a propulsion system is operated at full or partial thrust while the missile is restrained in the test stand. Sometimes improperly termed *static firing*.

captive flight. A flight wherein a guided missile, or component thereof, is carried on an aircraft in order to test the item under flight conditions. In this test the test article has some freedom for functioning but with restraints that permit reuse of the missile.

captive (ground) test. A technique of operating a missile on a test stand to determine or check its performance. Engines can be operated to full thrust and all conditions except those caused by actual flight can be simulated. Also termed *static test. See* firings.

captive missile. A test vehicle; a missile used to determine the compatibility of the propulsion system, the structure, and the subsystems under hot firing conditions and while constrained in a static position.

capture. (1) In nucleonics, a process in which a nucleus acquires an additional particle. (2) After launching, the process in which a missile having achieved flight speed is taken under control by the guidance system. (3) The process of roll stabilizing a missile–roll capture (q.v.).

capture maneuver. In space flight, change from an open (parabolic or hyperbolic) orbit to a closed orbit near a celestial body.

capture, roll. *See* roll capture.

cardan-mounted. A gimbal mounting system for a device requiring freedom of movement in one, two, or three degrees.

carp. A bombsight attachment for aid in the control of certain guided devices, such as the razon bomb.

carrier. (1) In electricity, an electromagnetic current or wave that may be modulated for transmission purposes; a carrier system (q.v.). (2) In analysis of a weapons system, that com-

ponent that brings the weapon or warhead (q.v.) to the target. (3) A handling device.

carrier. *Types of, see* coherent–; reinsertion–.

carrier frequency. In electronics, the basic frequency (q.v.) of the unmodulated radio wave emanated from a radio, radar, or other type of transmitter.

carrier suppression. A radio-telephonic transmission system whereby the carrier wave is not transmitted or radiated. *See* balanced modulation.

carrier system. In electronics, a system permitting transmission of independent communications over the same circuit. *See also* phase coherent carrier system.

carrier wave. The radio-frequency component of a transmitted wave, which may be modulated for transmission purposes.

cartesian control. A special kind of guided missile control dependent upon two sets of control surfaces, each producing movement perpendicular to the movement produced by the other.

cartesian coordinates. *See* inertial cartesian coordinates.

cascade control. An automatic control system in which the control units, linked in chain fashion, feed into one another in succession, each regulating the operation of the next in line. Sometimes termed *piggy-back control*.

case-bonded grain. In solid rocket usage, a grain (q.v.) cemented or bonded to the case or container to prevent burning on the surface adjacent to the container. See Fig. 22, page 259.

Cassegrainian mirror. A mirror mounted between the surface of a spherical (or parabolic) mirror and its focus. The purpose is to project the image formed by the outer portion of the incident rays. Named after Cassegrain, the astronomer, who invented it.

catapult. A fixed structure which accelerates a missile or aircraft. It must combine the function of directing and accelerating the missile during its travel on the catapult; it serves the same function for a missile as does a gun tube for a shell. *See* launcher.

catastrophic failure. *See* chance (catastrophic) failure.

cathode. A negative electrode, especially the electrode in a vacuum tube from which electrons are emitted.

cathode follower. A circuit in which the output load is connected in the cathode circuit of an electron tube, and the input is applied between the control grid and the remote end of the cathode load. The circuit is characterized by low output impedance, high input impedance, gain less than unity under most operating conditions, and an output voltage nearly independent of the current taken from the output terminals.

cathode-ray indicator. A cathode-ray tube (q.v.) with a calibrated screen to indicate position.

cathode-ray oscilloscope (CRO). An oscilloscope (q.v.) incorporating a cathode-ray tube, used especially as the indicator in a radar set to portray the echoes on its screen.

cathode-ray tube (CRT). A means for visually displaying electrical intelligence. An electron beam impinges on a fluorescent screen. This beam can be deflected in a vertical and horizontal plane by deflecting plates with electrical potentials which vary with the intelligence it is desired to display. The intensity of the beam can by varied similarly by the accelerating potential applied to the electrons. Because of the low inertia of electrons, an oscillograph (q.v.) using a CRT has an extremely fast response time (in the microsecond range) which is limited only by mechanical considerations such as screen intensity and film recording.

CAtk. Counterattack.

cavitation. The formation and collapse of vapor pressure bubbles due to the movement of a body through a fluid, or the effect of this action.

cavity magnetron. A magnetron having a number of resonant cavities forming the anode, used as a transmitting oscillator in the microwave frequencies.

cavity resonator. A space enclosed by a metallic conductor and excited in such a way that it becomes a source of electromagnetic oscillations, the size and shape determining the resonant frequency. It is used in ultra-high-frequency systems for which conventional types of oscillators are unsuitable. *See* klystron.

Cb. Cumulonimbus cloud (q.v.).

C-band. A radio-frequency band of 3.9-6.2 kilomegacycles/sec with wavelengths of 11.8 cm to 7.3 cm. It includes the top two sidebands of $S_{(Z)}$ through the bottom three sidebands of $X_{(Y)}$. See Fig. 8, page 105.

CC. (1) Command Center (q.v.). (2) Control Center. (3) Common Carrier.

Cc. Cirrocumulus cloud (q.v.).

CCE. Command Control Equipment (q.v.).

CCMTA. Cape Canaveral Missile Test Auxiliary; Cape Canaveral, Florida.

C.D. Confidential Document.

CDM. Contractor Developed Material.

CEA. Circular Error Average.

ceiling. (1) Short for *absolute ceiling* (q.v.). (2) A capability of any given airborne vehicle measured by its absolute ceiling. (3) The maximum height at which individuals can fly either with or without special equipment. (4) (a) A complete or almost complete overcast, particularly an overcast of clouds above a given area limiting vertical visibility; (b) the height of the lower surface of such an overcast. Used in assessing weather conditions; (c) clearness in the air for looking upward (e.g., "ceiling and visibility unlimited"). (5) The upper limit on assignments or on allocations (e.g., personnel ceiling).

ceiling. *Types of, see* absolute–; –zero.

ceiling-height indicator. An instrument for measuring the height of a cloud ceiling with the aid of a ceiling projector, the latter being a device which throws a spot of light on the underside of a cloud ceiling to aid in determining its height.

ceiling unlimited. The atmospheric condition when no ceiling exists. Formerly, an unlimited ceiling was assumed as long as there was a clear sky extending 9750 ft above the point of observation; since the advent of craft which fly in higher altitudes, this limit is no longer in effect.

ceiling zero. The atmospheric condition when a ceiling is at a height of 50 ft or lower.

ceilometer. An electronic device for measuring and recording the height of a cloud ceiling.

celestial altitude. The vertical angle between an observer's celestial horizon and a line joining a celestial body with the Earth's center. (It is the same as the angular altitude of a celestial body.)

celestial axis. The axis around which the celestial sphere apparently rotates by reason of the Earth's rotation. The celestial axis passes through the Earth's axis.

celestial coordinate. One or other of two coordinates on the surface of the celestial sphere used to locate a celestial body. Two sets of celestial coordinates are commonly used: the *equinoctial system* wherein the coordinates are a declination (q.v.) circle and an hour circle; the *horizon system* wherein the coordinates are the vertical circle that passes through the celestial body and an altitude circle.

celestial equator (equinoctial). The great circle in which the plane of the Earth's equator cuts the celestial sphere (q.v.).

celestial guidance. *See* celestial navigation.

celestial horizon. A great circle on the celestial sphere (q.v.), established by a plane passing through the center of the Earth, perpendicular to the zenith-nadir axis (q.v.) of an observer, and intersecting the celestial sphere; also, the plane that establishes this great circle. *See* parallax; rational horizon; sensible horizon.

celestial-inertial guidance. A system in which the basic inertial guidance (q.v.) of a missile is corrected by supplementary position and/or velocity information as obtained from celestial observations (e.g., optical or radio star trackers).

celestial intercept. In celestial navigation, an imaginary line extending from an assumed position to intercept a line of position and used to compute the altitude of a given celestial body; the distance and direction of a line of position from an assumed position. Sometimes termed *altitude intercept.*

celestial landfall. A method or procedure of reaching a destination by using as a course line a celestial line of position which goes through both the position of the vehicle and the destination. Often termed *landfall.*

celestial latitude. The angle in degrees between a point on the celestial sphere and the nearest point on the ecliptic (q.v.). It is reckoned positive northward from the ecliptic and negative southward.

celestial mechanics. The branch of astronomy concerned with the laws governing the motions of heavenly bodies.

celestial meridian. Any great circle on the celestial sphere (q.v.) that passes through its poles, especially either half of such a circle between the celestial poles (q.v.). A celestial meridian is a projection of a meridian on the Earth.

celestial navigation. Navigation by means of observations of celestial bodies. By this system a vehicle, suitably instrumented and containing all necessary guidance equipment, may follow a predetermined course in space with reference primarily to the relative positions of the vehicle and certain preselected celestial bodies. Determination of the local vertical to the Earth's surface is requisite.

celestial navigation guidance. The automatic directing of guided missiles through the employment of celestial navigation (q.v.). The missile is equipped with gyroscopes (q.v.), telescopes, mechanically or electrically recorded navigational tables, and other instruments and devices that sight stars, calculate positions, and direct the missile.

celestial pole. One of the poles of the celestial sphere (q.v.), corresponding to the north or

south pole of the Earth, assumed to extend into space along the line of the Earth's axis.

celestial radio tracking. A navigation technique wherein the microwave emanations of the Sun, Moon, or certain stars are used to ascertain their position with reference to the point of observation.

celestial sphere. An imaginary sphere of infinite radius considered to be concentric with the Earth. The points on it which appear to be stationary during its daily revolution are the celestial north and south poles, and are the points at which the Earth's axis extended would cut the celestial sphere. The plane of the Earth's equator cuts the celestial sphere in the *celestial equator* (q.v.), and the plane in which the Earth's orbit around the Sun lies cuts it in the ecliptic (q.v.). The celestial equator and ecliptic cut each other in two points. *See* equinox.

celestial triangle. An astronomical triangle on the surface of the celestial sphere (q.v.), whose vertices are the zenith, an elevated pole, and a celestial body.

cell. *Types of, see* fuel–; load–; thunderstorm–.

cellulose nitrate. Any of several esters of nitric acid used as explosives or solid rocket propellants, produced by treating cotton or some other form of cellulose with a mixture of nitric and sulphuric acids. Popularly termed *nitrocellulose.*

CENTAUR. A 3-stage satellite/space probe rocket vehicle consisting of the ATLAS (q.v.) for the first stage, a liquid hydrogen engine for the second stage, and a new engine for the third stage. Its mission is to provide heavy Earth satellites (6,000 lb payload) and probes to the Moon, Mars or Venus (1,000 lb payload to Mars).

center. *Types of, see* aerodynamic–; command–; command control–; control–; electronic data processing–; flexural–; shear–.

center frequency. The assigned frequency of an FM station from which deviation takes place in step with the audio signals impressed. Also termed *resting frequency.*

centerline. (1) A line running along the longitudinal center of any given object (e.g., a rocket). (2) A line perpendicular to the base line at its center between two radio transmitters. Signals sent out simultaneously from the transmitters will arrive at the same instant at any point along this line.

center of gravity. *See* center of mass.

center of lift. The mean of all the centers of pressure on an airfoil.

center of mass. The point at which all the mass of a body may be regarded as being concentrated, insofar as motion of translation is concerned. Commonly termed *center of gravity*.

center of percussion. In a rotating body, the point on a line passing through the center of rotation and the center of gravity at which force can be applied at a right angle to this line without causing a reaction at the center of rotation. The location of the center of percussion is expressed as the square of the radius of gyration divided by the distance between the center of gravity and the center of rotation.

center of pressure. The point on an airfoil at which the resultant of all aerodynamic forces apparently operates. For two-dimensional airfoils at supersonic speeds, it is slightly ahead of the midchord point, depending on the MACH number, thickness ratio, and type of cross section. For a flat plate of zero thickness and infinite aspect ratio (q.v.), the center of pressure is at the midchord.

center of pressure coefficient. With respect to an aerodynamic lifting surface (airfoil), the ratio of the distance of the center of pressure from the leading edge of an airfoil to the chord length.

center of pressure of an airfoil. The intersection of the chord of an airfoil (extended if necessary) and the line of action of the resultant air forces.

center of pressure travel. The movement, or the amount of movement, of the center of pressure (q.v.) along a chord of an airfoil as the latter is inclined through its normal angles of attack (measured from the leading edge, and expressed in percentage of the chord length).

center of twist. In structures, the point in a cross section of a beam that remains stationary when a torque is applied in that section.

centimeter. A unit of length measurement in the metric system (q.v.).

> 1 centimeter = 0.39370 in. = 0.01 meter
> = 10,000 microns = 10mm
> = 10^7 millimicrons = 393.70 mils
>
> 1 centimeter of mercury at 0°C
> = 0.013158 atmosphere
> = 0.44604 ft of water at 39.2°F
> = 0.19337 lb/sq in.
>
> 1 centimeter/sec = 0.03281 ft/sec
>
> 1 centimeter/sec² = 0.3281 ft/sec²

For centimeter-gram, see gram-centimeter.

centimeter-dyne. A unit of torque measurement in the metric system (q.v.).

> 1 centimeter-dyne = 1 erg = 7.3756 × 10^{-8} ft-lb = 0.001097 gm-cm
> = 8.85073 × 10^{-7} in.-lb

centimeter wave. A microwave one centimeter in length.

central control. In reference to Cape Canaveral Missile Test Center, a building which includes the Air Force management center in the operations center. The latter function is under the control of the Superintendent of Range Operations who is responsible for coordinating the activities of radar, timing, power communications, optics, range safety, range surveillance, interference monitoring, telemetry, and special instrumentation over all portions of the range that are involved in a test.

Central Intelligence Agency (CIA). An organization under the National Security Council that coordinates the intelligence activities of Government departments and agencies, correlates and evaluates intelligence relating to national security, and provides for disseminating this intelligence within the Government.

central timing system. A system that establishes a standard time reference for the operation of all time-based ground instrumentation equipment at a test site.

centrifugal compressor (radial compressor). An air compressor which imparts high kinetic energy (q.v.) to air in the form of centrifugal or radial air flow. A large proportion of the kinetic energy is subsequently converted into pressure potential energy in a diffuser system.

centrifugal flow jet engine. A turbojet engine that uses a centrifugal compressor (q.v.). It may be either an axial flow jet engine or a radial flow jet engine, or a combination of the two.

centrifugal force. The force which a rotating mass imposes upon the device which restrains it.

$$F_c = m\omega^2 r = \frac{w}{g}$$

where m = mass; $\omega = 2\pi$; r = radius; w = weight; g = gravity.

centrifuge. A machine for inducing artificial gravity by means of centrifugal force, used in testing the ability of equipment and personnel to withstand above-normal gravitational forces.

centripetal. Moving or directed toward the center of rotation.

CEP. Circular Error Probable (q.v.).

cepheid variable. A giant-type star that undergoes regular periodic changes in brightness due to internal pulsations. It is used in determination of distances.

ceramel (ceramet). A ceramic coated metal.

ceramic liner. A liner made of ceramic materials and fired to a high temperature, installed in the firing chamber of a rocket motor or jet engine to resist the heat and so protect the metal wall of the chamber.

ceramic, metal. *See* metal ceramic.

Cerenkov radiation. Radiation in the visible light range produced when charged sub-atomic particles traverse a transparent medium with a velocity exceeding that of light in that medium, sometimes termed *Cerenkov effect.*

certified component. A component (part, assembly) which has successfully passed a limited number of critical performance and environmental tests.

CFAE. Contractor Furnished Aeronautical Equipment.

CFE. Contractor Furnished Equipment.

CFP. Contractor Furnished Property (q.v.).

cg. Center of gravity. *See* center of mass.

cgs system of measurement. The centimeter-gram-second system, also known as the *absolute system of measurement*, based upon the length and weight units of the metric system (q.v.), and the second as the time unit. In this system, the units are: (a) distance—1 centimeter; (b) mass (or weight)—1 gram; (c) time—1 second. From these fundamental units are derived:

Unit of velocity	=	1 cm in one sec
Acceleration due to gravity (at Paris)	=	981 cm in one sec
Unit of force	=	1 dyne = 1/981 gram
Unit of work	=	1 erg = 1 dyne-cm
Unit of power	=	1 watt = 10,000,000 ergs/sec

See physical units and constants; systems of measurement.

chaff. Electromagnetic radiation reflectors in the form of narrow metallic strips used to create echoes for confusion of enemy radars. Chaff represents one type of confusion reflector (q.v.).

chain, LORAN. *See* LORAN chain.

chain reaction. A self-sustaining series of events. In a nuclear reaction, neutrons essential to the reaction are produced by the reaction in sufficient quantity to sustain or increase the reaction rate. It is any chemical or nuclear process in which some of the products of the process are instrumental in the continuation of the process.

chamber. *Types of, see* blast–; combustion–; firing–; motor–; plenum–; test–; thrust–.

chamber flight. A simulated flight in a decompression chamber, during which the occupant or occupants are subjected to atmospheric pressures encountered at various altitudes.

chamber pressure. The pressure existing in a liquid or solid rocket combustion chamber.

$$P_c = \frac{F}{C_f A_t} = \frac{\dot{w}}{C_w A_t} = \frac{\dot{w} C^*}{A_t g}$$

where F = thrust; C_f = thrust coefficient; A_t = throat area; $\dot{w}$ = weight flow; C_w = weight flow coefficient; C^* = characteristic velocity; g = acceleration of gravity.

See also effective chamber pressure.

chance (catastrophic) failures. Those failures which occur suddenly within the operational time period after all efforts have been made to eliminate design defects and unsound components and before any foreseen "wearout" phenomena have time to appear (e.g., the random "open" occurring in a resistor wire after several hundred hours of operation).

channel. (1) A system or means through which something passes or by which something is effected, as a channel of distribution, a channel of liaison. (2) *Through channels*—through a command channel or other military channel (e.g., command channel, technical channel, military channel, q.v.). (3) In electricity, an electrical path over which transmission is made from one station to another; a band of radio frequencies wide enough to allow a transmission, as a communication or telemetering channel.

channel. *Types of, see* control–; technical–; telemeter–.

channelized. A term pertaining to training, implying that a considerable amount of knowledge and skill peculiar to the equipment is required.

channel switching. Switching of different pickups permanently onto a subcarrier band after the original pickup has been switched off.

characteristic. *Types of, see* liquid rocket propellant–; military–; operational–; quality–; solid rocket propellant–; technical–.

characteristic impedance (Z_0). (1) The value of the terminating resistance which provides minimum reflections to the input of the network. (2) The characteristic impedance of free space is approximately 120π ohms.

characteristic length (L*). In rocket propulsion, the ratio of the chamber volume to its nozzle throat area is L^*; a measure of the length of travel available for the combustion of the propellants. To obtain the best performance possible the chemical reaction should be completed before the gaseous combustion products reach the entrance to the exhaust nozzle. The objective is to minimize L^* without introducing any significant reduction in the measured value of characteristic velocity due to incomplete reaction of the propellants.

$$L^* = \frac{V_c}{A_t} = \frac{\text{chamber volume}}{\text{throat area}}$$

characteristic velocity (C^*). (1) In rocketry, a measure of the effectiveness with which the chemical reaction of the propellants in the rocket motor produces the high-temperature, high-pressure gases.

$$C^* = \frac{V_i}{C_f} = \frac{g}{\dot{w}} P_c A_t = \frac{g}{C_w}$$

where V_i = exhaust velocity; C_f = thrust coefficient; g = acceleration of gravity ft/sec²; $\dot{w}$ = mass flow, lb/sec; P_c = chamber pressure, lb/sq ft.; A_t = nozzle throat area, sq ft; C_w = weight flow coefficient.

(2) In astronautics, the sum total of all the velocities that a rocket has to develop or dissipate by fuel consumption in the course of a given, specific journey.

characterization device. A device which adds or subtracts a value to a control signal in some predetermined relationship.

charge. *Types of, see* destruct–; propellant–; shaped–; space–.

charge/weight ratio. A term used in solid rocket design; the ratio of the weight of the propellant charge, including the inhibitor, to the total weight of the solid propellant rocket (charge and metal parts) including special fittings and attachments. *See* metal parts/weight ratio.

chart. *Types of, see* adiabatic–; azimuthal equidistant–; Bode–; constant pressure–; equidistant–; pseudoadiabatic–.

chart projection. Any one of the several methods by which the surface of the Earth or the celestial sphere (q.v.) is represented on a plane surface; a map or chart produced by one of these methods (e.g., Mercator projection, q.v.).

chatter. (Vernacular) A low-speed vibration which can be heard or felt in a piece of machinery or other equipment.

checkout. A test or procedure for determining whether a person or device is capable of performing a required operation or function. When used in connection with equipment, a checkout usually consists of the application of a series of operational and calibrational tests in a certain sequence, with the requirement that the response of the device to each of these tests be within a predetermined tolerance. For personnel, the term is sometimes used in the sense of a briefing or explanation to the person involved, rather than a test of that person's capabilities.

checkout operations. In a launch complex, the testing and calibration of the weapon system (q.v.) and its subsystems to establish a high confidence level of successful launch on command. Weapon system reliability and the desired confidence level establish the required periodicity of checkout operations; including the capability of malfunction isolation to those components or assemblies for which spares are stocked at the launch complex.

check valve. A valve that automatically prevents a reverse flow.

cheese antenna. A cylindrical reflector having two plates perpendicular to it spaced so as to permit the propagation of more than one mode in the desired direction of polarization.

chemical energy. A form of energy that requires initial work before it becomes useful (e.g., the heat of a match applied to a sheet of paper will release chemical energy as heat of combustion; a small spark can initiate the explosion of a mixture of hydrogen and chlorine leading to the evolution of heat of combination).

chemical fuel motor. A rocket engine that uses a chemical rather than a hydrocarbon as fuel.

chemical milling. The controlled removal of metal by masking that part to remain intact and then immersing the metal in an acid or alkaline etching bath at a controlled temperature for a carefully timed period to mill or etch away the unprotected areas. The process may be used on sheet metal, forgings, or extrusions.

chemical rocket. A basic type of propulsion using chemical propellants in either solid or liquid form. The energy limit is the molecular bond energy, the molecular weight, and the molecular dissociation. Specific impulses of up to 400 sec may be expected.

chemosphere. That part of the atmosphere (q.v.) extending from 20 to 50 miles in altitude. See Fig. 11, page 140.

Cheyenne fog. An upslope fog occurring on the eastern slope of the Rocky Mountains, and caused by the westward flow of air from the Missouri Valley.

chirping. A high-pitched, continuous-wave noise of varying frequency, heard in radio receivers and caused by an instability in the receiver or transmitter.

chirp system. A Bell Telephone Laboratories

developed matched filter technique used for long range radars to enhance signal levels.

chlorine heptoxide. A liquid rocket propellant *oxidizer*. See Table 3, page 157.

chlorine trifluoride (ClF$_3$). A liquid rocket propellant *oxidizer*. See Table 3, page 157.

choke. (1) In electricity, a coil used to impede the flow of pulsating direct current or of alternating current in a circuit. (2) In electronics, a groove in a metal surface, preventing the escape of microwave energy.

choke out. A condition that exists in a wind tunnel when a shock wave (q.v.) forms in the throat of the tunnel, blocking any further increase in air velocity.

chopper. (Vernacular) An electrical device for interrupting, at regular intervals, continuous wave signals either in a transmitter or receiver.

chord. *See* mean aerodynamic chord.

chromosphere. One of the atmospheric shells of the Sun. It lies above the photosphere (q.v.) and is best visible at time of total eclipse, but can be observed spectroscopically at other times.

chuffing. The characteristic of certain rockets to burn intermittently with relatively low frequency pressure oscillations and with an irregular puffing noise. Also termed *chugging, combustion resonance*.

chugging. Synonymous with chuffing (q.v.).

chute boot. A container on a sounding rocket (q.v.) to carry its parachute.

Ci. Cirrus cloud (q.v.).

CIA. Central Intelligence Agency (q.v.).

cine-theodolite. Missile-tracking equipment used to obtain position data up to about 100,000 ft. 35 and 70 mm cameras record azimuth (q.v.) and elevation. Approximate accuracies: distance —10 to 50 ft; angular—20 sec.

ciphony equipment. Any equipment attached to a radio transmitter or receiver or to a telephone for scrambling or unscrambling voice messages.

cir. Circular.

circle. *Types of, see* altitude–; hour–; null–; vertical–.

circle of confusion. In an optical system, the circular image of a distant point object as formed in a focal plane by a lens.

circle of equal altitude. A circle on the surface of the Earth, having as its center the substellar point of a given celestial body, from any point on or above the circumference of which the angular altitude of the body is the same. Also termed a *circle of position*.

circuit. (1) The path of an electrical current or of magnetic lines of force. (2) A radio or telephone communication link between two or more points capable of providing one or more communication channels.

circuit. *Types of, see* clamping–; closed–; integrating–; open–; parallel–; phase splitting–; plate–; printed–; push-pull–; push-pull parallel–; push-push–; quenching–; reflex–; series–; tank–; trigger–.

circuit breaker. An electromagnetic device attached to a circuit for automatically opening or interrupting a circuit when the latter is overloaded.

circuit diagram. A line drawing used in electrical and electronic design showing specific wire connections and individual parts such as resistors, potentiometers, coils, and capacitors.

circuit discipline. In communications, the observance of rules governing the use of equipment, prescribed frequencies, operating procedures, etc.

circuit ringing. The resonant sound heard in the receiver of a radio when cycles of scintillation are set up in a low frequency circuit by reception of a pulse of radio-frequency energy, to which the circuit is resonant.

circuitry. *See* printed circuitry.

circular error. (1) A bombing error measured by the radial distance of a point of bomb impact, or mean point of impact (q.v.), from the center of the target, excluding gross errors. (2) With an airburst atomic bomb, the bombing error measured from the point on the ground immediately below the bomb burst to the desired ground zero (q.v.).

circular error average. The bombing error in a given bombing attack, expressed as the average radial distance of the bomb impacts, or mean points of impact, from the center of the target.

circular error probable (CEP). A term describing the hitting accuracy of a guided missile measured at the target in a plane perpendicular to the trajectory for air targets, and in the ground plane for surface targets. Thus, it is that error which is just as likely to be exceeded as not. It is the radius of a circle that encompasses 50% of the probable points of impact. Also termed *circular probable error*.

circular orbital velocity. In astronautics, that velocity which enables a rocket to rise from the Earth and circle in orbit indefinitely (e.g., artificial satellite), but without attaining the escape velocity (q.v.) necessary to escape completely the gravitational attraction of the Earth. Also termed *orbital velocity*.

circular probable error. *See* circular error probable.

circular scanning. Radar scanning in which the direction of maximum radiation (beam axis) generates a plane or a right circular cone whose vertex angle may approach 180°.

circular system. A system for controlling guided missiles wherein the missile automatically sends out a signal to two radio stations, and times the echoes to keep itself on course.

circular velocity. The critical velocity at which a satellite (q.v.) will move in a circular orbit (q.v.) around its primary. Circular velocity is a special case of orbital velocity (q.v.), and one which is not likely to be obtained in practice owing to the accuracy of control needed.

circulation. (1) In meteorology, the motion of the air, caused by differential heating at the surface of the Earth, as distinguished from its motion of rotation with the Earth. (2) In aerodynamics, circulatory flow (q.v.). *See also* atmospheric circulation.

circulatory flow. In aerodynamics, the flow of air, hypothetically circular, about an airfoil profile in motion relative to the air. Based upon the observed reaction of a moving fluid in which a vertically immersed cylinder is rotated. If the immersed cylinder is stationary, the fluid streams pass the cylinder in symmetrical flow, and no cross-fluid forces act on the cylinder; if the cylinder is rotated, however, an asymmetrical flow is set up past the cylinder, resulting in a net sideward (or cross-fluid) force, corresponding to lift in an airfoil. The asymmetrical airfoil, in combination with the airstream moving past it, creates an effect analogous to that of the symmetrical cylinder rotating in a fluid.

circumlunar rocket. A rocket-propelled vehicle designed and operated to take off from Earth, travel to the Moon's orbit, circle the Moon, and return to Earth.

circumplanetary orbit. An orbit (not necessarily closed) about the Earth's Moon or a moon in general.

circumsolar orbit. The orbit (q.v.) of an artificial asteroid about the Sun, of the same kind as a planetary or natural asteroidal orbit.

cirrocumulus cloud. A cloud layer with an ice crystal content, composed of small flakes or masses of cloud without shadows. Patches of cirrocumulus, when gathered into regular group-

ings, give what is termed a "mackerel sky"; when without order or pattern, the patches give what is termed a "curdled sky." The cirrocumulus occurs at 20,000 to 40,000 ft.

cirrostratus cloud. A thin, whitish, stratiform cloud layer, having an ice crystal content and occurring at altitudes of 20,000 to 40,000 ft. Cirrostratus does not blur the outlines of the Sun or Moon, but gives them "haloes." When greatly diffused, it gives the sky a milky appearance.

cirrus cloud. A separate and detached thin stratiform cloud without shadows, having an ice crystal content and occurring in varied shapes, as tufts of hair, thin filaments, bands, feathered filaments, etc. Cirrus usually occurs at altitudes between 20,000 to 40,000 ft, but may be found at any level.

cislunar space. The space around the Earth within the Moon's orbit.

cisplanetary space. Space between the Earth's orbit and the orbit of the respective planet (e.g., *cis-Martian space:* space between Earth and Mars; *cis-Venusian space:* space between Earth and Venus).

city fog. A mixture of smoke and fog occurring over a city. Also termed *smog. See also* black fog.

civil twilight. That part of the twilight period that occurs, for computation purposes, when the Sun is between the horizon and a point about 6 degrees below the horizon, the latter measured at the middle of the Sun; the light diffused during this period. *See* twilight.

C-kill. *See* kill.

clamping circuit. In electricity, (1) A circuit that maintains either of the amplitude extremes of a waveform at a certain level of potential. (2) A circuit that clamps the base of a waveform to a given potential or current value.

class II explosive. Materials whose fire produces intense heat which is dangerous to personnel and equipment in the vicinity.

class IX explosive. Materials which can be expected to detonate when involved in a fire, and are subject to mass detonation by a detonating initiator.

classification of defects. A method of establishing acceptability of a product. The classification establishes need for rework or change to meet a specification or a set of standards.

classified. A security term applied to material or information whose disclosure to a prospective enemy would be inimical to the national interests.

clear ice. A transparent ice deposited in layers on the airfoils of an aircraft in flight. Also termed *glaze*. It may be either smooth or rough, and in some instances it causes deformation of the airfoil curve, resulting in greatly increased drag.

climatic test. A generic term describing any test designed to evaluate the ability of equipment to survive climatic conditions. Climatic tests usually include: sunshine, rain, hail, snow, sleet, wind, humidity, ice, aridity, sand, dust, temperature, fungus, salt spray, etc.

clinometer. An instrument for measuring an angle of elevation (q.v.).

clipper. In electronics, a device that gives output only when the input exceeds a critical value.

clipping. (1) Distortion in amplifiers produced by flattening of the plate current curve due to excessive grid current during positive grid swing. (2) Distortion in the AC component of a modulated wave when modulation amplitude exceeds that which brings the trough to zero. (3) Generation of approximately square waves by shunting biased diodes across the load, the bias determining the amplitude at which the peaks are to be clipped.

closed circuit. An electrical circuit over which the current passes without being broken; distinguish from an *open circuit* (q.v.).

closed circuit signaling. The sending of electrical signals over a closed circuit by increasing or decreasing the current.

closed cycle turbine. A gas turbine in which the working gas circulates continuously within a closed unit, heated by the combustion of fuel outside the circulating system. Also termed an *aerodynamic turbine*.

closed loop. A family of automatic control units linked together with a process to form an endless chain. The effects of control action are constantly measured so that if the controlled quantity departs from the norm, the control units act to bring it back. See Fig. 3.

closed loop flight tests. In missile applications those tests in which the guidance system signals are used to steer the missile. When the autopilot (q.v.) is used to stabilize the missile, the inner loop is said to be closed. See Fig. 3.

closed loop operation. A characteristic of servo-mechanisms or other devices in which feedback is used to indicate output errors and to correct the input accordingly.

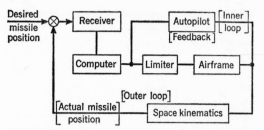

Fig. 3. Simplified block diagram of generalized guidance system. (A. S. Locke, *Guidance*, D. Van Nostrand)

closed loop testing. A test technique in which all dynamic elements of a missile system, including the guidance and aerodynamic characteristics, are physically used or simulated with all loops which are used in actual flight.

closed orbit. A circle or ellipse (q.v.) in a central force field (invariant elements).

closed space antenna array. An array (q.v.) in which the spacing of the elements is less than one-half wavelength.

closed system. A system which constitutes a feedback loop so that the inputs and controls depend on the resulting output (e.g., an automatic radar controlled fire control system).

cloud. A visible concentration of water particles or ice crystals suspended at a considerable height in the air.

cloud. *Types of, see* altocumulus–; altostratus–; anvil–; banner–; billow–; cirrocumulus–; cirrostratus–; cirrus–; crest–; cumulonimbus–; cumulus–; cumulus boa–; false cirrus–; foehn–; fractocumulus–; fractostratus–; helmet–; ice crystal–; lenticular–; mammatocumulus–; Moazagotl–; nimbostratus–; noctilucent–; riffle–; scarf–; steam–; stratocumulus–; stratus–; ten-tenths–; tonitro-cirrus–; wave–; wilson–; windrow–.

cloud base. The lower surface of a cloud.

cloud cover. Partial or complete cover of the sky by clouds.

cloud deck. The upper surface of a cloud.

cloud physics. The physical processes involved in the formation, movement, action, and effects of clouds; the science or knowledge of these processes.

cluster. A grouping together of solid or liquid rocket engines to provide a launching carriage or booster assembly.

cluster missile. *See* parallel cluster missile.

clutter. Unwanted signals, echoes, or images that appear on a radarscope and interfere with observation of the desired signals.

clutter. *Types of, see* ground (sea)–; radar–.

CNO. Chief of Naval Operations.

COC. Air Division Combat Operations Center.

coaxial line. An electrical cable having concentric conductors. Used as a transmission line for audio, radio, radar, and television signals.

COBRA. Ramjet test vehicle. Navy Bureau of Ordnance cognizance.

Type I: weight: 70 lb plus booster; diameter: 6 in.; booster had 4 fins.

Technical Direction: Applied Physics Laboratory/The Johns Hopkins University. A ramjet test vehicle used for data acquisition for the TALOS (q.v.) preprototype.

cobs. Bell-shaped deflection produced on an oscilloscope (q.v.) by frequency modulated, continuous-wave jamming.

cocooning. The action of spraying or otherwise enveloping a piece of equipment with a plastic protective substance.

co-declination. Polar distance.

code delay. An arbitrary interval of time introduced, in addition to other time intervals, between pulsed signals sent by master and slave transmitters. Also termed a *coding delay*.

code name. A generic name assigned to each guided missile to permit convenient reference to it in unclassified correspondence and oral discussions (e.g., NIKE, TALOS, ATLAS, TITAN, BOMARC, [q.q.v.]).

coder. An electronic device in a radar beacon (q.v.) or in an interrogator or interrogator-responser for coding pulsed signals.

code. *Types of, see* cyclic binary–; Gray–; reflective–.

coefficient. *Types of, see* aerodynamic–; ballistic–; center of pressure–; confidence–; correlation–; divergence–; drag–; influence–; Joule-Thomson–; lateral stability (and control)–; lift–; stability and control–; temperature–; thrust–; weight flow–.

coffee grinder. (Vernacular) A type of radio-direction-finder tuning device.

coherent carrier. A basic system referring to the principle involved in any transponder system, i.e., interdependence of a transmitter and receiver (e.g., in the DOVAP system, the missile is interrogated and after the carrier is received it is retransmitted at a definite multiple frequency for comparison).

coherent oscillator (coho). Oscillator used in moving target indicators (q.v.). A reference is provided by which the RF phase difference of successive received pulses can be established.

coho. *Coherent oscillator* (q.v.).

coil. *Types of, see* E-coil; loading–; magnetic biasing–; U-coil.

coincidence-type range finder. An optical range finder for use with one eye only.

co-latitude. A part of the observer's meridian on the celestial sphere (q.v.), being the angular distance from the observer's zenith to the elevated pole.

cold day. A synthetic temperature vs. altitude profile used for design. Cold day conditions cannot exist meteorologically, but represent a statistical envelope and hence should be used for design but not for performance calculations. Characteristics are shown in Fig. 25, page 267.

cold front thunderstorm. A frontal thunderstorm (q.v.) caused by a cold air mass underrunning a warm air mass.

cold low. A low-pressure atmospheric area of predominantly low temperature.

cold room. An environmental test chamber used to provide a low temperature area for evaluating equipment in this regime.

cold soak. The exposure of equipment to low temperature for a long period of time in a cold chamber to insure that the temperature of the equipment is lowered to that of the surrounding atmosphere or to permit tests at lower than ambient conditions.

cold tests, of resonant systems. In electronics, the testing of a microwave system with the tube in place, but in a nonoperative condition so that its electronic admittance is zero. The resonance frequency, loaded and unloaded Q, and the driving point admittance are quantities usually measured.

colinear array. An array of half-wave antennas in phase. The antennas are held in phase in order to produce maximum radiation in a plane perpendicular to the axis of the array.

collapse. The destruction of a target by crushing due to external pressure from a blast (implosion).

collector junction. In a semiconductor device, a junction normally biased in the high-resistance direction, the current through which can be controlled by the introduction of minority carriers.

collector ring. A hollow ring used to collect exhaust gases, as in a turbosupercharger.

collimation. The process of adjusting an instrument or device so that its reference axis is

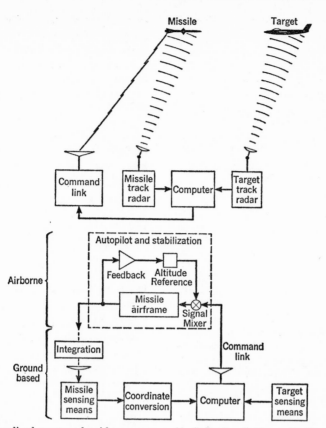

Fig. 4. Generalized command guidance system. (A. S. Locke, *Guidance*, D. Van Nostrand)

aligned in a desired direction within a predetermined tolerance.

collimator. An optical arrangement for collecting light from a source into a parallel beam. Often simply a converging lens with the source at its focus. It is an important part of spectroscopes (q.v.).

collision vector. A vector which, if maintained by a craft or missile, will end in collision at a given point between the craft or missile and some other object moving with a certain velocity.

combination fuze. A fuze (q.v.) combining two different types of fuzes (e.g., impact and time fuzes). It may be set so that either or both elements will function.

combustion. In propulsion, an exothermic chemical process usually producing high-temperature exhaust gases and light. Oxidation is generally involved. The process is slow compared to a chemical or nuclear explosion.

combustion chamber. (1) That area within which burning of the fuel-oxidizer mixture occurs in any combustion engine. (2) In rocket engines, the combustion chamber is the enclosed volume between the injector face and an imaginary plane across the throat of the nozzle. See Figs. 19 and 20, page 240.

combustion resonance. *See* chuffing.

combustion, screaming. *See* screaming combustion.

combustor. A name given to the assembly of flame holder (q.v.), igniter (q.v.), injection system, and combustion chamber (q.v.) of a ramjet engine. See Fig. 15, page 227. *See also* injector.

combustor, can. *See* can combustor.

comet. A nebulous body that revolves about the Sun in an elongated ellipse (q.v.).

comet orbit. An orbit (q.v.) with an initial, but not a final, restraint, such as used by instrumental comets.

command center (CC). In weapon applications, the center responsible for issuing target designations and firing commands.

command control center. A central station of an air defense system wherein information on enemy and friendly forces is collected and analyzed and appropriate commands are issued.

command control equipment (CCE). Equipment used in a weapon or command control center (q.v.) to select targets, perform countdown (q.v.) functions, and fire missiles.

command destruct. A system which destroys a missile, actuated on command of the Range Safety Officer, whenever missile performance degrades enough to be a safety hazard.

command-destruct signal. A radio signal intentionally used to operate the destruction device carried in a missile.

command guidance system. A system of missile control wherein intelligence transmitted to the missile from an outside source causes the missile to traverse a directed path in space. Missile command guidance systems in general require that the behavior of the missile (and of the target, if it is in motion) be monitored externally so that any deviation from a prescribed collision course may be computed, and the deviation communicated to the missile and interpreted by its guidance system so as to realign the missile flight path toward an intercept with the target. See Fig. 4, page 51 and Fig. 27, page 293.

command guided missile. A missile guided by a system that requires two radars, one to track the target, the other to track the missile. A computer combines the data from each radar to give the missile flight directions.

command post. The place from which a commander exercises his command function. Normally, each missile launch station and guidance station will have a command post.

common drive. As applied to a decommutator, counter stepping pulses.

common items. Those items of supply with application to two or more weapon systems (q.v.), subsystems (q.v.), or support equipment including components and spares related thereto.

commutation. (1) In telemetering, the sampling of various functions in a repetitive manner and using one band to transmit the information. *See* multiplexing. (2) In electricity, the mechanical process of converting alternating current, which flows in the armature of a direct-current generator, to direct current as furnished to the conductor.

commutator, airborne. *See* airborne commutator.

commutator jitter. Rapid changes in commutator angular velocity.

commutator switch. A rotary switch which is driven by a constant-speed motor. Used for time-sharing (q.v.), or sampling of several functions during each 360 degrees of rotation. The number of functions sampled and the amount of time allotted each function are both variable in the switch design.

compass. *Types of, see* fixed loop radio–; flux-gate–; gyro flux-gate–.

compensated amplifier. A broad band amplifier in which the range is extended by choice of tubes and by slight resonant effects. These are used as video amplifiers.

compensating component failure. A malfunction of one component of a system which nullifies the effect of failure of another component.

compensation. *See* data recording compensation.

complete round. *See* round.

complex. *Types of, see* launch–; target–.

complexity. The figure of merit or measure of the quantity of related parts or circuits. The total number of electronic parts (n) is often used as the measure. Complexity units are sometimes used as a preliminary and approximate measure.

complexity relationship. That relationship between complexity and failure rate which can be expressed as:

$$\lambda = nr_p$$

where λ = the failure rate for an equipment containing n number of parts each having the same probable failure rate, r_p. For equipments containing many different types of parts, each used under different conditions and thus yielding a different failure rate, the complexity relationship can be expressed by the equation:

$$\lambda = n_1r_1 + n_2r_2 + \ldots + n_pr_p$$

where n_1 = the number of parts having failure rate r_1; n_2 = the number of parts having failure rate r_2, etc., to n_p = the number of parts having failure rate r_p.

complexity units. An approximate figure of merit (q.v.) for complexity based on the sum of the number of tubes plus the number of relays in an equipment. The total number of parts in an equipment roughly approximates ten times the number of *complexity units*.

complex numbers. Numbers made up by the vector addition of real numbers (ordinary numbers) and imaginary numbers (numbers multiplied by $\sqrt{-1}$ termed i or j).

complex reflector. In electronics, a structure or group of structures having many radar-reflecting surfaces facing in different directions.

complex tone. (1) A sound wave produced by the combination of simple sinusoidal components of different frequencies. (2) A sound characterized by more than one pitch.

compliance. The mechanical element which opposes a change in the applied force. The energy involved is associated with the compression or twisting of a spring or other compliant element. Analogous to *electrical capacitance* (q.v.).

compliance. *Types of, see* mechanical–; rotational–.

component. A unit which is a self-contained element of a complete operating equipment and which performs a distinctive function necessary to the operation of that equipment (e.g., beacon, power unit, receiver, transmitting-tuning units, rotating antenna, modulator unit, amplifier unit, blower unit, gyroscope).

component. *Types of, see* certified–; dependent–; engine–; equipment–; independent–; inertial–; qualified–.

component failure. *Types of, see* compensating–; dependent–; independent–; partial–.

component part. An item not normally subject to further disassembly (e.g., resistors, capacitors, tubes, potted or molded items, etc.).

component stress. The stresses on component parts; from the reliability viewpoint, those factors of usage (or test) which tend to affect the failure rate of these parts, which factors include voltage, power, temperature, frequency, rise time, etc.

composite missile. A multiple-stage missile (q.v.).

composite modulation voltage. The voltage composed of all the combined output voltages of the subcarrier oscillators which are applied to any given RF transmitter as modulation.

composite propellant. A solid rocket propellant (q.v.) wherein oxidant and reductant occur as chemically and mechanically separate and distinct entities. The fuel acts as a binder and is usually a non-nitro containing an organic polymer (e.g., polyurethane or a polysulfide type of rubber). The oxidizer is usually an inorganic compound (e.g., ammonium nitrate or ammonium perchlorate). A plasticizer is used to make the fuel-binder pliable. See Table 5, page 214.

composite takeoff. The takeoff of a large missile carrying a smaller missile.

compound compressor. A jet-engine compressor using two or more different systems of compression.

compressibility. A condition that exists when air or other fluid has been compressed, as when air or other fluid passes through a shock wave (q.v.), especially in reference to the air around or against a vehicle flying at high speeds. Compressibility of air against or around a vehicle at transonic speeds (q.v.) may vary widely in degree, depending upon the design, giving rise in some instances to various aerodynamic effects (e.g., buffeting, shift in trim, aileron flutter, etc.).

compressibility burble. In aerodynamics, a disturbed flow of air produced by, and aft of, a shock wave (q.v.).

compressive stress. *See* total stress.

compressive waves. *See* shock wave.

compressor. A machine or apparatus for compressing something (e.g., for compressing air for delivery to the combustion chamber of an engine). Compressors are classified into two groups: (a) the *positive displacement compressors* include the reciprocating compressor, the displacement blower without compression, the displacement blower with compression; (b) the *centrifugal compressors* include the radial-flow compressor, the axial flow compressor, and the mixed flow compressor. These compressors are constructed in different ways and use various combinations of devices as in the *compound compressor,* the *multistage compressor,* the *single-stage compressor,* and the *supersonic compressor* (q.q.v.).

compressor. *Types of, see* axial–; centrifugal–; cómpound–; double-entry centrifugal–; mixed flow–; multistage–; positive displacement–; radial–; radial flow–; reciprocating–; single-stage–; supersonic–; two-stage–.

computer. (1) A term applied to calculating machines ranging from the Chinese abacus to electronic "brains." (2) In automation, it refers to machines which, once set up, perform a series of individual computations without outside tutoring.

computer. *Types of, see* analog–; digital–; logarithmic–; spherical trigonometric–.

ConAC. *C*ontinental *A*ir *C*ommand.

ConAD. *C*ontinental *A*ir *D*efense.

concept. *Types of, see* area rule–; entire job basis–; installations–; logistics–; operational–; polar–.

concussion fuze. A bomb fuze designed to function in the air in response to the concussion produced by the explosion of a preceding bomb. Also termed an *airburst fuze* or *air pressure fuze*.

condensation. In meteorology, (1) The act or process of changing from water vapor into water, and forming a cloud; the water so formed. (2) Sublimation (q.v.).

condensation trail. A visible trail of small water droplets or ice crystals formed under certain conditions in the wake of an aircraft. Also termed *contrail*.

condenser (capacitor). An electronic part consisting of two conducting surfaces separated from each other by an insulating material such as air, oil, paper, glass, mica, or ceramic. A condenser is capable of storing electrical energy. In radio circuits, condensers are used to block the flow of direct current while allowing alternating and pulsating currents to pass. The capacitance of a condenser is specified in *microfarads* and *micro-microfarads*. The capacitance of a parallel plate condenser in air is equal to the area of the dielectric divided by 4π times the thickness of the dielectric.

condenser. *Types of, see* blocking capacitor–; buffer–; by-pass–.

conditional instability. (1) The condition of a body of air the stability of which is dependent upon water vapor content and upward movement of the air. (2) In technical usage, conditional instability is said to exist in a body of air when the lapse rate of the air lies between the dry and pseudoadiabats (q.v.) on an adiabatic diagram (q.v.).

conductance. The capability of a material to carry electrical current.

$$G = \frac{1}{R} = \frac{1}{E}$$

where G = conductance, mhos (DC circuits); R = resistance, ohms; E = voltage, volts.

conductance. *Types of, see* mutual–; transconductance.

cone. The nose cone (q.v.) of a guided missile. Currently termed *reentry vehicle* (q.v.).

cone. *Types of, see* entrance–; exit–; inner–; MACH–; nose–; tail–.

cone marker beacon. *See* Z marker beacon.

cone of silence. (1) A cone-shaped extent of space extending upward from a radio-range transmitting station, and in which signals are unheard or greatly reduced in volume. (2) An approximately cone-shaped extent of space extending from a radar transmitting set and through which pulses are not sent because of inadequate antenna coverage.

confidence coefficient. *See* confidence level.

confidence firing. Periodic firings of a missile from an operational or training weapon system site for the purpose of providing personnel with refresher training and/or to provide data on reliability of the weapon system and its elements.

confidence interval. A statistical term establishing the difference between the upper and lower confidence limits.

confidence level. The percentage of statements, tests, etc., expected to be correct. The certainty with which data from a small group apply to a specific confidence interval. By using appropriate data and a selected confidence level (i.e., at a 95% confidence level the conclusions drawn will be in error only one time in twenty, *on the average*) the expected correct answers can be obtained. Synonymous with *confidence coefficient*.

confidence limits. The *computed* upper and lower limits of the desired value of a physical quantity.

CONFIDENTIAL. Of classified material, having such security status that its unauthorized disclosure could be prejudicial to the defense interests of the nation. The lowest classification now in use. *See* security classification.

configuration. The physical nature of an item. It denotes the physical arrangement of components which comprise a guided missile and its dimensions.

configuration. *Types of, see* Canard–; cruciform–.

confirm. To conduct tests to verify and substantiate the results of previous demonstrations. The degree of confidence with which one confirms a result depends, of course, on the number of successful repetitions of the same result.

conformal mapping. A method of diagrammatically representing the performance of a servo system (q.v.) Consider first the loop transfer function Y_0s, where in general s is a complex number of the form $s = \alpha + j\omega$. Corresponding to each value of s there is particular value of Y_0s. This can be shown by showing the value of s as a point in a complex plane called the s plane, and the corresponding value of Y_0 plane. Corresponding to a contour in the s plane there is a contour in the Y_0 plane. The shape of the latter depends on the function Y_0s, and hence on the parameters of the servo it represents. Thus, if the s plane is divided into a net of lines of constant α and constant ω, parallel to the axes, there is a corresponding pattern of lines in the Y_0 plane.

conformal projection. A mapping system wherein a surface in a given coordinate system is mapped or transformed into an alternate reference system without change in the angular relationship between any two points.

conformance. See quality of conformance.

confusion reflector. A reflector of electromagnetic radiation used to create echoes for confusion purposes against radars, guided missiles, and proximity fuzes (q.q.v.). See chaff; meaconing; rope; window.

conical scanning. Scanning (q.v.) in which the direction of maximum radiation (beam axis) generates a cone whose vertex angle is of the order of the beam width. Such scanning may be either *rotating* or *nutating,* depending upon whether the direction of polarization rotates or remains unchanged.

conic orbit. An orbit (q.v.) in a central force field (orbital elements invariant).

conservation of angular momentum. The principle that, in any system which is not acted upon by external forces, the total angular momentum remains unchanged. The law holds regardless of what takes place within the system.

conservation of energy principle. The principle that energy can neither be created nor destroyed, but can only be transformed. Therefore, the total amount of energy in any finite system is a constant, or Σ energy $= C$.

$$\text{IKE} + \Sigma U - \Sigma U - \text{FKE} = 0$$

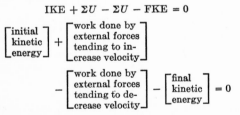

$$\begin{bmatrix} \text{initial} \\ \text{kinetic} \\ \text{energy} \end{bmatrix} + \begin{bmatrix} \text{work done by} \\ \text{external forces} \\ \text{tending to increase velocity} \end{bmatrix}$$
$$- \begin{bmatrix} \text{work done by} \\ \text{external forces} \\ \text{tending to decrease velocity} \end{bmatrix} - \begin{bmatrix} \text{final} \\ \text{kinetic} \\ \text{energy} \end{bmatrix} = 0$$

conservation of mass energy. The principle that energy and mass are interchangeable in accordance with the Einstein equation (q.v.).

conservation of momentum. The principle that the total momentum of a system is a constant:

$$M_{\bullet} + \begin{bmatrix} \Sigma Ft \\ \text{tending to} \\ \text{increase} \\ \text{velocity} \end{bmatrix} - \begin{bmatrix} \Sigma Ft \\ \text{tending to} \\ \text{decrease} \\ \text{velocity} \end{bmatrix} - M_t = 0$$

console. (1) A grouping of controls, indicators, and similar electrical or mechanical equipment which is used to monitor readiness of and/or control specific functions (e.g., missile checkout, countdown, or launch operations). Consoles are usually designed around desklike arrays as the working position for the operator. (2) The master instrument panel from which rocket and missile launchings are controlled.

console. *Types of, see* instrumentation–; master operational–; pre-launch–.

constant. *Types of, see* critical damping–; dielectric–; Karman–; *RC–; RL–;* solar–; time–.

constant-bearing course. That missile trajectory (q.v.) wherein the line-of-sight (q.v.) from the missile to the target maintains a constant direction in space.

constant-bearing navigation. That trajectory of a missile wherein it maneuvers so that the seeker is looking at the target in a direction that is fixed in space.

constant M control. A method of controlling a missile power plant in which the MACH number, M, rather than the velocity is held constant. It is sufficient to measure ram pressure and static air pressure with proper mechanization to keep M constant. Constant M is used because of the ease of measurements required for control and because most other parameters are a function of M rather than velocity. *See* MACH meter.

constant pressure chart. A chart of a given geographical area depicting variations of height above mean sea level of a constant pressure surface.

constant pressure surface. An atmospheric surface, either level or undulating, on which the pressure is the same at all points.

constant velocity control. A method of controlling a missile power plant to maintain constant velocity rather than constant MACH number. It is necessary and sufficient to measure ram air pressure, static pressure, and air temperature to establish the proper thrust control. Constant velocity control is used to avoid the need for a present position indicator (q.v.), velocity and time being used in computing range.

constellation. A configuration of stars associated by patterns in the sky. Constellations can be used to identify areas in the sky as states are used to designate areas in the United States. The principal constellations are:

Andromeda	Canis Major
Aquarius	Canis Minor
Aquila	Capricornus
Aries	Cassiopeia
Auriga	Cepheus
Bootes	Cetus
Camelopardalis	Cygnus
Cancer	Draco
Canes Venatici	Eridanus

Gemini	Perseus
Hercules	Pisces
Hydra	Sagittarius
Leo	Scorpius
Libra	Taurus
Lyra	Triangulum
Ophiuchus	Ursa Major
Orion	Ursa Minor
Pegasus	Virgo

See also stellar constellation.

construction weight. The weight of any crewless rocket exclusive of fuel. Usually termed *structural weight* (q.v.).

consumer's risk. The probability or risk of accepting a lot, for a given lot quality or process quality, whichever is applicable. It is usually applied only to quality values that are relatively poor.

contact fuze. A device which initiates warhead (q.v.) detonation after some interval of time following impact with a target surface. *See also* impact fuze.

contamination. The deposit of radioactive materials, such as fission fragments or radiological warfare agents, on any objective or surface which makes it hazardous.

contamination, residual. *See* residual contamination.

continental United States (ConUS). That part of United States territory that encompasses the contiguous forty-eight states, the District of Columbia, the coastal islands, the extent within the three-mile limit, including the surface, the extents under water, and the air-space above this territory. The states of Alaska and Hawaii, and the United States' possessions, are not included.

continuous linear antenna array. An infinite number of infinitesimally spaced sources. Some dielectric antennas and leaky-pipe antennas belong to this general class.

continuous wave radar (CW). A radar system in which a transmitter sends out a continuous flow of radio energy to the target which reradiates (scatters) the energy intercepted and returns a small fraction to a receiving antenna. Since both the transmitter and receiver are operating simultaneously and continuously, it is sometimes impractical to employ a common antenna, and usually two similar antennas are employed side-by-side and so oriented that only a small fraction of the transmitted power leaks directly into the receiver. The reflected wave is distinguished from the transmitted signal by the Doppler shift in radio frequency. The CW method has two important properties: (a) its

ability to distinguish moving targets against a stationary reflecting background; (b) a narrow bandwidth as compared to pulse radar (q.v.).

contour gradient. In meteorology, the rate of altitude increase of a constant pressure surface for any given distance.

Contr. Contract or contractor.

contracting officer. Any officer or civilian employee of any military department who, in accordance with departmental procedure, has been so designated, and has the authority to enter into and administer contracts and make determinations and findings with respect thereto, or any part of such authority and any authorized representative of a contracting officer acting within the limits of his authority.

contraction ratio. In a liquid rocket engine, the ratio of combustion chamber area to nozzle throat area.

contractor. *Types of, see* associate–; integrating–; prime–.

Contractor Furnished Property (CFP). All property used by a contractor in the performance of a contract, other than Government property.

contract status report. A periodic report which contains brief technical, operational, logistical, and managerial information required for the management, guidance, and evaluation of contracts.

contractual coverage. The existence of a legally binding document which requires a contractor to satisfy military requirements for supplies or services defined by such document.

contrail. A contraction of condensation trail (q.v.).

contra-injection. In a jet engine, the injection of fuel into the air stream in a direction opposite to the flow of air.

contraorbit missile. A missile sent backward along the calculated orbit (q.v.) of an approaching spaceship, satellite, or space weapon for the purpose of destroying it in a head-on collision with an explosive warhead (q.v.) or by missiles. Contraorbit attacks are considered much easier to accomplish than orbital attack; the anti-satellite missile is one of these weapons.

control. As related to a missile, the process of stabilizing the missile with respect to disturbances (such as gusts of wind) while simultaneously furnishing satisfactory responses to guidance signals.

control. *Types of, see* aerodynamic–; atmospheric–; attitude–; bang-bang–; barometric fuel–; boundary layer–; cartesian–; cascade–; central–; constant M–; constant velocity–; damage–; elevon–; fire–; gain–; ground–; lateral–; lead–; local–; material–; missile control and warning; nonatmospheric–; piggy-back–; proportional–; quality–; radar–; roll–; rail–; sensitivity time–; tailless (elevon)–; technical–; technical test–; thrust–; thrust vector–; wing–.

control accuracy. The degree of correspondence between the ultimately controlled variable and the ideal value.

control amplifier. As applied to a decommutator, an amplifier which amplifies and limits input information pulses, forming control circuitry actuating pulses.

control booster. Any device providing additional power for moving a control surface.

control building. A structure designed to house all instrument equipment, accessory equipment, and personnel necessary for the testing or launching of a missile. The control building is constructed to resist the effects of accidental explosion of the test article and may be a blockhouse (q.v.) if properly designed.

control center. The facility from which command is exercised over a group of missile launch complexes (q.v.).

control channel. An electrical or radio-frequency channel through which, or by means of which, control is exercised.

control force measuring system. An assembly of dynamometers, amplifiers, and indicators used to measure the control forces during a flight test (q.v.).

control grid. The grid of a vacuum tube to which direct-current voltage is applied to control the current of the anode.

controllability. The ability of a missile or aircraft satisfactorily to control its maneuvers in response to guidance intelligence.

controlled devices countermeasure. Any electronic countermeasure (q.v.) against guided missiles, pilotless aircraft, proximity fuzes, or similar devices.

controlled materials plan. A plan whereby the distribution to properly qualified claimants of basic critical materials (e.g., aluminum, copper, steel, steel alloy) is controlled and allocated by a central Government agency.

controlled temperature cabinet. An environmental test facility with automatic control accessories for testing ability of equipment to withstand high or low temperatures, temperature

shocks, and cycling. Cabinet sometimes includes humidity test capability.

controller. A device which receives a measured value of a variable from a sensor, compares that value with some reference value, and supplies a control signal to a control element to maintain the value of the variable within a certain range about the reference value.

controller, master operational. *See* master operational controller.

control panel. A surface or panel on which switches, rheostats, indicators, etc., are located for controlling and supervising equipment.

control point. In automation, the value of the controlled variable which, at any instant, the automatic controller operates to maintain.

control ratio. The ratio of the frequency response of the controlled variable to the reference input in a control system (q.v.). Under linear conditions, this ratio is expressed mathematically as:

$$\frac{C}{R} = \frac{G}{1 + GH}$$

where G = gain; H = feedback; C = controlled variable; R = input reference.

control surface. Any movable airfoil used to guide or control a vehicle in the air.

control system. (1) A coordinated group of components designed to exert a directing influence on other components. The system for properly maneuvering a missile in response to guidance intelligence; these usually include an autopilot, servos and control surfaces, or jets (q.q.v.). (2) a group of control consoles, housed in the blockhouse (q.v.), that monitor and launch a missile by utilizing radio and electronic control devices.

control system. *Types of, see* automatic–; damped aerodynamic righting attitude–; flight–.

ConUS. Continental United States (q.v.).

Convair. A division of General Dynamics Corporation; San Diego, California. Formerly Consolidated-Vultee Aircraft Corp.

convection. Motions resulting within a fluid owing to differences in temperature and density.

convection current. In meteorology, a current caused by convection (e.g., thermal convection); a thermal.

convective instability. In meteorology, the condition of a body of air having a distribution of temperature and moisture in such a manner that lifting of the body will cause it to become unstable. Also termed *potential instability*.

conversion graph. A graph used to convert the supplied calibration curve to the specific installation conditions of a telemetering installation.

conversion kit. A modification kit used to change a system for improved performance, modernization, reliability, etc. The kit is usually complete in every detail and may be used in the factory or field, but makeup of the kit may be different for these uses.

converter. (1) That section of a superheterodyne radio receiver which changes incoming modulated RF signals to a lower frequency known as the intermediate frequency; the converter section includes the oscillator and the first detector. (2) A device, usually rotary, changing electrical energy from one form to another (e.g., AC to DC, etc.).

converter. *Types of, see* frequency–; thermionic–.

converter frequency. Any circuit or device that accomplishes a frequency conversion, (e.g.) the mixer detector of a superheterodyne. Also an arc tube, a motor generator.

converting. (1) In nucleonics, the process whereby neutrons are used to transmit thorium-232 into uranium-233 or uranium-238 into plutonium-239. Term is less specific than breeding (q.v.). (2) In electrical parlance, changing from one type of power to another (AC to DC) or from one type of signal to another (AM to FM).

"cookie-cutter" intake. (1) A normal shock intake for a ramjet engine. (2) A sharp-edged intake for any air-breathing engine. See Fig. 5, page 73.

cooldown. The process of reducing the temperature of containers and associated piping for cryogenic materials (e.g., LOX, liquid nitrogen) to reduce thermal shock and boiloff by flowing LOX or liquid nitrogen through the container and allowing it to vaporize or boil off, thereby absorbing heat from the container to reduce its temperature.

cooling. *Types of, see* film–; regenerative–; sweat–; transpiration–.

cooling film. A cooling technique where a liquid is admitted through small holes into a jet or rocket engine combustion chamber or nozzle of a rocket near possible hot spots. Cooling is by evaporation of the liquid film.

cooperative systems. In instrumentation, systems which require transmission of information from a ground station (remotely) to a missile in flight, processing of the information by the missile-borne equipment, and re-transmission of the processed data to the originating and/or other remote ground stations (e.g., Azusa; DOVAP [q.q.v.]).

coordinate(s). Any one of two or more magnitudes that determine position.

coordinate. *Types of, see* celestial–; false–; generalized–; geographical–; inertial cartesian–; spherical–; test range–.

coordinated tooling. Tooling used to insure the matching of equipment or assemblies, particularly if from two sources of supply. Coordinated, or master, tooling provides assurance that parts or assemblies which fit the tools will fit with each other.

copper loss. *See* I^2R loss.

cordite. A colloidal rocket propellant composed of guncotton, nitroglycerin, and mineral jelly, mixed and formed with the aid of solvents.

CorEng. Department of the Army. *Corps of Engineers.*

Coriolis acceleration. When the apparent acceleration of a freely falling body relative to the Earth is considered, the additional acceleration involved that results in an eastward deviation of a falling body.

$$X = \tfrac{1}{3}\, \omega g t^3 \cos \phi = \tfrac{1}{3}\, \omega \sqrt{\frac{8h^3}{g}} \cos \phi$$

where ω = velocity of Earth; g = effective gravity; t = time of fall; ϕ = latitude; X = eastward distance; h = height of fall. For a vertically projected body:

$$X = \tfrac{4}{3}\, \omega g t^3 \cos \phi$$

The horizontal deviating acceleration,

$$y = 2\omega v \sin \phi$$

where v = horizontal velocity of the missile. *Note:* The sign of the Coriolis acceleration changes when the equator is crossed.

Coriolis force. Deflection of a projectile during its flight across the surface of the Earth, caused by the rotation of the Earth.

corner. In electronics, a sharp bend in a waveguide (q.v.).

corner frequency. A factor of a transfer function; the frequency at which lines asymptotic to the log-magnitude curve intersect.

corner reflector. A device used to increase the effective radar cross section (q.v.) of a target. See Fig. 7, page 83.

corona. (1) A halo, usually electrical in nature. Astronomically, usually refers to the ion halo around the Sun. (2) In electricity, a silent discharge very pale blue in color. *See also* solar corona.

CORPORAL. Surface-to-surface ballistic guided missile. Army designation: SSM-A-17. Latest version is designated CORPORAL F.

An outgrowth of the WAC-CORPORAL (q.v.) research project and roughly comparable to the German V-2. Length: 41 ft; body diameter: 30 in.; fin span: 84 in.; launching weight: 12,000 lb; burnout speed: MACH 3; range: 50 miles to 150 miles. Liquid propellant rocket engine; propellants are red fuming nitric acid and xylidine. Radar/Doppler guidance system.

Developed by the Jet Propulsion Laboratory. Prime Contractor: Firestone Tire and Rubber Co. of California. Airframe: Firestone. Engine: Ryan Aeronautical Co. Guidance system: Gilfillan Bros., Inc.

correction. *Types of, see* altitude–; azimuth ballistic–; parallax–.

correction maneuver. In space flight, change of orbit (q.v.) for the purpose of obtaining closer agreement with a pre-calculated orbit.

correlation coefficient. A statistical coefficient, P, which is a measure of the dependence of one quantity on another. If P is zero the quantities are independent.

corrosion. *See* fretting corrosion.

corrosion test. A test designed to determine the degree of adequacy of a part for withstanding corrosion. Usually a salt spray test is used.

CORVUS. Air-to-surface missile. Navy Bureau of Aeronautics cognizance.

Described as a large, long-range, winged vehicle using a solid sustainer motor. For use on carrier-based aircraft.

Prime Contractor: Temco Aircraft Corp.

cosecant-squared antenna. In electronics, an antenna designed to produce special polarization effects wherein the power density pattern varies as the square of cosecant of an angle defined by a line parallel to the earth's surface and the slant range line-of-sight. (This arrangement is used in airborne antennas to lay down a uniform electric field intensity along a line on the Earth's surface.)

cosecant-squared beam. An electronic beam that gives a coverage of approximately uniform intensity for both near and far objects. The intensity of the cosecant-squared beam over a part of its pattern in a specified plane, usually the vertical, is proportional to the square of the cosecant of the angle measured from a specified direction in that plane, usually the horizontal.

cosmic rays. Rays of extremely high penetrating power, thought to be produced beyond the Earth's atmosphere by transmutations of atoms continually taking place through interstellar space (q.v.).

cosmology. The science of the Universe in all its parts, laws and operations, so far as they can be known by observation and scientific inquiry.

cosmonautics. The science of space flight and travel in interstellar regions. *See* astronautics.

cost effectiveness. The aggregate cost of men and material and their required support which are needed to inflict a specified damage level on an enemy installation. A widely used concept in comparing the effectiveness of weapon systems (q.v.) and their influence on the military budget requirements.

cost-plus-fixed fee (CPFF). A method in which the fee earned by a contractor is established as a certain percentage of the originally estimated cost. The contractor is paid for all of his work but the fee is increased only with an increase in scope of contract.

COTAR. *Correlation tracking and ranging* system. A passive range instrumentation and/or safety system designed to provide position information by determining the angle between the remote ground-based antenna system and a missile transmitter (telemetering or other) by a phase comparison technique. The system, developed by Cubic Corp., does not require a separate transponder. It gives direction information only; range: 175-200 nm; single site, short baseline. *See also* ELSSE COTAR.

Coulmer array antenna. A planar antenna array consisting of non-resonant elements stacked vertically and horizontally with respect to each other. The result is both vertically and horizontally polarized waves to produce a high gain antenna.

coulomb. The unit of electrical quantity. A coulomb is the quantity of electricity transmitted by a current of one ampere in one second. It is also equal to the quantity of electricity contained in a condenser with a capacity of one farad (q.v.), when the same is subjected to an electromotive force of one volt.

$$1 \text{ coulomb} = 0.1 \text{ abcoulomb} = 0.0002778 \text{ ampere-hour} = 6.2425 \times 10^{18} \text{ electronic charges} = 1.036 \times 10^{-5} \text{ faraday} = 2.998 \times 10^9 \text{ statcoulombs}$$

1 coulomb/sq cm = 0.1   abcoulomb/sq cm
               = 6.452 coulombs/sq in.
               = 2.998×10^9 statcoulombs/ sq cm

1 coulomb/sq in. = 0.0155   abcoulomb/sq cm
              = 0.155 coulomb/sq cm
              = 4.647×10^8 statcoulombs/ sq cm

coulomb damping. *See* dry friction damping.

countdown. The step-by-step process of a weapon system (q.v.) checkout and flight readying leading to missile launching; it is performed in accordance with a predesignated time schedule and measured in terms of x-time (q.v.). The countdown usually is confined to the time from start of preparation at the test or loading area to the actual firing.

counter. *Types of, see* Eput–; scintillation–; tumble–.

counterbalance. That portion of a balanced aerodynamic surface (q.v.) lying forward of the hinge line (q.v.).

countermeasures. That part of military science which by the employment of devices and/or techniques has as its objective the impairment of the operational effectiveness of enemy activity.

countermeasures. *Types of, see* active electronic–; chaff–; confusion reflector–; controlled devices–; electronic–; passive electronic–; radar–.

counter output. As applied to a telemetering decommutator, a four-channel separator test point, output of the last counter stage on each separator.

coupled modes (principal modes). In mechanical systems, two frequencies found where the amplitude of the motion consisting of a combined rotation and translation is a maximum. These *coupled modes*, or *principal modes*, may be calculated from the uncoupled modes. The resonant frequencies thus determined are very near the natural frequencies of the system, and the deformation configurations are termed the *normal* or *principal modes of vibration*.

coupler. In electronics, any device which is used to transfer electromagnetic energy from one circuit to another. There are three principal ways in which energy can be introduced into and removed from waveguides and resonant cavities: (a) by placing a small loop of wire so that it "cuts" or couples the lines of force of the magnetic field (e.g., transformer); (b) placing an "antenna" or probe parallel to the lines of force of the electric field; (c) using external fields to link or contact the fields inside the guide or cavity by means of slots or holes in the walls.

coupler. *Types of, see* antenna multiplex–; directional–.

course. *Types of, see* constant-bearing–; great circle–; line-of-sight–; pursuit–; single-drift correction–; washboard–.

CPE. Circular Error Probable (q.v.).

CPFF. Cost-Plus-Fixed-Fee (q.v.).

crash program. A program set up under the pressure of an urgent requirement, the emphasis being upon speed even though the effects of such speed may be harmful to other existing programs or may require extra funding.

crater. The pit, depression, or cavity formed in the surface of the Earth by an explosion. The nearer to the surface the detonation occurs the shallower the crater.

crater depth. The maximum depth of a crater (q.v.) measured vertically from the deepest point of the pit to the original ground level.

crater diameter. The average diameter of a crater (q.v.) measured at the level corresponding to the original surface of the ground.

crater, lunar. *See* lunar crater.

craze. The development of a multitude of small surface cracks in a plastic, ceramic, or other material.

CRDF. Cathode-Ray Direction Finding.

CREE. Air Force test vehicle for parachute testing.

Altitude: 26 miles; speed: 3000 mph. Cluster of 3 boosted by a single rocket.

Development: Air Research and Development Command.

creep. A gradual deformation of ordinarily rigid materials. Creep occurs in the metal skin of missiles or space vehicles when it is weakened by excessive heat generated by air resistance at high speeds. Creep is usually a long-time phenomenon and is not a design consideration for missiles with short flight periods.

crepuscular rays. Solar rays made distinguishable by dust particles in the air when the Sun is shining upon them from behind a mountain or cloud or from near or below the horizon.

cresceleration. A progression of velocity increases or decreases per unit of time, in which each successive velocity increase or decrease is raised to a given power; the rate of such velocity increase or decrease (e.g., a velocity increase from 10 fps in the first second to 1000 fps in the next second would be cresceleration to the third power). Cresceleration may also be expressed in g's.

crest cloud. A cloud, stationary in position, that may occur along the crest of a long mountain ridge, caused by the upward deflection of humid winds and the consequent cooling by expansion. Also termed a *helmet cloud*.

criterion. *Types of, see* Nyquist–; Routh's stability–; strength-weight–.

critical altitude. The maximum altitude beyond which the propulsion system (q.v.) of a guided missile or aircraft will not perform satisfactorily.

critical angle. The greatest angle of incidence for which refraction of a ray traveling from one medium into an optically less dense medium is possible. For greater angles of incidence the ray will be totally reflected.

critical angle of attack. The angle of attack of an airfoil at which the flow of air about the airfoil changes abruptly in such a manner that lift is sharply reduced and drag is sharply increased. Also termed the *stalling angle of attack*.

critical damping. (1) In an elastic mechanical system subjected to a periodic force, the amount of damping just sufficient to prevent vibration from occurring if the system is displaced and then released.

$$c_c = 2\sqrt{km} = 2m\omega_n$$

where k = spring constant; m = mass; ω_n = circular natural frequency = $2\pi f$. (2) The threshold value of damping which will just prevent oscillation in an electrical system subjected to a periodic forcing function.

critical failure. A failure (q.v.) that judgment and experience indicate could result in failure of the entire weapon system (q.v.) other than catastrophic.

critical frequency. (1) The frequency at which radio waves transmitted vertically change from penetrating the ionized layer (q.v.) to being reflected back to the Earth's surface. Communication with bodies moving above the ionized layers must be made at frequencies above the critical frequency. (2) The resonant speed of a rotating shaft.

critical MACH number. The MACH number at which sonic velocity (q.v.) is attained at some point on the airframe (q.v.).

critical mass or size. In a fissionable material, the amount of material which will just support a chain reaction power level. This is related,

among other things, to the volume it occupies, or size.

critical materials. A general classification of raw and processed materials according to their strategic value, both in time of peace (stockpiling) and in time of war.

critical operation. A term which describes a limiting condition for ramjet operation. When the heat released by the burner is of such a magnitude that the back pressure at the exit to the subsonic diffuser causes the normal shock to be positioned at the inlet, then the operation is said to be critical.

critical speed. Any speed at which a given vehicle performance will change or end (e.g., the lowest speed of a missile at which proper control can be maintained; or the highest speed, either on the ground or in the air, at which a missile can be driven with safety; or the speed of a missile as a whole when a local point on the missile reaches the speed of sound).

critical temperature. That temperature above which a gas cannot be liquefied by pressure alone. The pressure under which a substance may exist as a gas in equilibrium with the liquid at the critical temperature is the *critical pressure*.

CRO. Cathode-Ray Oscilloscope (q.v.).

CROSSBOW. Air-to-surface missile. Air Force designation: GAM-67.

Missile is winged and air-launched. Westinghouse J81 (Rolls-Royce Soar) engine. Command guidance. Estimated speed: 500 knots.

Prime Contractor: Radioplane Division of Northrup Aircraft Co. Engine: Westinghouse. Guidance: Bendix Aviation Corporation.

crossing the trough. Process in an Earth to Moon voyage of passing from the influence of terrestrial gravity to the region of space (q.v.) where lunar gravity (q.v.) predominates.

cross-modulation. Modulation of a desired signal by an undesired signal.

crossover tube. A tube between the combustion chambers in certain jet engines, permitting the passage of flame for ignition purposes. *See* manifolding.

cross section. Types of, see neutron–; radar–.

cross-talk. The interference between nearby circuits, wherein signals in one circuit are undesirably reproduced in another, or other circuits.

crosswind. A wind blowing from such direction that its principal effect is to cause a vehicle to drift or move laterally; a wind that blows across something.

CRT. Cathode-Ray Tube (q.v.).

cruciform configuration. An aerodynamic configuration design used for highly maneuverable missiles in which the aerodynamic surfaces are identical and symmetrically located at right angles to each other around the missile body (e.g., TERRIER, TALOS, q.q.v.).

cruciform grain. A solid propellant rocket grain (q.v.) with a cruciform cross section. The grain is an external burning, partially restricted type. See Fig. 22, page 259.

cruise missile. A guided missile (q.v.), the major portion of whose flight path to its target is conducted at approximately constant velocity; it depends on the dynamic reaction of the air for lift, and upon propulsion forces to balance drag forces.

crushing stress. Compression stress.

cryogenic gyroscope. A gyroscope (q.v.) employing spinning electrons at near absolute zero temperature instead of the conventional spinning flywheel.

cryogenics. The science of physical phenomena in the temperature range below about −50°C (−58°F). More generally, cryogenics, or its synonym cryogeny, refers to methods of producing very low temperatures. One classification establishes the range as −300°F to absolute zero or −148°C to absolute zero (Linde).

cryogeny. The science of refrigeration. *See* cryogenics.

cryostat. Helium liquefier to produce very low temperature refrigerant.

cryotron. A high-speed low-impedance electronic switch with switching times approximately 10 millimicroseconds in duration. (An application of superconductivity, q.v.).

crystal. In electronics, a piece of quartz, silicon or other piezoelectric material ground to the proper thickness and size to produce a desired frequency when caused to vibrate. Crystals are used to generate accurately carrier frequencies, reference frequencies, rectifications, etc.

crystal controlled oscillator. An oscillator (q.v.) using a mechanically vibrating piezoelectric crystal with an energy transfer between mechanical vibrations and the electrical circuit, used in place of a resonant circuit as a stable frequency source.

crystal controlled transmitter. A transmitter whose carrier frequency (q.v.) is directly controlled by the electro-mechanical characteristics of a piece of material of crystalline structure (a crystal).

crystal correlation data. The data required for the fabrication of a specified part containing a crystal (q.v.) for use in electronic equipment.

crystal diode. A diode (q.v.) consisting of a semiconductor material, such as germanium or silicon, as one electrode, and a fine wire "whisker" resting on the semiconductor as the other electrode. Because of its low capacitance, the device finds considerable application as a rectifier or detector of microwave frequencies.

crystal filter. A highly selective tuning circuit employing a quartz crystal, sometimes used in the IF amplifier of a communications receiver to improve selectivity so as to permit reception of a desired station even when there is strong interference from other stations on nearby channels.

crystallization. (Obsolete) In metallurgy, the act or process of a material (e.g., metal) becoming brittle. This is an undesirable phenomenon and may be caused by subjection of metal to extremes of heat or cold.

crystal oscillator. An oscillator in which the frequency is controlled by a crystal.

crystal stabilized transmitter. A transmitter employing automatic frequency control (q.v.), in which the reference frequency is that of a crystal oscillator (q.v.).

Cs. Cirrostratus cloud (q.v.).

C-scope. A cathode-ray tube (q.v.) or screen that displays a signal with elevation indicated by a vertical displacement of the signal on the screen and azimuth (q.v.) by a horizontal displacement.

CST. Central Standard Time. *See* standard time.

CTCI. Contract Technical Compliance Inspection.

CTV. (Obsolete) Control Test Vehicle. A subsonic test vehicle developed as part of the Bumblebee Project (q.v.).

CTV-N-9. Military designation for the ground-to-air missile termed LARK (q.v.).

Cu. Cumulus cloud (q.v.).

cubic measurement.

1 cubic centimeter = 0.06102 cu in. = 10^{-6} cu meter = 1000 cu mm = 0.999973 ml = 0.033814 oz (U.S. fluid)

1 cubic foot = 28,317 cu cm = 1728 cu in.
         = 0.02832 cu meter = 0.03704 cu yd = 7.481 gal (U.S. liquid)
         = 28.316 l = 59.84 pt (liquid)
         = 29.92 qt (liquid)
1 cubic foot of water 39.2°F = 62.427 lb
1 cubic foot of water 62°F = 62.365 lb
1 cubic foot/second = 1.9834 acre ft/day
         = 0.646315 million gal/day
         = 448.83 gal/min
1 cubic inch = 16.387 cu cm = 0.554 oz (U.S. fluid)
1 cubic meter = 10^6 cu cm = 35.314 cu ft
         = 1.308 cu yd
         = 264.2 gal = 999.973 l
1 cubic millimeter = 0.001 cu cm
1 cubic yard = 27 cu ft = 0.76456 cu meter
         = 202.0 gal = 764.54 l

cumulative kill probability. If the single-shot probability is P_k, the P_{km} which results (assuming no progressive damage) from firing m shots at the target is:

$$P_{km} = 1 - (1 - P_k)^m$$

cumulative reliability. In the concept of establishing reliability by weighting or use of the learning curve, the heaviest emphasis is on the last missile or system tested (i.e., the one with the most advanced state of development, the most learning, etc.). In one approach the weights assigned the reliability of successive articles are as follows:

$$R_c = \frac{\sqrt{1}R_1 + \sqrt{2}R_2 + \sqrt{3}R_3 + \ldots + \sqrt{n}\,R_n}{\sqrt{1} + \sqrt{2} + \sqrt{3} + \ldots \sqrt{n}}$$

where R_c = cumulative reliability; $R_1 \ldots R_n$ = reliability of each missile.

cumulonimbus cloud. A heavy mass of cumuliform cloud with great vertical development, the summits of which rise in the form of mountains or towers, the upper parts having a fibrous texture and often taking the shape of an anvil. It has an ice or water content and occurs at altitudes between 1000 to 40,000 ft. It may deliver rain, snow, or soft hail.

cumulus boa cloud. A stream of low cumulus that embraces a mountain peak so as to suggest a boa neckpiece. Also termed a *boa cumulus cloud.*

cumulus clouds. Billowed heaps with flat bases and tufted tops. They have considerable shadow and often are very dark on the underside. Size and shape vary from flat small balls of cloud-cotton to great towers with valleys and ravines along the sides. The cloud is a low type, but can be found with bases from 500-1000 ft

and tops as high as 20,000 ft. It is composed of water droplets and may produce rain if well developed. Flat, fair-weather types are known as *cumulus humilis* and the well-developed variety as *cumulus congestus.*

curie. The number of nuclear disintegrations per second from a gram of radium (3.7×10^{10}) used as a unit of radioactivity.

current damping. A shunt damping resistor across the recording galvanometer to limit the frequency response of a measurement channel. Sometimes termed *dynamic* or *magnetic damping.*

curvature. *See* anticlastic curvature.

cutoff. (1) In electricity, the minimum negative direct-current voltage necessary to apply to the control grid of a tube in order to stop the flow of current in the anode. (2) (Vernacular) The instant cessation of thrust of a jet or rocket motor. *See* brennschluss.

cutoff frequency. The frequency at which the attenuation (q.v.) through a device reaches a certain predetermined value.

cutoff point. A point on the trajectory (q.v.) of a ballistic missile (q.v.) or other airborne object at which the fuel is exhausted or cut off.

cutoff receiver. A small RF receiver carried within a missile or high-altitude rocket operated by radio commands from the range safety officer. If the tracking devices indicate that the vehicle will stray from the range under continued operation of thrust, a signal is transmitted which is picked up and decoded by the cutoff receiver. Relays are then activated to stop the flow of propellants so that the vehicle will fall within the range or, alternatively, airborne explosive charges are detonated to destroy the missile while in flight.

cutoff velocity. The velocity at which thrust is terminated on a ballistic trajectory (q.v.) in order to obtain desired range.

curve. *Types of, see* ballistic–; calibration–; learning–; loxodromic–; OC–; S–N–.

CW Doppler radar. A radar which uses CW as distinct from pulsed radiation and the Doppler shift (q.v.) to perform its function. If the target is stationary, its presence may be *detected* by rectifying the energy returned from the target and displaying it upon a DC galvanometer. No other property of the target may be deduced except its presence and possibly its direction. If, however, the target is moving, its *radial velocity* also may be detected by comparing the echo frequency against the transmitted frequency. The echo radio frequency will differ from the transmitted frequency because of the Doppler effect. *See* Doppler.

cybernetics. A field of comparative study concerned with the controls inherent in the nervous system and the controls of certain mechanical or electronic machines such as digital computers.

cycle. One complete set of the recurrent values of a periodic quantity.

cycle. *Types of, see* duty–; limit–; minor–.

cyclic binary code. *See* Gray code.

cyclone. *See* tropical cyclone.

cyclonite. A white crystalline explosive, formula $(CH_2)_3N_3(NO_2)_3$, having high sensitivity and brisance. Also termed RDX. Cyclonite is used with other explosives or substances to form explosive mixtures.

cyclonic wind. *See* winds.

cyclostrophic winds. Winds which blow as a result of a pressure gradient and centrifugal force, but in the absence of Coriolis force (q.v.). They are, of necessity, cyclonic and restricted to equatorial zones which is the only place Coriolis force is zero. The cyclostrophic

component of a wind is the difference between the *gradient* and the *geostrophic* winds. Hurricanes are largely cyclostrophic winds until they travel north or south sufficiently to be effected by Coriolis force. *See also* winds.

cyclotron. An apparatus for imparting high speeds to atomic particles by magnetically accelerating them in spiral paths, used for bombarding atoms to produce transmutation and artificial radioactivity.

CYTAC. A system of determining hyperbolic lines of position by measuring the time relationship between two synchronized radio signals. CYTAC is similar to LORAN (q.v.) in principle but capable of greater accuracy and has a greater range of operation since it utilizes only the ground wave at 100 Kcs. Cycle matching is used for maximum accuracy.

CZR-1 camera. Missile-tracking camera equipment used to obtain primary trajectory data (launch to about 5000 ft). Approximate accuracies (out to 2000 ft) are: position, ± 3 ft; velocity, ± 14 fps. Camera speed is 30 frames/sec.

D

DAE. Data Acquisition Equipment (q.v.).

DAF. Department of the Air Force.

damage agent. An explosive carried within the warhead (q.v.) to be released against an enemy target (q.v.) to cause damage.

damage assessment. *Types of, see* detail–; indirect bomb–.

damage assessment table. A device for the graphic presentation of the results of damage assessment.

damage control. In naval usage, the means for controlling damage aboard ship incident to missile handling and launching and to enemy action.

damage radius. The distance at which, in terms of experience of theoretical calculations, certain types of damage can be expected from a specified type of explosive.

damage volume of missile. An envelope of swept-out volume defined by range-limit of the destructive agent carried by a missile.

damp. (1) To cause an oscillating needle or other indicator to come to rest. (2) To cause an oscillating object (e.g., rocket) to cease oscillating. (3) To absorb shock.

damped aerodynamic righting attitude control system (DARAC). An attitude control system used on reentry vehicles (q.v.) of ballistic missiles (q.v.) to insure that entry into the sensible atmosphere (q.v.) is such as to reduce the oscillation to reduce heating due to friction to a minimum.

damper. *Types of, see* dynamic–; Lanchester–; yaw–.

damping. (1) Usually refers to the checking of motion due to resistance, as by friction or similar cause. It is of special significance in connection with the diminishing amplitude of an oscillation (e.g., a pendulum swinging in the air). (2) The action of reducing the oscillations of a wavering body. Damping may be brought about by direct action, or by use of specialized instruments, or by friction.

damping. *Types of, see* aerodynamic–; cou-

lomb–; critical–; current–; dry friction–; structural–; viscous–.

damping decrement. *See* logarithmic decrement.

damping ratio (viscous damping ratio) (c/cₑ). The ratio of the actual damping coefficient for an oscillating mechanical system to the coefficient for a critically damped system.

$$f_d = \sqrt{1 - (c/c_c)^2}$$

where f_d = damped natural frequency, cps; f = undamped natural frequency, cps; c/c_c = damping ratio.

DAN. Research rocket. Air Force cognizance. Name is a combination of DEACON (q.v.) and NIKE (q.v.). Replaced by the NIKE-CAJUN (q.v.) which has an improved solid propellant charge.

DARAC. Damped Aerodynamic Righting Attitude Control system (q.v.).

DART. Research rocket for gathering weather information. Navy cognizance. (*Note:* The Army also uses the name DART to designate a surface-to-surface anti-tank missile. However, the two missiles are not similar in any other respect.)

Length: 40 in.; weight: 6.3 lb; speed: 3000 mph. Launched from a ship's five-inch gun and propelled by a rocket motor.

DART. Surface-to-surface anti-tank and anti-emplacement missile. Army designation: SSM-A-23.

Length: approximately 5 ft; wing span: 50 in.; fin span: 36 in.; firing weight: about 250 lb; cruising speed: more than 900 ft/sec; range: up to 5000 yd. Missile is electrically guided (optical/wire, gyroscope stabilized) by a trailing wire. Solid propellant rocket. It can be fired from fixed or mobile positions such as jeeps, weapon carriers, and helicopters by one man, if necessary.

Prime Contractor: Aerophysics Development Corp. (Curtiss-Wright Corp.). Airframe: Utica-Bend Division, Curtiss-Wright Corp. Engine: Grand Central Rocket Co. Guidance system: Aerophysics.

Program cancelled September 1958.

data. *Types of, see* crystal correlation–; metric–; position–; quick-look–; real-time–; raw–; restricted–.

data acquisition. That phase of data handling associated with obtaining, measuring, and/or recording the basic parameter(s) to be measured (e.g., the entire telemetering system is a part of the data acquisition system).

data acquisition equipment (DAE). Equipment used to acquire internal (e.g., telemetering) and external (e.g., camera) measurements of a missile performance. Contrast with *data reduction equipment* (q.v.).

data analysis. Analysis, for which design groups are responsible, of the reduced data returned from data processing control. This analysis determines the validity of a test and will determine conformance of the subsystems with design objectives and criteria, and performance specifications.

data handling. Encompasses the three operations of *data processing, data reduction,* and *data analysis* (q.q.v.). The specific application of these operations depends upon the nature of the data involved. Handling of data at the test site is oriented to the requirements for quickly determining overall test results and guiding of the next test sequence; handling of data for analysis is oriented to fundamental evaluation of subsystem performance.

data handling system. Automatically operated equipment engineered to simplify the use and interpretation of the mass of data gathered by modern instrument installations. Also termed *data reduction system.*

data processing. Includes development of engineering sequential motion picture film, re-recording of magnetic tape data into visual analog form, development of oscillograms, and duplication of magnetic tape and paper records. Raw data, in analog form, are forwarded to the appropriate subsystem design group. On the basis of these data and information on the test run, the design group edits the data and returns them with a data directive, outlining the desired data reduction. This processing is conducted for each test run.

data recording compensation. The compensation for error introduced in a recording by the recorder itself.

data reduction. That phase of data processing (q.v.) which includes the conversion of the basic acquisition system (e.g., telemetering) into properly corrected information usable to compare with the test objectives. Includes analog presentation of data (except quick-look); calibration, linearization, and presentation of data in numerical tabulation, coordinate plot, or other appropriate form; and tabulation of results of repetitive calculations required in reduction.

data reduction equipment. Equipment designed to convert data obtained by the data acquisition (q.v.) system into a form usable by the test designer. The data may be linearized, adjusted, calibrated, and/or corrected for systematic errors by the data reduction equipment.

data reduction system. *See* data handling system.

date line. *See* International date line.

datum line or plane. The base line or plane of reference from which calculations or measurements are taken.

dawn rocket. A rocket launched towards the east [from the dawn side (q.v.) of the Earth]. The takeoff velocity is *increased* by the orbital velocity (q.v.) of the Earth (18.5 miles per second). Contrast with *dusk rocket* (q.v.).

dawn side. That side of a planet or celestial body which points in the direction of its orbital movement. Contrast with *dusk side* (q.v.).

day. *Types of, see* Army hot–; cold–; hot–; ICAO–; mean solar–; polar–; sidereal–; solar–; standard–; tropical–.

day system. A bandwidth-conservation system which uses two quadrature carriers individually amplitude-modulated by separate and different modulating waves. The two modulated waves are added and applied to the transmitting medium. At the receiver, the transmitted wave is applied to a pair of product demodulators. Each demodulator is supplied with a carrier in phase with the corresponding component of the received carrier. The spectrum occupied is the same as it would have been for a single carrier.

db. Decibel (q.v.).

dbm. A signal strength measured as so many decibels above one milliwatt.

DBW. Differential Ballistic Wind.

dbw. A signal strength measured as so many decibels above one watt.

DCN. Design Change Notice.

DCO. Development Contract Office or Development Contract Officer; U.S. Navy.

DEACON. Research rocket. The DEACON with a NIKE (q.v.) booster is a CAJUN (q.v.). An unimproved DEACON is a DAN (q.v.). CAJUNS have replaced DANS. A DEACON launched from a balloon is termed a ROCKOON (q.v.). A DEACON launched from an aircraft vertically is a ROCK-AIRE (q.v.).

Prime Contractor: Allegany Ballistic Laboratory.

DEACON-LOKI. Two-stage solid-fuel rocket combination for upper atmosphere research. Navy cognizance. Composed of standard DEACON (q.v.) and LOKI (q.v.) rockets arranged in tandem. Successful firings by the Navy in the Antarctic.

dead band. In a servo system, a specific range of values in which an incoming signal can be altered without also changing the outgoing response. Sometimes termed *dead zone.*

dead-beat stability. A condition characteristic of, or induced in, certain oscillating systems, causing the system, when disturbed, to return to its original position without oscillation.

dead reckoning. The navigation process used to obtain the approximate position of a vehicle by integrating estimates of velocity, direction, wind, current, etc., over the period of time since the last established fix.

dead space. (1) A space within the range of a weapon but not covered by fire because of intervening obstacles, the nature of the ground, or the characteristics of the trajectory of the weapon. (2) In radio, a space or zone within the range of a radio transmitter, but in which a signal is not received. (3) In heat transfer, a space used for insulation. (4) In a hydraulic transfer valve, the range of input current around null (zero load flow) where the load flow of the valve remains essentially zero.

dead time. An interval following response to one signal or event during which a system is unable to respond to another.

debug. (Vernacular) To eliminate bugs (q.v.) or causes of trouble or malfunction from equipment.

debugging. A process of engineering "shakedown operation" performed as a means of eliminating system elements and circuits (proved incompatible with environmental and functional needs) by producing early failures. The weak or overstressed elements are caused to fail and are replaced by elements which are (statistically) of a normal quality not subject to a similar failure. The time necessary to weed out these early failures depends upon the total number of them in the equipment package (the quality of parts used) and upon the ultimate irreducible failure rate of the equipment. The debugging time seems to be controlled by the fact that the original defectives reduce to one-

half of their original number in a short period of operation, assuming all component *overstressing* has been alleviated. Sometimes termed *burn-in.*

debunching. In electronics, the phenomena in a klystron (q.v.) which work against the forming of electron bunches.

Debye length. In physics, the distance the positive and negative charges in a gas will be separated if the thermal energy of the gas is used for charge separation.

dec. Declination (q.v.).

decaborane. High-energy rocket or ramjet *fuel.* A boron derivative.

decay. *See* exponential decay.

decca navigation. *See* hyperbolic navigation.

deceleration. The action or process of velocity decrease; the rate of velocity decrease, often measured in *g*'s.

deception. *Types of, see* electronic–; imitative–; manipulative–; radar–; radio–.

deception meaconing. *See* meaconing.

decibel (db). A unit for expressing the magnitude of a change in sound or electrical power level. One db is approximately the amount that the power of a pure sine-wave sound must be changed in order for the change to be just barely detectable by the average human ear. The *bel* is the fundamental division of a logarithmic scale expressing the ratio of two amounts of power, the number of bels denoting such a ratio being *the logarithm to the base ten* of this ratio. The decibel is one-tenth of a bel. For example, with P_1 and P_2 designating two amounts of power, and n the number of decibels denoting their ratio:

$$n = 10 \log_{10} \frac{P_1}{P_2} \text{ db}$$

When the conditions are such that ratios of voltages or ratios of currents (or analogous quantities such as force or velocities, torques or angular velocities, pressures or volume currents) are the square roots of the corresponding power ratios, the number of decibels by which the corresponding powers differ is expressed by the following formulas:

$$n = 20 \log_{10} \frac{i_1}{i_2} \text{ db}$$

$$n = 20 \log_{10} \frac{e_1}{e_2} \text{ db}$$

where i_1/i_2 and e_1/e_2 are the given current and voltage ratios, respectively. A common reference level is zero db with one milliwatt into a 600-

ohm load; and sometimes 10^{-16} watts/sq cm pressure. In sound measurements the reference level is 0.0002 dynes per sq cm at 1000 cps. See Table 2, page 108.

deck motion predictor. A device to predict at given intervals, and at a time prior to missile firing, ship's motion about its fore and aft and athwartship's axes in such a manner as to permit firing a missile at a desired condition of ship's attitude and motion.

declination. (1) The angular difference in direction between magnetic north and true north, or between grid north and true north; hence *magnetic declination* and *grid declination* (q.v.). (2) In astronomy and celestial navigation, the angular distance of a celestial body from the celestial equator (q.v.) measured through 90° and named north or south as the body is north or south of the celestial equator measure on an hour angle (q.v.). (3) As regards a celestial sphere (q.v.), the angular distance from the celestial equator, expressed in degrees and positive if the point is north of the celestial equator, negative if it is south of it. Declination corresponds to latitude on the Earth.

declination. *Types of, see* co-declination; grid–.

decoder. A device, usually in the airborne portion of the guidance system, which accepts only properly coded guidance and command signals. (Coding is used to avoid enemy and friendly jamming, increase traffic handling, and to permit increased data transmission on one link.)

decoder, digital-analog. *See* digital-analog decoder.

decontamination. Removal of radioactive materials.

decoy. A countermeasure device intended to divert a guided missile or other weapon from its proper target.

decrement. *Types of, see* damage–; logarithmic–.

deep space. *See* space.

deep water burst. An underwater nuclear burst in which the center of detonation is at a depth of at least 1000 ft.

defensive firepower. The capacity of a target to inflict damage on an attacker.

defensive missile. One which is used to thwart an enemy attack which is proceeding against friendly forces or resources. An *offensive missile* is used to destroy enemy forces or resources which could be employed at a later time.

defensive radar. A radar designed and located

to provide early warning of enemy attack. *See* distant early warning.

deflagration. The slow combustion of a low explosive, as compared to the detonation of a high explosive.

deflection angle. An angle that measures the departure of a moving object from its directed course. It is the angle of a deflection shot between the line of sight (q.v.) to the target and the line of sight to the aiming point.

deflection error. The distance between the point of impact or the mean point of impact and the center of the target measured at right angles from the line of a vehicle's approach.

deflection probable error (DEP). The probable bombing error due to deflection, expressed in terms of distance between two lines parallel to the line of flight and equally distant from the desired mean point of impact (q.v.).

deflector. *Types of, see* blast–; flame–.

deflector plate. *See* flame deflector.

deformation. The amount of change in the linear dimension of a body, caused by the application of an external load.

deformation, plastic. *See* plastic deformation.

defuse. To remove the fuse (q.v.) from a warhead (q.v.), or other explosive.

degenerative feedback. *See* inverse feedback.

DEGN. Diethyleneglycol dinitrate (q.v.).

degradation (creeping) failures. Those failures (q.v.) which occur gradually as a result of change in value of some part parameter (e.g., the deterioration of the tube G_m below some critical value; drift in resistor values, etc.).

degree, electrical. *See* electrical degree.

degree. (measurement) 1 degree (angles) = $\frac{1}{360}$ circle = 60 minutes = 0.01745 radian = 3600 seconds.

degrees of freedom. (1) The number of independent coordinates necessary for the unique determination of the position of every particle in a dynamical system. Each degree of freedom is represented by a coordinate which can vary with time independently of all the rest. Thus a single particle which may move anywhere in three-dimensional space has three degrees of freedom. A particle constrained to move on a surface has two degrees of freedom, etc. (2) In the statement of the *phase rule*, one of that number of variable factors such as pressure, temperature, or concentration which must be fixed to define completely the state of the system. (3) The number of independent meshes, or the number of independent circuits that may be selected in a network.

dehorn. (Vernacular) The process of removing a fuse.

DEI. Development Engineering Inspection (q.v.).

delay. *Types of, see* absolute–; code–; ignition–.

delayer. A substance mixed with the propellant of a solid propellant rocket to decrease the rate of combustion.

delay fuze. Any impact fuze (q.v.) incorporating a means of delaying its action after contact with the target.

delay line. In electronics, an artificial transmission line employing lumped constant elements to provide a predetermined time for a waveform to traverse a line. (Delay times of 1 microsecond are readily obtainable; longer times are difficult because of the large number of sections required to provide sufficient delay and still give sufficiently high cutoff frequencies.)

delay time. In delay line applications, the elapsed time between 50% amplitude of the input pulse leading edge and the 50% amplitude of the output leading edge.

delivered specific impulse. In rocket usage, the actual specific impulse obtained at any altitude and at actual chamber pressure. Contrast with the same I_{sp} at sea level or a different chamber pressure.

Dellinger effect. In radio, a sudden ionospheric disturbance in the daylight portion of the Earth, affecting sky-wave transmission. (Named for the American physicist, John Howard Dellinger.)

DELTA. A National Aeronautics and Space Administration (q.v.) satellite deep space probe (q.v.) launching rocket. 1st stage—liquid rocket Aerojet engine. 2nd stage—liquid rocket Aerojet engine. 3rd stage—solid rocket—Allegany Ballistics Laboratory.

Capable of putting a 250 lb payload in a 300 mile orbit.

Delta 58-1 and 2. According to the International Geophysical Year code system used for identifying Earth satellites, this is the Russian SPUTNIK III satellite and the separated last stage of the rocket launching vehicle. See Table 6, page 245.

delta noise. In electronics, the "time" correction function of white noise is a delta function; a mathematical entity of unity area and of infinite height and zero width.

deluge system. A water washdown system installed on missile test stands or launch stands to permit inundation in case of fire or other accident.

demodulation. The reverse of modulation. Demodulation is the process of extracting the audio or video frequency component from the modulated RF signal. Commonly termed *detection* (e.g., the function of the second detector in a superheterodyne radio receiver).

demodulation, phase locked. *See* phase locked demodulation.

demonstrate. To conduct tests to prove the possibility of, or capability for, something. In general, a single successful test will complete a *demonstration*.

density. The mass of a body divided by its volume; the amount of matter in a unit volume of a substance. The density of water is the basis of comparison; e.g., the density of the Earth is 5½ times as heavy as a ball of water of the same size. *See also* physical units and constants.

density. *Types of, see* acceleration spectral–; air–; ballistic–; bulk–; power spectral–; spectral–; structural–.

density altitude (HD). The theoretical altitude of any place or point in the air determined by the altitude at which its air density would place it in standard atmosphere.

density specific impulse. The product of the specific impulse (q.v.) of a propellant (q.v.) and the average density of the fuel and oxidizer.

DEP. Deflection Probable Error (q.v.).

Department of Defense (DOD). (1) The entire military establishment of the United States. (2) A main subdivision of the executive branch of the federal government in Washington, D.C., charged with the administration, management, and policy determinations of the entire military establishment of the United States.

dependent component. In reliability studies, those components which interact significantly with the rest of the system.

dependent component failure. A malfunction of a component which is the direct result of the failure of another component.

depleted uranium. Uranium ore or slag having less than the natural content (0.7%) of the easily fissionable uranium-235.

depot. *See* maintenance depot.

depot-level maintenance. *See* maintenance depot.

depression. In meteorology, the designation for an extensive area of relatively low barometric pressure.

depression, dew point. *See* dew point depression.

depressor. *See* flash depressor.

depth. *See* crater depth.

derating. A design technique of limiting the required functional performance of a part or component when it is to be subjected to a severe environment (q.v.) or required to operate for a long period with high reliability.

derax. (Obsolete) An early name for radar; probably derived from the word *detector* plus *range* plus *x*.

derivative. *Types of, see* resistance–; stability–.

derivative action. Control operation in which the speed of a correction is made according to how fast the system error is increasing (same as *rate action*).

derived environment. A classification comprising natural uncontrolled environments; it includes temperature, humidity, rain, snow, ice, sleet, hail, wind and gusts, fog, lightning, sand, dust, dirt, fungus, pressure, salt spray, static electricity.

descent path. The flight path leading from an orbit in space to the surface of a celestial body.

design. *Types of, see* battleship–; limit–; logical–; preliminary–; quality of–; unitized–.

design altitude. The altitude or range of altitude at which a vehicle or airborne equipment is designed to function with optimum efficiency.

design bandwidth. The frequency deviation any device is intended to achieve with full-range stimulus.

design competition. A competition in which different manufacturers or companies submit design plans and drawings for a vehicle, device or system that will meet certain military specifications or requirements.

design contract. A contract to have a component, system, vehicle, or other piece of equipment produced in prototype (q.v.) form only according to a given design.

design criteria. Those design data which, when collated and integrated, represent the restraints required to establish design characteristics of a system, facility, device, or element. These follow design requirements (q.v.).

design load. In stress analysis, a specified load below which a structural member or part should not fail. It is the *probable maximum applied load* multiplied by the *factor of safety* (q.v.). Also in many cases, an appropriate *basic load* (q.v.) multiplied by a *design-load factor* (q.v.).

design objective. A non-contractual means of specifying certain desirable performance or operating characteristics. (Frequently it is used when a design feature is difficult to validate; e.g., very high reliability requirements, probability of survival of blast, etc.)

design requirements. Those design constraints established to limit features, size, performance, and requirements on other systems. These precede design criteria (q.v.).

design stage. The stage in the development of a vehicle, equipment, or system in which its design is being prepared.

design study. An analytical study showing the capabilities or characteristics to be expected from a component, system, vehicle, element, etc., if constructed to a given design.

design temperature. A temperature to which high-speed aerodynamic bodies must be designed in order to resist. It is based on the boundary layer temperature:

$$t = 0.84 \frac{V^2}{12,000} \quad \text{for laminar flow}$$

$$t = 0.90 \frac{V^2}{12,000} \quad \text{for turbulent flow}$$

where t is in °F and V is in fps.

design type test. Type (qualification) tests (q.v.) performed on early production equipment; i.e., equipment manufactured with production tooling.

design weight. The target gross weight of a part, component, system, or vehicle arrived at by adding up the weights of materials and elements expected to go into it in accordance with the requirements and criteria for its design. Differentiate from *specification weight, design objective, actual weight.*

destruct. The deliberate action of detonating or otherwise destroying a rocket, missile or vehicle after it has been launched, but before it has completed its course. Destructs are executed when a missile gets off its plotted course or functions in such a way as to become a hazard. *See* command destruct.

destruct charge. An explosive charge installed on a missile to destroy the missile or key components or parts.

destructive agent. Material contained in warheads such as explosives, corrosive chemicals, biological or radiological agents, etc., which damage or destroy the target.

destructive testing. The intentional operation of an equipment or portion thereof to ultimate failure. This type of test is often used to establish safety factors and end-use limitations.

destructor. An explosive or other device for intentionally destroying a missile or aircraft, or a component thereof.

DETA. Diethylene triamine (q.v.).

detached shock. In supersonic aerodynamics, the flow condition occurring when the shock wave (q.v.) created at the leading edge (q.v.) of a body is not attached to the body but has moved ahead. The shock wave will acquire a smooth, rounded configuration in the immediate vicinity of the leading edge. This condition occurs if the wedge or cone angle exceeds a certain value for a given M; or for any blunt body in a supersonic stream. The flow immediately behind a detached shock is *subsonic* (q.v.).

detailed damage assessment. A type of detailed photo-interpretation report, concerned with damage assessment. These reports cover the functional analysis, the structural analysis, the damage assessment, the target complex, and the special photo-intelligence report.

detail specification. A detail description, prepared by the designer, of a particular model, element, or component which cites all specific design, construction, and test criteria.

detection. *Types of, see* passive–; radar storm–.

detector. *Types of, see* impact–; proximity–; square-law–.

detonating wave. The rapidly moving wave set off within an explosive by detonation, creating such high pressure as to cause explosion.

detonation (explosion). (1) An extremely rapid reaction, in which an oxidizer and a fuel combine with large evolution of heat. (2) The release of warhead damage agents (q.v.), usually by initiating a series of explosive elements arranged in a "chain." A *high-order detonation* or "true detonation," proceeds with very high speed, generally several thousand feet per second. A *low-order* detonation is a partial, or relatively slow, explosion, generally caused by accidental or inadequate initiation. The term *detonation* is not to be confused with *deflagration* (q.v.), which may consume the same explosive materials, but at a rate usually of the order of inches per second.

detonator. A combination of a primer (q.v.) and another less sensitive explosive charge. Electrical type is detonated by a current of approximately one-half ampere. Typical material is tetryl in the form of a reconsolidated pellet.

development. The application of known techniques and principles to produce a desired result from the discoveries of research. In the development stage a device is visualized and its performance is anticipated. Development is characterized by deliberate planning, by ingenuity, and by synthesis of knowledge in many fields. The result of development is the creation of plans or models for a new device, and the demonstration by test that the prototype of the device fulfills the objective of the development.

development engineering. Creation of a design, parts of which make use of new facts discovered by research.

Development Engineering Inspection (DEI). An official inspection of a product or system, held on a date fixed by contract and in accordance with military regulations. It is essentially a mockup (q.v.) of a weapon system (q.v.) including the missile, support equipment, and launch control equipment; sometimes limited to an inspection of an *element* of a weapon system.

development model. A model used to develop and/or perfect the proposed design of a component, subsystem, or system.

deviation. A contractual change to a specification or work statement; a temporary change or departure from a particular requirement of a contract or other document. Generally, deviations are granted prior to the existence of equipment and waivers are granted on equipment if it does not conform to the specification. *See* waiver.

deviation. *Types of, see* frequency–; maximum system–; total frequency–.

deviation of a signal. In telemetering, the frequency change from the center frequency governed by the amplitude of the modulating system. The modulating signal does not vary the amplitude of the carrier but does shift the frequency and power to different sidebands.

deviation ratio. (1) In electronics, an index describing FM waves. It is the ratio of maximum frequency deviation to highest audio frequency. (2) In telemetering applications, the amount of the frequency shift of a subcarrier signal as the function of the signal level. (3) In telemetering, the ratio of one-half the subcarrier bandwidth divided by the cutoff frequency of the low pass filter:

$$\alpha = \frac{0.5 \text{ bandwidth}}{\text{frequency of low pass filter cutoff}}$$

deviation sensitivity. The ratio of frequency deviation to the amplitude of input function (e.g., cps/volt or cps/psi).

device. *Types of, see* homing–; jettison–; thrust termination–.

DEW. Distant Early Warning (q.v.).

dew. Condensed water vapor. If air in contact with any surface is cooled at the surface to a temperature below its dew point, some of the water vapor present in the air will condense onto the cool surface as liquid water or dew. When temperatures are below freezing, hoarfrost forms instead.

DEW line. A line of radar stations at about the 70th parallel on the North American continent, financed by the American Government but undertaken in cooperation with the Canadian Government.

dew point. The temperature at which the actual content of water vapor in the atmosphere is sufficient to saturate the air with water vapor. If the atmosphere contains much water vapor, the dew point is higher than in the case of drier air, so that the dew point is an indication of the relative humidity of the atmosphere.

dew point depression. The lowering of the dew point by decreasing water content or pressure.

DF. (1) Radio direction finder. (2) Radio direction finding.

DGZ. Desired Ground Zero.

diagram. *Types of, see* atmospheric sounding–; block–; Bode–; force-vector–; free body–; nozzle–; schematic–; wiring–.

DIAMONDBACK. Air-to-air guided missile. Navy Bureau of Ordnance cognizance. Reported to be an improved version of the SIDEWINDER (q.v.) with a greater range as the primary difference.

diaphragm. Usually a thin circular disc of highly resilient material, flat or ribbed and capable of being distended by pressure and returning to its original position upon release of the pressure. Commonly used to convert changes of liquid or gas pressure into a proportional mechanical deflection.

diatomic gas. Gas consisting of two atoms or having two replaceable atoms, having a valence of two.

diborane (B_2H_4). A liquid rocket propellant *fuel*. See Table 3, page 157. Heat content is 32,000 Btu/lb.

Didion-Bernoulli method. A method of computing ballistic trajectories (q.v.) which gives accurate results if the launch quadrant angle is less than 20° and if the drag is proportional to the square of the velocity. This implies applicability is limited to rockets with burnout velocities less than about 800 ft/sec. *See* Otto-Lardillon method; Siacci method.

dielectric. A nonconducting substance or material through which, however, induction, magnetic lines of force, or electrostatic lines of force may pass. Air, porcelain, glass, mica, and wood are dielectrics.

dielectric constant. In electronics, the relative permittivity of the dielectric material as compared to vacuum. It is measured by determining how many times greater the capacitance of a capacitor is with the dielectric between the plates than with air.

dielectric loss. In electronics, energy loss in the dielectric of a capacitor due to hysteresis effects. The losses show up as heat. The effects are analogous to magnetic losses in steels. Heating of the dielectric increases the power factor, which in turn increases the heat losses. *See* hysteresis loss.

dielectric strength. In electronics, the maximum voltage that a dielectric can withstand without rupture. Also termed *insulating strength*. Expressed in *volts per millimeter*. The dielectric strength of air is 4000, oil 16,000, and mica and glass 50,000.

diergolic (non-hypergolic). A property of liquid rocket propellants (oxidizer and fuel) that do not react spontaneously when brought into contact but require an auxiliary ignition system to initiate combustion.

diethyleneglycol dinitrate [$CH_2CH_2(ONO_2)$] (DEGN). A solid rocket propellant organic nitrate *oxidizer*. It is basically an unstable compound and capable of oxidizing the organic material; used in double-base solid propellant rockets.

diethylene . triamine . ($NH_2CH_2CH—NHCH_2$ CH_2NH_2) (DETA). A liquid rocket propellant *fuel*. See Table 3, page 157.

differential analyzer. An analog computer used especially for the solution of ordinary differential equations, linear and nonlinear.

differential ballistic wind. A hypothetical wind equal to the difference in velocity between the ballistic wind (q.v.) and the actual wind at release altitude.

differential pressure pickup. An end instrument (q.v.) which measures the difference between two pressure sources and translates this difference into a usable quantity (e.g., change of inductance or resistance).

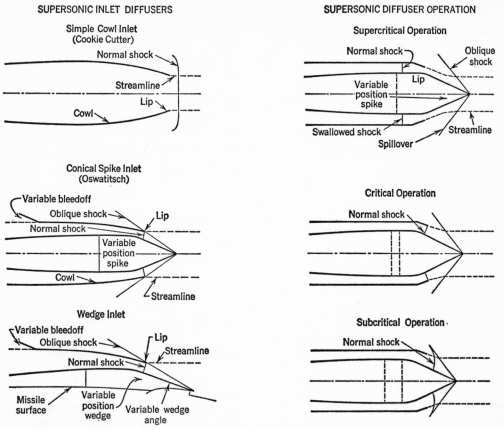

Fig. 5. Diffuser characteristics. (R. Herman, *Supersonic Inlet Diffusers, An Introduction to Internal Aero-dynamics*, Minneapolis-Honeywell Regulator Co.)

diffuser. A diverging duct designed to reduce the velocity of a stream of fluid without loss of total head and so to recover pressure head as kinetic head is reduced. Successful operation of a diffuser depends on having both a suitable shape of duct and a well behaved flow at the entrance. See Fig. 5, and Fig. 15, page 227.

diffuser. *Types of, see* Ferri–; Kantrowitz-Donaldson–; normal shock–; oblique shock–; Oswatitsch–; perforated inlet–; spike–; subsonic–; supersonic–.

diffuser, area ratio of. The ratio of the outlet cross-sectional area of a ramjet diffuser to the inlet cross-sectional area.

diffuser buzz. In ramjet engines, an oscillatory phenomenon with alternate swallowing and expelling of the normal shock system resulting in pressure variations throughout the diffuser. Buzz can occur only when the normal shock is expelled outside the cowl intake lip.

diffuser efficiency. (1) The ratio of the actual pressure increase realized by the diffuser to the theoretical pressure increase realized in an isentropic process. (2) The ratio of the stagnation pressures after and before the diffuser. (3) The ratio of actual change in enthalpy to the ideal change in enthalpy for passage from ambient to diffuser pressure.

diffuser recovery. In ramjet engine applications, the ratio of actual ram pressure ratio to theoretical ram pressure ratio. See Fig. 16, page 228.

diffuser spillover. That part of the approaching free air stream that does not enter a jet engine diffuser directly but is spilled over the lips. See Fig. 5.

diffusion kernel. In mathematics, a Green's function of the elementary diffusion equation. Sometimes termed *Yukawa kernel. See* kernel.

digit. *See* binary digit.

digital-analog decoder. A device for converting information available in digital form into a form suitable for utilization by an analog device. (*Encoders* are used to convert analog to digital form.)

digital computer. A computer (q.v.) in which quantities are represented in numerical (as distinct from analog) form and which generally is made to solve complex mathematical problems by iterative use of the fundamental processes of addition, subtraction, multiplication, and division.

digital transducer. A coupling device used to pass discrete pieces of data to another component or system.

dilation. *See* time dilation.

dimazine $[(CH_3)_2NNH_2]$. A synthetic rocket *fuel*.

DING-DONG. *See* GENIE.

diode. A two-electrode device, having an anode and a cathode, which has marked unidirectional characteristics.

diode. *Types of, see* crystal–; junction–.

dip (magnetic inclination). The angle, in the plane of the magnetic meridian, that a compass magnet is inclined to the horizontal.

dipole. In nucleonics and electronics, (1) A combination of two electrically or magnetically charged particles of opposite sign which are separated by a very small distance. (2) Any system of charges, such as a circulating current, which has the following properties: (a) no forces act on it in a uniform field; (b) a torque proportional to sine θ, where θ is the angle between the dipole axis and a uniform field, does act on it; (c) it produces a potential which is proportional to the inverse square of the distance from it.

dipole. *Types of, see* electric–; magnetic–.

dipole antenna. In electronics, a center-fed antenna, which is constructed to be approximately one-half as long as the wavelength it is designed to transmit or receive, essentially a resonant transmission line system. Also termed *half-wave antenna*.

direction. The angular measure, usually from true north, to a point of interest. At any point along a trajectory (q.v.) it is the inclination of the trajectory to the meridian of the point, measured clockwise from 000 degrees at true north through 360 degrees.

directional antenna. An antenna which radiates or receives radio waves more effectively in or from some directions than others.

directional coupler. A device used to extract a small amount of RF power from one waveguide to another as means for measurement of transmitter frequency, or to obtain the spectrum of the transmitted pulse or receiver sensitivity (used in conjunction with a slotted guide or line).

directional gyroscope. A gyroscopic instrument for indicating direction. It contains a free gyroscope which holds its position in azimuth (q.v.) and thus indicates angular deviation from the course.

directional stability. In aerodynamics, stability of a missile with reference to disturbances about its normal axis, i.e., disturbances which tend to cause yawing.

direction finder. *See* VHF/UHF direction finder.

direct manhours. Those manhours (q.v.) directly chargeable to such operations or functions as engineering, shops and production, and product support, i.e., labor readily identifiable with the product.

director. *See* electrical director.

direct ray. A radio wave which travels a direct path from one point to another without being reflected from the ionosphere (q.v.).

direct writing oscillograph. A recording instrument. The basic principle of most oscillographs is the D'Arsonval movement. This is essentially a suspended coil in a magnetic field. Current passing through the coil imparts torque to the coil. A pen is attached to the coil to provide a record (direct writing). It has a long response time—about 0.01 sec being a maximum. Accuracies of about 5% to 10% may be expected in typical applications.

disarm. (unarm) The act of rendering an armament system incapable of operation by interrupting the explosive train.

disassociation. An effect of a high-speed missile upon the atmosphere it encounters; i.e., the breaking down into atomic form of the molecules of nitrogen and oxygen. At MACH numbers between about 10 and 14 this is the major change in molecular structure. Electronic excitation and ionization are minor portions of the process.

DISCOVERER. A 2-stage satellite launching vehicle sponsored by ARPA (Advanced Research Projects Agency). The first stage is a THOR (q.v.) and the second stage uses a Bell Hustler liquid rocket engine (using JP5 and RFNA). The payload can vary up to 150 lb. The second stage, which orbits, weighs 7,000 lb. See Table 6, page 245.

DICOVERER Project. A Department Of Defense (Advanced Research Projects Agency) sponsored program aimed at orbiting a number of 1300-lb satellites to be used to develop early warning satellites [MIDAS (q.v.)], means for safe return to Earth of an orbiting vehicle, manned satellites, etc. Polar orbits with launchings at Vandenberg Air Force Base are planned.

discrimination. *See* target discrimination.

discriminator. In electronics: (1) A device wherein amplitude variations are derived in response to frequency or phase variations. (2) A circuit used in connection with counters, having the property that only pulses falling between two limits of amplitude (one of which may be O or ∝) are recorded. (3) A special type of detector circuit used after amplification in the IF stage to establish whether the IF deviates from the correct value. (4) In telemetering, this covers several types of tubes and circuits whose specific function is to demodulate, or remove the intelligence from the FM signal. The voltage output of a discriminator is proportional to the frequency excursion of an FM signal, and the polarity of the output voltage is dependent upon whether the frequency excursion is higher or lower than the center frequency (e.g., in a radio receiver, that stage which converts the frequency-modulated signals directly to audio-frequency signals).

discriminator. *Types of, see* limiting–; microwave–; pulse averaging–; subcarrier–.

discriminator bandwidth (pass band). The total width (lowest to highest frequency) of the band of frequency components accepted by the discriminator equipment over which the output voltage is directly proportional to the frequency deviation of the input signal.

discriminator cabinet. As applied to a telemeter receiving station, the standard relay rack containing six or seven discriminators and a blower assembly.

discriminator calibration. The recording or checking of output voltage at three or more points of a discriminator output signal with a known frequency applied.

discriminator linearity. A means of expressing the linear relationship between the input frequency and the output voltage of a discriminator.

discriminator output stability. A measure of the change in initial balance conditions with respect to time.

discriminator standby stability. A measure of the change in initial balance conditions after lengthy periods of time with no input signal.

discriminator tuning unit. A device which deter-

mines the frequency at which a discriminator will operate. It is sometimes constructed as a plug-in replaceable unit.

dish antenna. In electronics, a continuous or perforated concave antenna usually contoured to a parabolic shape used for transmitting and/or receiving radio frequency waves.

dish, radar. *See* radar dish.

dispersion. The scatter of impact points of a group of missiles about a particular aiming point.

dispersion area. In guidance, that area enclosing the intersections of a large number of missile trajectories with a perpendicular plane just in front of the target; used to analyze the performance requirement of guidance and armament systems.

displacement aircraft rocket launcher. A type of aircraft rocket launcher (q.v.) that swings rockets from the carrying position on an aircraft into firing position.

displacement gyroscope (free attitude). A sensing instrument for establishing a space-reference for a missile which makes use of a gyroscope's inherent characteristic of tending to maintain its spin axis fixed in space. The gyroscope is mounted on gimbals which give it two degrees of freedom. See Fig. 21, page 254.

dissociation. (1) The breaking of the electronic bonds between the molecule nuclei resulting from high-temperature air particles impacting with each other with high energy. Molecules dissociate into other molecules, atoms, or ions. The impact energy required is the *energy of dissociation*. (2) The decomposition of burned gases in the combustion chamber (q.v.) of a rocket, resulting in a loss of heat energy.

distance. *Types of, see* astronomical–; great circle–; line-of-sight–; miss–; rhumb line–; zenith–.

distance measuring equipment (DME). A generalized term pertaining to guidance, range instrumentation, or safety systems (q.q.v.) designed to indicate the radial distance between two locations.

distance modulus. A convenient method of expressing large distances in terms of magnitudes; the apparent minus the absolute magnitude of a star. The apparent magnitude can be measured and the absolute magnitude deduced.

Modulus, *Magnitudes*	Distance, *Parsecs*
14	6,000
16	16,000
18	40,000
20	100,000

See magnitude.

distant early warning (DEW) system. A line of radars for the detection of incoming targets at a considerable distance from the air defense system which must be alerted.

distortion. With respect to a waveform, a condition in which the output characteristic of a unit is not a faithful reproduction of the input function. The peak amplitudes of all spurious pulses overshoot or undershoot at the 100% or the 0% levels (relative to the pulse amplitude with a specified input pulse), respectively, and expressed (in per cent) as:

$$\text{per cent distortion} = \frac{a}{E_0} \times 100$$

where a = overshoot amplitude, volts; E_0 = output voltage.

It appears in circuits as: (a) nonlinear distortion or amplitude distortion; (b) frequency distortion; (c) delay distortion or phase-shift distortion.

distortion. *Types of, see* amplitude–; harmonic–; hysteresis–.

distribution. *Types of, see* binomial–; Gaussian–; normal–; Poisson's probability–; Rayleigh–.

disturbed orbit. Orbit (q.v.) in a non-homogeneous gravitational field. Such an orbit is not a truly closed orbit (its elements vary).

dither. A force of controlled amplitude and frequency applied to a servo-motored transfer valve, so the valve is constantly in small amplitude motion and cannot stick at its null position. Also termed *buzz*.

divergence. (1) An atmospheric condition in which air flows outward from a given region. (2) In aerodynamics, the action of an aerodynamic surface when under the influence of oscillating loads; the amplitude increases for each cycle of deflection.

divergence coefficient. The correction factor for the divergence angle of the conical exit section of a nozzle:

$$\lambda = \tfrac{1}{2} + \tfrac{1}{2} \cos \alpha$$

See Fig. 6.

diversity radar. Two complete radars tied together electronically. Also triple diversity. (Diversity is used to reduce jamming susceptibility and increase detection range.)

diversity reception. Radio reception that uses two or more sources of signal energy. To minimize the effects of fading, a resultant signal is obtained by combining or selecting two or more

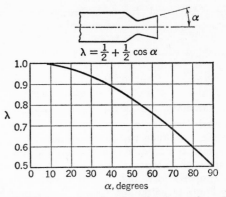

Fig. 6. Divergence angle correction factor for a De Laval nozzle as a function of the divergence angle. (Bonney, Zucrow & Besserer, *Aerodynamics, Propulsion, Structures & Design Practice*, D. Van Nostrand)

sources of signal energy carrying the same modulus.

divider. *See* frequency divider.

dividing network. A circuit whose output is reduced in value, but proportional to the input.

D-kill. *See* kill.

D layer. The lowest layer of the ionosphere (q.v.). This layer, occurring at between 25 and 50 miles above the Earth's surface, with a maximum of ionization, absorbs some of the radio energy reflected by the E and F layers (q.q.v.). See Fig. 11, page 140.

DME. Distance Measuring Equipment (q.v.).

DME ground beacon. A ground beacon employed in distance measuring equipment (q.v.).

DMPI. Desired Mean Point of Impact.

DN. Department of the Navy.

DO. Defense Order.

doctrine. *See* tactical doctrine.

documentary film. That film which is obtained primarily to provide a general historical record of a test or other event.

DOD. Department of Defense (q.v.).

DOFL. Diamond Ordnance Fuze Laboratory.

dog house. (Vernacular) A protuberance that houses instruments on a rocket's otherwise smooth skin.

doldrums. *See* intertropical front.

Doppler effect. The apparent change in frequency of a sound or radio wave, reaching an observer or radio receiver, caused by a relative speed and consequent change in distance or range, between the source and the observer or the receiver during the interval of reception.

Doppler frequency. *See* Doppler shift.

Doppler radar. Radar, either CW or pulsed, which utilizes the Doppler frequency shift of a reflected echo due to relative motion of target and radar. (For comparable maximum range performance, the peak power of a pulsed radar is likely to be on the order of hundreds of kilowatts and that of a CW Doppler radar in tens of watts. The average powers of these two radar systems, however, will be equal if they are designed to have the same maximum range capability.) A Doppler system, unless gated, is capable of unambiguous tracking under the special condition that only one moving target exist within the antenna beam. This condition is no different than that encountered in a pulsed radar, in that some special feature of the target, usually its range, allows it to be selected from all others for tracking. In a Doppler system only two means of selection are available, namely, *Doppler signal frequency* and *Doppler signal amplitude*. The basis of selection is usually Doppler frequency and the mechanism is commonly a highly selective tunable filter such as is contained in commercial wave analyzers. Narrowing the filter bandwidth gives a greater amount of definition, just as reducing the range gate duration in a pulse radar improves definition.

Doppler shift. In radio technology, a Doppler phenomenon analogous to that occurring in sound propagation. The amount of the shift is doubled because of the two-way transmission (to the target and return). The comparison between the transmitted and received frequencies results in a difference, or beat frequency, sometimes termed the *Doppler frequency, f_D*:

$$f_D = 77.7 \frac{V}{\lambda}$$

where V = target radial velocity, knots; λ = transmitted wavelength, cm.

Doppler velocity and position (DOVAP). A range instrumentation and safety system used to determine velocity and position by using electromagnetic radiation. An airborne frequency doubler is utilized as are Doppler beat frequencies at several ground stations to provide range data (by counting cycles which represent the sum of velocities for the propagation paths). Direct velocity measurement is provided.

DORAN. A Doppler ranging system (elliptical) using phase comparison to establish missile range. It is very similar to DOVAP (q.v.).

dose (dosage). The amount of nuclear radiation delivered to a specified area or volume, or to the whole human body.

dosimeter. An instrument for measuring the total dosage of nuclear radiation, in roentgens or milliroentgens, received in a given period.

double amplitude. *See* peak-to-peak amplitude.

double-balanced modulator. *See* ring modulator.

double-base propellant. A solid rocket propellant consisting of gelatinized colloidal nitrocellulose (the matrix) and nitroglycerin (the plasticizer) with the addition of certain stabilizers. Since both materials contain nitro groups attached to oxygen and carbon atoms, each is, in effect, a homogeneous or integrated propellant containing both fuel and oxidizer. See Table 5, page 214.

double-entry centrifugal compressor. A single-stage, radial-flow compressor in which the impeller vanes are double, placed back-to-back but delivering air to the same diffuser. Distinguish from a *multistage compressor*.

double pulsing station. A LORAN (q.v.) station that belongs to two pairs and emits pulses at two pulse rates.

doubler. (1) In electronics, a vacuum-tube circuit in which the output circuit is tuned to twice the frequency of the input circuit. Also a *voltage doubler circuit*. (2) In structures, a reinforcement (usually sheet metal) used to provide extra metal around cutouts or where additional strength is needed.

double sampling. Sampling inspection in which the inspection of the first sample leads to a decision to accept, to reject, or to take a second sample. The examination of a second sample, when required, always leads to a decision to accept or to reject.

double side band transmission. In electronics, transmission of the sum and difference frequencies of the modulating and carrier signals; It is the standard broadcast type of transmission.

double side band transmitter. A transmitter which transmits the carrier frequency and both side bands resulting from the modulation of the carrier by the modulating signal.

double wedge (section) airfoil. An aerodynamic surface of symmetrical wedge shape. The wave drag is:

$$C_{Dw} = \frac{4r^2}{\sqrt{M^2 - 1}}$$

where r = ratio of maximum thickness to chord of the cross section; M = MACH number.

DOVAP. *DO*ppler *V*elocity *A*nd *P*osition (q.v.).

DOVE. Air-to-surface and air-to-underwater missile. Military designation: XASM-N-4.

Prime Contractor: Eastman Kodak Co.

downdraft. A draft of atmospheric air that moves downward, the opposite of an updraft. Generally encountered in thunderstorms, downdrafts often attain great velocities.

downgrade. To assign a lower security classification to a document, piece of equipment, or the like, than that previously assigned.

down range. In missile testing, the area over which missiles fly. At the Air Force Missile Test Center (q.v.) down-range stations are maintained on islands in the down-range area for range safety and instrumentation purposes.

down-range stations. In missile testing, a facility providing for communications, range clearance, inflight safety, weather reporting, telemetry reception (and transmission via the submarine cable to other stations up and down range for recording control), optical and radar-tracking (sub-cable permits radar-tracking aid to acquisition). See AFMTC.

downstairs. (Vernacular) In the lower atmosphere, near the ground or water.

downsun. In a direction away from the Sun; with the Sun at one's back.

down the slot. (Vernacular) A successful flight of a missile down the test range and within the left and right range limits established by range safety personnel.

down-time. The calendar time in which a system is *not* considered in condition to perform its required function.

downwash. A wing-tail aerodynamic interference effect which affects the lifting efficiency of aft surfaces when these are either controlling or stabilizing a missile about its center of gravity. This effect will cause positive trim angles of attack (q.v.) to exist with wing control types even though the wing hub may be located on the overall missile center of gravity. The downwash produced by a given angle of attack increases as the aspect ratio is reduced.

DPO. Development Planning Objective.

DR. Dead Reckoning (q.v.).

drag. The resistance of a missile to motion in a fluid. In a supersonic missile it is generally made up of three different types: (a) *wave drag,* (b) *skin friction,* and (c) *drag due to normal force.* The total of the wave drag—that is, drag forces due to pressures acting on the missile at zero angle of attack—and the skin friction is usually referred to as the *zero-lift drag,* whereas the component of normal force acting in the airstream direction (and existing

solely owing to the resultant normal force) is referred to as the *lift-drag.* The zero-lift drag is made up of the total pressure drag of the body, wings, and tails as well as the pressure effect of any protuberances, plus the skin friction acting over the entire body surfaces.

drag. *Types of, see* aerodynamic–; burner–; form–; induced–; interference–; parasite–; profile–; ram–; skin–; structural–; wave–; wing–; zero-lift–.

drag coefficient. (1) A coefficient that gives the relative air resistance of a particular aerodynamic configuration. (2) A coefficient used in calculating the drag component of forces in an atomic blast.

drag due to normal force. See drag.

drag rise. The rapid increase in parasitic drag that a vehicle not designed for high speeds encounters as it approaches the speed of sound (q.v.).

drag-weight ratio. A useful aerodynamic ratio relating the total drag of a missile to the total weight.

drawing. *Types of, see* end product–; schematic–.

DRE. Data Reduction Equipment.

drift. (1) In a gyroscope (q.v.), the displacement of the gimbals due to bearing friction, weight of lead wires, anisoelastic effects, mass unbalance, etc. (2) In an amplifier (and other electronic devices) the departure of the characteristic output from the desired value; due to circuit unbalance, temperature, etc. (3) In guidance, the gradual motion of a missile away from the desired trajectory; caused by misalignments, electrical biases, etc.

drift. *Types of, see* gyroscope–; output–; radar–.

driftmeter. An instrument for measuring or determining the drift of a vehicle by visual sighting of points or objects on the ground.

drift space. In electronics, the portion of a klystron (q.v.) in which faster electrons catch up with slower ones to form bunches.

drizzle. See atmospheric drizzle.

DRL/UT. Defense Research Laboratory/The University of Texas; Austin, Texas.

drone. A remotely controlled pilotless aircraft used as a target or to perform tasks hazardous to a human pilot (e.g., probe a nuclear cloud, target practice, etc.).

drone, target. See target drone.

drop aircraft rocket launcher. A type of aircraft rocket launcher (q.v.) that drops the rocket before ignition.

drop test. (1) An environmental linear acceleration test used to establish capability of equipment to withstand handling or drops in service. (2) A generic term categorizing tests in which the equipment is dropped in a tower, from a height, etc.

drop, vertical. *See* vertical drop.

dry fog. A fog-like haze of suspended particles with low moisture content, such as occurs near a forest fire or after an explosion.

dry friction. Friction between solid surfaces without benefit of a lubricant.

dry friction damping. The damping in a mechanical system resulting primarily from friction forces which are independent of velocity displacement. The damping force is equal to the coefficient of friction times the normal force.

dry load. *See* sand load.

dry run. A "dummy" test usually complete in detail except for actual operation of the equipment; used to develop crew skills and to assure readiness for a full-scale test.

dry stand. A type of rocket launcher (q.v.) having a flame deflector (q.v.) which is not liquid-cooled.

DTE. Data Transmission Equipment.

DTMB. David Taylor Model Basin; Carderock, Maryland.

DUCK. Air-to-air defense missile. Air Force cognizance.

Armament for long-range and supersonic bombers as a bombardment missile. Initially probably a part of the weapon system for the Convair B-58 Hustler bomber. Turbojet engine.

Prime Contractor: Fairchild Engine and Airplane Corp. Airframe: Fairchild. Engine: Fairchild. Guidance system: Fairchild.

duct. *See* aero-thermodynamic-duct.

ducted fan jet engine. A kind of turbojet engine in which a propeller or fan forces low-pressure air through ducts directly into the hot turbine exhaust at the turbine exhaust pressure.

ducted solid propellant rocket. A type of missile system which uses a solid reductant (fuel) contained in a duct with air serving as the oxidant. This type of rocket is known as a *solid propellant ramjet* and is not a pure rocket system; i.e., it is an air-breathing engine (q.v.).

dud. A missile or armament which fails to operate during preparation, launching, or flight.

dummy load. In electronics, a waveguide (q.v.) or coaxial device which is able to absorb power from a waveguide or coaxial transmission line without allowing any of it to be radiated or reflected back toward the source. It must present a smooth impedance match (q.v.) in order to prevent reflections, and the energy fed into it must be dissipated as heat.

dunking pulse. (Vernacular) The recycling pulse employed in some amplitude selection circuits.

duplex. The capability of an equipment to perform two independent functions simultaneously (e.g., simultaneous firing from several launchers). Contrast with *simplex* (q.v.).

duplexer. In electronics, that portion of a microwave circuit where the TR (transmit-receive) switch and the ATR (anti-transmit-receive) switches are located.

duraluminum. (obsolete) A term used to denote 2014T (formerly 14ST); an alloy of aluminum used extensively in aircraft construction, light but relatively hard and strong.

dusk rocket. A rocket launched towards the west [from the dusk side (q.v.) of the Earth]. The takeoff velocity is *diminished* by the orbital velocity (q.v.) of the Earth (18.5 miles per second).

dusk side. That side of a planet or celestial body which points away from the direction of its orbital movement. Contrast with *dawn side* (q.v.).

duty cycle. In electronics: (1) The time interval consumed by a device on intermittent duty in starting, running, stopping, and idling. (2) The ratio of this time interval to the total time of one operating cycle. (3) The ratio of the pulse width or time to the interval between like portions of successive pulses.

$$\text{duty cycle} = \frac{t_0}{T}$$

where t_0 = pulse width in seconds; T = time in seconds from leading edge to leading edge.

dynaforming. A metal-working process in which explosive charges are used to obtain desired forms. The process is applicable to aluminum alloys, magnesium alloys, 17-7 Ph steel, 4130 steel, etc. Thicknesses of 0.015 to 0.5 in. have been worked.

dynamical analogies. The formal similarities among the differential equations of electrical, mechanical, and acoustical systems which make possible the reduction of mechanical and acoustical systems to electrical networks and the solution of such problems by electrical circuit theory.

dynamical similarity. (1) Describes two geometrically similar fluid flows when the flow field of one may be transformed into the flow field of the other by the same change of length and velocity scales that was necessary to make the boundary conditions identical. If the equations of motion of the flow are made non-dimensional by expressing velocities and lengths as fractions of these scales, these equations contain a number of non-dimensional coefficients that determine the character of the flow. The general condition for dynamical similarity is that all these coefficients should be the same for the two flows. The coefficients commonly used are the REYNOLDS *number*, the PRANDTL *number*, the GRASHOF (or RAYLEIGH) *number*, the MACH *number*, and the FROUDE *number*. (2) In a structural system, the use of a model with the same stiffness, resonant frequencies, mass distribution, etc., as required to perform dynamic tests in a wind tunnel or under other dynamic conditions.

dynamic behavior. A term which describes how a control system or an individual unit performs with respect to time.

dynamic damper. A short pendulum-like counterweight attached to a crankshaft in order to damp out or reduce engine vibration.

dynamic hysteresis loop. Of a core, the curve of magnetization versus applied magnetomotive force per unit length obtained when the magnetic material is cyclically magnetized at some specified rate. The magnetization at any instant is the average flux density over the entire core section. The applied magnetomotive force per unit length at any instant is that required to provide the flux and rate-of-change of flux implicit in the test or operating specifications. Also termed *AC hysteresis loop, flux current loop, flux-ampere-turn loop.*

dynamic lift. The lift given a vehicle by the dynamic force produced from an airfoil. Distinguished from the lift imparted to an aerostat by a lighter-than-air gas.

dynamic mock-up. A laboratory-type mock-up (q.v.) of the (usually) controls system with mechanical springs simulating the engine (or other forcing function) support structure. It is used for *functional* testing.

dynamic pressure (total head) (q). The pressure exerted upon a body by a fluid which is brought to rest against it. For an incompressible fluid, the dynamic pressure is the sum of the local pressure and the kinetic energy per unit volume.

$$q = \tfrac{1}{2}\,\rho V^2 = 0.7 p M^2$$

where ρ = density, slug/ft; V = velocity, ft/sec; p = pressure, lb/sq ft; M = MACH number. See Table 1, page 81.

dynamic range. The ratio between maximum signal and basic noise level. Both the maximum signal and the noise level can be variously defined according to harmonic distortion levels and pass bands.

dynamics. A branch of mechanics that treats of the motion of bodies and of the forces acting upon bodies in motion or in process of changing motion. *Dynamics* deals with the causes of motion, as opposed to *kinematics*, which deals with its geometric description, and to *statics*, which deals with the conditions for lack of motion.

dynamics, fluid. *See* fluid dynamics.

dynamic stability. In aerodynamics, the characteristic motion of a missile as it returns to its steady-state condition after a disturbance has produced an unbalanced moment. The natural frequency of this "weathercock" (q.v.) oscillation and the time-to-damp-to-half amplitude (q.v.) are the usual criteria for dynamic stability.

dynamo. A member of a general class of machines capable of transformation of electrical into mechanical energy, or vice versa. The word is a shortened form of dynamo-electric. A feature of all dynamo machines is the employment of magnetic induction in effecting the transformation. The essential parts of an ordinary dynamo are the *armature* and the *field*. One of these is mounted on a rotating shaft, and the other is stationary. In ideal cases, such as DC dynamos and separately excited AC dynamos, the machine is reversible; i.e., it may be used either as a motor or a generator.

dynamometer. An end instrument which translates force (tensile or compressive) into a usable quantity (e.g., change of inductance or resistance).

dynamotor. A combination electric motor and DC generator having two, or more, separate armature windings, and a common set of field poles. One armature winding, receiving direct current, operates as a motor producing rotation, while the other operates as a dynamo or generator, generating voltage. Used to convert low DC voltages for application as an electronic tube plate supply.

DYNA-SOAR. *Dynamic soaring.* A competitive study project under the direction of the United States Air Force (USAF) and the National Aeronautics and Space Administration (NASA) to develop an orbital bomber (q.v.) for reconnaissance and/or strategic bombing manned aircraft with a trajectory initially ballistic and a skip-glide reentry. Competitive teams for the phase I study are composed of the following companies: General Electric, Thompson-Ramo-Wooldridge, North American Aviation (Autonetics and Missile Divisions), Aerojet-General, Boeing, Martin, Bell, Minneapolis-Honeywell, Goodyear, Bendix, Chance-Vought, and American Machine and Foundry. Scope was changed in March 1959 to make it an unpowered glider boosted to near-satellite speeds.

dynatron. A four-electrode vacuum tube so designed that secondary emission of electrons from the plate causes the plate current to decrease as plate voltage is increased giving a negative resistance characteristic. Used in oscillator circuits.

dyne. A unit of force that will accelerate a particle having a mass of one gram, one centimeter per second per second.

$$1 \text{ dyne} = 0.0010197 \text{ gram} = 2.2481 \times 10^{-6} \text{ lb}$$
$$1 \text{ dyne/cm} = 1 \text{ erg/sq cm}$$
$$1 \text{ dyne/sq cm} = 10^{-6} \text{ bar}$$
$$1 \text{ dyne-centimeter} = 1 \text{ erg} = 7.3756 \times 10^{-8} \text{ ft-lb} = 0.001097 \text{ gm-cm} = 8.85073 \times 10^{-7} \text{ in.-lb}$$

dynetric balancer. A device used in balancing individual units of equipment revolving at varying speeds.

TABLE 1. Pressure of air coming to rest from various speeds*

Air speed, fps	Impact pressure, lb/ft²		Air speed, fps	Impact pressure, lb/ft²	
	Incompressible	*Adiabatic*		*Incompressible*	*Adiabatic*
0	0.000	0.000	300	107.03	108.97
10	0.119	0.119	310	114.28	116.50
20	0.476	0.476	320	121.78	124.30
30	1.070	1.070	330	129.51	132.36
40	1.903	1.903	340	137.47	140.69
50	2.973	2.975	350	145.68	149.30
60	4.281	4.285	360	154.12	158.17
70	5.827	5.833	370	162.80	167.32
80	7.611	7.621	380	171.72	176.75
90	9.633	9.649	390	180.88	186.47
100	11.892	11.916	400	190.27	196.46
110	14.390	14.424	410	199.91	206.74
120	17.125	17.174	420	209.78	217.31
130	20.098	20.166	430	219.89	228.17
140	23.308	23.401	440	230.22	239.30
150	26.758	26.877	450	240.81	250.76
160	30.444	30.600	460	251.65	262.50
170	34.368	34.567	470	262.69	274.55
180	38.530	38.784	480	274.00	286.89
190	42.931	43.242	490	285.54	299.55
200	47.569	47.952	500	297.30	312.50
210	52.444	52.909	550	359.73	382.10
220	57.558	58.119	600	428.12	459.94
230	62.909	63.580	700	582.71	642.28
240	68.500	69.293	800	761.10	863.93
250	74.327	75.263	900	963.27	1130.2
260	80.392	81.488	1000	1189.2	1447.3
270	86.694	87.966	1100	1439.0	1823.0
280	93.234	94.708	1200	1712.5	2266.0
290	100.01	101.71	1300	2009.8	2786.8
			1400	2330.9	3397.2
			1500	2675.7	4111.2

* NACA Tech. Rept. 316.

E

EAFB. (1) Edwards Air Force Base, the Air Force Flight Test Center (AFFTC) (q.v.), Mojave, California. (2) Eglin Air Force Base, Florida.

EAGLE. Air-to-air and air-to-surface missile. Air Force cognizance.

A "highly sophisticated" missile to be married to a fighter plane which will act only as a platform. Range is 50-100 miles. Bendix is the contractor.

E & ST. Employment and Suitability Test (q.v.).

EAPD. Eastern Air Procurement District.

early. Warhead detonation (burst) during the period after S and A (q.v.) activation but before target detection.

early bird. A missile which arrives at the intersection of the missile-target trajectories prior to the arrival of the target.

early failure. Those failures (q.v.) which occur early in the life of an equipment at a rate in excess of the rate to be expected due to chance. Failures due to inherent weaknesses built into the equipment during fabrication in excess of inherent design weaknesses.

early warning system. Part of an air defense system usually comprising search radars, whose function is to detect and identify attacking enemy aircraft in time to permit effective use of the system's air defense weapons.

Earth. *Types of, see* atmosphere of the Earth; nonrotating earth.

Earth-grazers. Minor planets which have orbits (q.v.) which bring them well within the orbit of Mars, and thus close to the Earth. The most famous of the group is *Eros*. It is an irregularly shaped body with a diameter of 15 miles. In 1931 it passed within 17 million miles of the Earth, proving very useful as an aid to determine the value of the astronomical unit (q.v.). The next close approach will be in 1975. Other Earth-grazers are *Albert* (minimum distance from the Earth, 20 million miles; diameter 3 miles); *Amor* (10 million miles, 10 miles); *Apollo* (7 million miles, 2 miles); *Adonis* (1½

million miles, 1 mile); and *Hermes* (200,000 miles, 1 mile). The closest approach on record is that of Hermes in 1937, when the minimum distance was 400,000 miles.

Earth mass and dimensions. The equatorial diameter of the Earth is 7,927 miles; the polar 7900, giving a polar compression of 1 part in 296. The escape velocity (q.v.) is 7 miles per second. The Earth is the largest of the inner group of planets, though only very slightly superior to Venus. Its mass is 6×10^{21} tons.

Earth motion. There are 5 principal motions of the Earth: (a) *rotation:* Earth turns on its axis once a day in an eastward direction at a speed which varies with the latitude (e.g., a point on the equator moves more than 1,000 miles per hour; movement at the poles is zero); (b) *revolution:* Earth revolves eastward around the Sun once in the span of a year. Average speed is 18½ miles per second; (c) *precession:* The axis of the Earth wobbles (like a spinning top) westward around a line joining the poles of the ecliptic (q.v.). One wobble is accomplished approximately every 25,800 years; (d) *solar motion:* the Sun (carrying the entire solar system) is moving nearly in the direction of the star Vega at the rate of 12 miles per second; (d) *galactic motion:* the Sun (and all planets in the system) revolves around the center of our galaxy (q.v.) once in approximately 200,000,000 years at the rate of 175 miles per second.

Earth orbit. Earth revolves around the Sun at a mean distance of 93,000,000 miles, the *perihelion* (q.v.) distance being 91.4 million miles and the *aphelion* (q.v.) distance being 94.6 million miles. The orbital eccentricity is 0.017, less than that of any other major planet except Venus and Neptune. The mean velocity is 18.47 miles per second.

Earth pendulum (84-minute pendulum; Schuler pendulum). A pendulum with a length equal to radius of the Earth and a natural period of 84 minutes. It has the property of being insensitive to Earth's rotation. Penduluous systems having the same period are similarly insensitive and are therefore widely used in gyroscope reference systems.

$$T = 2\pi \sqrt{\frac{L}{g}} = 2\pi \sqrt{\frac{3963 \times 5280}{32 \times 3600}} = 84 \text{ min}$$

Earth rotation period. The axial rotation period of the Earth is 23 hours 56 minutes, and the inclination of the axis 23°27′.

Earth's rate. The apparent angular motion of a space-stabilized gyroscope caused by the Earth's turning on its axis (at 15° per hour). Gyroscope drift (q.v.) is measured as a fraction of Earth's rate.

ECARL. Expendable Cluster Aircraft Rocket Launcher. *See* FFAR.

ECCM. Electronic Counter-CounterMeasure(s).

echo area. That part of a radar target that effectively returns echoes to the transmitter. Also termed *radar cross section, scattering cross section.* The effectiveness of a radar target in sending back echoes depends upon its size and shape, especially upon the contours of its surface.

Tuned λ/2 dipole	$0.22\lambda^2$
Small sphere with radius = a, where a/λ = 0.15	$9\pi a^2 (2\pi a/\lambda)^4$
Large sphere with radius = a, where a/λ = 1	πa^2
Corner reflector with one edge = a (maximum)	$4\pi a^4/3\lambda^2$
Flat plate with area = A (normal incidence)	$4\pi A^2/\lambda^2$
Cylinder with radius = a, length = L (normal incidence)	$2\pi L^2 a/\lambda$
Small airplane	200 ft²
Large airplane	800 ft²
Small cargo ship	1500 ft²
Large cargo ship	160,000 ft²

Fig. 7. Target echoing area. (L. N. Ridenour, *Radar Systems Engineering*, McGraw-Hill Book Co.)

echo box. A device connected to a radar transmitter to reradiate transmitted pulses for testing purposes and for timing the receiver to the transmitter.

echo, permanent. *See* permanent echo.

ECL. Equipment Component List.

ecliptic. (1) Plane of Earth's orbit around the Sun. It is used as a reference plane for other interplanetary orbits. (2) Ecliptic is also the name for the apparent path of the Sun through the constellations as projected on the celestial sphere (q.v.).

ECM. Electronic CounterMeasures (q.v.). *See also* countermeasures.

E-coil. An inductor consisting of an open-face stack of E laminations with a coil wound on the middle leg of the stack. The E-coil assembly is usually potted in a protective case.

ecosphere. From a medical standpoint, that part of the atmosphere in which normal breathing may be exercised, extending upward to about 13,000 ft above sea level. Also termed the *physiological atmosphere.*

ECP. (1) Engineering Change Proposal (q.v.). (2) Engineering Change Proposed.

EDP. Electronic Data Processing.

EDPC. Electronic Data Processing Center (q.v.).

EDPS. Electronic Data Processing System (q.v.).

effect. *Types of, see* Dellinger–; Doppler–; Hall–; Joule-Thomson–; MACH–; Monroe–; nonisoelastic–; Peltier–; pinch–; ram–; scale–; Schottky–; shot–.

effective angle of attack. That part of a given angle of attack (q.v.) that lies between the chord of an airfoil and a line representing the resultant velocity of the disturbed airflow. This angle is measured on a finite wing, but it has the same effective magnitude as that of an angle of attack for infinite aspect ratio (q.v.) measured on a theoretical airfoil between the chord and the direction of the undisturbed airflow.

effective area. The area within which a projectile containing a high explosive charge must explode in order to do effective damage.

effective aspect ratio. In aerodynamics, the aspect ratio (q.v.) of an airfoil of elliptical planform that, for the same lift coefficient (q.v.), has the same induced drag coefficient (q.v.) as the airfoil or combination of airfoils under consideration.

effective atmosphere. That portion of the atmosphere (q.v.) which effectively influences a particular process or motion; the outer limits vary according to the terms of the process or motion used.

effective burning time. In solid rocket performance calculations, an arbitrary quantity defined as the total impulse from the time 90% of effective thrust is reached at the start to 90% of thrust at decay. The 90% value is arbitrary.

effective chamber pressure. In rocketry, the area under the chamber pressure time curve between the two points indicating 90 per cent of rated thrust divided by the time interval between these points.

effective echoing area of target. In radar terminology, the area of a hypothetical target, normal to the incident beam, which reradiates equally in all directions all the energy incident on it, and produces at the receiver a signal equal to that produced by the actual target. The value of A_e for an actual target depends on many factors, and can only be found empirically. For an average aircraft it is of the order of 10 to 100 sq ft. See Fig. 7, page 83.

effective exhaust velocity. Of a rocket engine, the average axial velocity of the jet stream (q.v.) leaving the exhaust nozzle; a fictitious velocity used because the variables can be measured with a high degree of accuracy.

$$V_j = g \frac{F}{\dot{w}} = gI_{sp}$$

where F = thrust, lb; $\dot{w}$ = weight flow, lb/sec; g = acceleration of gravity, ft/sec^2; I_{sp} = specific impulse, sec.

effective impulse. The impulse equal to that portion of the thrust-vs.-duration curve between the "90 per cent of rated" ordinates on a plot made of the complete firing of a rocket engine.

effective launcher length. The relation between the active and effective launcher length is:

$$l_{\text{eff}} = \frac{V^2}{2G_e}$$

where V = actual velocity at launching; G_e = effective acceleration after launching.

effective (mechanomotive) force. In calculating loads on a structure imposed by complex forces, the effective force is the root mean square of the instantaneous forces over a complete cycle. The unit is the *dyne*.

effective sound pressure. *See* sound (acoustomotive) pressure.

effective static stability. In aerodynamics, the slope of the moment coefficient vs. normal force coefficient curve; the extent to which a vehicle is arrowlike stable.

effective vehicle thrust. The resultant force in the direction of motion of an airborne vehicle, owing to the components of all pressure forces in excess of ambient atmospheric pressure, acting on all inner surfaces of the vehicle parallel to the direction of motion.

effective wind. A calculated wind equal in speed and direction to the average of any given number of varying actual winds, used especially in sound ranging and weather observation.

efficiency. The ratio of output to input.

$$\text{efficiency} = \frac{\text{output}}{\text{input}}$$

efficiency. *Types of, see* adiabatic–; ballistic–; diffuser–; external–; isolator–; overall–; thermal–; wake–.

EHF. Extremely High Frequency (30,000-300,000 mcs).

Einstein equation. A fundamental equation expressing the equivalence of energy and mass:

$$E = mc^2$$

where E = energy; m = mass converted; c = velocity of light. One kilogram of uranium or plutonium must be fissioned to yield the energy equivalent of 20,000 tons of TNT (which is 2×10^{13} cal = 8.4×10^{20} ergs = 2.3×10^7 kwh).

elastic axis. In structures, the locus of the shear centers of the cross sections of a beam.

elasticity. The ability of a body which has been deformed by an applied force to return to its original shape when the force is removed. Characteristics of the stress-strain relation vary with the material. Each of the several types of elasticity is probably due to the action of intermolecular forces which are in equilibrium only for certain configurations.

elasticity. *Types of, see* anomalous–; modulus of–.

elastic limit. The least stress that will cause permanent set (strain remaining after removal of stress) of a material.

E layer. That part of the ionosphere (q.v.) with a maxima of ionization that persists both day and night from above 55 miles to 85 miles, immediately below the F layer (q.v.). Sometimes termed the *Heaviside layer* or the *Kennelly-Heaviside layer*. See Fig. 11, page 140.

electrical capacitance. In an electrical system, the circuit element which opposes a change in voltage. It is analogous to compliance in a mechanical system.

electrical degree. One of the 360 equal parts of an alternating current (AC) cycle.

electrical director. An electrical device for tracking a moving target and, by using information from radar or from a range finder, for computing firing data. *See* moving target indicator.

electrical impedance. The ratio of the effective value of the potential difference between the terminals to the effective value of the current, there being no source of power in the portion of the circuit under consideration. The unit is the *abohm*.

electrical interference. Refers specifically to interference (q.v.) caused by the operation of electrical apparatus that is not designed to radiate electromagnetic energy.

electrical reactance. In an electrical system, a circuit element which is part of the electrical impedance (q.v.). The unit is the *abohm*. Analogous to *mechanical resistance* (q.v.).

electrical system. A system adapted for the transmission of electrical currents consisting of one or all of the electrical elements: resistance, inductance, and capacitance (q.q.v.) which, added vectorially, constitute the electrical impedance.

electrical units. The fundamental electrical units are: (a) ohm; (b) ampere; (c) volt; (d) coulomb; (e) farad; (f) henry; (g) watt (q.q.v.).

electric dipole. In electronics, a dipole (q.v.) which is made up of a positive and a negative charge which are of equal strength and are placed at a small distance apart so that no macroscopic net charge is present and yet an electric field is generated.

electroforming. The electrolytic deposition of metal upon a conducting mold to make a desired metal object, e.g., precision tubing or medals. The mold is often of graphite-coated wax, so that it can be removed by melting.

electrogravity. The science which deals with control of gravity, and seeks ways to explain it, shield it, and put it to work.

electro-interference. Any electrical disturbance created by producing an undesired response in, or causing malfunctioning of, any electrical or electronic equipment.

electrojet. Current sheet or stream moving in an ionized layer (q.v.) in the upper atmosphere of a planet. On Earth, electrojets move around the equator following the subsolar point and also in polar regions where they give rise to auroral phenomena; generally caused by solar activity.

electrolyte. A chemical substance, either liquid or paste-like, used in a battery, cell, or capacitor (q.v.) to generate or store electric current.

electromagnetic radiation. Radiation made up of oscillating electric and magnetic fields and propagating with the speed of light. Includes gamma radiation, X-rays, ultraviolet light, visible light, infrared radiation, radar and radio waves.

electromagnetic spectrum. The full range of wavelengths of electromagnetic radiation.

electromagnetic units (emu). The system of units based upon the study of magnetism quite apart from electrical charge, except as electric currents give rise to magnetic fields. The *unit magnetic pole*, which is an imaginary entity useful in setting up the system, is defined (in analogy to a statcoulomb, q.v.) as a magnetic pole of sufficient strength to exert a force of one dyne on a similar pole one cm away. An *emu ampere* is defined as the current in a circular loop of wire of one-cm radius which will cause a force of 2π dynes to act on a unit pole placed at the center of the loop.

electromagnetic waves. Periodic fluctuations in space of electric and magnetic fields which act in directions perpendicular to each other and to the line of propagation.

electromotive force (EMF). The force which moves electricity in a current, measured in volts.

electron. A very small negatively charged particle. Electrons appear to be uniform in mass and charge and to be one of the basic units of which atoms are made. The negatively charged electrons surrounding an atomic nucleus form an *atom* (q.v.). Each electron has 1/1840 the mass of a light hydrogen atom.

electron beam. (1) A stream of electrons moving at high velocity, e.g., in a cathode-ray tube. (2) A cathode ray.

electron coupled oscillator. An oscillator (q.v.) which employs electron coupling between the oscillator and the output or load, using a vacuum tube as the medium of the coupling.

electron gun. A device used in a cathode-ray tube (q.v.) to form, accelerate, and focus an electron beam.

electronic countermeasures (ECM). Refers to that major subdivision of the use of electronics which involves actions taken to reduce the effectiveness of enemy equipment and/or tactics employing or affected by electromagnetic radiation. *See* active electronic countermeasures; passive electronic countermeasures.

electronic data processing center (EDPC). A center that maintains automatically operated equipment, including computers, engineered to simplify the use and interpretation of the mass of data gathered by modern instrument installations. Capable of automatically handling information fed to it from widely scattered points.

electronic data processing system (EDPS). Part of the Air Materiel Command network for logistics (q.v.) support.

electronic deception. The radiation or reradiation of electromagnetic energy in a manner intended to mislead the enemy in the interpretation of data received by his electronic equipment.

electronic fuze. A fuze (q.v.), (e.g., the radio proximity fuze), set off by an electronic device incorporated in the fuze.

electronic jamming. An action involved in electronic countermeasures (q.v.), being the radiation or reradiation of electromagnetic waves to impair the use of a specific segment of the radio spectrum. Usually termed *jamming*.

electronic missile acquisition (EMA). A measuring system for providing angular data (azimuth and elevation angle) by a phase comparison of RF signals received from a missile.

electronics. That branch of physics which treats of the emission, transmission, behavior, and effects of electrons. Practical application of electronics has been made through such devices as vacuum tubes, cathode-ray tubes, photoelectric cells, etc.

electronic skyscreen equipment (ELSSE). A missile trajectory measuring system used to provide azimuth data. Telemetering transmitters or other airborne transponders may be used for a signal source; usually used for range safety.

electronics warfare (EW). Warfare in which electronic instruments are used, e.g., in radio communications, guided missile control, target detection, etc.

electron-multiplier phototube. A vacuum-type phototube that employs secondary emission to amplify the electron stream emitted from the illuminated photo-cathode. The electron stream impinges in turn on each of a series of reflecting electrodes termed *dynodes*, at each of which secondary emission adds electrons to the stream. In one tube, an amplification of approximately 2000 to 2,000,000 times is obtained with nine dynodes. Also termed *photoelectric electron-multiplier tube* and *multiplier-phototube*.

electron trajectory. In vacuum tubes, the path which an electron follows in going through the space between electrodes.

electron tube. Any completely evacuated or gas-filled tube used to control the flow of electrons in a circuit. Vacuum tubes, phototubes, mercury-vapor rectifier tubes, and cathode-ray tubes are all electron tubes. They are largely used for amplification purposes.

electrostatic units (esu). The simplest system of notation for calculations which involve only stationary charge and, therefore, do not deal

at all with magnetism. The *esu coulomb* is defined as the amount of charge which will exert a force of one dyne on an equal charge one centimeter distant. An *esu ampere* is an esu coulomb per second. Electrostatic units are sometimes termed *statcoulombs, statvolts, statfarads*.

element function. In electronics, the radiation pattern of a single antenna element of an antenna array (e.g., the radiation pattern of one dipole of a bank of dipoles used to feed a broadside array). *See* antenna array.

element, lumped constant. *See* lumped constant element.

element of a physical system. (1) An element or circuit parameter in an electrical system defines a distinct activity in its part of the circuit. In the same way, an element in a mechanical rectilineal, mechanical rotational, or acoustical system (q.q.v.) defines a distinct activity in its part of the system. The elements in an electrical circuit are *electrical resistance, inductance,* and *electrical capacitance* (q.q.v.). The elements in a mechanical rectilineal system are *mechanical rectilineal resistance, mass,* and *compliance* (q.q.v.). The elements in a mechanical rotational system are *mechanical rotational resistance, moment of inertia,* and *rotational compliance* (q.q.v.). The elements in an acoustical system are *acoustical rseistance, inertance,* and *acoustical capacitance* (q.q.v.). (2) A part, device, piece part which constitutes a portion of a system—usually physically identifiable (an entity).

elephant ears. (Vernacular) Thick plates that reinforce the hatches and holes in a missile's body.

elevation quadrant. A measure of launcher elevation position. The measurement may be made with a gunner's quadrant.

elevation, target. *See* target elevation.

elevon control. *See* tailless (elevon) control.

ellipse. The geometrical form of the orbit (q.v.) of one celestial body revolving around another. Earth's orbit around the Sun is an ellipse distorted by the presence of other planets. *See* Kepler's laws.

ellipse. *Types of, see* braking–; tangential–; transfer–.

ellipsoid. *See* reference ellipsoid.

elliptical orbit. The orbit (q.v.) described by a body with less than escape energy but more than one-half escape energy [e.g., an Earth satellite (q.v.)].

ELSSE. *Electronic skyscreen equipment (q.v.).*

ELSSE COTAR. A passive range instrumentation system using, on the ground, the skyscreen system to receive data transmitted from any airborne transponder, which may be used for other purposes (e.g., FM/FM telemetering transmits at a satisfactory frequency for this system).

EMA. Electronic Missile Acquisition (q.v.).

emagram. In meteorology, a chart showing temperature on a linear scale and pressure on a logarithmic scale.

emergency maintenance. A maintenance procedure instigated because of a failure (q.v.).

emergency power supply (EPS). Device used to supply electrical power for certain range safety components during missile flight.

EMF. ElectroMotive Force (q.v.).

emission. *See* thermionic emission.

emissive power. Total for a surface: the amount of energy of all wavelengths radiated per sec into a solid angle of 2π steradians (e.g., a hemisphere).

EML. Equipment Modification List.

empennage. The assembly at the rear end of an aircraft or missile comprised of the horizontal and vertical stabilizers and their associated control surfaces. Also termed the *tail assembly*.

emplacement. *See* permanent emplacement.

employment and suitability test. A missile test which corresponds to an operational suitability test for aircraft.

emu. Electromagnetic units (q.v.).

encoder (analog-digital). A device for converting information available in analog computer form into a form suitable for understanding by a digital computer. (*Decoders* are used to convert digital to analog form.)

end bow. A member giving a rounded outline to the tip of a wing, control surface, or the like.

end burner. *See* restricted propellant, and Fig. 22, page 259.

end burning grain. *See* restricted burning grain; restricted propellant; Fig. 22, page 259.

end-fire antenna array. Parallel antenna elements with currents 180° out of phase, which radiate the greater part of their energy along the line of the antennas.

end-fire array. A linear or cylindrical radar antenna array (q.v.) that emits its radiation from one end.

end instrument. An instrument for measuring a quantity within a missile for transmission by telemetering (q.v.); a transducer (q.v.) or pickup.

end instrumentation calibration. The process of determining the response characteristics of a device by measuring the electrical output signal while an accurately known physical stimulus is applied to the input. Usually, the process is repeated for a number of different values of input stimulus.

end item. A final combination of end products (q.v.), component parts, and/or materials that is ready for its intended use (e.g., a missile, a mobile guidance unit, a launcher).

end organ. An *end instrument, pickup, transducer* (q.q.v.); a device for measuring a quantity for transmission by a telemetering system (an obsolescent term). *See* telemetering pickup.

endothermic. In thermodynamics, a term descriptive of an absorption of heat or other energy.

end play. The longitudinal back-and-forth play of a shaft.

end product. Any material, part, subassembly, or assembly in its final completed state, as governed by specifications, drawings, provisions of contract or order, or other requirements.

end product drawing. A drawing showing an *end product* (q.v.). An end product drawing covering the detail of an individual part should include all dimensions, tolerances, notes, and other data necessary to describe fully the size, shape, and other characteristics of the part as it appears in its completed state, but should not include references to intermediate steps in the production process, such as roughing operations with dimensions and limits pertaining thereto, or to specific manufacturing methods.

endurance limit. A limiting stress, below which metal will withstand, without fracture, an indefinitely large number of cycles of stress. If the term is used without qualification, the cycles of stress are usually such as to produce complete reversal of flexural stress. Above this limit failure occurs by the generation and growth of cracks until fracture results in the remaining section. The effect of repeated reversal of stresses is to cold-work the material, and the results produced are the same. From tests that have been made, the endurance limit for steel appears to be obtained at 10^7 cycles and is approximately one-half the tensile strength. In plotting the results of these tests the load per square inch and the number of cycles are used as coordinates and are termed *S-N curves*. In actual practice, allowances should be made for stress raisers such as notches, unequal stress applications, etc., and design varied accordingly. *See* S-N curves.

energizer. That component of a hydraulic system or other energy system that produces pressure and circulates the liquid or other working medium in the system.

energy. The ability to do work. *See* physical units and constants.

energy. *Types of, see* chemical–; conservation of energy principle; conservation of mass energy; escape–; hysteresis–; kinetic–; nuclear–; orbital–; potential–; radiant–; RF–.

energy level. The distribution of the electrons in an atom among the various orbits they can occupy. If an electron jumps from one orbit into another smaller one, it loses energy which is emitted as radiation of a particular wavelength. An electron also can absorb radiated energy by jumping into a greater orbit. The first event will lower, and the second raise the energy level of the atom in which it occurs. The lowest energy level of an atom is called its *ground state.*

engine. *Types of, see* air-breathing–; by-pass–; heat–; jet–; reaction–; regenerative–; rocket–; vernier–; solar–.

engine accessory. A part or assembly connected to, or used with, an engine, but not essential to its operation (e.g., generator, hydraulic pump, etc.).

engineering. *Types of, see* development–; environmental–; product–; production–; systems–; transition–; value–.

engineering change proposal (ECP). The medium utilized by a contractor for formally proposing and processing engineering changes affecting safety, deviation from contract specifications, requirements for performance interchangeability, or appreciable weight or cost, or requiring action in regard to retrofit (q.v.), service bulletins, or technical orders.

engineering drawings. Drawings usable for the complete fabrication, inspection, and identification of all details, assemblies, and components of the finished product for which these drawings are made. These drawings do not include *production drawings* which are made in addition to engineering drawings on a missile or support system, and are used solely for a contractor's plant facilities.

engineering maintenance. The logistic (q.v.) function of devising and developing maintenance systems, procedures, practices, techniques, and policies.

engineering support personnel. Those individuals expending effort in support of a technical development program, e.g., draftsmen, technicians, mechanics, technical secretaries, etc. This category of personnel can be utilized as *direct manpower* or *indirect manpower.*

engineering surveillance film. That photographic data acquired primarily to show the detail functioning of a missile or a component either before or during flight. Normally, high resolution is paramount in these data. Timing is included on such film as needed.

enthalpy. A thermodynamic concept defined by the equation:

$$H = E + PV$$

where H = the enthalpy; E = energy; P = pressure; V = volume of a system. At constant pressure the change in enthalpy measures the quantity of heat exchanged by the system with its surroundings.

entire job basis concept. In contracting, a contract written on an "entire job" basis; the contractor agrees to *complete* within a reasonably accurately estimated period of time, research and development (q.v.) which will require, in addition to engineering reports, the delivery of such hardware (q.v.) as flyable experimental model(s), breadboard model(s), unique spare parts, and special test equipment.

entrance cone. That segment of a wind tunnel through which the air flows into the test chamber.

entrapped propellant. At engine shutdown, that mass of propellant below the interface (q.v.) of the propellant pump and feed system. *See also* trapped propellant.

entropy. (1) The unavailable energy in a thermodynamic system; the measure of this. (2) In information theory, the measure of the uncertainty of our knowledge.

environment. The aggregate of all the conditions and influences which affect the operation of equipments and components (e.g., physical location and operating characteristics of surrounding equipments and/or components; temperatures, humidity, and contaminants of surrounding air; operational procedures; acceleration, shock and vibration; radiation; method of utilization, etc.).

environment. *Types of, see* derived–; induced–; production-to-target–; semi-automatic-ground–.

environmental engineering. That phase of engineering devoted to the study of cause and effect of the several environments (q.v.) in which equipment must live. Particularly, for missiles, this includes: vibration, shock and impact, temperature, climatology, fungus, corrosion, pressure, acoustics.

environmental protection. Unique steps taken to protect equipment from any or all of the following environments: shock, vibration, temperature, corrosion, abrasion (sand, dirt, dust, snow, hail, ice), moisture (humidity, snow, ice, hail, rain), pressure, lightning, wind, sunshine, noise, fungus.

EO. Engineering Order.

EODP. Engineering Order Delayed for Parts.

EPS. Emergency Power Supply (q.v.).

Epsilon 58-1. According to the International Geophysical Year code system used for identifying Earth satellites, the U.S. launched EXPLORER IV. It was launched on July 26, 1958, and the 38.4-lb payload is expected to orbit for about 4 years. See Table 6, page 245.

Eput. *Events per unit time. See* Eput counter.

Eput counter. An electronic device for high speed counting.

Eput meter. A device which measures frequency by counting the number of cycles for a given time interval.

equalizer. *See* thrust equalizer.

equation of time. A mathematical formula by which apparent time may be found by adding or subtracting a certain number of time units to or from mean time in accordance with a prepared table. The range in time units is from +16 minutes to −14 minutes.

equations of motion. A set of equations, generally in differential form, which when solved yield information concerning the subsequent motion of a particle or system of particles whose initial conditions are known. The initial conditions are specified by the initial position and initial velocity. A knowledge of the resultant force acting on the system at any instant is also necessary. There are several equivalent forms in which the equations of motion may be expressed.

equator. Of a rotating sphere, the line joining the points on the surface which are equidistant from the two poles of the axis of rotation. The plane in which the equator lies cuts the axis at right angles in the center of the sphere. At the equator, centrifugal force and angular velocity are greater than anywhere else on the surface of the sphere.

equator. *Types of, see* celestial–; magnetic–.

equatorial mount. A mechanical device on which is mounted some device for star tracking

(q.v.). A telescope when so mounted and tracking a star generates a right circular cone of revolution in one sidereal day (q.v.).

equidistant azimuthal projection. A map so designed that all radial lines drawn from its center are true in distance and direction; the method used in making such a map. The distortion in area increases rapidly from the center of the map (the point of tangency) toward the circumference.

equidistant chart. Any one of several aeronautical charts used for strategic planning purposes on which great circle routes and distances may be readily determined. There are 17 of these charts. All, except two, cover the world, each compiled on an equidistant azimuthal projection (q.v.) centered on a point indicated by the name of the chart. The charts are of different scales, 8 being 1:87,400,000; 3 being 1:55,000,000; 2 being 1:47,423,730; 1 being 1:18,328,012; and 1 being 1:8,288,111.

equigravitational point. The point between two astronomical bodies at which the respective gravitational fields are equal and opposite, so that a mass falls toward neither.

equilibrium. *Types of, see* force–; frozen (steady-state)–; moment–; shifting–; static–.

equilibrium pressure. In a solid propellant rocket, the internal gas pressure which provides a rate of gas discharge through the nozzle equal to the rate of gas generation. It depends upon rocket geometry, the burning rate of the propellant, and the initial temperature of the grain (q.v.). The relationship between pressure (and hence thrust) and initial grain temperature is approximately linear. The impulse does not change appreciably over the usual temperature ranges; therefore the change in thrust is accompanied by an inverse change in duration.

equilibrium temperatures. In outer space applications, solar radiation on a surface perpendicular to the Sun's rays will give surface temperatures as follows:

$$t = \frac{712\sqrt[4]{\alpha}}{\epsilon - 460}$$

where α = absorptivity surface area; ϵ = emissivity of the surface; t = equilibrium temperature, °F.

equinox. A moment at which the Sun's center crosses the *celestial equator* (q.v.) as seen from Earth's center. During its annual journey around the ecliptic (q.v.), the Sun crosses the celestial equator twice, resulting in two equinoxes each year: the *vernal equinox* occurs about March 21 and marks the official beginning of spring; the *autumnal equinox* occurs near September 22 and marks the beginning of autumn. At those dates, day and night are of roughly equal length all over Earth.

equiphase zone. A region within which the difference in phase of two radio signals is indistinguishable.

equipment. A combination of parts, assemblies, or subassemblies capable of functional operation by itself and separately housed (e.g., an antenna, antenna tuner, radio transmitter and transmitter modulator, radio altimeter, turbo-pump, fuze, etc.).

equipment. *Types of, see* ancillary–; base support–; ciphony–; command control–; data acquisition–; data reduction–; distance measuring–; electronic skyscreen–; field support–; fixed–; ground handling–; ground support–; Government-furnished–; Government-furnished airborne–; guidance station–; installed–; life characteristic of–; prototype–; self-destruction–; special list of–; tentative table of–; thrust termination–; unit essential–; unit mission–; unit support–.

equipment component. A group of parts, subassemblies, or assemblies combined in a separate housing and used as an element of an equipment (e.g., antenna tuner, radio transmitter, or transmitter modulator if each is in separate housing).

equipment component list (ECL). A publication that prescribes the components of individual kits and organization sets of equipment required for the performance of specific duties, functions, or support of end items (q.v.) of equipment.

equipment failure rate. The ratio of the number of equipments which fail or malfunction (f) within a given period of time (t) to the total number of equipments (N) at the start of a test period; i.e., $\lambda = f/N$. This figure of merit is sometimes referred to as the *failure hazard*. A plot of the hourly failure hazard obtained from a life test and smoothed by means of a moving average will reveal the life characteristics of an equipment.

equipment (hardware) specification. A specification which spells out in some detail the requirements for equipment. An extreme example is a set of working drawings; a minimum example is a set of preliminary or conceptual drawings.

equisignal beacon. A radio transmitter that creates an equisignal zone (q.v.) or zones.

equisignal zone. An on-course zone lying within the overlapping zones of any two signal patterns transmitted by radio, as between the "A" and "N" patterns in an Adcock radio range (q.v.).

equivalence ratio. The ratio of the stoichiometric (q.v.) air-to-fuel ratio to the experimental air-to-fuel ratio in an air-breathing engine.

equivalent airspeed. Calibrated airspeed corrected for compressibility error. Under conditions of compressibility, true airspeed is computed from equivalent airspeed rather than directly from calibrated airspeed.

equivalent altitude. An altitude that would supply the same amount of oxygen to the respiratory system as that provided in a pressurized cabin, through an oxygen mask, etc.

equivalent bhp. The brake horsepower equivalent to a jet engine's thrust; 2.6-lb thrust equals one horsepower under static conditions.

equivalent flat-plate area. A theoretical frontal area that would create the same parasitic drag (q.v.) as that of a given nacelle, fuselage, complete vehicle, or other air-resistant member. Also termed *equivalent frontal area*.

erasing head. A device for obliterating any previous recordings on a tape or wire recorder. It may be used for preconditioning magnetic media for recording purposes.

erector. A system for raising or lowering a complete missile, or its stages, from the horizontal to the vertical position.

erg. The unit of work or energy in the cgs system (q.v.); the work done when one dyne of force causes a displacement of one cm along the direction of force. *See* physical units and constants–; systems of measurement.

$$1 \text{ erg} = 9.480 \times 10^{-11} \text{ Btu} = 2.389 \times 10^{-11}$$
$$\text{cal-kg} = 1 \text{ dyne-cm} = 7.3756 \times 10^{-8}$$
$$\text{ft-lb} = 1.0197 \times 10^{-3} \text{ gm-cm} = 10^{-7}$$
$$\text{joule} = 1.0197 \times 10^{-8} \text{ kg-meter}$$

$$1 \text{ erg/sec} = 5.689 \times 10^{-9} \text{ Btu/min} = 4.426 \times 10^{-6} \text{ ft-lb/min} = 7.376 \times 10^{-8} \text{ ft-lb/sec} = 1.341 \times 10^{-10} \text{ hp} = 10^{-10} \text{ kw} = 10^{-7} \text{ watt}$$

$$1 \text{ erg/sq cm} = 1 \text{ dyne/cm}$$

$$1 \text{ erg-sec} = 1.50975 \times 10^{26} \text{ Planck's constants}$$

erosion. (1) In a solid rocket, deformation of propellant due to heat, radiation, and gas velocity leading to erosive burning (q.v.). (2) The loss of material in such mechanical elements as a rocket nozzle.

erosive burning rate. In a solid propellant

rocket, the increase in burning rate (q.v.), under normal conditions, which is incident to the sweep of gases over a burning propellant surface.

error. *Types of, see* absolute–; average–; beamwidth–; circular–; deflection–; deflection probable–; fixed–; hysteresis–; mean–; mean absolute–; probable–; pulse-length–; random–; receiving station–; relative–; spot-size–; supply voltage–; systematic–; temperature–; vectoring–; vibration–.

error acceleration. The change in output of a device being subjected to an acceleration as compared to the output of the instrument under no acceleration.

error ratio. The frequency response (for a control system) of the system error with respect to the reference input. Under linear conditions, the ratio is expressed mathematically as Ye/R. In simple systems where the system error is equal to the actuating signal, the actuating ratio becomes the error ratio:

$$\frac{Ye}{R} = \frac{E}{R} = \frac{1}{1+G}$$

where G = gain of the system.

error signal. (1) In servomechanisms, the signal, frequently a voltage applied to the control circuit, that indicates the misalignment between the controlling and the controlled members. (2) In tracking systems, a voltage, depending upon the signal received from the target, whose sign and magnitude depend on the angle between the target and the center of the scanning beam.

escape energy. The energy per unit mass which must be imparted to a missile to give it escape velocity (q.v.). A body possessing escape energy in the form of kinetic energy has escape velocity. The escape energy for a body already in orbit (q.v.) is the difference between total orbital energy and full escape energy.

$$\text{escape energy} = mg_R R$$

where m = mass of the body; g_R = gravitational force at surface of the Earth, R. For escape from Earth: 8.74×10^5 Btu/slug. For escape from the solar system: 70.4×10^5 Btu/slug.

escape maneuver. In space flight, change from a closed orbit (q.v.) to an open orbit (q.v.) near a celestial body.

escape parabola. *See* parabola of escape.

escape velocity. That velocity required by a missile or space vehicle in order to escape from Earth's gravitational field. If escape energy

(q.v.) is entirely in the form of kinetic energy, the body has escape velocity.

$$V_e = R \sqrt{\frac{2g}{R+h}}$$

where V_e = escape velocity, fps; g = gravity at the Earth's surface, fps²; R = radius of Earth, ft; h = altitude, ft. The escape velocity of the Earth is just over 7 miles per sec, or 36,900 fps. Once a body moving upwards has exceeded this speed, its own momentum will carry it away from Earth in a hyperbolic orbit and it will never return under the influence of gravity. Escape velocity does not allow for air resistance, but in all practical cases the velocity will not be attained until heights are reached at which air resistance is so low that it can, for this purpose, be disregarded. Following are a few calculated escape velocities:

	miles/sec	*ft/sec*
Earth	7.0	36,900
Moon	1.47	7,750
Mercury	2.2	11,600
Mars	3.1	16,360
Venus	6.3	33,200

E-scope. A radarscope which presents the range of a target by a horizontal displacement of the target signal on the face of the scope, and the elevation by a vertical displacement.

ESSO BEE. Research missile. Navy Bureau of Ordnance cognizance. One of the Bumblebee project (q.v.) missiles. Named after the fuel manufacturer (Esso Research Laboratories).

EST. Eastern Standard Time. *See* standard time.

esu. Electrostatic units (q.v.).

ESV. Earth Satellite Vehicle.

ETC. Estimated Time of Completion.

ethanol (C_2H_5OH). A liquid rocket propellant *fuel.*

ethyl alcohol (C_6H_5OH). A liquid rocket propellant *fuel.* See Table 3, page 157.

ethyl decaborane ($C_2H_5B_{10}H_{13}$) (EDB). A liquid rocket propellant *fuel.*

ethylene diamine ($C_2H_4N_2H_4$). A liquid rocket propellant *fuel.*

ethylene oxide (C_2H_4O). A liquid monopropellant.

ethyl nitrate ($C_2H_5NO_3$). A liquid rocket propellant *oxidizer.*

ethyl silicate. A liquid rocket propellant *fuel.* See Table 3, page 157.

ETO. Engineering Test Order.

Eureka. A radar beacon used in a Rebecca-Eureka system (q.v.).

evaluation. *Types of, see* operational–; technical–; weapon–.

evaluation tests. Tests conducted by a development agency comprising examinations, investigations, or other observations necessary to determine the technical adequacy of the materiel undergoing test. Pilot or experimental models are subjected to these tests at the various laboratories and proving grounds prior to initiation of procurement of a production model.

E-vector. The vector representing the electric field of an electromagnetic wave. In free space it is perpendicular to the direction of propagation and to the *H*-vector representing the associated magnetic field.

EW. (1) Early Warning. (2) Electronics Warfare (q.v.).

EWR. Early Warning Radar. *See* early warning system.

EX-8. Underwater-to-underwater missile. Navy cognizance.

Designed to give the Navy an ultra-high speed underwater anti-submarine missile. Designated as a rocket- (or hydro-duct-) powered torpedo with speeds up to and perhaps exceeding 150 knots. Reportedly a new method of cavitation control was developed to decrease drag and noise.

exchanger. *See* heat exchanger.

exchange ratio. A systems engineering (q.v.) tool utilized to trade the effect of one parameter for another to evolve an optimum or otherwise desirable result (e.g., weight vs. range of a ballistic missile).

excitation. *Types of, see* hard–; impulse–; parametric–; shock–; soft–.

exciter. (Vernacular) (1) The oscillator that generates the carrier frequency of a transmitter. (2) A part of a transmitting antenna array (q.v.) directly connected to the source of power and including a reflector or director. (3) A device for producing variable forces at varying frequencies and used to vibrate beams, missiles, components, etc.

exhaust cone. An assembly behind the turbine wheel of a turbojet engine, consisting of an inner cone surrounded by an outer cone or casing, the open end of which forms the exhaust nozzle. The function of the exhaust cone is to collect and direct discharge gases from the turbine wheel.

exhaust nozzle. *See* exit nozzle.

exhaust velocity. The velocity with which burned gases leave the combustion chamber of a rocket. A measure of the performance of the rocket propellants (i.e., the higher the performance, the greater the exhaust velocity). It is also associated with specific impulse (q.v.) by the equation:

$$\text{exhaust velocity} = \text{specific impulse} \times g$$

where g = acceleration due to gravity. Typical values for exhaust velocities of modern propellants, at ground level, are 6000-7500 fps. These figures represent about half the theoretical maximum obtainable from normal chemical propellants. It is theorized that atomic propulsion units may give exhaust velocities of 25,000 fps or more.

exhaust velocity. *Types of, see* effective–; theoretical–.

exit cone. That part of a wind tunnel through which the air leaves the test chamber.

exit nozzle. That part of a ramjet or rocket engine used to accelerate the hot gases at the combustion chamber exit to a high velocity. A well-designed nozzle will have a velocity coefficient (ratio of actual to ideal gross thrust per lb of gas flow) of 0.97 to 0.99 at the design pressure ratio. *See* velocity thrust, and Fig. 6, page 76.

exosphere. The outermost layer of the atmosphere in which the air particles travel in elliptical orbits with infrequent collisions. It comprises approximately 1/3000 of the Earth's atmosphere. See Fig. 11, page 140.

exothermic. A thermodynamic term descriptive of an evolution of heat or other energy.

exotic fuels. A broad and nondefinitive classification of high-performance propulsive fuels. *See* free radicals; ion propulsion; photon propulsion; plasma jet; zip fuels. See Table 4, page 187.

expanded scope. In electronics, a magnified portion of a presentation on a radarscope.

expansion, optimum. *See* optimum expansion.

expansion ratio. In rocketry, the ratio of nozzle exit area to the nozzle throat area. It is always greater than unity.

expansion wave. A phenomenon of supersonic aerodynamics which occurs whenever air flows around a corner; that is, when the air tends to turn away from the air in the adjacent stream layer. It is a pressure wave, or kind of shock wave, that has the effect of decreasing the density of air as the air passes through it. Distinguish from *shock wave* (q.v.).

expendable construction. A method of construction for propellant tanks of high-performance rocket vehicles. The tanks are made in independent sections. As propellants are exhausted from each tank in turn, the tank is jettisoned. Thus the amount of dead weight carried at each instant is minimized accordingly. This improves the overall mass ratio (q.v.), gives a greater burnout velocity, and results in improved performance.

experimental mean pitch. Zero-thrust pitch.

experimental missile. (1) A missile built to try out an idea, or to try for certain capabilities or characteristics. (2) A missile that embodies a new principle or a new application of an old principle. Usually designated by the symbol "X" in model designations. Distinguish from *service test missiles.*

experimental status. The status of an item that has not been developed to the point where service tests might be made with it.

EXPLORER I. The first U.S. satellite to be successfully placed in an Earth-circling orbit. On January 31, 1958, at 10:55 p.m. EST, a U.S. Army JUPITER-C launching vehicle left Cape Canaveral, Florida, in a trajectory that placed a satellite developed by the Jet Propulsion Laboratory of the California Institute of Technology in an elliptic orbit. The EXPLORER satellite is the 80-inch, solid propellant last stage of the vehicle. The 6-inch diameter body weighed 30.8 lb, after burnout, including approximately 18 lb of instruments in its nose cone. See Table 6, page 245.

explosive. *Types of, see* class II–; class IX–; high–; inert–; low–.

explosive train (explosive chain). In missile armament, a series of explosive elements including primer, detonator, and booster (q.q.v.), arranged to permit warhead explosion to be initiated from relatively weak fuze signals.

exponential decay. A characteristic reduction in amplitude, quantity, etc., which occurs frequently in nature. It is the decrease in the amount of a particular substance present according to the equation:

$$A = A_0 e^{-\lambda t}$$

where A and A_0 are the quantities present at times t and zero, respectively, and λ is a constant characteristic of the substance involved in the process.

exponential horn. A horn whose cross-sectional area varies exponentially with its length. It is an impedance-matching (q.v.) device between a diaphragm and free space and has a low cutoff value dependent on the taper.

extensometer. An instrument used to measure extension, expansions, or deformations in a material.

exterior ballistics. The science concerned with the motion and behavior of projectiles in flight; as distinguished from interior ballistics (e.g., solid propellant rocket internal mechanics).

external efficiency. The efficiency with which an engine converts the total kinetic energy developed into forward propulsion, expressed by the ratio between the energy employed in propulsion and the total energy developed. This is often termed *ballistic efficiency* when applied to the engine or motor of a rocket or other jet propelled missile, and termed *mechanical efficiency* when applied to an internal combustion reciprocating engine.

extraplanetary space. Space beyond a particular planetary orbit as seen from the Sun (e.g., extra-trans-Plutonian space).

extraterrestrial space. That space outside of Earth's atmosphere. *See* atmosphere of the Earth.

eye. In meteorology, the center of a cyclonic type storm. The eye averages 14 miles in diameter, with no precipitation, very light winds, and sometimes a clear sky and a complete calm.

eyelid. Either of two movable parts at the rear of a jet engine which, by an eyelid-like action, regulates the size of the opening in the exhaust nozzle. It is used for thrust control.

F

face-hardened armor. An alloy-steel, heat-treated to produce an especially hard surface on one side.

facilities. All areas, structures, apparatus, utilities, etc., that contribute to the operation of a company, base, program, etc. Brick and mortar, non-severable outfitting utilities are invariably considered to be facilities. Contrast with *ground support equipment* (q.v.).

facility. *Types of, see* research and development–; supporting–.

factor of safety. A design criterion, usually the ratio of the load that would cause failure of a member or structure to the load that is imposed upon it in service. It also may be used to represent the ratio of failure to service value of speed, deflection, voltage, temperature, or other stress-producing factor.

factor of safety. *Types of, see K* factor–; ultimate–; yield–.

factor of utilization. A design parameter, the ratio of the allowable stress to the ultimate strength. For cases in which stress is proportional to load, the factor of utilization is the reciprocal of the factor of safety.

factors. *Types of, see* form–; G factor; growth–; limit load–; load–; magnification–; material–; –of safety; –of utilization; overshoot–; power–; Q factor; scale–; structural–; temperature recovery–; tiploss–; ultimate factor of safety; ultimate strength load–; yield factor of safety; yield strength load–.

fade. Of radio reception, to fluctuate in intensity.

fade, target. *See* target fade.

FAGMS-S. Army designation for surface-to-surface ballistic missile termed SERGEANT (q.v.).

fail-safe. In missile testing, a control providing for the automatic selection of an alternative action in case of malfunction. If a fail-safe control receives data indicating a malfunction in the missile or support equipment, it will cause an abort of the test. In the case of a less serious malfunction, the test may proceed by bypassing the faulty subassembly or component.

failure. Any physical phenomenon, no matter how small, which prevents a missile from achieving its objective.

failure. *Types of, see* abortive–; associated–; chance (catastrophic)–; compensating component–; component–; critical–; degradation–, early–; independent component–; initial–; meantime between failure; non-critical–; technical–; time limit–; wearout–.

failure classes. In one set of definitions there are four classifications of causes of failure: (a) early failure; (b) chance failure; (c) wearout failure; (d) catastrophic failure (q.q.v.). *Also see* failure modes.

failure classes, physical cause. The physical causes of failure (q.v.) may be classified as follows: (a) *design oversight:* the condition is correctable by changing design parameters and/or specified materials; (b) *low safety factor:* specified use of materials at or near their strength limits; (c) *excessive variance:* the use of materials or combinations of materials whose statistical variability is such that the equipment has a high probability of failure; (d) *production engineering:* the use of manufacturing or assembly techniques which produce unsatisfactory deviations from the prototype; (e) *workmanship:* individual variations from specified or normal manufacturing or assembly techniques; (f) *inspection:* failure to detect a defect when methods for detection are available or can be developed; (g) *process drift:* gradual shift of a processing technique to the point at which one or more parameters are intolerable; (h) *handling and storage:* subjection of an equipment to non-use conditions in excess of normal or specified conditions; (i) *adjustment or checkout:* use of procedures or operating techniques for adjustment of checkout which cause failure of an equipment or its parts.

failure classes, severity. Relative severity of failure (q.v.) may be classified as follows: (a) abortive; (b) critical; (c) time limit; (d) non-critical; (e) associated (q.q.v.).

failure modes. A classification system for failures of a missile system: (a) *chance:* random, encountered in unusually severe environments, unpredictable and unavoidable conditions during the operating period. Described by the chance failure distribution. A statistical failure; (b) *wearout:* occurs owing to wearing away of material or by using up a potential until the component reaches a condition where it can no longer operate according to specifications. Described by the normal or Gaussian distribution, or better, by the binomial distribution (q.v.); (c) *initial:* a component is defective at the time it is required to operate. The result of design errors, manufacturing errors, storage, assembly, handling, transportation, etc. Described by simple probability.

failure probability. One means of calculating the probability of failure of a component, based on the operations of the component and the possibility of a reduced margin of safety.

$$P_f = \frac{P_o P_i + (1 - P_o)P_s}{1 - P_o + P_o P_i}$$

where P_f = probability of occurrence of a component failure under specified conditions; P_o = probability of occurrence of a manufacturing error that will cause failure; P_i = probability of occurrence of an inspection missing a manufacturing error; P_s = probability of occurrence of a strength-stress scatterband overlap.

failure rate. A numeric or figure of merit (q.v.) that expresses the frequency of failure occurrence which can be observed over specified time intervals when observing equipments or component parts. This parameter is λ in the exponential failure law when the occurrence of failures is random in the time domain:

$$P_s = e^{-\lambda t}$$

where P_s = probability of occurrence; t = time.

failure rate, equipment. *See* equipment failure rate.

fair. (1) To streamline a part of an aircraft for reducing a wind resistance or drag. (2) Of an external part, to fit into another part so as to present a streamlined surface.

fairing. An auxiliary member or structure of a missile whose primary function is to reduce the aerodynamic drag or to protect the part against aerodynamic forces. Usually it acts to shape outside surfaces in conformance with aerodynamic streamlines.

FALCON. Air-to-air missile. Air Force designation: GAR-1D, GAR-2, and GAR-9.

Length: 77.8 in.; wing span: 20 in.; body diameter: 6.5 in.; firing weight: 110 lb (earlier

models weighed 122 lb); burnout speed: over MACH 2; operational range: about 5 miles. The FALCON is carried for salvo by interceptors. It employs a solid rocket sustainer. The GAR-1 has semi-active radar guidance; GAR-2 has infrared guidance; GAR-9 carries an atomic warhead.

Prime Contractors: Hughes Aircraft Co. Airframe: Hughes. Engine: Thiokol Chemical Corp. Guidance system: Hughes.

fall-back. That portion of the material carried into the air by a nuclear explosion which ultimately drops back into the crater formed by an underground or surface burst, or into the water in the immediate vicinity of the site of the burst in the case of a water shot.

fall-out. A deposit of radioactive material created by a nuclear explosion that has settled out of the air or from contaminated water.

fall-wind. A wind blowing down a mountainside; or any wind having a strong downward component. Fall-winds include the *Foehn, mistral, bora, williwaw,* etc.

false cirrus cloud. (1) A light delicate ice cloud that forms out of the top of a cumulonimbus (q.v.). (2) Tonitro-cirrus or a scarf cloud.

false coordinate. An artificial coordinate established to insure that all points in a grid zone will have positive coordinated numbers.

fan beam. A fan-shaped radar beam, broad in the vertical plane and narrow in the horizontal plane.

fanny. (Vernacular) A radio device attached to an airborne search receiver for homing on a jamming or radar signal.

FAP. Frequency Allocation Panel, a Government agency.

farad. A unit measure of electrical capacity. A farad is the capacity of a condenser to hold one coulomb of electricity under a pressure of one volt.

$$1 \text{ farad} = 10^{-9} \text{ abfarad} = 10^6 \text{ microfarads}$$
$$= 8.988 \times 10^{11} \text{ statfarads}$$

Far Side Project. Test missile for space navigation. The Air Force Office of Scientific Research is the sponsor of the project.

Designed to reach a height of 4000 miles using four solid propellant stages: first stage is four Thiokol RECRUIT (q.v.) rockets; the second is a single RECRUIT; the third is composed of four Grand Central motors now used in ASP (q.v.) sounding rockets; and the fourth stage is a single ASP motor. The four stages weigh 1900 lb, and are launched from a balloon developed by

General Mills, Inc. Stage one is fired by a radio signal from the ground after the balloon reaches 19 miles above Earth.

Prime Contractor. Aeronutronic Systems, Inc.

fastar. A radar system utilizing fast scanning and fast pulse repetition rate without loss of resolution or range.

Fastax camera. A high-speed motion picture camera used for observation of missiles at launch and for studying vibration phenomena in the laboratory. Frame speeds approach 7500 per sec. Accuracy between frames is measurable to about ±¼%.

fathometer. A sonar device for measuring the depth of water beneath a ship.

fatigue. (1) The phenomenon of the progressive fracture of a metal by means of a crack which develops and spreads under repeated cycles of stress. *See* endurance limit. (2) The weakening of metal or other material due to microscopic changes in molecular structures caused by vibration or exposure.

FBM. Fleet Ballistic Missile (q.v.).

FBMS. Fleet Ballistic Missile System (q.v.).

Fc. Fractocumulus cloud (q.v.).

FCC. Federal Communications Commission.

FCS. Federal Catalog System.

feed. In electronics, that part of a radar antenna that consists of the end of the energy transmission line together with the immediately adjacent parts, which radiates or "feeds" radio-frequency energy to a reflector.

feedback. That part of a closed loop system (q.v.) which brings back information about the condition under control for comparison to the target value. See Fig. 3, page 49.

feedback. *Types of, see* acceleration–; degenerative–; inductive–; inverse–; negative–; position–; positive–; structural–.

feedback signal. In a control system, a signal responsible to the controlled variable. This signal is returned to the input of the system and compared with the reference signal to obtain an actuating signal which then returns the controlled variable to the desired value.

feedback test. *See* structural feedback test.

feed system. *See* pressure feed system.

feint attack. A simulated attack intended to draw enemy fire.

Felix. A name for a type of target-seeking bomb. The essential element in the bomb is a nose unit that homes on heat-generating machines.

fence. A radar warning network, considered as a barrier against surprise attack. Usually termed *radar fence.*

fence, radar. *See* radar fence.

Ferri diffuser. *See* Oswatitsch diffuser.

ferry rocket. In astronautics, a manned rocket designed for transporting personnel between Earth and the terminal orbit.

FFAR. Forward-Firing Aerial Rocket.

FFAR. Folding Fin Aircraft, Rocket. Operational air-to-air rocket.

Weight: 18 lb; diameter: 2.75 in.; length: about 3 ft. Fuel is ballistite type; rocket is unguided. Fired in clusters of 7 and 19 from an expendable cluster aircraft rocket launcher (ECARL) (e.g., MIGHTY MOUSE, q.v.). Fins unfold after leaving launching tube; used to decrease dispersion.

fidelity. *See* high fidelity.

fiducial line. An accurately located and known reference line used for alignment of the airframe or guidance system (q.v.); frequently a line to which gyroscope axes are referred.

field assembly area. That area of a missile support base where missiles are received, checked out, maintained, stored, or otherwise handled before being sent to a test or launch stand.

field assembly hangar. A building in a field assembly area (q.v.) provided for the assembly and checkout (q.v.) of a complete missile.

field intensity. In electricity, the intensity, measured in terms of strength or pressure, exerted by the lines of force in a magnetic, electrostatic, or radio field.

field level maintenance. That maintenance authorized for, the responsibility of, and performed by designated maintenance activities in direct support of using organizations. This category of maintenance normally includes: intermediate and major inspection of equipment; the repair of unserviceable parts, assemblies, subassemblies, and components; the local manufacture of non-available parts; testing, calibration, and reclamation as authorized.

field, magnetic. *See* magnetic field.

field of search. In electronics, the space that a radar set or installation can cover effectively.

field strength pattern. The same as radiation pattern (q.v.) except that actual field strength values are used rather than relative ratios.

field support equipment (FSE). That portion of the unit mission equipment (q.v.) for technical operation units which permits their operations from a "bare strip."

field test. A service test of an equipment by putting it into actual use in the field.

figure. *Types of, see* Lissajous–; noise–; –of merit.

figure of merit. (1) A property or characteristic of a tube, coil, or other electronic device which makes it suitable for a particular application. A quality to be looked for in choosing a piece of equipment, e.g., amplification factor is a figure of merit to a triode for use as an audio-frequency amplifier tube. For maximum AC power in a triode a figure of merit is the product of amplification factor and transconductance. Both of these depend solely on tube design. Often figures of merit involve circuits, such as that for broad-banding of amplifiers. This is the transconductance of the tube divided by the sum of the input and output capacitances. (2) For control systems, the gain margin, G, and phase margin, β. Desired values are: G from 0.5 to 0.8, and β from 35 to 45 degrees.

fillet. A faired surface or piece that smooths the flow of air at an internal angle.

film classification. *Types of, see* engineering surveillance–; documentary–.

film cooling. A method of cooling rocket motors in which a small amount of fuel or inert liquid is injected into the motor at low net pressures through holes upstream from hot spots; the liquid adheres to the wall and spreads out as a film; in evaporating, pronounced cooling of the hot areas is obtained.

filter. In electronics, a network employing lumped constant elements, used to select or reject signals in predetermined frequency ranges.

filter. *Types of, see* active–; balanced low pass–; band-elimination–; band-pass–; band-rejection–; crystal–; high-pass–; inverse feedback–; low pass–; mechanical–; microwave frequency–; notch–; octave–; structural–; wave–.

filter/amplifier. A component which isolates, matches the filter impedance, and amplifies the subcarrier signal before applying it to a discriminator for demodulation.

filter bandwidth. The range of frequencies passed by a bandpass filter to which the filter provides uniform or minimum attenuation (q.v.) within a prescribed amount.

fin. (1) A fixed or adjustable vane or airfoil affixed longitudinally to an aerodynamically or ballistically designed body for stabilizing purposes. (2) In specific senses: (a) a vertical stabilizer; (b) a carbon fin; (c) a cooling fin.

fin. *Types of, see* folding–; horizontal–.

finder. *See* height finder.

fineness ratio. In aerodynamics, the ratio of the length to the maximum diameter of a stream-lined body. *See* slenderness ratio.

fin-stabilized projectile. Any projectile (e.g., rocket) steadied in flight by fins.

fire. (Vernacular) To launch a missile.

fire. *Types of, see* ripple–; salvo–.

fireball. The luminous sphere which begins to form a few millionths of a second after a burst of an atomic bomb.

FIREBEE. Target, also used as a tactical, missile. Military designation: Q-2. Navy designation: KDA-1. Army designation: XM-21.

Length: 17.3 ft; takeoff weight: 1,848 lb; wing span: 11.2 ft; altitude: 8 miles; range: 750 miles (80 minutes flight time); speed: MACH 0.9. Uses one solid propellant rocket for boost and turbojet for cruise.

Prime Contractor: Ryan Aeronautical Co. Airframe: Ryan. Power plant: Fairchild Engine & Airplane Co., Aerojet General Corp., Continental Motors Corp.

FIREBIRD. An air-to-air rocket. Military designation: XAAM-A-1 or XAAM-N-1.

Length: 10 ft; wing span: 3 ft; diameter: 6 in.; weight: 600 lb. Solid fuel motor. Radar guided with homing head and proximity fuze. Booster launched. Trapezoidal, swept back, plastic tail fins.

Prime Contractor: Ryan Aeronautical Co.

fire control. (1) A means of controlling fire power of a gun. A fire control system usually consists of a gun director, a computer, and the gun on its trainable and elevatable mount. The gun director tracks the target; the computer establishes predicted future position of the target; the gun is directed according to the output of the computer. (2) Term sometimes applied to missile guidance when exercised outside the missile.

fire point. The temperature, as determined by testing, of a lubricating oil when it gives off a vapor that will continue to burn steadily. Contrast with *flash point* (q.v.).

firepower. *See* defensive firepower.

firing. *Types of, see* blow-down–; captive–; confidence–; flight–; flight readiness–; hot–; mock–; static–.

firing chamber. The combustion chamber (q.v.) in a rocket motor or rocket engine.

firing key. A device, either electrical or mechanical, which when actuated will initiate an action to launch a missile.

firing system tester. An electrical device for testing the continuity or other electrical characteristics of a rocket-firing system.

firing tables. For ballistic missiles, precomputed trajectories (q.v.) for given launch points and targets.

firing test. *See* flight readiness firing test.

first light. In nautical usage, the beginning of nautical twilight in the morning, occurring when the Sun reaches a position 12° below the horizon.

fishtail. (Vernacular) A transition piece (q.v.).

fission. *Types of, see* atomic–; nuclear–; spontaneous–; ternary–.

fission products. Elements and/or particles created by nuclear fission (q.v.). In addition to uranium and plutonium, these may consist of more than 40 different radioactive elements: barium, iodine, cerium, arsenic, silver, tin, cadmium, and others.

fit and function part. A part designed for a specific assembly.

fittings. Structural elements used to join mechanically two or more parts, usually designed for two loading conditions: *limit load* and *ultimate load* (q.q.v.).

five-by-five. (Vernacular) Of radio signals or reception, meaning "loud and clear." The phrase is derived from a scale set up for showing numerically the strength and clarity of radio reception.

fixed area exhaust nozzle. An exhaust nozzle on a jet engine the opening of which is of a fixed size, no provision being made for varying the size of the opening.

fixed bias. A constant bias obtained from a given source, as from a battery generator.

fixed equipment. *See* installed equipment.

fixed error. A term used in precise alignments, the offset between a preset position and the observed median value.

fixed frequency transmitter. A radio transmitter designed to operate at a single frequency.

fixed loop radio compass. A radio compass having a loop antenna fixed in position. The plane of the fixed loop antenna is perpendicular to the longitudinal axis of the vehicle in which it is situated. The compass has a left-right indicator, the needle of which is centered when the vehicle is headed directly toward or away from the transmitting station to which the receiver is tuned.

fixed surface. An airfoil, fin, or stabilizer that is more or less rigidly fixed to the body of a vehicle. While fixed surfaces are often adjustable, they are so-called to distinguish them from the movable ailerons, elevator, etc., or from a rotary wing, tail or flipper system.

fizz pot. (Vernacular) A booster rocket on a vehicle.

FK. Faker track.

FL. Focal Length.

flame. The body of burning gases in a jet engine or rocket motor.

flame attenuation. A phenomenon occurring when microwave energy is directed through the exhaust gases from rocket or jet engines. The attenuation (q.v.) varies with the microwave frequency, the direction and power of the beam, the characteristics of the exhaust flow, the propellant, combustion efficiency, and altitude.

flame bucket. In liquid rocket engine test stands, the structure used to deflect the engine exhaust gases (often water-cooled).

flame deflector. A large structure beneath a thrust mount or stand that deflects exhaust gases away from the firing complex. Wet and dry types are used. For repetitive firing or for long duration "hot" tests, wet stands are used in which a large volume of water under high pressure is caused to flow over the face of the deflector. Dry deflectors or spikes are used for short exposure times.

flame holder. A device inserted in the combustor (q.v.) of an air-breathing engine designed to stabilize (or hold) a flame.

flameout. The extinguishment of the flame in a jet engine. *See* acceleration blowout; brennschluss.

flame propagation. In a jet engine, the process by which the flame is made to continue burning in a combustion chamber after the initial ignition.

flame shield. Sandwich (or other) type rigid insulation that protects portions of a missile (e.g., attachment frames, thrust mount, and load struts) from heat reflected from the jet exhaust gases or from flareback due to pressure differentials during firing.

flap. (1) Any rudder attached to a rocket or missile and acting either in the air or within the jet stream. (2) (Vernacular) A technical argument, discussion, or conference. (3) A boot-like sealing element used in solid propellant rockets to guard against unwanted burning which might occur on propellant surfaces owing to inadequate bonding of the propellant and liner.

flaperon. A kind of control surface used both as a flap and as an aileron.

flare. (1) A pyrotechnic device that emits a bright light, used for illumination, signaling, or identification. (2) In electronics, an overly bright return on a radarscope, which loses definite shape because of its excessive brightness. (3) In rocketry, the flared inside curve of some types of rocket nozzles.

flare. *Types of, see* marker–; solar–.

flash depressor. A substance used to reduce the flash from a solid-fuel rocket.

flash point. The temperature, as determined by testing, of a fuel or oil when it gives off a vapor that will flash or ignite momentarily. Contrast with *fire point* (q.v.).

flat-out. (Vernacular) At full speed; at full capacity.

F layer (F₁ and F₂). That part of the ionosphere with a maximum of ionization. The F_1 layer is the region of 135 to 145 miles altitude, and the F_2 layer is the region of 190 to 230 miles altitude. See Fig. 11, page 140.

F₂ layer. The single ionized layer normally existing in the F region in the night atmosphere, and the higher of the two layers normally existing in the F region in the day hemisphere. See Fig. 11, page 140.

fleet ballistic missile (FBM). An intermediate range ship-launched ballistic missile. *See* POLARIS.

fleet ballistic missile system (FBMS). The United States Navy Bureau of Ordnance program developing missiles to be launched from nuclear-powered submarines. *See* POLARIS.

flexural center. In structures, the point in a cross section of a beam at which a shear force can be applied without producing a rotation of that section in its own plane.

flexural line. In structures, for a given loading on a beam, the line on which the loading may be applied so that no twist results at any section of the beam.

flexure. The relative motion which occurs between structural parts of a missile, aircraft, or ship. Flexure adversely affects the use of such a structure as a reference for direction-sensitive devices.

flight. The smallest Air Force organization possessing both launch and guidance capability.

flight. *Types of, see* captive–; chamber–; interstellar–; free–; line-of-sight–; nolo–; space–.

flight certification test. A component test to prove the capability of a component to function properly in a minimal flight environment (usually temperature and vibration). The test is less stringent than a flight qualification test.

flight control system. A system having three functions: (a) to maintain missile stability about the pitch, roll, and yaw axes; (b) to receive command signals from the guidance system and convert these signals into mechanical movements of the engines to change the missile course; (c) to turn (pitch) the missile onto the proper target heading in the early moments of flight.

flight firing. Hot firing of a missile engine during flight (e.g., an altitude start).

flight line maintenance. Maintenance performed on equipment while installed in its normal operating position. In electronics maintenance, it usually implies "black box" (q.v.) or "down-to-plug-in-components" maintenance. The term is somewhat parallel, but not always identical to *organizational maintenance*. Distinguish from *shop maintenance*.

flight missile. A test vehicle; a missile that is capable of boosting or sustaining itself for flight. Contrast with *ground test missile* or *hangar queen* (q.v.).

flight path. The path of the center of gravity of a missile with reference to the Earth or with reference to a coordinate from a fixed point relative to the missile.

flight path angle. The angle between the velocity of a missile and the local horizontal.

flight rating test (FRT). In engine applications, tests made to establish adequacy for use in flight tests; essentially a qualification test (q.v.).

flight readiness firing (FRF). A firing or "hot" test, usually on liquid rocket engines (q.v.) and for short durations, conducted while a missile is secured to the launcher, to determine that the propulsion system (q.v.) is "ready" for a flight test (q.v.).

flight table. A rate, roll, and/or tilt table used for gyroscope (q.v.) testing. It is used to check gyroscope position and/or rate outputs.

flight test. Tests conducted to determine system performance, design verification, operational characteristics, reliability, and sequencing while a missile is in flight.

flight test, closed loop. See closed loop flight test.

flotation. In hermetically sealed integrating gyroscopes (q.v.), a means of relieving the gimbal bearing load by floating the enclosed wheel assembly in a liquid. For a single-axis gyroscope this liquid may be used for damping by controlling the viscosity.

flow. *Types of, see* circulatory–; free molecular–; incompressible–; inviscid–; isentropic flow through a converging nozzle; laminar–; shear–; slip–; streamline–; transition–; turbulent–; two-dimensional–.

fluid dynamics. The study of the motion of Newtonian fluids, including viscid and inviscid, compressible and incompressible flow together with the phenomena associated with free surfaces and buoyancy forces caused by gravitational fields. The phrase carries the implication that the study is carried out from the physical, rather than the practical engineering, standpoint.

fluid mechanics. The study of the mechanical properties of fluids, including *hydrostatics* (q.v.), *hydrodynamics* (q.v.) and *gas dynamics* (compressible flow). *See* mechanics.

fluorine. A liquid rocket propellant *oxidizer*. See Table 3, page 157.

flutter. (1) In aerodynamics, an oscillation of definite period set up in any part of an aerodynamically active component by a momentary disturbance and maintained in a steady airstream by a combination of the aerodynamic, inertial, and elastic characteristics of the member itself. (2) In communication practice: (a) distortion due to variations in loss resulting from the simultaneous transmission of a signal at another frequency; (b) a similar effect due to phase distortion; (c) in recording and reproducing, the deviations in reproduced sounds from their original frequencies, which result in general from irregular motion during recording, duplication or reproduction. The colloquial term *wow* is defined in the same way, but is commonly applied to relatively slow variations (e.g., one to five or six repetitions per second) which are recognized aurally as pitch fluctuations, in contra-distinction to the roughening of tones, which is the most noticeable effect of rapid fluctuations. A constant difference in pitch such as results from a difference in the average speeds during recording and reproduction is not included in the meanings of the terms *wow, flutter,* and *drift* (q.q.v.). By an extension of their meanings, the terms *flutter* and *wow* are used to designate variations in speed itself or variations in recorded wavelengths. Although most recorded sound comprises multitudes of tones, it is convenient to refer to *flutter* as variations in frequency, assuming the recorded sound to have been a single, steady tone.

flutter, panel. *See* panel flutter.

flutter speed. The speed for constant amplitude motion. *See* allowable flutter speed.

flux. In electricity, the electric or magnetic lines of force within a given field.

flux. *Types of, see* neutron–; solar–.

flux-ampere-turn loop. *See* dynamic hysteresis loop.

flux current loop. *See* dynamic hysteresis loop.

flux-gate compass. (1) A direction-sensing element activated by the Earth's magnetic field and used in a gyro flux-gate compass (q.v.) or in a Gyrosyn (q.v.) compass. Sometimes termed a *flux valve.* (2) Short for gyro flux-gate compass.

fly back. In electronics, the return of the tracing beam in a plan position indicator (q.v.) tube to the starting point after having reached the end of its trace; the time required for this return.

flying missile. (Vernacular) A self-propelled or robot missile [e.g., a guided missile; a ballistic missile(q.q.v.)].

flying range. The capability of a missile or aircraft that indicates how far it can fly under given operating conditions.

flying stovepipe. (Vernacular) A ramjet engine (q.v.).

flyobrpt. Flying object report.

FM. (1) Frequency Modulated. (2) Frequency Modulation (q.v.).

FM data system. A data acquisition system consisting (in its simplest form) of: (a) a frequency generator which transforms intelligence signals generated by a transducer (q.v.) or pickup with a variable frequency; (b) a transmission link; (c) a discriminator to reconvert the variable frequency into a reproduction of the original intelligence.

FM/FM. A method of modulation using the principle of frequency modulation (q.v.) at two points in a complex transmitting system. In the FM/FM telemetering system the first FM takes place when the subcarrier oscillators are frequency modulated by the pickup intelligence. The second FM is applied when the various subcarrier oscillators frequency modulate the VHF radio (RF) signal which is eventually transmitted and received by the receiving equipment and demodulated.

FM/FM telemetering. A standard telemetering system of the frequency division multiplexed type used at all missile development centers in the United States. The 18 subcarrier bands are frequency modulated and the RF carrier is also frequency modulated; hence the term FM/FM. The information capacity of each channel is proportional to the particular subcarrier center frequency since each subcarrier is deviated by a constant percentage.

FM/PM. A system of multiple modulation where the RF stage is modulated using phase modulation (PM) (q.v.). The final resultant of a phase modulated system is frequency modulation (q.v.) if no phase reference signal is transmitted.

FM radar. A kind of radar set or system using a frequency modulated transmission signal.

foehn cloud. A stationary cloud on the windward slope or peak of a mountain or mountain chain, formed by the condensation of rising air. Also termed a *foehn wall.*

foehn wind. On the lee side of mountains, air flowing downhill and warmed adiabatically as it descends. *See* adiabat.

fog. (1) A visible concentration of water particles or ice crystals touching the surface of Earth or suspended near the surface, and interfering with visibility at the surface. Distinguish from *cloud* (q.v.) and *haze* (q.v.). (2) A like concentration of fine particles other than those of water or ice, often mixed with those of water or ice.

The Air Force distinguishes between a suspended fog and a cloud by establishing an arbitrary maximum height for a fog base as fifty feet. A cloud just touching the top of a mountain is usually termed *stratus,* while if the cloud mist extends for a distance down the sides of the mountain, it is often termed *fog.* Fogs are variously classified, as by the way they are formed, by their contents, or by the places where they occur. One classification puts them into two broad categories: the *air-mass fogs* and the *frontal fogs* (q.v.). In the former category are the *advection fog,* the *radiation fog,* and the *upslope fog* (q.q.v.). In the latter are the fogs associated with *fronts* (q.v.).

fog. *Types of, see* advection–; air mass–; black–; Cheyenne–; city–; dry–; frontal–; frost–; ground–; ice–; land–; radiation–; sea–; steam–; upslope–; wet–.

folding fin. A fin on a rocket or missile hinged to remain flat or retractable until the vehicle is in flight.

follow-up system. A colloquialism for servomechanism (q.v.).

foot. A unit for the measurement of length.

1 foot = 30.480 cm = 12 in. = 0.3048 meter = $\frac{1}{3}$ yd

1 foot of water at 39.2°F = 0.02950 atm. = 0.8826 in. of mercury at 32°F = 62.427 lb/sq ft = 0.4335 lb/sq in.

1 foot/min = 0.01136 mile/hr

1 foot/sec = 30.480 cm/sec = 0.5921 knot = 0.6818 mile/hr

1 foot/sec² = 30.480 cm/sec²

1 foot-candle = 1 lumen/sq ft = 10.764 lumens/sq meter

1 foot-pound = 0.0012854 Btu = 0.0003239 cal-kg = 1.356 × 10⁷ dyne-cm = 1.356 × 10⁷ ergs = 3.766 × 10⁻⁷ kwhr = 0.0003766 watt-hr

1 foot-pound/hr = 3.766 × 10⁻⁷ kw

1 foot-pound/min = 0.001285 Btu/min = 2.259 × 10⁵ ergs/sec = 0.01667 ft-lb/sec = 3.030 × 10⁻⁵ hp = 2.260 × 10⁻⁵ kw = 0.02260 watt

1 foot-pound/sec = 0.07712 Btu/min = 1.356 × 10⁷ ergs/sec = 60 ft-lb/min = 0.001818 hp = 0.001356 kw = 1.356 watts

force. The action of one body upon another body, which changes or tends to change their relative motions, positions, sizes, or shapes. A force has four characteristics: (a) magnitude; (b) direction; (c) sense; and (d) point of application; therefore, it is a vector quantity. Forces are measured in *grams, kilograms, pounds, tons* (q.q.v.), etc. A force that pulls on a body and tends to lengthen it in the direction of pull is termed *tension.* A force that pushes or presses on a body and tends to shorten it in the direction of the force is termed *compression. See also* physical units and constants.

Force Equivalents

dynes × 10⁶	kilograms	pounds	poundals
1	1.020	2.248	72.33
	0.00848	0.3518	1.85933
0.9807	1	2.205	70.93
1.99149		0.34334	1.85084
0.4448	0.4536	1	32.17
1.64819	1.65667		1.50750
0.01383	0.01410	0.03108	1
2.14067	2.14916	2.49249	

force. *Types of, see* aerodynamic–; centrifugal–; Coriolis–; effective–; electromotive–; frictional–; *g* force; gradient–; inertial–; line of force; mixed–; perturbative–.

force coefficient. *See* aerodynamic forces and moments.

force equilibrium. A system of forces is in force equilibrium when the resultant force of the system is zero. Expressed mathematically as:

$$\Sigma F = 0$$

forced vibration. Vibration of a body resulting

from application of external force during an explicit time interval.

force requirements. The manpower and personnel required by an armed service using a weapon system (q.v.) for a defined mission.

force-vector diagram. A diagram in which the forces acting on a body are represented by vectors which will form a closed polygon if connected tip to tail.

forcing function. The description of the characteristics and identity of a source of excitation. The function may be *linear, nonlinear, harmonic, random*. The response is a function of the input, the damping, and the inertial characteristics of the forced member.

foreign intelligence. Information gathered by one nation in an effort to evaluate another nation's political and military capabilities and intentions.

form drag. Drag (q.v.) caused by variations of pressure around a moving body. An extreme case is that of a flat plate, where the pressure is greatly increased on the forward face and greatly reduced behind the plate. At speeds less than that of sound, form drag may be reduced by using an elongated shape with a rounded nose and pointed tail.

form factor. A factor used in establishing a figure of merit (q.v.) or other criterion for packaging of electronic components and elements. It is used to give an indication of packaging efficiency or space utilization.

forward scatter. Extended range radio-wave propagation attained by forward scatter from the ionosphere (q.v.).

Foucault gyroscope. A gyroscope in which the wheel is supported by gimbals so that it is allowed to turn freely about any axis, and the parts are balanced to prevent gravity from exerting a torque on the wheel.

four-channel separator. A telemetering (q.v.) unit containing four counter stages and associated circuitry, necessary power supply for these circuits, and four plug-in gates (q.v.).

Fourier series. A series of sine and cosine terms of integral-multiples of frequency. It is used in evaluating the coefficients of harmonics of complex waves.

four-way valve. (pressure-drain-load-load) A hydraulic valve which uses four orifices to control the load flow or pressure for bi-directional motion. One pair of orifices is used for each direction. Basically, the four-way valve operates as *two three-way valves* in push-pull (q.v.). As the movable member moves in one direction, the load pressure between the other pair decreases. Because of this push-pull action the four-way valve produces a greater force output, is more linear over a larger range, and is less susceptible to supply pressure variations; it has the disadvantage of increased cost. In servo applications the four-way valve is most commonly used. Four-way valves may be *closed center* or *open center* types.

fraction. *Types of, see* propellant mass–; web–.

fractocumulus cloud. A small, ragged cloud or grouping of clouds.

fractonimbus cloud. A low, ragged, detached fragment of cloud which either rises out of a warm surface after rainfall or is dragged out of a crest cloud by a passing wind. Sometimes termed *scud* or *steam cloud* (q.v.).

fractostratus cloud. A layer of cloud broken up into segments by wind or mountain tops.

frag. (1) Fragment or fragmentary. (2) Fragmentation. (3) Fragmentation bomb.

fragmenting warhead. A warhead (q.v.) specifically designed to emit a maximum number of specially shaped fragments having optimum propagation properties. The blast effect which accompanies the emission of the fragments is a secondary effect and is not generally considered in the assessment of the effectiveness of the fragmenting warhead.

Frahm frequency meter. A frequency meter consisting of a row of steel reeds, each having a different natural frequency. All are excited by an electromagnet that is fed with the alternating current whose frequency is to be measured. That reed vibrates whose frequency corresponds most nearly with that of the current.

frame. In telemetering, one commutator revolution.

frame of reference. A set of lines or surfaces used as a system of reference for defining coordinates that describe positions, velocities, etc.

frangible booster. A booster rocket (q.v.) in which the container is made of material which can be burst into small parts by an explosive charge to render the expended case harmless. It is used to diminish damage to friendly installations from booster cases.

Fraunhofer region. In antenna applications, the characteristic flow of energy from an antenna as though it were coming from a point source near the antenna.

free air. (1) That portion of the atmosphere (q.v.) undisturbed by objects on the surface of the Earth, as by mountains or buildings. (2) In meteorology, that portion of the free air above the range of recording instruments on the surface. (3) In aerodynamics, nonturbulent air; air undisturbed by a moving body, as by an airfoil. (4) In contexts regarding atomic explosions, air sufficiently remote from surfaces or objects that an explosive effect (e.g., blast) is not modified by reflected shock or scattering objects.

free ascent. The part of a rocket's ascent under its own inertia after the fuel is exhausted.

free body diagram. A diagram showing all forces acting on a body or portion of a body which has been isolated by replacing all contacting or attached objects with forces representing their effect on the body isolated.

free fall. A condition of unrestricted motion in a gravitational field. In a rocket coasting without power, the rocket and all of its contents are equally under the influence of gravity, irrespective of the distance from Earth, and the entire rocket is in free fall. *See* weightlessness.

free flight. The flight of a guided missile or space vehicle after the fuel is exhausted or shut off.

free flight angle. The acute angle between the horizontal and the longitudinal axis of a guided missile or space vehicle at the beginning of its free flight.

free-free. A beam free from support in two of three mutually perpendicular axes.

free-free mode. A characteristic description of the shape of a missile body in flight (i.e., unsupported or unrestrained). The body is free to conform to the imposed steady state or oscillatory forces. The first bending frequency is the lowest free-free mode.

$$\omega = n^2 \sqrt{\frac{gEI}{w}}$$

where the number n depends on the boundary conditions. The following lists numerical values of $(nl)^2$ for the first three modes.

	$(n_1 l)^2$	$(n_2 l)^2$	$(n_3 l)^2$
	fundamental	*second mode*	*third mode*
free-free:	22.4	61.7	121.0

free gyroscope. A gyroscope mounted in two or more gimbal rings so that its spin axis is free to maintain a fixed orientation in space. See Fig. 21, page 254.

free molecular flow. Physical property of a gas in which the mean free path of a molecule is large compared to its size. It is usually arbitrarily limited to the point where the path is ten times the molecular diameter; especially signifi-

cant in the outer reaches of the atmosphere (q.v.).

free oscillation. (1) In electricity, an oscillatory current continuing to flow in a tuned circuit after cessation of the impressed voltage. (2) In structures, an oscillatory motion continuing after cessation of the exciting force.

free radical propellants. High-performance propellants whose energy results from the recombination of metastable atoms or radicals obtained from the splitting of certain chemical compounds (e.g., atomic hydrogen recombines into molecular hydrogen—theoretical $I_{sp} \simeq 1500$ sec). See Table 4, page 187.

free rocket. A rocket having fixed fins but no control surfaces.

free vibration. Vibration of a body occurring without external forces being applied during the time the phenomenon is occurring.

freezing level. In meteorology, the lowest level in the atmosphere (q.v.) at which a freezing temperature prevails.

frequency. In a periodic phenomenon, the number of cycles occurring per unit of time, or which would occur per unit of time if all subsequent cycles were identical with the cycle under consideration. The frequency is usually the *cycle per second.* For an undamped mechanical system, the frequency is:

$$f = \frac{1}{2\pi} \sqrt{\frac{k}{m}}$$

where k = spring constant, lb/in.; m = mass = w/g = weight/acceleration of gravity.

frequency. *Types of, see* audio–; basic–; beat–; carrier–; center–; converter–; corner–; critical–; cut-off–; Doppler–; fundamental–; fundamental natural–; harmonic–; heterodyne–; infrared–; intermediate–; Langmuir–; low–; natural–; pulse repetition–; radar pulse repetition–; radio–; reference–; resonant–; resting–; servo corner–; subcarrier–; very high–; very low–; video–; weathercock–.

frequency control. *See* automatic frequency control.

frequency converter. Any circuit or device that accomplishes a frequency conversion (e.g., the mixer detector of a superheterodyne, an arc tube, a motor generator).

frequency deviation. (1) In amplitude-modulated or continuous-wave transmission, the amount by which the carrier frequency (q.v.) varies from its assigned value. (2) In frequency modulation, the peak difference between the instantaneous frequency of the modulated wave and the carrier frequency. (3) The number of cycles of excursion from band center in one direction or another.

$$f_d = f_{max} - f_{center} = f_{center} - f_{min}$$

(4) In the FM/FM telemetering system ±7.5% deviation of the subcarrier frequencies (q.v.) is used. A deviation of ±15% is sometimes used at 22 kc and higher.

frequency distortion. Distortion which occurs as a result of failure to amplify or attenuate equally all frequencies present in a complex wave.

frequency divider. A device delivering output voltage at a frequency that is a proper fraction of the input frequency. Usually the output frequency is an integral submultiple or an integral proper fraction of the input frequency. *See* harmonic conversion transducer.

frequency intelligence. In telemetering, the rate of change of the subcarrier frequency which contains the transmitted information.

frequency-modulated transmitter. A radio transmitter which transmits a frequency-modulated wave.

frequency modulation (FM). A method of modulating a radio-frequency carrier by causing the frequency of this carrier to vary above and below the quiescent value, at a rate determined by the audio or other modulating signal to be transmitted. The amplitude of the carrier remains constant.

frequency range. In communications, any part of the electromagnetic spectrum contained within given frequency limits; the range of a piece of communication equipment for transmitting or receiving within a given segment of the electromagnetic spectrum.

frequency ratio. As applied to telemetry inductance end instruments, the ratio of the highest calibration frequency to the lowest calibration frequency. A measure of sensitivity.

frequency response. The output characteristics of a unit with respect to various frequency inputs. It may be specified for a certain frequency, or represented as a graph covering a band of frequencies. It is sometimes expressed as per cent or decibels (db) down from the flat portion.

frequency response analysis. A method of evaluating a control system (q.v.) by introducing a varying rhythmic change (e.g., alternating current) into a process or control unit to see what effect, if any, this change will have. This method of analysis is used to predict what the addition of new equipment will mean to the operation of

a control system or to assess off-design performance.

frequency response function. A term which is descriptive of the performance of a component in a dynamic system, i.e., the Fourier transform of the impulse response. It is also the ratio of the Fourier transform of the network output to the Fourier transform of the network input.

frequency response method. A technique for analyzing servomechanism (q.v.) performance. It utilizes the fact that a linear system, when subjected to a sinusoidal disturbance, will demonstrate a steady-state sinusoidal response of the same frequency but differing in phase and amplitude from the input. The characteristics of the servo are then defined in terms of resulting change in amplitude and the phase shift over the frequency regime of interest. This method gives stability information directly from the open-loop transfer function.

frequency response of a system. The steady-state ratio of magnitude and the difference in phase of the output with respect to a sinusoidal input. The range of frequency and conditions of operation and measurement must be specified.

frequency response survey. A frequency survey made to determine resonant response characteristics of system or subsystem structures.

frequency sensitivity. As applied to telemetering end instruments, the frequency sensitivity of the instrument is equal to the difference between the frequencies corresponding to the two ends of the instrument's range divided by the mean of the two frequencies. This may be expressed as a percentage:

$$\text{frequency sensitivity in per cent} = \left[\frac{f_{max} - f_{min}}{\frac{1}{2}(f_{max} + f_{min})} \right]$$

frequency shift. *See* incremental frequency shift.

frequency spectrum (RF). The range of frequencies of interest in radio and radar applications. See Fig. 8.

frequency tolerance. The maximum number of frequencies from the assigned frequency that a carrier wave is permitted to depart in transmitting a carrier wave.

frequency tripler. An amplifier having an output frequency three times that of the input.

fretting. Physical damage caused by mechanical chafing, rubbing, or wearing away.

fretting corrosion. Fretting (q.v.) acceleration by corrosive action.

FRF. Flight readiness firing (q.v.).

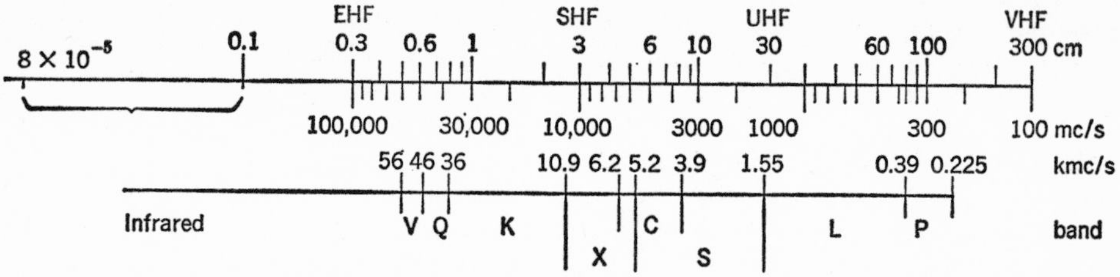

Classification	*Frequency Range*	*Wavelength Range*
Very low frequency (VLF)	10-30 kc	30,000-10,000 meters
Low frequency (LF)	30-300 kc	10,000-1000 meters
Medium frequency (MF)	300-3000 kc	1000-100 meters
High frequency (HF)	3-30 mc	100-10 meters
Very high frequency (VHF)	30-300 mc	10-1 meters
Ultra high frequency (UHF)	300-3000 mc	100-10 cm
Super high frequency (SHF)	3000-30,000 mc	10-1 cm

	Band Frequency (mc/sec)	*Wavelength* (cm)
P	225-250	133-77
L	390-1550	77-20
S	1550-5200	20-5.8
C	3900-6200	11.8-7.3
X	5200-10900	5.8-2.5
K	10900-36000	2.5-0.8
V	46000-56000	0.6-0.5
Q	36000-46000	0.8-0.6

Fig. 8. Frequency, wavelength, and band nomenclature. (C. W. Besserer, *Missile Engineering Handbook*, D. Van Nostrand)

friction. The resistance to relative movement of two surfaces in contact with another. The *coefficient of friction* is equal to the ratio of the friction force to the normal force:

$$f = \frac{F_f}{F_p}$$

where F_f = friction force; F_p = normal force.

friction. *Types of, see* anelasticity–; dry–; internal–; kinetic–.

frictional forces. Types of forces used to overcome friction in a mechanical system: (a) *static:* a discontinuous force independent of the output until the static friction is broken; (b) *coulomb:* a constant force substantially independent of velocity and opposite to the motion; (c) *viscous:* a force proportional to velocity of the output member.

friction layer. (1) In meteorology, the lower layer of the troposphere (q.v.), in which the friction of the air against Earth's surface affects the movement of the air. It is considered to be anywhere from 1500 to 3000 ft thick. (2) The boundary layer (q.v.) in an airflow.

front. *Types of, see* intertropical–; occluded–; polar–; pressure–; quasi-stationary–; secondary–; shock–; stationary–; upper–; warm–; weather–.

frontal fog. Any fog associated with a front, in which lowering temperatures and evaporation from falling rain meet at dew points where condensation results, e.g., a fog occurring in a cold air mass beneath a frontal surface.

frontal surface. (1) In meteorology, a slanting or sloping surface or layer of discontinuity existing between two air masses having different characteristics. Also termed a *front.* (2) In missiles, the cross-sectional area presented to the airstream.

frontal thunderstorm. A thunderstorm occurring at, or associated with, a frontal surface (q.v.). Three types of frontal thunderstorms are recognized: *cold-front thunderstorm; squall-line thunderstorm; warm-front thunderstorm* (q.q.v.).

front-to-back ratio. The ratio of the effectiveness of a directional antenna, microphone, or loudspeaker toward the front and toward the rear.

frontogenesis. In meteorology, the origination or creation of a front by the motion and meeting of different air masses; the process by which this takes place.

frontolysis. The dissolution or breaking up of a frontal surface (q.v.).

front-to-rear ratio. In antenna terminology, the ratio of the effectiveness of a directional antenna as measured toward the front and the rear.

frost. (1) A feathery deposit of minute ice crystals or grains upon a surface or object, formed directly from vapor in the air. (2) The process by which such ice crystals are formed. (3) Any temperature at which frost forms. Frost often forms when the close-lying air is above 32°F, especially in calm, clear weather when radiation or evaporation reduces a surface temperature to a point of freezing or below.

frost. *Types of, see* hoarfrost; permafrost.

frost fog. Ice fog; specifically, a thin or light ice fog (q.v.).

frozen (steady-state) equilibrium. A rocket performance term pertaining to characteristics of the combustion process in the nozzle (q.v.). The specific impulse is calculated on the basis of frozen chemical reactions at the nozzle entrance section. Frozen equilibrium assumes no secondary reactions. *See* shifting equilibrium.

FRS. Frequency Response Survey.

FRT. Flight Rating Test (q.v.).

fruit pulse. A pulse reply received as the result of interrogation of a transponder (q.v.) by interrogators not associated with the responsor in question. Also termed *fruit.*

Fs. Fractostratus cloud (q.v.).

FSA. Federal Security Agency.

F-scope. A radarscope which presents the azimuth (q.v.) error angle of a target by a horizontal displacement of the target spot on the face of the scope and the elevation of the target by a vertical displacement.

FSE. Field Support Equipment (q.v.).

FSN. Federal Stock Number.

ft/sec (fps or F/S). Feet per second.

fuel. In a rocket engine, any material that is mixed with an oxidizer to support and maintain combustion.

fuel. *Types of, see* exotic–; high-energy–; JP–; pyrophoric–; solid–; zip–. Also see Table 3, page 157.

fuel-air mixture. The mixture of fuel and air in the combustion chamber (q.v.) of an engine at any given fuel-air ratio (q.v.).

fuel-air ratio. The ratio of fuel to air as supplied to the combustion chamber (q.v.) of an engine.

fuel cell. (1) A device for the conversion of chemical energy directly into electrical energy on a continuous basis. (Contrast with a *battery* which makes this conversion on a batch basis.) (2) A bladder or container used to separate fuel from the pressurizing gas.

fuel control. *See* barometric fuel control.

fuel consumption. *See* thrust specific fuel consumption.

fuel dope. Any antiknock substance added to a fuel. Also termed a *detonation suppressant.*

fuel specific impulse. In rocketry, the thrust developed by burning one pound of fuel in one second, or the ratio of the thrust to the fuel mass flow.

fuel-weight ratio. In rocketry, the ratio of the weight of a rocket's propellant to the weight of the unloaded rocket. Also termed the *fuel-structure ratio.*

full automatic aircraft rocket launcher. A type of aircraft rocket launcher (q.v.) requiring only operation of the firing switch to fire and launch a number of rockets automatically.

full emission turbine. A turbine which employs a continuous series of jets or nozzle segments that direct a gas stream against all blades simultaneously.

full-wave rectifier. A radio tube, selenium rectifier, or other device which rectifies an alternating current in such a way that both halves of each input AC cycle appear in the pulsating rectified output. A full-wave rectifier tube contains two separate diode (q.v.) sections, one passing current during one alternation, and the other passing current during the opposite cycle. Bridge rectifier circuits are often used for full-wave rectification.

function. (1) A term referring to an activity of an armed service in the furtherance of war (e.g., minelaying is a *function* of the U.S. Navy). (2) The useful result of an operation of a component or equipment. (3) A characteristic description of the mechanization of a mathematical relation.

function. *Types of, see* array–; element–; forcing–; frequency response–; transfer–.

functional reliability. The probability that all components, units, or major units in a system will function within their specified operating tolerances for a specified length of time and under specified environments.

functional test. A test of a piece of equipment to prove or determine the functional or operational performance characteristics of the whole and of its various components and assemblies.

function indicator. An indicating instrument used to plot any two variable quantities whose values can be proportional to either voltage or current (e.g., pen recorder, cathode-ray tube).

fundamental. The lowest frequency component of a complex vibration, sound, tone, or electrical signal.

fundamental frequency. (1) The lowest possible frequency of vibration of a system characterized by normal modes of vibration (e.g., a vibrating string or organ pipe). (2) The greatest common divisor of the component frequencies of a periodic wave or quantity. (3) The frequency of a sinusoidal quantity which has the same frequency as the periodic quantity.

fundamental natural frequency. The lowest of a set of natural frequencies.

furfural alcohol ($C_4H_3OCH_2OH$). A liquid rocket propellant *fuel*.

fuse. (1) A slow burning device to transmit a flame—used to detonate a warhead (q.v.) via a booster (q.v.). (2) A safety device used to limit to a predetermined value some characteristic (e.g., electrical current).

fuse. *Types of, see* Bickford–, Miner's–; safety–.

fusetron. A kind of electrical fuse (q.v.) that will bear an overload for a short period of time before failing.

fusion. *Types of, see* atomic–; latent heat of–; nuclear–.

fuze. That component of the armament which recognizes the optimum time for destruction of a target by a missile and initiates explosive elements leading to the detonation of the warhead (q.v.) at that time. Commonly termed the *intelligence element of a warhead, S and A, fuze system*, etc.

fuze. *Types of, see* airburst–; allways–; ambient–; antidisturbance–; barometric (baro)–; combination–; concussion–; contact–; delay–; electronic–; hydrostatic–; impact–; inertial–; influence–; instantaneous–; long-delay–; longitudinal (antenna)–; mechanical time–; medium delay–; non-delay–; nose–; radio–; radio proximity–; superquick–; supersensitive–; time–; transverse (antenna)–; variable time–; VT–.

fuze agents. Natural phenomena utilized for the purpose of recognizing target characteristics useful for fuzing.

fuze range. The range of a projectile before its fuze detonates the charge.

G

g. *See* gravity; *g* force.

G_m. Designation for the mutual conductance of a vacuum tube. See *transconductance*.

g/a. Glide angle.

gage pressure. Pressure measured with zero equal to atmospheric pressure.

gain. (1) The increase in a signal (or other quantity) as it passes through a control system or a specific control element. If a signal gets smaller, it is said to be attenuated. Alternatively, gain can mean the sensitivity of a device to changes. (2) A general term used to denote an increase in signal power in transmission from one point to another. See Table 2.

TABLE 2. Conversion table, gain to decibels.

M	m, db	M	m, db
0	$-\infty$	4	+12*
1/100	-40	8	+18*
1/10	-20	10	+20
1/4	-12*	16	+24*
1/2	$-$ 6*	20	+26*
0.707	$-$ 3*	32	+30*
1	$-$ 0	100	+40
1.414	$+$ 3*	1000	+60
2	$+$ 6*		

* These values are approximate but are accurate enough for servo design.

M = magnitude of transfer function = $\dfrac{\text{output}}{\text{input}}$

m = corresponding magnitude in db.

gain. *Types of, see* alpha–; antenna–; antenna power–; beta–; loop–; transducer–; transducer insertion–; transmission loss or gain; warhead–.

gain control. (1) A control connected so that it can change the over-all gain of an amplifier or system. (2) Any volume control.

gain margin. The amount by which the magnitude of the loop ratio of a static system is different from unity at phase crossover. It is frequently expressed in the number of decibels below unity gain at a selected frequency for which the phase magnitude is 180°.

gain of an antenna. A rating used in comparing a complex antenna or antenna array usually with a simple doublet antenna.

gain stabilized. (1) Of an amplifier, designed so that a change in external conditions (input signal, power supply voltage, etc.) or internal conditions (tube characteristics, etc.) will have a minimum effect on the gain. (2) Of a servo system, stabilized by reducing the open loop gain of the system below the critical value for the particular system.

gal. A unit of measurement relating the gravitational constant G, mass of the Earth M, and its flattening e:

$$\frac{GM}{a} = \left(\frac{ag_o}{1 + e}\right)$$

where g_o = mean equatorial gravity $\simeq$ 980 cm/sec = 980 gals; a = equatorial radius.

galactic nebulae. Clouds of interstellar matter whose presence is revealed either because they are illuminated by a bright star or because they noticeably weaken the light from stars in a particular region of the sky.

galactic space. Interstellar space (q.v.), in general within the respective galactic system.

galaxy. A spiral system of stars; our galaxy, a disc-shaped aggregation of stars called the Milky Way, includes our solar system, far out on one of its spiral arms.

galaxy noise. Noise with the same characteristic as thermal-electronic noise which comes from the general direction of the Milky Way.

GALCIT. (1) Guggenheim Aeronautical Laboratory, California Institute of Technology. (2) A rocket project started before World War II which led eventually to the production of the WAC CORPORAL (q.v.).

gale. A wind that blows between 39 and 75 miles an hour. On Beaufort's scale (q.v.) a gale (including the whole gale) is between a strong breeze and a hurricane, with a force of 8 through 11.

galvanometer. (1) A sensitive current-responsive indicator. (2) In telemetering, galvanometers are used in electromechanical oscillographs. They consist of a small coil or loop of wire suspended in a magnetic field. A small mirror is attached to the coil or loop. When current is applied the mirror moves angularly, deflecting a light beam which is recorded to give an indication of the value of the signal causing the displacement.

GAM. Guided Aircraft Missile (q.v.).

GAM-63. Air Force designation for the air-to-surface rocket-powered robot bomber termed RASCAL (q.v.).

GAM-67. Air Force designation for the air-to-surface missile termed CROSSBOW (q.v.).

GAM-72. Air Force designation for the air-to-surface countermeasure diversionary missile termed GREEN QUAIL (q.v.).

GAM-77. Air Force designation for the air-to-surface missile termed HOUNDDOG (q.v.).

Gamma 58. According to the International Geophysical Year code system used for identifying Earth satellites, this is the American EXPLORER III (q.v.) launched March 26, 1958, from Cape Canaveral, Florida. The 31-lb payload orbited until late June, 1958. See Table 6, page 245.

gamma (ray) radiation. In nucleonics, high-energy electromagnetic radiation with a wavelength of about 10^{-12} cm that has tremendous penetrating power and is dangerous to living tissues.

gantry. A frame structure raised on side supports to span a missile, usually traveling on rails and used for erecting and servicing large bombardment-type missiles. Typically can be positioned directly over the launching site and rolled away just prior to firing.

GAPA. Surface-to-air missile. Air Force cognizance.

Early experimental antiaircraft missile. BOMARC (q.v.) was the follow-on project.

Prime contractor: Boeing Airplane Co.

Program terminated in 1949.

GAPA. Ground-to-Air Pilotless Aircraft.

gap-filler radar. An auxiliary radar antenna used to cover gaps in the main radar antenna pattern.

GAR. (1) Guided Aircraft Rocket (q.v.). (2) Guided Airborne Rocket.

GAR-1, GAR-1D, and GAR-2. Air Force designation for the air-to-air missile termed FALCON (q.v.).

GAR-8. Air Force designation for the air-to-air guided missile termed SIDEWINDER I (q.v.).

GAR-9. Air Force designation for the version

of the FALCON (q.v.) designed to carry an atomic warhead.

gas. *Types of, see* diatomic-; monatomic-; pressure-.

gas generator. A combustion chamber (q.v.) used to provide hot gases for a turbine or motor to drive the propellant pumps of a rocket engine (q.v.) or to provide a source of gas at some predetermined pressure program. Gas generators are usually operated fuel-rich to maintain the container temperature at reduced values.

gasoline (C_8H_{28}). A liquid rocket propellant *fuel*.

gassing. (1) The production of gases from one or more of the electrodes during electrolysis. (2) Liberal production of gas in a storage battery when charging is continued after the battery is completely charged.

gassy tube. A high-vacuum or other tube in which a leak has developed, admitting air; a "soft" tube.

gas turbine. (1) A mechanical unit that spins or rotates in reaction to a current of gas passing through or over it, the flow of gas being direct from the combustion or explosion of fuel. Distinguish from a *steam turbine*. (2) A gas-turbine engine; a power plant or engine that utilizes a gas turbine to generate mechanical power, especially to turn the compressor in a jet engine or to turn certain accessories or generators used in a missile or jet aircraft.

GAT. Greenwich Apparent Time (q.v.).

gate. (1) In radar or control terminology, a sensitivity-control arrangement to pass signals only in a small, selected fraction of the principal time interval. Unwanted signals are thus rejected. (2) In propulsion, a range of air-fuel ratios in which combustion can be initiated.

gate. *Types of, see* airborne-; information-.

gate-closing pulse. In electronics, the stimulus in the form of a pulse to close the information gates.

gate-opening pulse. In electronics, the stimulus in the form of a pulse serving to open the information gates.

gauss. A common unit for the measurement of magnetic fields. The magnetic induction at a point is one gauss when the maximum voltage that can be induced in a conductor moving through the point with a velocity of one centimeter per second is one emu volt.

> 1 gauss = 1 EM cgs unit of magnetic flux density = 1 maxwell/sq cm = 1 line/sq cm = 3.336×10^{-11} stat-weber/sq cm = 10^{-8} weber/sq in.

Gaussian distribution. *See* normal distribution.

Gâvre retardation function. A method of computing ballistic trajectories (q.v.) particularly applicable to high-angle fire at supersonic velocities. Ballistic tables for this case are based on the Gâvre law. If sufficient accuracy cannot be obtained this way, it is necessary to use numerical integration based on any desired resistance law. *See* Didion-Bernoulli method; Otto-Lardillon method.

GB. Glide Bomb (q.v.). *See also* glomb.

GBL. Government Bill of Lading.

GCA. Ground Controlled Approach (q.v.).

GCC. Ground Control Center.

GCI. Ground Controlled Interception.

GCR. (1) Ground Controlled Radar. (2) Grand Central Rocket Company, a division of Food Machinery Corp.

GCT. Greenwich Civil Time. *See* Greenwich mean time.

GEE. A medium-distance radio navigation system for air. Position is determined by measuring the difference in the time of arrival of synchronized pulses broadcast by a master and two slave stations.

GEE-H. A combination of the GEE and H electronic navigation systems, in which the GEE equipment is modified so that distances can be determined from transmitting stations on the ground with the aid of an airborne interrogator.

geepound. (Vernacular) The slug (q.v.).

gegenschein. A faint light area of the sky always opposite the position of the Sun on the celestial sphere. It is believed to be the reflection of sunlight from particles moving beyond the Earth's orbit.

genemotor. A rotary voltage converter in which, usually, two windings are used on the rotor and one on the stator. The two rotor windings terminate in separate commutator and brush sets. Generally used to convert a low DC voltage to a high DC voltage, as for mobile transmitters, amplifiers, etc.

generalized coordinates. In deriving the equations of motion of many dynamic problems, generalized coordinates are used to provide a set of coordinates in which the forces of constraint do not appear.

general operational requirement (GOR). The initial requirements established by the military services for a weapon system. These represent the boundary conditions for the development plan and program.

generator. *Types of, see* gas–; impulse–; sawtooth–; signal–; vortex–.

GENIE. Air-to-air missile with a nuclear warhead. Air Force designation: MB-1. Formerly known as DING-DONG, BIRD DOG, HIGH CARD, and TING-A-LING.

Length: estimated at 9 ft; diameter: about 17 in. over the warhead; firing weight: about 1000 lb. Solid sustainer motor (missile formerly was to use a liquid propellant motor but has been changed to solid fuel propulsion). No guidance system.

Prime Contractor: Douglas Aircraft Co. Air frame: Douglas. Engine: Aerojet General Corp.

geodesic line. The shortest line on the curved surface of the Earth between two points.

geodesy. The study of the Earth's dimensions, elasticity, mass, and local variations of gravity.

geographical coordinate. Either of two intersecting lines of latitude and longitude determining a position on the surface of the Earth.

geographic pole. One of the two points where Earth's axis of rotation cuts its surface. All geographic meridians meet at the poles. Since the magnetic poles are at a considerable distance from the geographic poles, compass needles do not as a rule point exactly towards the geographic poles. Earth's axis of rotation differs slightly from its axis of symmetry. The difference causes a wandering of the precise location of the geographic poles in cycles of 432 days, over a range of about 60 ft, and hence corresponding small changes in latitudes all over the Earth. The motions of land masses in relation to the poles have been termed *polar wandering*.

geographic position. The position of a given celestial body in relation to Earth. The geographical position of a body is defined as its substellar, subsolar, or sublunar point.

geoid. The figure or shape of Earth defined by the mean level of the ocean. It is an oblate spheroid (approximately an ellipsoid of revolution flattened at the poles).

geopotential. The increase in potential energy per unit mass lifted from mean sea level to a point against the force of gravity. The basic unit of geopotential is the *standard geopotential meter* where one standard geopotential, m^1, is defined to be an increment of potential energy per unit mass equal to 9.80665 joules kg^{-1} (or m^2sec^{-1}); i.e., 1 m^1 = 9.80665 m^2sec^{-2}. *Physical concept:* One standard geopotential meter is vertical distance through which one kilogram mass must be lifted against the force of gravity to increase its potential energy by 9.80665 joules. Accordingly, the geopotential meter length decreases as a function of altitude.

GEOREF grid. The grid used on U.S. Air Force aeronautical charts for identifying the location of any point or area in the world; the system involved in the use of this grid. Formerly termed *World Geographic Grid*. In this system the world chart is divided into 24 parallel north-south strips 15° wide numbered from *A* through *Z* (omitting *I* and *O*), beginning at the South Pole. Each quadrangle is subdivided into 15 lettered units eastward and 15 lettered units northward. These are lettered from *A* through *Q* (omitting *P* and *O*). Each one-degree quadrangle is subdivided into 60 numbered minute units. Minute units may be subdivided further into decimal parts.

geostrophic wind. The wind that is the result of a balanced pressure gradient and Coriolis force (q.v.). Geostrophic winds blow in straight or nearly straight lines. Low pressure is to the left of the wind direction in the Northern Hemisphere when the observer stands with his back to the wind. *See also* winds.

getter. An alkali or alkaline earth metal introduced into a vacuum tube during manufacture and vaporized after the tube has been evacuated to absorb any gases which may have been left by the vacuum pump. The silvery deposit on the inside of the glass envelope of a tube, usually near the tube base, is the result of getter vaporization.

***g* factor.** (limit) The ratio of the maximum acceleration that an object can withstand to the acceleration of gravity. It is equivalent to the ratio of the maximum accelerating force that the object can withstand to the weight of the object. The *g* factor for an object depends in part on the time duration of the accelerating force.

GFAE. (1) Government-Furnished Airborne Equipment (q.v.). (2) Government-Furnished Aircraft Equipment. (3) Government-Furnished Aeronautical Equipment.

GFE. Government-Furnished Equipment (q.v.).

GFM. Government-Furnished Material.

***g* force.** Force exerted upon an object by gravity or by reaction to acceleration or deceleration, as in a change of direction; *g* is the measure of the gravitational pull required to accelerate a body at the rate of about 32.16 ft/sec/sec.

GFP. (1) Government-Furnished Property (q.v.). (2) Government-Furnished Procurement.

GHA. Greenwich Hour Angle (q.v.).

GHE. Ground Handling Equipment (q.v.).

ghost signal. An unwanted echo on the screen of a radar indicator.

gibbous. Of moon or planet, the phase when more than half the disc appears illuminated; i.e., between "half moon" and "full moon."

gimbal. A mechanical frame containing two mutually perpendicular intersecting axes of rotation. See Fig. 17, page 230.

gimbal lock. Catastrophic malfunction of a two-axis gyroscope in which the normally orthogonal gimbals become aligned, i.e., the precession angle θ reaches 90°; usually results from excessive angular motion of a missile. See Fig. 21, page 254.

gimmick. The colloquial name given to a small capacitor (1-5 micromicrofarads) formed from two insulated wires twisted together.

G layer. An ionized layer thought to exist at a height of 300-400 miles in Earth's atmosphere. See Fig. 11, page 140.

glaze. *See* clear ice.

glide bomb. A winged missile powered by gravity. The wing loading is so high that it is incapable of flight at the speeds of modern bombardment aircraft. Such a missile therefore must be carried rather than towed.

glide missile. One which has for its midcourse and reentry or terminal phases a trajectory essentially flat or gliding with respect to Earth's surface. No power is required, and the actual trajectory shape is a function of entry angle to the sensible atmosphere (q.v.) and the aerodynamic configuration (W/C_DA).

glide trajectory. A long-range missile trajectory in which the initial powered flight is followed by a reentry glide at optimum lift/drag ratio in the upper portions of the atmosphere (q.v.). The glide portion may be accompanied by maneuvers to avoid countermeasures (q.v.). *See* glide vehicle.

glide vehicle. A hypersonic (q.v.) vehicle with a power boost similar to a long-range ballistic missile (q.v.) but with lifting surfaces to provide an optimum lift/drag reentry in the sensible atmosphere. Contrast with *skip vehicle*. *See* glide trajectory.

glint. The pulse-to-pulse variation in amplitude and apparent origin of reflected radar signal, owing to the reflection of the radar beam from a body which is changing its reflecting surface in an extremely rapid manner, such as would exist in pulses reflected from a rapidly spinning airplane propeller.

glitter. *See* glint.

glomb. *Glide bomb.* A glider (LNT-2) adapted by the Navy for use as a glide bomb; it is loaded with destructive charges and towed to the target area where, upon release, it is guided to its target by radio from a mother plane.

glow plug. An electric heating element which is used to raise a rocket propellant (q.v.) to its auto-ignition temperature.

glycol. A thick alcohol, $C_2H_4(OH)_2$ used as a coolant in liquid-cooled engines.

GM. Guided Missile (q.v.).

GMT. Greenwich Mean Time (q.v.).

gnomonic projection. A portrayal of Earth's surface in which the meridians and parallels of latitude are projected to a plane tangent to the Earth at one point (e.g., North Pole).

go-getter. (Vernacular) A control mechanism for automatic guidance of a rocket to its target.

go juice. (Vernacular) Jet fuel.

goniometer. (1) An instrument for measuring the angles between the reflection surfaces of a crystal or a prism. (2) A radio receiver and directional antenna system for determining the angle of arrival of incident waves. (3) Autosyn (q.v.) phase shifters driven by a common gear train.

go-no-go testing. A testing technique in which a signal is obtained which indicates that the system either is or is not functioning properly. No measure of performance is given and no degradation of operating characteristics can be measured. Go-no-go testing may be made open or closed loop (q.q.v.) and on any level of assembly.

GOOSE. Air-to-air missile and/or surface-to-surface missile. Air Force designation: for weapon system: WS-123A; for the missile itself: SM-73. Also known as BULL GOOSE and BLUE GOOSE. Program canceled in December, 1958.

Length: estimated from 20 to 30 ft; span: about 13 ft; speed: MACH 1.25; maximum altitude: 80,000 ft; range: estimated in excess of 500 nm. Turbojet J83 engine. Radio command guidance system. B-58 armament for decoy assignments. Prime Contractor: Fairchild Engine and Airplane Corp. Airframe: Fairchild. Engine: Fairchild. Guidance system: radio command: Fairchild. Control system: Kollsman Instrument Corp.

GOR. General Operational Requirement (q.v.).

GORGON. Air-to-surface missile. Military designation: XSAM-N-5.

Prime Contractor: The Martin Co.
Status: program phased out; never operational.

Government-furnished airborne equipment (GFAE). Equipment furnished by the Government for installation in airborne vehicles and for which the title remains with the Government.

Government-furnished equipment (GFE). Equipment furnished by the Government for an end item (q.v.) and for which the title remains with the Government.

Government-furnished property (GFP). Equipment or material provided by the Government to a contractor to be used by the contractor in the development, production, or testing of items to be delivered to the Government or to be incorporated by the contractor for delivery to the Government. *See* Government-furnished airborne equipment.

GOX. *Gaseous oxygen.*

GPI. Ground Position Indicator.

gradient. *Types of, see* contour–; pressure–; temperature–.

gradient force. In meteorology, the force of gravity exerted down a slope of a constant-pressure surface, or the force on a constant-altitude surface resulting from differences in atmospheric pressure.

gradient wind. A wind that blows parallel to curved isobars in a field of unchanging pressure. This wind does not blow at Earth's surface, because of friction. It is realized at 1500 ft and occurs when the centrifugal, Coriolis, and pressure-gradient forces (q.q.v.) are in balance. *See also* winds.

grain. In solid-propellant rockets, the mass of the propellant.

grain. *Types of, see* case-bonded–; cruciform–; end burning–; internal star-shaped–; multiple–; multiple-perforated single cylindrical–; restricted burning–; star–; tubular–.

grain. (measure) A unit of weight measurement.

1 grain = 0.06480 gram = 0.00229 oz (avoirdupois) = 1/7000 lb (avoirdupois)

grain volume. In solid propellant rockets, the volume occupied by the propellant.

$$V_p = \frac{(\text{chamber volume})(\text{volume of propellant})}{\begin{bmatrix}\text{volume of} \\ \text{propellant}\end{bmatrix} + \begin{bmatrix}\text{void} \\ \text{space}\end{bmatrix} + \begin{bmatrix}\text{liner} \\ \text{volume}\end{bmatrix}}$$

gram. A unit of weight or force measurement.

1 gram = 980.665 dynes = 15.4324 grains = 0.001 kg = 1000 mg = 0.03527 oz (avoirdupois)

1 gram-centimeter = 9.297 $\times$ 10^{-8} Btu = 2.3427 $\times$ 10^{-8} kg cal = 980.665 dyne-cm = 980.665 ergs = 7.233 $\times$ 10^{-5} ft-lb = 9.80665 $\times$ 10^{-5} joule

1 gram/cu cm = 62.43 lb/cu ft

1 gram/liter = 1000 parts/million

1 gram/sq cm = 0.73556 mm of mercury at 0°C = 2.04817 lb/sq ft = 0.01422 lb/sq in.

gram calorie. A unit of heat measurement; the quantity of heat required to raise the temperature of 1 gram of water 1 degree centigrade. Also termed *small calorie.*

1 gram calorie = 0.001 kilogram calorie

granular ice. Ice formed when droplets freeze without completely breaking into a film of water.

graph. *Types of, see* conversion–; time function–.

grass. (Vernacular) In electronics, radio noise interference; denotes visible effects of random noise on an oscilloscope (q.v.) display.

gravisphere. The space surrounding Earth in which the Earth's gravitational attraction is predominant. Approximately coincident with the diameter of cislunar space (q.v.), but sometimes assumed to be approximately 1 million miles.

gravitation. Force of attraction that exists between all particles of matter everywhere in the universe. Between any pair of bodies, it is proportional to the mass of each and inversely proportional to the square of the distance between them.

gravitational anomalies. Irregular distribution of the gravitational field over the Earth's surface.

gravitational loss. The loss of efficiency of a rocket escaping from the Earth occasioned by the time required for escape velocity (q.v.) to be reached. If the rocket could attain escape velocity instantly, it would require no more than the theoretical minimum of energy to escape. But an actual rocket cannot do this; it is limited by the power of its motors. For each second that the rocket spends in accelerating, the gravitational attraction of the Earth retards it by about 32 fps (roughly 20 mph). Even if the period of acceleration were as short as 100 sec (corresponding to an improbably great average acceleration of over 10 g) it would involve a loss of 2930 fps, which is not negligible even in comparison with the Earth's escape velocity.

gravity. The gravity acceleration for objects at the surface of the Earth, slightly modified by centrifugal force, the shape of the Earth, etc. The term is also applied to a similar force on other bodies in space.

gravity – 980.665 cm/sec^2 = 32.174 fps^2

gravity. *Types of, see* artificial–; lunar–; specific–; zero–.

gravity (as a function of altitude). The Earth's gravitational field at altitude varies as follows:

$$g_h = g_e \left(\frac{R_e}{R_e + h} \right)^2$$

where g_e = acceleration of gravity at sea level, fps^2; R_e = radius of the earth, ft; h = altitude, ft.

gravity (force of, on a rotating earth). If F is the force of attraction between two bodies of mass m_1 and m_2, when separated by a distance d:

$$F = G \frac{m_1 m_2}{d^2}$$

The quantity G is termed the *universal gravitational constant* and is generally assigned the numerical value of 6.66 $\times$ 10^{-8} with the dimensions of cm^3/gram sec^2, where F is given in dynes, m_1 and m_2 in grams, and d in centimeters.

gravity (non-rotating earth). The acceleration force exerted on terrestrial bodies by a fictitious earth which is homogeneous, stationary, isolated, and spherical. Used as a mathematical artifice in certain trajectory computations.

gravity simulation. Use of centripetal (q.v.) force to simulate weight reaction, in a condition of free fall (q.v.); possibly achieved by spinning a vehicle to use the centripetal force of the outer periphery on bodies within the vehicle to replace the normal weight reaction experienced at the Earth's surface.

gravity turn. Employed in ballistic missiles (q.v.) to obtain a trajectory (q.v.) in which the gravity component is just cancelled by a component of the thrust vector; i.e., the thrust vector is parallel to the velocity vector.

gravity (vertical component at any latitude, ϕ). The vertical component of gravity decreases inversely as the square of the distance between the center of the Earth and a unit mass, and the centrifugal force increases as a function of the same distance.

$$g_\phi = 978.046(1 + 0.005296 \sin^2 \phi - 0.000007 \sin^2 2\phi)$$

gravity well. Analogy in which the gravitational field is considered as a deep pit out of which a space vehicle has to climb to escape from a planetary body.

gray body. A radiator whose spectral emissivity remains constant through the spectrum, being in a constant ratio, less than unity, to that of a complete radiator (black body q.v.) at the same temperature.

Gray code. In digital computer applications, a modified binary code (q.v.) used for analog-to-digital conversion. The principle of operation is based on the change of only one element in a system at a time when passing from one digit to the next. Also termed *cyclic binary* or *reflective code*.

great circle course. The shortest path between two points on a spherical Earth. The path is coincident with the circular arc whose radius is equal to that of the Earth, and whose center of curvature is located at the center of the Earth.

great circle distance. The shortest distance along the surface of the Earth (sea level) connecting two points. The great circle distance (q.v.) between two points not at sea level is taken as the great circle distance between the vertical projections of the two points upon the sea level surface.

Greek alphabet.

	Greek	English			Greek	English
A	α	Alpha	a	N	ν	Nu	n
B	β	Beta	b	Ξ	ξ	Xi	x
Γ	γ	Gamma	g	O	o	Omicron	ŏ
Δ	δ	Delta	d	Π	π	Pi	p
E	ε	Epsilon	ĕ	P	ρ	Rho	r
Z	ζ	Zeta	z	Σ	σ	Sigma	s
H	η	Eta	ē	T	τ	Tau	t
Θ	θ	Theta	th	Υ	υ	Upsilon	u
I	ι	Iota	i	Φ	φ	Phi	ph
K	κ	Kappa	k	X	χ	Chi	ch
Λ	λ	Lambda	l	Ψ	ψ	Psi	ps
M	μ	Mu	m	Ω	ω	Omega	ō

green house. (Vernacular) A check station where simulated flight tests are conducted.

GREEN QUAIL. Air-to-surface countermeasure diversionary missile. Air Force designation: GAM-72.

B-58 armament; carries no warhead, but is equipped with electronic countermeasures equipment. Turbojet engine. Preset autopilot guidance system.

Prime Contractor: McDonnell Aircraft Corp. Airframe: McDonnell. Guidance system: Summers Gyroscope Co.

Greenwich apparent time (GAT). Apparent time measured with reference to the Greenwich meridian (q.v.).

Greenwich civil time. Greenwich mean time (q.v.).

Greenwich hour angle (GHA). The angle of a celestial body from the Greenwich meridian (q.v.) projected on the celestial sphere (q.v.), measured westward from the projected Greenwich meridian to the hour circle passing through the body, from 0 through 360 degrees.

Greenwich mean time (GMT). Prior to Jan. 1, 1925, the astronomical day beginning at Greenwich mean noon was used in navigational almanacs, and mean solar time reckoned from this origin was called Greenwich mean time. Since 1925, time has been reckoned from midnight instead of noon, in order to bring navigational and civil practice into conformity. In communications practice, the symbol Z is used to designate Greenwich mean time. *See* zebra time.

Greenwich meridian. The meridian on which the Royal Observatory at Greenwich, England is located; the zero meridian from which longitude is measured. *See* prime meridian.

Greenwich sidereal time (GST). Sidereal time (q.v.) measured with reference to the Greenwich meridian (q.v.).

grid. (1) In electronics, an electrode mounted between the cathode and anode of a radio or electronic tube to control the flow of electrons from cathode to anode. The grid electrode is usually either a cylindrical-shaped wire screen or a spiral of wire through which electrons can readily move. (2) A part in the rear section of a rocket motor, which supports the powder grain (q.v.) but allows enough clearance for the propellant gases to escape to the nozzle (q.v.). (3) The pattern of intersecting lines set up in accordance with a grid system, and superimposed upon charts, aerial photographs, etc., to permit ready location of points on the ground.

grid. *Types of, see* control–; GEOREF–; polar–; suppressor–; screen–; United States–; universal transverse Mercator–; world polyconic–.

grid bias. The direct current voltage applied between the control grid and the cathode of a vacuum tube. Often termed *bias*.

grid declination. The difference between true north and grid north (q.q.v.), usually shown graphically on maps in marginal information. Grid declination is measured by an angle from true north and designated *east* or *west* as the case may be.

grid north. The direction indicated by the arbitrary vertical line of a grid, usually found on military maps or charts. *See* magnetic north; true north.

gross thrust. A factor of thrust used in calculating the net thrust of a jet engine, and equal to the entire thrust output of the engine. Quantities required to evaluate gross thrust are the total pressure of the gas, the stagnation temperature of the gas, the static pressure of the gas, and the area of the exhaust nozzle.

ground. An electrical conductor connected to Earth, or a large conductor whose potential is taken as zero (e.g., the metallic frame of a missile). A ground may be the undesirable, inadvertent, or accidental path taken by an electrical current; or it may be the deliberate provision of conductors well connected to the Earth by means of plates buried therein, or similar device.

ground abort. An instance in which a vehicle is prevented from taking off by failure (q.v.).

ground antenna data link system. Electronic equipment which provides an RF link between test equipment and equipment under test.

ground control. (1) The guidance given a missile in flight by a person on the ground. (2) The electronic equipment or network used in exercising this control.

ground controlled approach (GCA). A method of landing aircraft in poor visibility by directing the operation with the aid of a ground radar station.

ground fog. A shallow fog that clings to the ground; a fog not exceeding the height of a man.

ground guided missile. A missile guided by control from the ground.

ground handling equipment (GHE). Equipment used to accomplish a prime mover function and other mechanical functions connected with readying a missile for test or other use.

ground missile. A test vehicle; a complete missile, without propellant and armament, that is used for actual ground handling tests and may be vibration tested in the laboratory to simulate flight and captive loading conditions. It is referred to in the vernacular as *hangar queen.*

ground potential. The potential with respect to the ground or Earth. It is usually zero, but can be of some other value as in an AC-DC radio receiver.

ground return. A return on a radar receiver caused by radar pulses reflected from the ground. Also termed *ground clutter; ground flutter; land return. See* radar clutter.

ground (sea) clutter. Unwanted radar echoes from terrain (or sea) in the vicinity of a target which tend to obscure it.

ground shock. The magnitude, direction, pattern, energy content, and duration of a shock

wave at a given point on the surface or below the surface of the Earth resulting from a nuclear explosion of a given magnitude and burst position.

ground speed. The horizontal component of the velocity of an aircraft or missile relative to the Earth's surface beneath it.

ground start. A propulsion-starting sequence through ignition to main stage (q.v.) which is initiated and cycled through to completion on the ground. It involves use of liquid fuel or liquid oxidizer or both from a pressurized ground supply, instead of missile tanks, during the countdown (q.v.), ignition phase, thrust buildup, and liftoff (q.v.) of a liquid propellant rocket. This system permits the missile to take off with full tanks, at correct weights. At liftoff, plumbing connections come apart as breakaway couplings. This is in contrast to an in-flight or "air" start where the starting sequence and power buildup occur in flight at sometime after launch.

ground support equipment (GSE). All ground equipment that is part of the complete weapon system (q.v.) and must be furnished to insure its support. Included in the GSE are all implements or devices required to inspect, test, adjust, calibrate, appraise, gage, measure, repair, overhaul, assemble, disassemble, transport, safeguard, record, store, actuate, service, launch, and otherwise support and maintain the functional operating status of a weapon system, subsystem, end item, or component (q.q.v.). *Test* GSE is ground support equipment used to support a missile development program. *Operational* GSE is ground support equipment used in an operational weapon system.

ground-to-air (surface-to-air) missile. A missile launched from the surface (ground or ship) for the purpose of intercepting an airborne vehicle (e.g., airplane, missile). Generally used for antiaircraft defense and may be of short- or long-range type [e.g., NIKE, TALOS, TERRIER, TARTAR, BOMARC (q.q.v.)].

ground-to-ground (surface-to-surface) missile. A missile launched from the surface (land or sea) against surface targets. Two categories are used: (a) missiles to be used for long-range type of offense (e.g., MATADOR, SNARK, MINUTEMAN, REGULUS, q.q.v.); (b) missiles of much shorter-range type used for support of ground troops (e.g., LACROSSE, CORPORAL, SERGEANT, q.q.v.).

ground vector. In air navigation, a vector representing the track and ground speed of a missile, and forming a part of the wind triangle (q.v.).

ground vibration survey (GVS). A test conducted under laboratory conditions to determine frequency response characteristics of a system or its subsystem during vibration. The GVS normally consists of a *frequency response survey* and a *mode shape survey* (q.v.).

ground waves. (1) The waves formed in the ground by an explosion. They are of three types: (a) *longitudinal waves* (compression); (b) *transverse waves* (shear); and (c) *surface waves* (similar to water ripples). They can be induced by direct ground shock (e.g., a ground or sub-surface burst) or by blast transmitted through the air (as in any type of burst). (2) In electronics, the energy which reaches a radio receiving antenna from a transmitter by travel along the surface of the Earth rather than by reflection from the ionosphere (q.v.).

ground zero (G.Z.). In nucleonics, that point on the surface of the Earth directly below, at, or above the detonation point of an atomic bomb.

group velocity. In electronics, the velocity with which a signal is transmitted along a wave [numerically different from *phase velocity* (q.v.), only if the medium is such that the phase velocity varies with frequency].

growth factor. A factor defining the increase in weight, volume, power, or any other parameter caused by the addition of some feature (e.g., an increase in a missile payload causes an increase in gross weight, etc.). The ratio of the latter to the former is the *growth factor.*

G-scope. A modification of the F-scope (q.v.), in which the bright spot of the signal shows "wings" as the distance to the target diminishes.

GSE. Ground Support Equipment (q.v.).

GSS. Ground Support System.

GST. Greenwich Sidereal Time (q.v.).

G string. (1) (Vernacular) A round, solid, dielectric-coated single wire used as a waveguide (q.v.) for the transmission of microwave energy. For many frequencies ordinary copper magnet wire coated with enamel or synthetic enamel may be employed. (2) A string tuned to the G-tone, e.g., the lowest string on a violin,

g-suit. A garment for covering parts of the body below the chest, so designed as to exert pressure to prevent or retard the pooling of the blood below the heart during exposure to abnormal *g* forces. Also termed *antiblackout suit* and *anti-g suit.*

G-system. A special system for drawing grid (q.v.) lines on aeronautical charts used in polar air navigation, in which the lower branch of the Greenwich meridian (q.v.) is arbitrarily chosen in establishing grid north (q.v.).

GTTS. Gyroscope Transfer Table (q.v.).

GTV. Guidance Test Vehicle.

guard band. In electronic propagation, a narrow band of unassigned frequencies located between adjacent assigned frequency channels in certain portions of the radio spectrum to prevent interference between stations.

guidance. Concerning missiles, the processes of intelligence-gathering and maneuvering required to reach a specified destination, with special connotation on the flight path and on the information for determining the proper course whether computed externally or within the missile itself.

guidance. *Types of, see* active homing–; beam rider–; celestial–; celestial inertial–; celestial navigation–; command–; dispersion area–; homing–; hyperbolic–; inertial–; midcourse–; passive homing–; preset–; radar repeat-back–; radio inertial–; radio navigation–; semiactive homing–; stellar–; television repeat-back–; terminal–; terrestrial reference–; track command–.

guidance station. A ground or ship facility that has the capability of directing missiles in flight.

guidance station equipment. The ground-based portion of missile guidance systems necessary to provide ground-based guidance during missile flight; specifically, it includes tracking radar, rate measuring equipment, data link equipment, and computer and test and maintenance equipment integral to these items.

guidance system. A system which obtains and develops target information for the determination of the desired flight path of a missile and communicates this intelligence in the form of commands to a missile flight-control system. A guidance system may be inertial, self-contained within the missile, or the guidance function may be performed by various combinations of ground and airborne components.

guidance system. *Types of, see* airborne–; beam rider–; command–; inertial–; inertial gravitational–; inflight–; homing–; onboard–.

guidance tapes. Magnetic or paper tapes that are placed in a missile or its computer, containing information needed to program desired events in the missile during flight.

guided aircraft missile (GAM). A guided missile launched or designed for launching from an aircraft.

guided aircraft rocket (GAR). A rocket-powered guided missile designed to be launched from an aircraft in flight. *See* FALCON.

guided missile (GM). An unmanned vehicle moving above the Earth's surface, whose trajectory or flight path is capable of being altered by a mechanism within the vehicle. One system of designating guided missiles: *surface-to-surface* —missiles launched from ground stations or ships against ground installations, surface vehicles, or surface ships. *See* ground-to-ground missiles; *surface-to-air*—missiles launched against airborne aircraft, airships, or other guided missiles. *See* ground-to-air missile. Other classifications exist, with similar variations (*air-to-air, air-to-surface*); however, in all cases, the words *surface* and *air* are governing. *See* model designation.

guided missile. *Types of, see* ballistic–; command–; ground–.

guided missile ships. Ships of the U.S. Navy carrying guided missiles as part of their armament. These include:

Type	Designation	Missile	Class
Large cruiser			
Hawaii	CB 3	TALOS	Alaska
Heavy cruisers			
Boston	CAG 1	TERRIER	Baltimore
Canberra	CAG 2	TERRIER	Baltimore
G.M. heavy cruisers			
Los Angeles	CA 135	REGULUS	Baltimore
Helena	CA 75	REGULUS	Baltimore
Macon	CA 132	REGULUS	Baltimore
Toledo	CA 133	REGULUS	Baltimore
Nuclear power G.M. cruiser	CLGN	TALOS	new construction
G.M. light cruisers			
Galveston	CLG 93	TALOS	Cleveland
Providence	CLG 82	TALOS	Cleveland
Frigate			
King	DLG 10	TARTAR	Mitchell
Cootz	DLG 9	TARTAR	Mitchell
—	DLG 14	TERRIER	
G.M. destroyers			
8 authorized	DDG	TARTAR	new construction
Gyatt	DD 1	TERRIER	Gearing
Submarines			
1 authorized (nuclear-powered)	SSG (N)	REGULUS	new construction
Seadragon (nuclear-powered)	SSN (N)	REGULUS	new construction
Attack submarines			
Grayback	SSG 574	REGULUS II	Tang
Growler	SSG 577	REGULUS II	Tang
Firestone		REGULUS II	
Tunny	SSG 282	REGULUS I	Bolas
Barbero	SSG	REGULUS I	
FBM submarines			
9 authorized (nuclear-powered)	SSBN	POLARIS	new construction
G.M. ships			
Norton Sound	AVM-1	experimental ship	
Mississippi	EAG 128	experimental ship (scrapped)	

guided missile system. (1) The guided missile itself including all airborne systems (preferred usage). (2) A combination of a guided missile and its ancillary launching, external guidance, test, and handling equipment which together accomplish a mission (e.g., destruction of a target). *See* weapon system.

guided rocket. (1) A guided missile having rocket propulsion. (2) Short for guided aircraft rocket.

gun. *Types of, see* electron–; light gas–; space–.

gunk. (Vernacular) (1) An undesirable, nondescript material, usually semi-solid. (2) A solvent for grease.

gun launcher. A gun adapted to launching guided missiles (q.v.).

gust load. The load, usually expressed in *g*'s, imposed by rising or descending air currents upon a vehicle flying straight and level.

gusts. Transient but rapid fluctuations of wind velocity. Gusts are the result of turbulent air flow. Gusty winds usually vary radially in direction.

gutter. In an air-breathing engine, the portion of a flame holder (q.v.) which is grooved to improve stability of the flame-holding operation.

GVS. Ground Vibration Survey (q.v.).

G-weight. A weight, free to move axially in a missile frame, which is used to measure acceleration. *See* accelerometer.

gyration. *See* radius of gyration.

gyro. (Vernacular) Gyroscope (q.v.).

gyro flux-gate compass. A compass in which a triangular flux gate, horizontally stabilized by a gyroscope (q.v.), senses the horizontal component of Earth's magnetic field, and, being fixed with respect to the aircraft, reacts to each change in heading by a change in current, the current being converted through an amplifier into mechanical motion on the dial of a master indicator. Sometimes termed *flux-gate compass.*

gyropilot. Automatic pilot (q.v.).

gyroscope. A wheel or disc mounted to spin rapidly about an axis and also free to rotate about one or both of two axes perpendicular to each other and to the axis of spin. The spinning gyroscope either offers considerable resistance, depending upon its angular momentum, to any torque which would tend to change the direction of the spin axis, or, if free, changes its spin axis in a direction perpendicular to the torque and to the original spin axis. See Fig. 21, page 254.

gyroscope. *Types of, see* air bearing–; body mounted–; cryogenic–; directional–; displacement–; Foucault–; free–; hermetically-sealed integrating–; integrating–; integrating (pendulous) accelerometer–; pendulous integrating–; rate–; single degree of freedom–; slave–; spinning–; unbalanced–; vibratory–.

gyroscope drift. The difference between the actual and theoretical line of direction of a gyroscope (q.v.) due to three general sources: (a) unbalance—due to unsymmetry of manufactured parts, temperature, etc.; (b) bearing friction—due to gimbal friction (spin axis friction does not cause precession if the friction is symmetrical); (c) gimbal inertia.

gyroscope position pickoff. An end instrument (q.v.) which translates gyroscope gimbal position into an analog quantity (e.g., change of inductance or resistance).

gyroscope precession. The force-motion relationship of a spinning gyroscope (q.v.) resulting from Newton's law of motion: "The time rate of change of angular momentum of a body about any given axis is equal to the torque applied about the given axis."

$$T = I\omega_r\Omega$$

where T = torque; I = inertia of the gyro rotor about the spin axis; ω_r = rotor speed; Ω = angular velocity about the output axis. Precession is always in such a direction as to align the direction of rotation of the rotor with the direction of rotation of the applied torque.

gyroscope reference system. A system that maintains a constant spatial reference. If a missile deviates from this reference, an error signal proportional to the deviation is generated by the gyroscope reference system. This signal is modified and used as a corrective signal to bring the missile back to the desired flight path.

gyroscope-stabilized platform. In inertial guidance, a gyroscopically stabilized platform for mounting accelerometers (q.v.) to maintain them fixed in either a space or an Earth reference system despite changes in missile position and attitude. See Fig. 24, page 266.

gyroscope torquing. The process of applying an external signal to the gimbals of a displacement gyroscope (q.v.) as a means of programming the position of the reference axes. Torquers may be operated on AC or DC.

gyroscope torquer hysteresis. The residual torque in a DC torquer resulting from the magnetic memory of the torque generator when the excitation is removed.

gyroscope transfer table (GTTS). A portable precision gyroscope instrument designed to transfer physically the direction of *vertical* and the *true north* from a reference instrument (normally a ship's inertial navigation system) to another part of the ship's navigation or fire control systems or to a missile.

gyroscopic horizon. A gyroscope instrument that indicates the lateral and longitudinal attitude of a vehicle by simulating the natural horizon. A single degree of freedom gyroscope.

Gyrosyn. In full, Gyrosyn compass. A trade name for a compass that consists of a directional gyroscope stabilized with the horizontal component of the Earth's magnetic field by means of a flux gate (q.v.). The flux gate detects the direction of the lines of force and transmits the information electrically to a precession device. Repeaters are a part of the Gyrosyn or Gyrosyn system.

G.Z. Ground zero (q.v.).

H

hachure. Any of a number of short lines used on a map or chart for shading and indicating relief on the ground.

hail. Pellets of ice ranging from about $\frac{1}{16}$ in. in diameter to as much as 4 or 5 in. Hail stones are often transparent, but more frequently are translucent, being formed of alternate layers of clear and opaque ice. Hail usually falls from thunder storms.

hair hygrometer. A hygrometer (q.v.) that measures humidity by means of the variations in a specially treated strand of hair.

half-life. In nucleonics, the time required for a radioactive substance to lose half its activity by radioactive decay; i.e., the time required for a radioactive element to change half its original mass into a new, and usually less radioactive, element.

half power (point). In an antenna pattern, the power on each side of the main lobe which is 3 decibels down.

half-wave antenna. *See* dipole antenna.

half-wave rectifier. A circuit, vacuum tube, or other electrical device that uses one alternation of an alternating current to produce a pulsating direct current. Contrast with *full wave rectifier* (q.v.).

Hall effect. A phenomenon occurring in an electrical conductor. When a conductor is placed with its plane at right angles to a magnetic field, an electrical potential will develop between electrodes on opposite edges when a current flows parallel to the edges.

hangar. *See* field assembly hangar.

hangar queen. (Vernacular) An inert missile used for experimental purposes. *See* ground missile.

hangfire. (Vernacular) The delayed ignition of a rocket propellant or igniter.

HAPO. Hanford Atomic Products Operation; operated by General Electric Company for the Atomic Energy Commission.

hard base. A launching base (q.v.) that is protected against a nuclear blast by a structure or a terrestrial cover (natural or man-made); the structures are designed for a specified amount of overpressure and displacement. *See* soft base.

hard excitation. In a control system, the self excitation which occurs in the presence of a signal larger than the minimum which causes instability.

hardness. (1) A term which qualifies a target's vulnerability to damage, particularly from a nuclear explosion. (2) The property of an installation, facility, or equipment that will prevent an unacceptable level of damage resulting from bombardment.

hardness, base. *See* base hardness.

hard points. Structurally reinforced areas on a missile's exterior surface which are suitable for supporting it during handling and stowage.

hard structure. A structure designed to withstand nuclear weapon effects of a stated magnitude.

hard tooling. Synonymous with permanent tooling; used for production runs and applications requiring a high degree of interchangeability.

hard tube. A vacuum tube that has been evacuated to a high degree.

hardware. (1) A category sometimes used to designate certain equipment or supplies made entirely or largely of metal and manufactured for use in the field. (2) A point-of-view term for the physical aspect of a thing used, as distinguished from its capability or function.

hardware, body. *See* body hardware.

hardware specification. *See* equipment (hardware) specification.

HARE project. *H*igh *A*ltitude *R*amjet *E*ngine. A ramjet development project in which the oxygen required for combustion is obtained from a catalyst activated recombination of oxygen atoms. Estimated operational altitude is 60 miles.

harmonic. In electronics, a component frequency of a periodic quantity which is an integral multiple of the fundamental frequency.

harmonic conversion transducer. A conversion

transducer (q.v.) in which the useful output frequency is a multiple or a submultiple of the input frequency. Either a *frequency multiplier* or a *frequency divider* is a special case of harmonic conversion transducer.

harmonic distortion. In electronics, a nonlinear distortion characterized by the appearance in the output of harmonics other than the fundamental component when the input wave is sinusoidal. Harmonic distortion is sometimes termed *amplitude distortion.*

harmonic frequency. In physics, a frequency (q.v.) which is an integral multiple of a fundamental frequency (q.v.).

harmonic interference. Frequency interference in a data channel due to the fact that another channel has a harmonic frequency that falls in the band of the first channel.

harness. Wires and cables so arranged and tied together that they may be inserted and connected or removed after disconnection, as a unit.

hartley. In communication theory, a unit of information which is generally defined as being equal to 3.219 bits (q.v.).

HARVEST MOON. A proposed manned satellite with a first stage based on the NAVAHO (q.v.) booster design consisting of several rocket engines of many thousands of pounds thrust and a manned reentry body (q.v.).

hash. (Vernacular) In electronics, radio noise interference; electrical noise produced by a mechanical vibrator or by the brushes of a generator or motor.

HASP. Surface-to-air *h*igh *a*ltitude research *s*ounding missile. Navy cognizance.

The missile is fired from a 5-in. rifle and reaches an altitude of 60 miles carrying a 6-lb package of complex electronic equipment for high-altitude weather research; it partially replaces weather balloons.

Development: Naval Ordnance Laboratory.

HAWK. Surface-to-air missile. Army cognizance; Marine Corps plans an adaptation.

Length: 16 ft 4 in.; span: 47 in.; body diameter: 16 in.; firing weight: more than 1000 lb; burnout speed: MACH 2.8; slant trajectory range: more than 15 miles. Solid propellant rocket engine. Semiactive monopulse radar. Launcher can fire three missiles in rapid succession. The HAWK is transportable by aircraft or helicopter. Fire control handled by Missile Master.

Prime Contractor: Raytheon Manufacturing Co.

Airframe: Northrop Corp. Engine: Aerojet-General Corp. Guidance system: Raytheon.

haze. (1) A concentration of water vapor, lighter than fog or clouds, but thick enough to reduce visibility. (2) A smoke concentration laid down around or over a friendly force or area sufficiently heavy to hinder enemy observation from the ground, but not so heavy as to impede friendly operations.

HD. Density altitude (q.v.).

HE. High explosive (q.v.).

head. *Types of, see* airspeed–; RF–.

heading. The direction in which a missile or vehicle heads at any particular moment, usually measured in an Earth reference system.

head-on wind. A head wind blowing directly against the front or head of a vehicle, opposed to its direction of flight.

head resistance. The resistance of the air against the front of an object moving forward through the air. *See* drag.

headwind. A wind blowing from such a direction that its principal effect is to retard the groundspeed of a vehicle in flight. Roughly, any wind coming in toward the nose from a direction within 45 degrees either side of the longitudinal axis may be considered a headwind. Contrast with *tail wind* (q.v.).

HEAP. High Explosive Armor Piercing.

heat. *Types of, see* latent heat of fusion; mechanical equivalent of–; radiant–; solar–; specific–.

heat engine. Any engine or motor that converts heat energy into mechanical energy or motion (e.g., jet engine, rocket engine).

heater. An electric heating element for supplying heat to an indirectly heated cathode in an electron tube.

heater, pebble bed. *See* pebble bed heater.

heat exchanger. (1) In a general sense, any device used to cool a liquid or gas by transferring heat to another liquid or gas. (2) In a turbojet engine, a device or system whereby heat is transferred from the turbine exhaust to another part of the engine and used to heat the air or fuel entering the combustion chamber.

heating. *Types of, see* aerodynamic–; hysteresis–; thermal–.

heat seeker. (Vernacular) A guided missile or the like incorporating a heat-sensitive device for homing (q.v.) on heat-radiating machines or installations, such as an aircraft engine (airborne target) or a blast furnace (surface target).

heat shield. The protective structure necessary to prevent destruction of a reentry body (q.v.) incident to aerodynamic heating. A material *sink* may be used to absorb heat, or ablating materials similarly may be used.

heat sink. A device which absorbs heat energy.

heat transfer (transference). Heat energy can be transferred from one place to another by three methods: (a) *conduction*—in which heat energy moves from one body or portion of a body to another in contact with it without displacing the particles of the body; (b) *convection*—the transfer of heat energy within a gas or liquid by the motion of a portion of the gas or liquid from the place where the heat is received to the place where the heat is given up; (c) *radiation*—the transfer of heat which is continually given off by bodies in the form of radiant energy.

heat units. The units of heat measurement. Those commonly used are: (a) the gram-calorie (q.v.) or small calorie; (b) the British thermal unit (Btu) (q.v.). The value most commonly accepted among American engineers as the work equivalent of heat is 1 mean Btu = 777.5 ft-lb; and the mean gram calorie = 4.183 joules. The United States Bureau of Standards uses the following:

$$59°F\text{-}Btu = 778.2 \text{ ft-lb}$$
$$20°C\text{-}calorie = 4.183 \text{ joules}$$

Heaviside-Kennelly layer. The region of the ionosphere (q.v.) that reflects certain radio waves back to Earth; the E layer (q.v.). See Fig. 11, page 140.

heavy press program. An Air Force sponsored program for the development and construction of eleven heavy-duty forging and extrusion presses.

sense, has a specific gravity one-tenth greater than that of ordinary water; it freezes at about 4°C. It is used as a moderator in certain types of nuclear reactors.

HEI. High Explosive Incendiary.

height finder. In radar, any radar set that measures and determines the height of an airborne object.

height-range indicator. Any radarscope that gives the height and range of a target.

helical scan. In radar, a type of radar scan (q.v.) in which a given point on a radar beam traces a helical path in space. In helical scanning, the transmitting antenna revolves about its vertical axis while changing its angle of elevation.

heliography. The science of the study of the Sun, its properties, and characteristics.

helium, liquid forms I and II. Liquid helium undergoes a change in its physical properties at 2.189°K, the so-called lambda-point. The form stable between the critical temperature and the lambda-point is termed *liquid helium I*, and that stable between the lambda-point and absolute zero is termed *liquid helium II*. Since the transformation is one of higher order, without latent heat at the lambda-point, the two liquid forms are never co-existent. The lambda-transformation does not occur in liquid helium with isotopic weight 3.

helium wind tunnel. A test tunnel using helium as the working medium. Advantages are: low liquefaction temperature, stability of the gas (i.e., does not disassociate like air at high MACH numbers).

helix antenna. In electronics, an antenna used where circular polarization is required.

LOCATION OF HEAVY PRESSES

Operator	Location	Type of Press
		Extrusion:
Alcoa	Lafayette, Ind.	14,800-ton Schloemann
Kaiser Aluminum	Halethorpe, Md.	8,000-ton Loewy (2)
Harvey Aluminum	Torrance, Calif.	8,000-ton Loewy
		12,000-ton Lombard
Curtiss-Wright	Buffalo, N. Y.	12,000-ton Loewy
Dow	Madison, Ill.	14,000-ton Hidraulic
		Forging:
Alcoa	Cleveland, Ohio	35,000-ton United
		50,000-ton Mesta
Wyman-Gordon	N. Grafton, Mass.	35,000-ton Loewy
		50,000-ton Loewy

heavy water. Water in which the hydrogen of the water molecule consists entirely of the heavy hydrogen isotope of mass two (e.g., deuterium oxide, D_2O). Heavy water, in its specific

helmet cloud. A crest cloud (q.v.). Sometimes termed a *helm cloud*.

helping wind. A wind blowing from such direction as to advance the groundspeed of a vehicle.

henry. The unit of inductance (q.v.). A henry is the inductance of a coil in which a current varying at the rate of one ampere per second will induce one volt. The one volt induced does not include the electromotive force (q.v.) necessary to overcome the resistance of the circuit. The millihenry (one thousandth of a henry) is the unit used in rating coils and electromagnets.

$$1 \text{ henry} = 10^9 \text{ abhenrys} = 1000 \text{ millihenrys} = 1.113 \times 10^{-12} \text{ stathenry}$$

Henry's law. The principle that the solubility of a gas in a liquid at a constant temperature is directly proportional to the pressure.

HERMES. Research missile. Army Ordnance was cognizant service.

Design was based on Wasserfall (q.v.). Liquid propellant rocket engine.

Prime Contractor: General Electric Co.

Status: Phased out.

hermetically sealed integrating gyroscope (HIG). An integrating gyroscope (q.v.) in which viscous damping (q.v.) replaces the spring restraint of the rate gyroscope. As a result, the restraining force exerted by the viscous damper is proportional to gyroscope precession rate, instead of being proportional to precession displacement, as in a rate gyroscope (q.v.). See Fig. 9.

heterodyne. In electronics, two alternating currents of different frequency, when "mixed" in a nonlinear impedance device (e.g., a rectifier), generate a current having the sum-and-difference-frequencies, either or both of which may be selected by properly tuning or filtering the output. This phenomenon is known as *heterodyne action,* and is put to practical use in the superheterodyne radio receiver circuit. *See* intermediate frequency.

heterodyne frequency. In electronics, a separate frequency produced by the combining of two different frequencies, equal either to the difference between, or the sum of, the original two frequencies. Contrast with *beat frequency* (q.v.).

heterogeneous propellant. Solid rocket propellants where oxidant and reductant occur as separate, distinct entities. *See* composite propellant.

heterogeneous reactor. A nuclear reactor in which the fissionable material and moderator are arranged as discrete bodies (usually according to a regular pattern) of such dimensions that a nonhomogeneous medium is presented to the neutrons (e.g., homogeneous reactor, q.v.).

heterosphere. That part of the atmosphere above the homopause (50 miles) as classified by Chapman (Composition Atmosphere). See Fig. 11, page 140.

HF. High Frequency (3000-30,000 kc/sec).

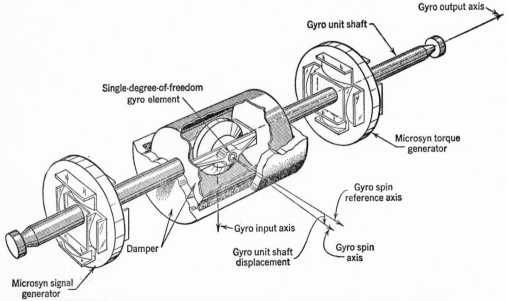

Fig. 9. Integrating gyro unit. (U.S. Air Force, *Guided Missiles,* McGraw-Hill)

HF/DF. High Frequency Direction Finding.

HGE. Ground Handling Equipment (q.v.).

HIG (gyro). Hermetically sealed Integrating Gyroscope (q.v.).

high altitude. Generally, any altitude at which height constitutes a special problem (e.g., adapting to the rarefied atmosphere, to the cold, or similar phenomena peculiar to high altitudes). High altitude also can be used to mean: (1) An action, operation, or performance carried out at a high altitude (e.g., interception, test, etc.); or (2) Equipment designed for use at high altitude (e.g., high-altitude aircraft rocket).

HIGH CARD. *See* GENIE.

high-energy fuels. Fuels with higher heat content than the hydrocarbon fuels (usually in the range of 25,000 Btu/lb). Boron compounds are frequently the basic ingredient.

high explosive (HE). Any powerful, nonatomic explosive characterized by extremely rapid detonation and having a powerful disruptive or shattering effect. Distinguish from a *low explosive*.

high fidelity. A term applied to an audio component, amplifier, or system. Ideally, it is the ability to reproduce faithfully (i.e., with a minimum of distortion) the full audio range of frequencies. While no universal standards have been set up, this range is generally agreed to be approximately 20-20,000 cycles. However, the term is often loosely applied to units whose range falls short of these limits. Also termed *hi-fi*.

high flux reactor. A nuclear reactor designed to operate with high neutron flux. Since a high flux results from a high rate of fission per unit volume, a high flux reactor operates at high power density.

high order detonation. Complete and especially rapid detonation (q.v.).

high-pass filter. In electronics, a wave filter (q.v.) having a single transmission band extending from some critical or cutoff frequency, not zero, up to infinite frequency. The value of the components may be selected as follows:

$$L = \frac{R}{4\pi f_c} \quad \text{and} \quad C = \frac{1}{4\pi f_c R}$$

The cutoff frequency is:

$$f_c = \frac{1}{4\pi\sqrt{LC}}$$

where L = inductance, henrys; C = capacitance, farads; R = load or terminating resistance, ohms

(R is approximately the same value as the input or source resistor).

high pressure area. In meteorology, a region of high atmospheric pressure (q.v.).

high Q. (1) An electrical circuit having a high ratio of reactance to effective resistance. (2) A mechanical system with low internal damping.

high-speed stall. A stall occuring when the speed becomes so great as to induce a wing or other airfoil into a critical angle of attack, resulting in turbulent separation.

high-temperature belt. A region of Earth's atmosphere at an altitude of about 35 miles. The temperature of the belt is about 80°C compared with −60°C at 15 miles and −30°C at 55 miles. The high temperature of the layer is probably associated with the presence of ozone, a form of oxygen having three, instead of two, atoms in its molecule. See Fig. 25, page 267.

high velocity aircraft rocket (HVAR). Any air-to-ground aircraft rocket specially designed for high velocities (e.g., a rocket 6 ft in length developed by the United States during World War II and nicknamed HOLY MOSES, q.v.). The HVAR was first used operationally in 1944.

hinge. *Types of, see* alpha–; lag–.

hinge axis. The axis about which a control surface (q.v.) swings.

hinge line. A line coincident with, or marking the axis about which a control surface (q.v.) swings.

hinge moment. The tendency of an aerodynamic force (q.v.) to produce motion about the hinge line (q.v.) of a control surface (q.v.). Technically, the hinge moment is the product of the aerodynamic force acting at the center of pressure (q.v.) of a control surface and the perpendicular distance from the center of pressure to the hinge line.

hit probability. The probability of hits being made on a target out of a given number of missiles directed at the target.

hoarfrost. Any white or silver frost; the normal kind of frost.

hog horn. In electronics, a microwave feed horn of special shape which allows the input energy from a waveguide (q.v.) to approach from the same direction as the horn opening.

Hohmann orbit. *See* tangential ellipse.

hold. (1) (Vernacular) The unscheduled delay or pause in the launching sequence or countdown (q.v.) of a missile or space vehicle. (2) To refrain from firing (e.g., as at a target). (3)

To hold an article or piece of equipment in order to determine its condition.

holdback. A device or mechanism whose function is to retain a missile on the launcher until it is desired to launch and until certain conditions requisite to successful launching are met. *See* launch.

holder. *See* flame holder.

hold parameter. A test situation, circumstance, or condition which requires that a testing sequence not proceed until the hold (q.v.) condition is resolved.

Holloman Air Development Center. *See* AF-MDC.

HOLY MOSES. A high velocity aircraft rocket (q.v.) developed during World War II.

Gross weight: 140 lb; propellant weight: 24 lb; payload: 52 lb; length: 6 ft; diameter: 5 in.; range: 1500 yd. Had four fins; solid propellant motor.

homer. (Vernacular) Homing guidance system (q.v.). *See also* target seeker.

homing device. Any device incorporated into a guided missile to home it on a target. Such a device may use light waves, radio waves, heat waves, etc. In the case of a moving target, a homing device may be designed either to maintain a steady pursuit course directly toward the target, or to maintain a lead angle (q.v.) while intercepting on a collision course.

homing guidance. *Types of, see* active–; interferometer–; passive–; semiactive–.

homing guidance system. A guidance system by which a missile steers itself toward a target by means of a self-contained mechanism which is activated by some distinguishing characteristic of the target. Homing guidance systems fall under one of three general types: *active homing, passive homing,* and *semiactive homing* (q.q.v.). *See also* radar illumination.

homing, radar. *See* radar homing.

homing range. The maximum distance at which a homing device (q.v.) incorporated into a vehicle becomes effective in respect to a target or to a homing station.

homogeneous armor. An alloy-steel armor, heat-treated for uniform hardness throughout. Contrast with *face-hardened armor* (q.v.).

homogeneous propellant. A solid propellant rocket fuel in which the oxidant and reductant (or a mixture of monopropellant materials) occur as a single, or colloidal entity; often termed *colloidal*. An example of this type of propellant is *ballistite* or *cordite* where nitrocellulose is colloided with another monopropellant such as nitroglycerin and other additives to provide the proper combustion characteristics and physical properties.

homogeneous reactor. A nuclear reactor in which the fissionable material and moderator (if used) are combined in a mixture such that an effectively homogeneous medium is presented to the neutrons. Such a mixture is represented either by a solution of fuel in the moderator or by discrete particles having dimensions small in comparison with the neutron mean free path (e.g., heterogeneous reactor, q.v.).

homopause. The altitude (50 miles) at which the composition of the atmosphere (q.v.) changes (Chapman nomenclature). See Fig. 11, page 140.

homosphere. That part of the atmosphere from sea level up to the homopause (50 miles) as classified by Chapman (Composition Atmosphere). See Fig. 11, page 140.

HONEST JOHN. Surface-to-surface unguided "free" ballistic missile. Army designation: M-31.

Length: 27 ft 3 in.; body diameter: 30 in. at warhead, 23 in. along motor; span of fins: 109 in.; firing weight: 5980 lb; burnout speed: MACH 1.5; maximum range: 35,000 yd. Uses a 1500-lb atomic warhead. Solid propellant rocket engine. Stability is obtained by spinning with four small rockets and canted fins.

Prime Contractor: Douglas Aircraft Co. Airframe: Douglas, Emerson Electric Manufacturing Co. Engine: Hercules Powder Co.

honeycomb. (1) (Vernacular) A grid used in certain wind tunnels to straighten airflow. (2) Structural material in which a configured filler of metal or plastic is bonded to two face sheets of (usually) sheet metal; has a high strength to weight ratio and high stiffness to weight ratio.

Hooke's law. The principle that within the proportional limit, the deformation (strain) produced is directly proportional to the force (stress) applied.

HOPI. A medium range air-to-surface missile. Navy cognizance.

Capable of carrying a hydrogen warhead (minimum weight on the order of 650 lb). Designed for carrier aircraft.

Development: Naval Ordnance Test Station; China Lake, California.

horizon. (1) The line formed by the apparent meeting of Earth and sky as observed from any point (e.g., *apparent horizon, natural hori-*

zon, visible horizon, q.q.v.). (2) A plane that runs through the eye of an observer, or a plane parallel to that plane, at right angles to the vertical (e.g., *bubble horizon, rational horizon, sensible horizon,* q.q.v.). (3) A line that indicates such a plane on a flight instrument (e.g., *artificial horizon,* q.v.).

horizon. *Types of, see* apparent–; artificial–; bubble–; celestial–; gyroscopic–; natural–; radar/radio–; rational–; sensible–; visible–.

horizontal attitude. An attitude of a vehicle in which the horizontal axes are in a plane at right angles to a plumb line.

horizontal axis. (1) Either the lateral or the longitudinal axis of a vehicle; usually in reference to both. (2) In a gyroscope (q.v.) or gyroscopic body, an axis of precession (q.v.) that lies more or less horizontal.

horizontal fin. Any fin mounted horizontally on a vehicle and extending outward on one side only, to which an elevator is attached. Sometimes termed a horizontal *stabilizer* (q.v.).

horizontal stabilizer. (1) The horizontal component of a vehicle's empennage extending on both sides of the fuselage or boom. (2) Also applied to a part of this component on only one side of the fuselage; hence, the plural form "horizontal stabilizers" and hence, references to the right or left horizontal stabilizer.

horizontal target complex. An industrial target complex consisting of potential targets related by their being in the same industry. *See* target complex.

horizon tracker. A device for establishing the vertical by precisely tracking the visible horizon simultaneously in mutually orthogonal directions.

horn. (1) A short lever attached to a control surface (q.v.), to which the control cable or other operating line or rod is attached. Often distinguished by a modifier signifying the control surface to which it is attached (e.g., elevator horn). (2) In electronics, a horn-shaped radiator sometimes used at the end of a waveguide (q.v.) or other transmission line to direct radiation in a special pattern.

horn. *Types of, see* exponential–; hog–; hypex–; inverse exponential–.

horn antenna. In electronics, the flared end of a radar waveguide (q.v.), designed for efficient radiation of energy from within the guide to free space and over a comparatively wide frequency range.

horsepower. A unit of power measurement.

1 horsepower = 2545 Btu/hr = 42.418 Btu/min = 0.70695 Btu/sec = 10.688 cal (kg/min) = 7.457 $\times$ 10^9 ergs/sec = 33,000 ft-lb/min = 550 ft-lb/sec = 1.0139 metric hp = 0.7457 kw = 745.7 watts

1 horsepower (electrical) = 2545.9 Btu/hr = 42.432 Btu/min = 0.7072 Btu/sec = 7.46 $\times$ 10^9 ergs/sec = 1,980,791 ft-lb/hr = 33,013.2 ft-lb/min = 550.22 ft-lb/sec = 746 joules/sec = 0.746 kw = 746 watts

1 horsepower-hour = 2545 Btu = 641.3 cal, kg = 1.98 $\times$ 10^6 ft-lb = 2.6845 $\times$ 10^6 joules = 0.7457 kwhr

horsepower. *Types of, see* indicated–; jet–; thrust–.

hot day. A synthetic temperature vs. altitude profile used for design. Hot day conditions cannot exist meteorologically but represent a statistical envelope and hence should be used for design but not for performance calculations. Characteristics are shown in Fig. 25, page 267.

hot firing. Actual firing of a missile propulsion system while in a captive or restrained mode.

hot line. (Vernacular) A communication channel providing instantaneous communication without switching.

hot start. The starting of a jet engine in such a manner as to cause the engine to exceed its normal operating temperature.

HOUNDDOG. Air-to-surface missile. Air Force designation for weapon system is WS 131 B and for missile itself is GAM-77.

Length: approximately 40 ft; launching weight: about 20,000 lb; cruising speed: estimated at MACH 1.7; range: 500 miles. Turbojet engine. An advanced, strategic missile of the "stand-off bomb" type. Designed to provide armament for the B-52G. It is simpler than the RASCAL (q.v.) (now operational with SAC) and has a longer range.

Prime Contractor: North American Aviation. Airframe: Missile Development Div., North American Aviation. Engine: Pratt & Whitney Aircraft Div. Guidance: Autonetics Div., North American Aviation, Inc.

hour. *Types of, see* man-hour–; zero–.

hour angle. The angular distance between two given hour circles (q.v.) on the celestial sphere (q.v.). Specifically the local hour angle (q.v.).

hour circle. Any great circle on the celestial

sphere (q.v.) passing through both celestial poles, used as a line of angular distance or of time measured eastward between the vernal equinox (q.v.) and any given celestial body through which a given hour circle passes. An hour circle is not a projection of a particular meridian on the Earth, because the hour circle moves with the movement of the body. The meridian is fixed. *See* right ascension.

HPF. Highest Probable Frequency.

HPT. High Pressure Test.

HRI. Height Range Indicator.

H-scope. A modified version of the B-scope (q.v.).

H-system. A radar navigational system by which a fix is obtained by airborne equipment which establishes the direction of, and measures the distances from, two radar beacons on the ground. The principal H-systems used are the *GEE-H, Micro-H, Rebecca-H,* and *SHORAN.*

HTV. Hypersonic Test Vehicle (q.v.).

humidity. Moisture or dampness in the atmosphere. There are two classifications of humidity: (a) absolute humidity (q.v.) and (b) relative humidity (q.v.).

hunt. (1) Of an aircraft or guided missile: (a) to make weaving motions about its median flight path, as in longitudinal or phugoid oscillation, or to vary in flight speed, as if seeking a new angle of attack, flight path, etc.; (b) to yaw repeatedly. (2) Of a radar scanner, to oscillate or swing of its own accord, owing to some flaw in the driving system. (3) Of a servo, to oscillate or swing about some null position.

hunting. The undesirable oscillation of an automatic-control system such that the controlled variable swings on both sides of the predetermined reference value without settling on it.

hurricane. A term applied to extra-tropical storms in the Atlantic Ocean. Over all oceans, near the equator, with the exception of the South Atlantic, there develop occasionally tropical cyclones which are intense vortices covering relatively large areas. As they move away from the equator, they usually intensify. All are the same type of storm. Surface pressure in a hurricane is very low at the center or eye of the storm but rises rapidly outward toward the periphery. Because of the large pressure gradient, winds are of high velocity, blowing counterclockwise in the Northern Hemisphere and clockwise south of the equator.

HVAP. High Velocity Armor-Piercing rocket.

HVAR. High Velocity Aircraft Rocket (q.v.).

H-vector. The vector representing the magnetic component of an electromagnetic field. *See E-*vector.

hybrid junction. Waveguide arrangement with four branches which, when the branches are properly terminated, has the property that energy can be transferred from any one branch into only two of the remaining three. In common usage, this energy is equally divided between the two branches.

hybrid liquid-stolid rocket. (1) A solid propellant rocket (q.v.) employing either an auxiliary liquid propellant or some other working fluid (e.g., air). (2) A self-igniting rocket using 90% peroxide and polyethylene as a fuel combination.

hydraulics. The science of the dynamics and statics of liquids, particularly water, in connection with engineering problems. *See* mechanics.

hydrazine (N_2H_4). A liquid rocket propellant *fuel.* See Table 3, page 157.

hydrazine hydrate ($N_2H_4 \cdot H_2O$). A liquid rocket propellant *fuel.*

hydrodynamics. The study of the dynamics of fluid motion, especially the steady motions of an incompressible, inviscid fluid. *See* mechanics.

hydrogen (H_2). A liquid rocket propellant *fuel.* See Table 3, page 157.

hydrogen peroxide (H_2O_2). A liquid rocket propellant *oxidizer.*

hydromatic. Pertaining to hydraulically operating mechanisms that function automatically.

hydrosphere. The aqueous envelope of a planet.

hydrostatic fuze. A fuze (q.v.) that functions under the influence of water pressure. It may be set to explode at a predetermined depth.

hydrostatics. A branch of physics dealing with the pressure and equilibrium of liquids, or of bodies immersed in liquids. *See* mechanics.

hygrometer. An instrument for measuring and indicating either the relative humidity or the dew point of the air. *See* hair hygrometer; psychrometer.

hygroscopicity. The tendency of a substance to absorb moisture; an undesirable quality in explosives.

hyperbolic guidance. The guidance or control of a guided missile (q.v.) in which the difference in the time delay of radio signals transmitted simultaneously from two ground stations, arriving at the missile at different time intervals, controls the position of the missile. This system is based upon the geometric theorem that the locus of all points of fixed difference in distance from two base points is a hyperbola.

hyperbolic navigation. A general method for determining lines of position by measuring the difference in distance of the navigator or navigating apparatus from two or more stations of known position. The difference in distance is determined by measuring the difference in time of arrival of signals transmitted from two or more stations. Although a great variety of signaling methods are theoretically possible, only radio waves are now commonly used in hyperbolic navigation. One system, using continuous wave signals, is known as DECCA. LORAN and GEE are systems using signals transmitted as pulses. One transmitting station is the *master station*, with the other stations or station, separated from 75 miles to 1200 miles, being *slave stations*. The cycle of transmission always begins at the master station and the signal travels out in all directions. The arrival of the master signal at the slave station "triggers off" the slave which, in turn, transmits a signal. Points of constant difference in time of arrival of the two or more signals will fall on hyperbolas, with the transmitters at the foci. The accuracy of the line of position which can be established by the navigator or the navigating apparatus varies from 200 yards to 2 miles depending upon the distance and orientation of the observer or the receiver from the base line between stations and upon the type of system and equipment used. Although the navigator's equipment differs in details for GEE, DECCA, and LORAN, the fundamental characteristics are all the same. In the DECCA and GEE systems, the master station operates in conjunction with two or more slave stations. In the LORAN system, the master station operates with one slave station. SHORAN is a short-range system.

Systems now in use: LORAN, GEE, CYTAC, SHORAN, and LORAC use pulsed radio energy; DECCA uses CW radio energy.

hyperbolic trajectory. The path of a body if the speed, and therefore the energy, exceeds escape energy. The body describes a hyperbolic curve with the Earth at the focus, and will never return.

hypergolic. Self-igniting.

hypergolic propellant. A propellant system which is capable of spontaneous ignition or contact. Also termed *auto-igniting propellant.*

hypersonic. (1) Aerodynamic flow at high supersonic velocities, of the order of $M = 5$ or greater. (2) Velocities at which time of missile passage is of the same order as *relaxation time;* that is, the time for gas molecules to reach equilibrium after sudden change in conditions. In such a domain, gases must be treated as discrete particles rather than as a continuum. Measurements of relaxation times of gases are incomplete, but there are indications that MACH numbers of the order of ten must be regarded as hypersonic. Velocities that are not hypersonic at sea level may become so at high altitude, as relaxation times will be longest where densities are relatively low.

hypersonic test vehicle (HTV). High-speed research vehicle in connection with Inter-Continental Ballistic Missile programs.

Two-stage missile using solid fuel; 1st stage: 7 rockets, 5 ft long, 9 in. diameter fired simultaneously. 2nd stage: 4 rockets, 5 ft long, 6 in. diameter fired simultaneously. 3rd stage: 2-ft nose cone. Can accelerate a test vehicle to MACH 7 in 2 sec. Approximately 6 sec after firing of 2nd stage, the fins are blown off the nose cone so that it starts to tumble and returns to Earth at approximately 100 mph. Total length: 12 ft; both stages have triangular fins of different size. Development: Aerophysics Laboratory and Curtiss-Wright Corp.

hypex horn. An acoustic horn designed to give accentuated response at low frequencies.

hysteresis. In general, the phenomenon exhibited by a system whose state depends on its previous history. This term usually refers to *magnetic hysteresis,* of importance in alternating-current machinery. When a ferromagnetic material (e.g., iron) is placed in a magnetic field, a certain amount of energy is involved in bringing about its magnetization. If the field is a rapidly alternating one, the material may become noticeably warm. It appears that the repeated changes of orientation in whatever it is within the substance that responds to the reversals of field are opposed by something like viscous friction. *Electric hysteresis* is a somewhat analogous phenomenon exhibited by dielectrics (q.v.) in the electric field, and gives rise to heating in AC condensers. Some solids exhibit what is termed *elastic hysteresis,* in which the variables corresponding to H and B in the magnetic case are the stress and the strain or deformation. Elastic bodies such as metals operating at stresses below the proportional limit also undergo hysteresis.

hysteresis distortion. The distortion of voltage and/or current waveforms in circuits containing magnetic components, which is caused by the nonlinear hysteresis effect.

hysteresis energy. The energy used per cycle of operation to overcome the effect of hysteresis (q.v.).

hysteresis error. The error present when an instrument or circuit element is experiencing the hysteresis effect.

hysteresis, gyroscope torquer. *See* gyroscope torquer hysteresis.

hysteresis heating. The temperature rise caused by the expenditure of hysteresis energy (q.v.).

hysteresis loss. In electronics, energy loss in a magnetic substance exposed to a constantly changing magnetic field. The loss is due to internal friction, and appears as heat. It is proportional to the area enclosed in the hysteresis loop.

I

I_{sp}. *See* specific impulse; ideal specific impulse.

IAD. International Astrophysical Decade (q.v.).

I & M. Installation and Maintenance.

IAS. (1) Institute of Aeronautical Sciences (q.v.). (2) Indicated Airspeed.

IBDA. Indirect Bomb Damage Assessment (q.v.).

ICAO. International Civil Aviation Organization.

ICAO atmosphere. A standard atmosphere promulgated by the International Civil Aviation Organization. This standard atmosphere includes characteristics (e.g., properties, composition, etc.) from sea level to 100,000 ft (the Minzner extension from 65 to 100,000 ft). *See* Fig. 25, page 267.

ICAO day. A standard day (q.v.) based on the ICAO standard atmosphere. See Fig. 25, page 267.

ICAO phonetic alphabet.

A	Alpha	G	Golf	N	November	T	Tango
B	Bravo	H	Hotel	O	Oscar	U	Uniform
C	Charlie	I	India	P	Papa	V	Victor
D	Delta	J	Juliet	Q	Quebec	W	Whiskey
E	Echo	K	Kilo	R	Romeo	X	Xray
F	Foxtrot	L	Lima	S	Sierra	Y	Yankee
		M	Mike			Z	Zulu

ICBM. InterContinental Ballistic Missile (q.v.).

ice. *Types of, see* clear–; granular–; rime–.

icecap. A perennial tract of snow and ice covering the land (e.g., the Greenland Icecap). This term is not properly applied to the ice covering the North Pole.

ice-crystal clouds. At temperatures below about 15°F water vapor changes to solid water directly without the intermediate liquid-water stage. Cloud particles form directly on sublimation nuclei as ice crystals, and such clouds are then composed of ice-crystal particles. Cirro-form clouds are of the ice-crystal group.

ice fog. A radiation fog consisting of ice crystals, formed under conditions of clear skies, very low temperature, and little or no wind. Sometimes termed *frost fog* (q.v.).

ice nucleus. Any minute particle around which an ice crystal forms.

ICFATCMUTAL. "Individual is cleared for access to classified material up to and including."

icing. (1) The act or process of atmospheric moisture freezing upon the surfaces of a vehicle; the condition in which this phenomenon takes place. (2) The minimum level or altitude at which ice forms on a vehicle under given conditions.

iconoscope. A cathode-ray tube for picking up and televising a scene, employing a photosensitive plate and electron gun that scans the image.

ICUS. Inside Continental United States.

ICW. Interrupted Continuous Wave (q.v.).

ideal rocket. A rocket motor or rocket engine that would have a velocity equal to the velocity of its exhaust jet gases; assumed as a criterion in rocket design.

ideal (or theoretical) specific impulse (I'_{sp}). The maximum realizable impulse obtainable from a given combination of propellants; calculated from thermo-chemical relations. The difference between the ideal and measured specific impulse (I_{sp}) is due to heat losses, incomplete combustion of propellants, flow losses, and variations in back pressure. I_{sp} usually ranges from 0.93 to 0.98 of I'_{sp}.

$$I'_{sp} = \frac{C'_f}{c'_w} = 6.93\lambda \sqrt{\frac{T_c}{M}} \sqrt{\frac{2k}{k-1}} (Z_t)$$

where M = molecular weight of gases; k = specific heat of gases; $Z_t = 1 - (P_a/P_c)^{k-1/k}$; P_a = ambient pressure, lb/sq in.; P_c = chamber pressure, lb/sq in.; T_c = combustion temperature, °R; λ = divergence coefficient (see Fig. 6, page 76); C'_f = ideal thrust coefficient; c'_w = ideal weight flow coefficient.

identification. *Types of, see* –, friend or foe; target–.

identification, friend or foe (IFF). A method of automatic identification of an aircraft or ship. A coded challenging transmission received by a correctly adjusted receiver in a friendly vessel causes the automatic transmission of an identification signal usually on another frequency.

identification switch. In telemetering, a key switch used to identify a data channel by short circuiting or opening the input galvanometer leads.

IF. Intermediate Frequency (q.v.).

IFB. Invitation For Bid.

IFF. Identification, Friend or Foe (q.v.).

IFLTT. Intermediate Focal Length Tracking Telescope (q.v.).

IFRB. International Frequency Registration Board.

IFT. In-Flight Test.

igloo. (Vernacular) A dome-shaped or rounded structure, usually made of reinforced concrete and earth, normally used for the storage of explosives or rockets.

igniter. A device used to initiate burning of a fuel mixture or a propellant in a ramjet (q.v.) or rocket combustion chamber. A pilot-burner in a ramjet may serve the same purpose.

igniter, pyrogen. See pyrogen igniter.

ignition delay. The time lag between introduction of fuel into the combustion chamber of a jet or rocket engine and the start of combustion.

ignition, self-piloting. See self-piloting ignition.

ignition system. The system associated with rocket or jet engines which provides for igniting the propellant.

IGOR. Intercept Ground Optical Recorders (q.v.).

IGS. Inertial Guidance System (q.v.).

IGY. International Geophysical Year (q.v.).

IIP. Instantaneous Impact Prediction (q.v.).

IJAJ. Intentional Jitter AntiJam.

IJJU. Intentional Jitter Jamming Unit.

illumination. See radar illumination.

IM. Interceptor Missile (q.v.).

IM 70. Air Force/Army designation for the surface ship-to-air guided missile termed TALOS (q.v.).

IM-99 and IM-99B. Air Force designation for the surface-to-air missile termed BOMARC (q.v.).

image antenna. An imaginary antenna assumed, for mathematical purposes, to be located below the surface directly beneath a real antenna. The image antenna is a mirror of the actual antenna. Waves transmitted by the real antenna are reflected from a depth equal to the height of the antenna.

image point. With an airburst atomic bomb, a hypothetical point beneath the surface of the Earth, equal in depth to the height of the exploding bomb. (The image point is a source of radiating reflected shock.)

image rejection. The characteristic of a receiving system to attenuate signals which are displaced from the local oscillator frequency by the proper amount to generate an IF (q.v.) signal but appear on the wrong side of the local oscillator frequency.

imitative deception. The transmission of messages in the enemy's communication channels with the intention of deceiving the enemy.

IMO. International Meteorological Organization.

impact area. (1) The area in which a missile and/or its payload strikes the surface of the Earth. The *intended impact area* is the target area. (2) The area along the line-of-flight (q.v.) where jettisoned parts will strike the surface of the Earth after separation from a missile at staging (q.v.) (e.g., stage-one impact area; booster rocket impact area).

impact area, booster. See booster impact area.

impact detector. A device that generates a voltage upon impact with a surface. It is generally used to fire a warhead.

impact fuze. A fuze, e.g., for a bomb, in which the action is initiated by the force of impact. Sometimes termed a *contact fuze* (q.v.).

impact point. (1) A point along the line-of-flight (q.v.) where jettisoned parts will strike the surface of the Earth or sea after stage separation. (2) The location on the Earth where a missile strikes.

impact point, nominal. See nominal impact point.

impact predictor. A scheme or mechanism for continuously estimating the coordinates of a missile impact point (q.v.), usually based on present position information obtained by optical or electronic tracking. Equations are solved and trajectories and time-to-go are estimated by ground computers. The information may be used by the range safety officer or for an early assessment of performance to assist in making a decision for firing the next round.

impact pressure. The pressure existing when a moving stream of fluid strikes a surface which brings part of the fluid abruptly to rest. The recovered pressure is roughly equivalent to the stagnation pressure for subsonic flow. See Table 1, page 81.

impedance. The complex ratio of a forcelike

quantity (force, pressure, voltage, temperature, or electric field strength) to a related velocity-like quantity (velocity, volume velocity, current, heat flow, or magnetic field strength). The terms and definitions under the term *impedance* pertain to single-frequency quantities in the steady state, and to systems whose properties are independent of the magnitudes of these quantities. These quantities can be represented mathematically by complex exponential functions of time. Under these conditions the factors involving time cancel out in the ratios called for, leaving complex numbers independent of time. Solutions based on complex exponential functions under these conditions give the solution for real sinusoidal oscillations. Because of the similarity of electrical, mechanical, and acoustical transmission theory, the same terminology is used in the three cases. Where confusion is likely to occur, the proper term should be prefixed to the general term (e.g., acoustic transfer impedance); i.e., while acoustics is a branch of mechanics, it is found convenient to distinguish an acoustic system from a mechanical one whenever elastic wave motion is an essential feature. While a strict application of the impedance concept implies the restrictions given above, it is common practice to extend the term impedance to situations involving nonsinusoidal quantities or nonlinear systems. Such extensions should be accompanied by an explanatory statement.

The symbol for impedance is Z and the *ohm* is the unit.

$$Z = \sqrt{R^2 + X^2}$$

where R = resistance of the circuit; X = reactance of the circuit.

impedance. *Types of, see* acoustical–; characteristic–; electrical–; input–; matching–; mechanical rectilineal–; mechanical rotational–; output–; point–; rotational–; source–; terminal–.

impedance match. The condition existing when two coupled circuits are so adjusted that their impedances will provide for some optimum performance (e.g., maximum power transfer, minimum distortion, etc.).

impedance pads matched. A variable level control design to match both input and output impedances regardless of the setting.

impinging injector. A liquid rocket engine injector in which the oxidizer and fuel are mixed by the intersection of jet streams at a predetermined point.

implosion. A sudden inward burst of particles

or gases that brings pressure upon the center of something. *See* collapse.

improvement threshold. In angle-modulation systems, the condition of unity for the ratio of peak carrier voltage to peak noise voltage, after selection and before any nonlinear process such as amplitude limiting and detection.

impulse. (1) A force lasting over a comparatively short period of time. (2) In specific senses: (a) a sudden and brief rise of current or voltage in a circuit; (b) the force exerted by a shock wave (q.v.) from an explosion; (c) the area under the thrust time curve for jet or rocket engines; for constant thrust, the product of thrust and time (units: lb/sec); (d) the detonative force delivered by a primer when fired. (3) A pulse of electronic energy. (4) A vector quantity defined by the time integral of the force F acting on a particle over a finite interval, e.g.:

$$\int_{t_1}^{t_2} F \, dt$$

for the interval from t_1 to t_2. The impulse-momentum theorem states that the impulse equals the change in momentum experienced by a particle during the corresponding time interval.

impulse. *Types of, see* air specific–; effective–; fuel specific–; ideal specific–; over-all specific–; specific–; volume–.

impulse excitation. A method of producing oscillator current in a circuit in which the duration of the impressed voltage is relatively short compared with the duration of the current produced.

impulse generator. A device for producing very short pulses of high voltage, usually by charging capacitors in parallel and discharging them in series.

impulse maneuver. *See* maneuver.

impulse noise. Noise characterized by transient disturbances separated in time by quiescent intervals. The frequency spectrum (q.v.) of these disturbances must be substantially uniform over the useful pass band of the transmission system.

impulse-reaction turbine. A turbine which employs the principles of both the impulse and reaction systems. Normally the reaction occurs in increasing effect towards the rotor blade tips, and no reaction occurs at the blade roots.

impulse turbine. A turbine which imparts energy by the use of a high-velocity low-pressure gas flow through the rotor blades.

impulse-weight ratio. In rocketry, the ratio of

total impulse to takeoff weight; a criterion of the excellence of the overall design of the complete rocket.

$$R_{I/W} = \frac{I}{W_o}$$

IMU. (1) Inertial Measurement Unit (q.v.). (2) Interference mockup.

inch. A unit of length measurement.

1 inch = 2.5400 cm = $\frac{1}{12}$ ft = 1000 mils = $\frac{1}{36}$ yd

1 inch of mercury at 32°F
= 0.03342 atm. = 3.38639 × 10⁴ dynes/sq cm = 1.13299 ft of water at 39.2°F = 345.31 kg/ sq meter = 70.727 lb/sq ft = 0.49116 lb/sq in.

1 inch of water at 39.2°F
= 0.0024583 atm. = 2490.8 dynes/sq cm = 0.07355 in. of mercury at 32°F = 5.2022 lb/ sq ft = 0.036126 lb/sq in.

incompressible flow. In aerodynamics, a flow of air around a moving body, with negligible change in pressure and density from its free-air state. It occurs around vehicles at relatively low speeds.

incremental frequency shift. A method of superimposing incremental intelligence upon another intelligence by shifting the center frequency of an oscillator by a predetermined amount. Sometimes referred to as *on-off measurement*.

independent component failure. A malfunction of a component which does not affect the probability of vital failure of another component.

independent components. In reliability studies, those components whose reliability is independent of the remainder of the system (e.g., no functional or environmental interaction).

indeterminate structure. A statically indeterminate structure is one which cannot be solved by the equations for static equilibrium. These equations state that the components of the forces acting on a body, taken in any two directions, must be equal to zero and that the sum of the moments of these same forces, taken around any moment center, must equal zero. If the axial stresses in the members of a structure are changed by altering the length of one of the members a very small amount, the structure is classified as indeterminate. When there are more *reactions* than equations for static equilibrium, the structure is externally indeterminate. After these reactions have been calculated the stresses in the members of the structure become statically determinate unless

internally indeterminate, that is, contain redundant members. In general, statically indeterminate structures can be analyzed by methods such as the energy theory or the deflection theory, although some are so complicated that the analyst must resort to experimental methods. The analysis of any indeterminate structure requires a knowledge of the size, shape, and elastic properties of the individual members.

index. *Types of, see* modulation–; performance–; reliability–.

indicated horsepower. The total horsepower developed by an engine, equal to the friction horsepower plus the brake horsepower, as indicated by appropriate calculations.

indicator. *Types of, see* aspect–; ceiling-height–; cathode-ray–; function–; height-range–; master–; moving target–; plan position–; present position–.

indicial admittance. The response of a physical system to a unit step function.

indirect bomb damage assessment (IBDA). The means, usually independent of the guidance system (q.v.), for confirming the detonation of a nuclear explosion, its position with respect to the target and the resulting damage.

indirect manhours. The hours expended on auxiliary work done in support of manufacturing, product support, and engineering; i.e., labor in performance of essential services, management and/or administration, that is not identifiable with the product.

induced angle of attack. The difference between the actual angle of attack (q.v.) and the angle of attack for infinite aspect ratio (q.v.) of an airfoil for the same lift coefficient (q.v.).

induced drag. That part of the total drag on a vehicle induced by the airflow about the lifting surfaces. The airflow that causes lift causes drag in proportion to the square of the lift.

induced environment. A classification comprising environments caused by the operation, location, and/or previous environmental state of a missile; it includes vibration, shock, aerodynamic heating, erosion (in flight), electromagnetic effects, force.

induced roll. Missile roll motions resulting from induced rolling moments (q.v.).

induced rolling moments. The moments resulting from aerodynamic forces which act to roll a missile during flight at angles of attack (q.v.) other than zero. They are encountered under conditions of large lateral accelerations, particularly when large angles of attack are used. These induced moments may be attributed to: (a) wing tip effects; (b) wing root effects; (c) separation effects on body and wing surfaces; (d) sweepback effects; (e) downwash effects or interference on the tail surface. In general, anything which affects the symmetry of the missile during a lateral maneuver at large angles of attack is apt to produce rolling moments.

inductance. (1) That property of an electric circuit or of two neighboring circuits which determines the electromotive force induced in one of the circuits by a change of current in either of them. (2) In an electrical system, that circuit element which opposes a change in current. The unit is the *abhenry*.

inductance. *Types of, see* mutual–; self–.

inductance-controlled oscillator. An oscillator whose frequency is controlled, within limits, by a variable inductance (e.g., variable reluctance pickups; accelerometers, dynamometers, pressure pickups, etc.).

induction. An electromotive force (q.v.) is induced in any conductor in a magnetic field when the intensity or direction of the magnetic field is changed. If the conductor forms a closed circuit, an induced current is produced.

inductive feedback. In electronics, feedback of energy from the plate circuit of a vacuum tube to the grid circuit through an inductance or by means of inductive coupling.

inductive reactance. Reactance due to the inductance of a coil or other part in an alternating-current circuit. Inductive reactance is measured in *ohms*, and is equal to the inductance in *henrys* multiplied by the frequency in *cycles*, times the number 2π. Inductive reactance therefore increases with frequency.

inductor or pickup inductor. Consists of a coil winding on a laminated core. As used in pickups (q.v.) the inductor is variable and uses a pad of high-permeability alloy to vary the inductance. The position of the pad determines the total air gap, thereby controlling the reluctance of the magnetic path which in turn controls the inductance of the coil.

inertance. In an acoustical system, that element that opposes a change in volume current; related to acoustical inertial energy. The unit is the *gram per centimeter to the fourth power*.

inert explosive. An explosive which can withstand severe environmental and handling loads without danger of spontaneous detonation.

inertia. A measure of the reluctance of a body to change its translational and rotational ve-

locities (including changes from zero). For transitional motion, inertia and mass are equivalent.

inertia. *Types of, see* moment of–; thermal–.

inertia fuze. A kind of impact fuze (q.v.) that functions by inertial force. Upon impact of the projectile to which an inertia fuze is attached, either a striker will fly forward against a primer or detonator, or the primer or detonator will move forward against a fixed firing pin.

inertial activator. A mechanical device employing springs that absorb energy from a velocity change and release this energy to activate a circuit.

inertial Cartesian coordinates. Three mutually perpendicular coordinate axes (X, Y, Z), located in inertial space; X is positive to the east, Y is positive to the north, and Z is positive up (altitude).

inertial components. A generic term for gyroscopes and accelerometers used in inertial guidance systems (q.v.).

inertial force. The force produced by the reaction of a body to an accelerating force, equal in magnitude and opposite in direction to the accelerating force. Inertial force endures only so long as the accelerating force endures.

inertial gravitational guidance system. A system which is independent of information other than gravitational effects, obtained from outside a missile. The sensitive elements of the system make use of the principle of Newton's second law of motion.

inertial guidance. An onboard guidance system (q.v.) for missiles and satellite vehicles where gyroscopes, accelerometers, and possibly a gyroscope-stabilized platform (q.q.v.) satisfy guidance requirements without use of any ground-located components. This system is jam-proof and entirely automatic, following a predetermined trajectory. The sensitive elements of the system make use of the principle of Newton's second law of motion. See Fig. 10, page 134 and Fig. 24, page 266.

inertial guidance system (IGS). A dead-reckoning missile guidance system that employs sensitive elements which respond to the Earth's gravitational field and to inertial effects in accordance with the Newtonian laws of motion. The system therefore is not dependent on information obtained from transmitters outside the missile. See Fig. 10, page 134.

inertial measurement unit (IMU). A gimbal system used in inertial guidance systems (q.v.), or other applications requiring a stable refer-

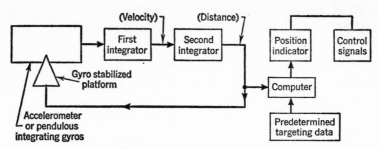

Fig. 10. Schematic of inertial guidance system.

ence, on which are mounted gyroscopes for orientation and accelerometers or velocity meters for measuring purposes. See Fig. 24, page 266.

inertial navigation system. A system which is functionally the same as inertial guidance (q.v.) except as to end use. It is essentially a form of dead-reckoning device. This means that the geographic position (latitude and longitude or equivalent) of both the starting point and destination must be known and must be set into the equipment. An inertial navigation system usually requires two or three accelerometers to sense aircraft/missile motion in the north-south direction, east-west direction, and in some applications, in the vertical direction.

inertial space. An assumed stationary frame of reference. A nonrotating set of coordinates in space, relative to which the trajectory of a space vehicle or long-range missile is calculated.

inertial system. A system which is able to determine the displacement of its carrying vehicle from its starting point by measuring the accelerations of the vehicle relative to the Earth.

inertial velocity meter. *See* velocity meter.

infantry mil. *See* mil.

infect. To sow the air above an area with a confusion reflector (q.v.) such as chaff.

inferior planets. Mercury and Venus, between the Earth and the Sun. *See* superior planets.

inflight calibration. A method of supplying an accurate, highly stable calibrating voltage during flight to amplifiers, oscillators, etc., in order to periodically calibrate telemetering (or other) equipment. In this way environmental effects on the electronic components are held to a minimum. The accuracy of the system is then a function of the stability of the calibrating signal.

inflight guidance system. *See* onboard guidance system.

influence coefficients. Constants of proportionality which permit determination of a given parameter at one point when certain related characteristics are known at another point.

influence fuze. A proximity fuze (q.v.).

influence line. Usually pertains to a particular section of a structural beam, and is a curve so drawn that its ordinate at any point represents the value of the reaction, vertical shear, bending moment, or deflection produced at the particular section by a unit load applied at the point where the ordinate is measured. An influence line may be used to show the effect of load position on any quantity dependent thereon, such as the stress in a given truss member, the deflection of a truss, the twisting moment in a shaft, etc.

information. *Types of, see* qualitative personnel requirements–; strategic–.

information amplifier. An amplifier serving to amplify, with negligible distortion, an input-information wave train to usable amplitudes.

information channel. *See* telemeter channel.

information gate. A gate (q.v.) which passes only the information contained on one intelligence or information channel of a data transmission system.

information pulse. As applied to a commutated data transmission system, an individual sample of a commutated intelligence. Compare with *commutator switch* (q.v.).

information theory. The application of statistics and probability theory to communication engineering.

infrared. A portion of the electromagnetic spectrum in which the wavelength is between 0.3×10^{-5} cm and 7.6×10^{-5} cm. It falls between the visible light and the microwave regions of the spectrum. See Fig. 8, page 105.

infrared frequency. In the electromagnetic spectrum, the range of invisible radiation frequencies which adjoins the visible red spectrum and extends to microwave radio frequencies.

infrasonic. Having a frequency below the audible range. Frequencies above the audible range are termed *ultrasonic* or *supersonic* (q.v.).

inhabited space vehicle. *See* space vehicle.

inherent stability. In aerodynamics, stability of a missile owing solely to the disposition and arrangement of its fixed parts; i.e., that property which causes the missile, when disturbed, to return to its normal attitude of flight without the use of the control system or the interposition of any mechanical device.

inhibitor. (1) An inert material surrounding a solid propellant rocket grain to limit burning except on desired surfaces. (2) A substance added to certain propellants to reduce hygroscopicity or the tendency to absorb moisture.

initial failure. A failure (q.v.) which occurs when a component is defective at the time it is required to operate. Can be the result of design errors, manufacturing errors, storage, assembly, handling, transportation, etc.

initial mass. The mass of a rocket missile at the beginning of its flight.

initial operational capability (IOC). A term used to describe, comprehensively, the initial adequacy of a weapon system to be used in the field operationally but not necessarily having operational characteristics.

initial velocity. The velocity of a rocket, relative to the launcher, immediately after leaving the launcher.

initiation. The application of a fuze signal to the first elements of an explosive train (q.v.).

initiator. A sensitive explosive that detonates to initiate the action in an explosive train (q.v.). An explosive such as lead azide, combining the properties of sensitivity, low energy, and low brisance is commonly used as an initiator.

injection pressure. The pressure difference between the total pressure at the propellant outlet orifice and the pressure in the combustion chamber of a liquid rocket engine.

injector. In liquid rocket engines, the device which functions to direct, mix, and atomize the propellants to provide a proper mixture for combustion.

injector. *Types of, see* impinging–; non-impinging–; spray–.

injuries. *See* mechanical injuries.

inlet (diffuser). The intake or scoop used to supply air to a ramjet or turbojet diffuser by converting the kinetic energy of the air approaching the inlet to a high pressure by slowing the air to a subsonic speed in an efficient manner. See Fig. 5, page 73.

innage. (1) The amount of a liquid or other bulk commodity left in a container after transportation or storage. (2) The amount of fuel left in a fuel tank.

inner body. Any closed body located in a ramjet, or other duct, around which the air taken into the diffuser or engine must flow. See Fig. 15, page 227.

inner cone. A cone-shaped part in the tail pipe of a turbojet engine (q.v.), just aft of the turbine wheel, forming part of the exhaust cone.

inner liner. The inner shell of a combustion chamber in certain jet engines, inserted to diffuse the compressed air in the chamber and maintain an efficient flame pattern. Also termed *burner basket, flame holder,* or *flame tube.*

inner loop. In guided missile control systems, the feedback loop consisting of the control system and missile aerodynamics as contrasted to the outer loop which includes the external-guidance system dynamics. See Fig. 3, page 49.

input. (1) In electricity, the power or energy delivered to an electrical or electronic device. (2) In maintenance or assembly, the quantity of unrepaired or unassembled articles that come in. (3) (Vernacular) Any idea or contribution offered on a problem under consideration.

input impedance. The impedance (q.v.) presented by a circuit when looking at it through its input terminals; i.e., the impedance seen by the preceding circuit.

insertion loss. The loss of energy attributed to the insertion, between two circuits, of another circuit. Sometimes expressed as db or per cent loss; e.g.:

$$\text{db loss} = 20 \log \frac{E \text{ input} - E \text{ output}}{E \text{ input}}$$

where E = voltage.

insertion power gain of an electric transducer. The ratio of (1) the power developed in the external termination of the output with the transducer inserted between generator and output termination to (2) the power developed in the external termination of the output with the generator connected directly to the output termination.

insertion voltage of an electric transducer. The complex ratio of (1) the alternating component of voltage across the external termination of the output with the transducer inserted between the generator and the output termination to (2) the voltage across the external termination of the output when the generator is connected directly to the output termination.

inspection. Examination of an item to determine compliance with established standards and/or specifications.

inspection. *Types of, see* development engineering–; periodic–; preliminary engineering–; visual–.

inspection and repair as necessary (IRAN). A term used to identify the maintenance work under which depot-level activities inspect and repair as necessary, as contrasted with complete disassembly and overhaul.

instability. (1) In meteorology, a condition that exists in the atmosphere when air is unquiet and easily displaced mechanically, causing air currents. Instability exists when the lapse rate is greater than the adiabatic rate (q.v.), causing rising air to accelerate. *See* conditional instability; convective instability. (2) In missiles, a dynamic condition of flight in which the forces are destabilizing. *See* unstable oscillations.

instability. *Types of, see* conditional–; convective–; potential–; thermal–.

instability line. Synonymous with squall line (q.v.).

installation. A separately located defined area of real property in which an armed service exercises real property interest or has jurisdiction over real property. Real property, as used here, includes lands and interest therein, buildings and structures, utility systems, runways, and installed equipment. Installation is synonymous with Air Force Base, Naval Base, etc.

installations concept. A broad over-all statement of the installations operation to be performed. It contains an outline of the objectives, assumptions, criteria, and capabilities needed in the preparation of the installations plan (q.v.).

installations plan. The projected method of obtaining the goals prescribed in the installations concept (q.v.). The plan is developed from the guidance contained in the concept.

installed equipment. Nonexpendable or expendable recoverable equipment permanently attached to or integrated into real property in such a manner that it cannot be removed without causing substantial physical damage or change to the real property.

instantaneous fuze. A superquick fuze (q.v.).

instantaneous impact prediction (IIP). The prediction of the anticipated impact point of a missile or reentry body by means of a ground-based computer using appropriate tracking data. The impact location is continuously predicted and the data are used for range safety.

instantaneous sound pressure. *See* sound (acoustomotive) pressure.

Institute of the Aeronautical Sciences (IAS). A United States nongovernment organization founded in 1932 for advancing and coordinating research in the arts, sciences, and techniques applied to aviation, for disseminating aeronautical knowledge, and furthering the proficiency and prestige of its members in the aeronautical professions.

instrument. *Types of, see* end–; recording optical tracking–.

instrumental space vehicle. *See* space vehicle.

instrumentation. Devices used to gather quantitative data on a guided missile system (q.v.) or its components while these are operating or being tested.

instrumentation. *Types of, see* airborne–; photogrammetric–; range–.

instrumentation console. The console, housed in the control building, which controls all ground instrumentation equipment, including the central timing system.

instrumentation section. On research and development missiles, a section of the missile housing the telemetering equipment, range safety receiver, tracking responder, antenna, power supply, and signal conditioners.

insulating strength. *See* dielectric strength.

intake. *Types of, see* "cookie-cutter"–; multiple shock–.

integrated weapon system training (IWST). The consolidated instructional period in which personnel qualified in their respective specialties are trained to perform simultaneous and sequential duties and tasks involved in the accomplishment of an assigned operation or set of related operations. Detailed instruction is given all members of a team in performing required time-phased sequential duties and tasks.

integrating accelerometer. A device whose output signals are proportional to vehicle velocity or distance traveled (depending on number of integrations) instead of acceleration.

integrating circuit. A circuit whose output voltage is proportional to the product of the instantaneous applied input voltages and their duration. Such circuits are made to give outputs proportional to input frequency and amplitude.

integrating contractor. A contractor to a military service, usually an associate contractor (q.v.), to whom the service has assigned the additional task of resolving interface (q.v.) considerations to insure proper operation and timely development of a complete weapon system (q.v.).

integrating gyroscope. An adaptation of the familiar rate gyroscope (q.v.); both have only a single degree of freedom. The restraining force exerted by the viscous damping is proportional to the gyroscope precession *rate* instead of the displacement. *See* HIG (gyro).

integrating (pendulous) accelerometer gyroscope. A gyroscope capable of sensing and integrating a linear acceleration to obtain the resultant velocity. It is unsymmetrically suspended so that acceleration produces a precession force resulting in an angular displacement of the gyroscope axis proportional to the time integral of the acceleration.

integration. *See* pseudo integration.

intelligence. Information or data to be transmitted or telemetered. (Compare with modulation.) The stimulus applied to pickups.

intelligence, frequency. *See* frequency intelligence.

intensity. *See* field intensity.

intercept. *Types of, see* altitude–; celestial–.

intercept ground optical recorder (IGOR). A long focal length telescopic camera mounted on a Mk 63 gun carriage used for missile test range instrumentation. It is usually fitted with a 35-mm or a Mitchell camera (q.v.). The primary telescope has an 18 in. diameter and 108 in. focal length. Range coverage up to 110,000 ft is attainable.

interceptor lead-angle. The angle between the flight path of an interceptor on a collision course with a target and the interconnecting line-of-sight.

interceptor missile (IM). A guided missile used to intercept enemy aircraft.

interchangeability. *Complete interchangeability:* the ability to interchange without restriction, like equipment or portions thereof in manufacture, maintenance, or operation. *Selected interchangeability:* when all components manufactured to the same general specifications are not completely interchangeable. When this is the case the component parts are often placed in classes so that there will be complete interchangeability in each class.

intercontinental ballistic missile (ICBM). A missile flying a ballistic trajectory (q.v.) after

guided powered flight, usually at velocities in excess of 20,000 fps and capable of operating over ranges in excess of 3500 nautical miles. Common design features are multiple stages (q.v.) and a detachable payload or reentry body (q.v.). Types include: ATLAS, MINUTEMAN, TITAN (q.q.v.).

interface. (1) The boundary (electrical, mechanical, performance, or other) between two systems or components; the coupling or interdependence of systems or elements. Characteristics are usually specified by installation, interface, or coordination drawings and specifications and by coordinated tooling. (2) The boundary between two media, especially as transited by a propagated wave.

interference. (1) In aerodynamics, the occurrence when the aerodynamic reactions of one surface or component of an aircraft interfere with those of another; the resultant effects from this occurrence. *See* drag interference. (2) In electronics, any electrical or electromagnetic disturbance that causes undesirable responses in electronic equipment. *See also* electrical interference.

interference. *Types of, see* –drag; electric–; electro–; harmonic–; radio-noise–.

interference compliance test. A radio noise and electrical interference test of a complete weapon system (q.v.) to determine whether there is an effect on performance of the airborne and ground equipment by noise—both external and internal.

interference drag. Drag caused by projections which disturb the air flow around the object (e.g., the wings and tail of a missile). It is minimized by fairing all projections and interstices.

interferometer. An apparatus used to produce and show interference (q.v.) between two or more wave trains coming from the same luminous area, and also to compare wavelengths with observable displacements of reflectors, or other parts, by means of interference fringes. An interferometer is frequently used to obtain quantitative information on flow around bodies in wind tunnels.

interferometer homing. A homing guidance system (q.v.) in which target direction is determined by comparing the phase of the echo signal as received at two antennas precisely spaced a few wavelengths apart.

intergalactic space. Space between galaxies.

interhemispheric. Of or pertaining to flight between the Western and Eastern Hemispheres.

interior ballistics. That branch of ballistics

(q.v.) concerned with the combustion of propellants, the development of gas pressures, and the motion of projectiles. Also termed *internal ballistics*. Interior ballistics of a rocket deals with the burning of the propellant inside the rocket, together with associated phenomena such as gas escapement, pressure, etc.

interlock. A device used to govern a sequence of operations to prevent injury to personnel or damage to equipment.

intermediate focal length tracking telescope (IFLTT). 35-mm and 75-mm cameras with 40- and 80-in. lenses for high-speed tracking of missiles during early portions of the trajectory.

intermediate frequency (IF). In superheterodyne radio reception, the frequency resulting from the combination of the received frequency with a locally generated frequency, usually equal to their difference. Its use facilitates amplification and detection.

Intermediate-range ballistic missile (IRBM). A generic term defining a missile flying a ballistic trajectory (q.v.) after guided powered flight and capable of a range of 800 to 1500 nautical miles. Types include: THOR, JUPITER, POLARIS (q.q.v.).

intermittent jet. A pulsejet engine (q.v.).

intermodulation. Interference between the component frequencies of a complex wave when the wave is applied to a nonlinear impedance. Intermodulation is evidenced in the form of beats between the component frequencies or their harmonics. The action produces deflections and frequencies which are not present in the original intelligence transmitted.

internal ballistics. Interior ballistics (q.v.).

internal friction. *See* anelasticity.

internal power supply. A power supply specifically installed within a missile.

internal star-shaped grain. *See* star grain. See Fig. 22, page 259.

International Astrophysical Decade (IAD). A world program of scientific investigation proposed by Dr. Krafft Ehricke.

International date line. At any one moment, two calendar dates are effective simultaneously over different parts of the globe, separated by the International date line. The date line sets a definite though arbitrary limit to the areas over which the two calendar dates apply. The line follows the 180th meridian through the middle of the Pacific Ocean, diverging occasionally so as to include the whole of an island group on one side or the other. When crossing

this line on a westerly course, a day is "lost," and the date must be advanced accordingly. The reverse is true for an easterly crossing. For one instant only each day, when it is midnight on the date line, does the whole world share the same calendar date.

International Geophysical Year (IGY). A worldwide program of research on the Earth and its atmosphere during the period July, 1957, through December, 1958.

interplanetary atmosphere. The sparse layer of atmosphere (q.v.) throughout the solar system. Thought to be an extension of the corona of the Sun, it was discovered in 1957 by the scientists cooperating in the International Geophysical Year (q.v.).

interplanetary space. The space between the planets.

Inter-Range Instrumentation Group (IRIG). A working group of Air Force-Army-Navy representatives charged with standardizing missile test range instrumentation (e.g., telemetering standardization).

interrogator (interrogation). An electronic device for transmitting challenging or interrogating pulses for reception and response by a transponder (q.v.); also the radio or radar beacon used for this purpose. (2) An *interrogator-responser* which combines a transmitter for sending pulses interrogating a transponder and a receiver for receiving and displaying the answering pulses of the transponder.

interrupted continuous wave (ICW). In electronics, a continuous wave that is interrupted at a constant audio-frequency rate.

interstellar flight. Flight between stars, strictly between orbits around stars. The shortest interstellar flight from the solar system is to Proxima Centauri, a distance of 24×10^{12} miles. Traveling at the speed of light, an interstellar space vehicle would take $4\frac{1}{2}$ years for such a journey, and a similar time for the return.

interstellar space. Space between suns or solar systems.

intertropical convergence zone. A zone in which the trade winds of the Northern and Southern Hemispheres converge, often marked by overcast skies, strong squalls, thunderstorms, etc.

intertropical front. In meteorology, the boundary between the trade wind system of the Northern and Southern Hemispheres. It manifests itself as a fairly broad zone of transition commonly known as the *doldrums*.

interval. *Types of, see* confidence–; radar reflection–; reflection–; vertical–.

intra-planetary space. Space between the Sun and the orbit of the respective planet (e.g., intra-Mercurial space).

inverse exponential horn. An acoustical environmental test device used to produce high-energy sound waves. The cross-sectional area varies with length as the inverse of the usual exponential horn configuration (q.v.).

inverse feedback. A vacuum-tube circuit arrangement in which a voltage is fed back from the plate circuit to the grid circuit; used in radio-frequency circuits to improve the stability, and in audio-frequency circuits to reduce distortion and thus permit greater undistorted power output. Also termed *degeneration, negative feedback,* and *stabilized feedback.*

inverse feedback filter. In electronics, a resonance bridge circuit used at the output of a high-selectivity amplifier, such as an oscillator or wave analyzer. Impedance is adjusted so that the feedback output is zero for the resonant frequency, but increases rapidly as frequency departs from this value.

inverse Mercator projection. In cartography, a special case of the transverse *Mercator projection* (q.v.), being that projection which results if the cylinder on which the Earth's surface is projected is placed tangent to the Earth at a meridian.

inverse peak voltage. The peak-voltage value existing across a rectifier tube during that half of the cycle in which current does not flow. It is the limiting voltage that a gas or vapor rectifier can stand without breakdown.

inverse recovery time. In electronics, the time required for a crystal diode (q.v.) to reach a certain prescribed impedance level in the back direction on switching from the high conducting state.

inverse square law. The principle of the gravitational attraction between two point masses diminishes as the square of the distance between them.

$$g_r = g_R \left(\frac{R}{r}\right)^2$$

where g_r = gravitational force at distance r; g_R = gravitational force at Earth's surface, radius R.

inverse square law attenuation. In acoustic applications, a decrease in the sound pressure level of 6 db for each doubling of the distance.

inversion. (1) The temperature below the stratosphere (q.v.) normally decreases with altitude. When temperature increases with altitude, normal conditions are inverted, and the condition is said to be an *inversion.* Inversions in the troposphere (q.v.) are usually restricted to shallow layers of air which most frequently occur in the lower 5000 ft above the surface. In low latitudes the stratosphere has a slight inversion more or less permanently. (2) The transformation of an optically active substance into one having the opposite rotatory effect, without essential change of chemical composition.

inversion. *Types of, see* temperature–; trade–.

inverter. An electrical device for converting direct current to alternating current (AC to DC).

inviscid flow. Fluid flow neglecting the effects of viscosity.

IOC. Initial Operational Capability (q.v.).

ionization. (1) The process of charging neutral atoms or molecules either positively or negatively. (2) The process causing gas to become a conductor of electricity.

ionized layers. Layers of increased ionization within the ionosphere (q.v.). There are believed to be caused by solar radiation, and are labeled the D, E, and F layers (q.q.v.). They are responsible for absorption and reflection of radio waves and are important in connection with communication and the tracking of satellites and other space vehicles. See Fig. 11, page 140.

ion jet. A reaction motor in which a gas is ionized and accelerated to high velocities by means of an electrical field; the reaction from the acceleration provides the thrust. See Table 4, page 187.

ionosphere. That part of the atmosphere extending from 30 miles to 250 miles altitude. Regions of ionization (approx. maxima):

> D layer—35 to 40 miles
> E layer—70 to 80 miles
> F_1 layer—135 to 145 miles
> F_2 layer—190 to 230 miles

The ionosphere consists of layers of highly ionized air capable of bending or reflecting certain radio waves back to the Earth. Ionization results principally from ultraviolet solar radiation. Some seasonal and day-to-night variation is expected. See Fig. 11, page 140.

ion propulsion. A means of obtaining propulsion for space ships by expelling heavy molecules which have been vaporized by an electric arc from a combustion chamber. As the positively charged molecule (ion) leaves the chamber an electric field accelerates it and the stream

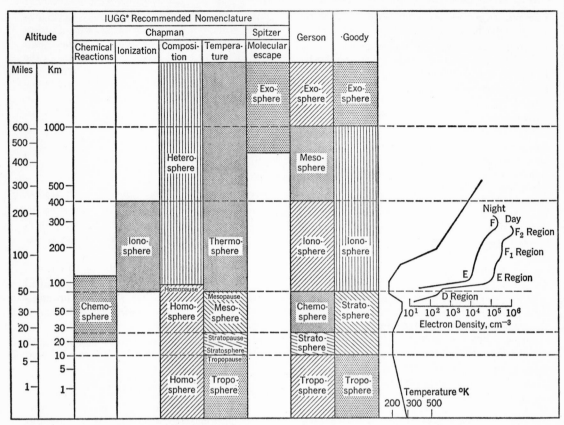

* International Union Geodesy and Geophysics

Fig. 11. Comparison of atmosphere nomenclature. *Source:* Chart prepared by G. W. Wares for "Atmospheric Shells," Chap. 1 in *Handbook of Geophysics for Air Force Designers*, Geophysics Research Directorate, AFCRC, November, 1957.

of ions provide the thrust required for forward motion. The recombination aft of the chamber prevents space charge effects which would counteract the thrust. See Table 4, page 187.

ion rocket. An advanced concept for a power plant for space vehicles in which a nuclear reactor ionizes a working medium and the resulting ions and electrons are accelerated to extreme speeds by an electric field produced by a "conventional" electric source (which is powered by the reactor). Estimated max. I_{sp} is 10^5 sec, but thrust to weight ratio is very small. See Table 4, page 187.

IPBM. (1) InterPlanetary Ballistic Missile; (2) (Vernacular) Inter-Pad Ballistic Missile—one which barely lifts off its launching pad.

IPS. Instrument Power Supply.

I²R loss. Power loss in transformers, generator, connecting wires, and other parts of a circuit due to current flow, I, through the resistance, R, of the copper conductors. Also termed *copper loss.*

IRAN. Inspection and Repair As Necessary (q.v.).

IRBM. Intermediate Range Ballistic Missile (q.v.).

IRE. Institute of Radio Engineers.

IRIG. Inter-Range Instrumentation Group (q.v.).

IRIS. Research sounding rocket.

Length: 14.83 ft; diameter: 12 in. Uses solid propellant fuel; reaches an altitude of 200 miles; payload: 100 lb; weight: 1000 lb. For upper-atmosphere experiments. Similar to AERO-BEE-HI (q.v.).

Prime Contractor: Atlantic Research Corp.

IRT. Interrogator-Response-Transponder. *See* interrogator.

isallohypse. A line on a chart connecting points having values of equal change in height.

isentropic flow through a converging nozzle. A constant-energy process which is representative of the gas flow in a De Laval nozzle.

island. A section in a missile duct where service lines (e.g., oil, fuel, hydraulic) are faired over to prevent failure from vibration and to reduce drag.

isobar. (1) In meteorology, a line conceived or considered to join points having the same barometric pressure; a line on a chart or weather map representing this line. (2) In chemistry, either of two atoms or elements having the same atomic weight but different atomic number.

isoclinic lines. Lines connecting points bearing equal magnetic dip angles (q.v.). Isoclinic lines are the counterpart of latitude lines in the geographical system and are rightly parallelled to the equator. The line connecting points having a zero vertical component (e.g., zero dip angle) is the *magnetic equator*.

isoclinic wing. A wing designed to twist as it bends so as to counterbalance the loss of tip incidence.

isodynamic change. A change in the state of a system in which the inertial energy of the system remains constant.

isodynamic lines. Lines having equal magnetic intensity in the *horizontal* plane.

isoelastic. The property of a body to experience a strain throughout which is proportional to the stress. This property is important in gimbal-mounted gyroscopes where a missile acceleration may produce distortions and unwanted precessions unless the gimbals and gyroscopes are isoelastic.

isogonic lines. Lines connecting points having equal magnetic declination (q.v.). Isogonic lines are the counterpart of longitudinal lines in the geographical system. The two lines along which the magnetic declination is zero are termed *agonic lines*.

isogram. In meteorology, a line on a map or chart connecting points of equal value of some meteorological or climatological phenomenon (e.g., an isobar, an isopleth, an isotherm).

isogriv. A line on a map or chart which joins points of equal magnetic variation from grid north (q.v.).

isolation network. A network inserted between two other circuits where it is disadvantageous to connect them directly to each other. The usual reasons for this network include: (a) impedance matching (q.v.); (b) transforming the type of feed, or connections; (c) loading effects; (d) minimizing energy feedback; (e) instrumentation isolation.

isolator. Any material or structure which tends to diminish the effect of shock or vibration on any item.

isolator efficiency. In an elastic system, the ratio of the energy absorbed by an isolator at a particular load and deflection (or stress and strain) to the product of the particular load and the deflection (or stress times strain).

isoline. In meteorology, an isogram or isopleth (q.q.v.).

isomer. (1) In meteorology, a line on a map or chart indicating an equal proportion of some meteorological phenomenon (e.g., rainfall). (2) In physics and chemistry, any of two or more compounds, substances, or isotopes having the same molecular formulas; i.e., the same constituents, but different structures or arrangements of those constituents, giving rise to different properties.

isopropyl alcohol ($CH_3CHOHCH_3$). A liquid rocket propellant *fuel*. See Table 3, page 157.

isopleth. In meteorology, a special kind of isogram (q.v.), showing the occurrence of frequency of a meteorological phenomenon in relation to two variables.

isotach. A line on a chart connecting points representing equal values of speed.

isotherm. A line drawn on a map or chart through points having equal temperature. Isotherms may be drawn to represent either the temperature at any particular time, or the average temperature for a specified period.

isothermal change. A change in the pressure and/or volume of a gas in which the temperature remains constant.

isothermal region. An atmospheric layer or shell above the troposphere (q.v.), considered to have uniform temperature. The isothermal region, extending from above 11 km to 32 km (7 to 19 miles), shows large departures from the isothermal assumption. It is thickest over the poles, thinnest (even absent) over the equator. It lies just above the tropopause, and coextends with a layer termed the stratosphere (Wares and Chapman). See Fig. 11, page 140.

isotopes. Elements occupying the same place in the periodic system, having the same nuclear charge, but differing somewhat in atomic weight. Most of the ordinary inactive elements have been shown to consist of a mixture of isotopes.

isotropic antenna. In electronic theory, an ideal, hypothetical antenna that radiates or receives equally well in all directions. The isotropic antenna serves as a reference in considering the directional properties of actual antennas.

isotropic warhead. A warhead whose damage effect is the same in all directions.

Max range of isotropic *fragmentation* warhead $\simeq \sqrt[2]{\text{warhead wt.}}$

Max range of isotropic *blast* warhead $\simeq \sqrt[3]{\text{warhead wt.}}$

IU. Interference Unit.

ivory tower. (Vernacular) A vertical stand to hold a missile while testing its engine.

IWST. Integrated Weapon System Training (q.v.).

J

jack box. (Vernacular) In electricity, a box with connections or switches for changing circuits.

jam. To make the transmissions of a radio unintelligible; to make a radio or radar set ineffective, either by the use of countertransmissions or by the use of a confusion reflector (q.v.).

JAMAG. Joint American Military Advisory Group.

jammer. (Vernacular) An electrical device for jamming (q.v.) electronic signals.

jammer. *Types of, see* automatic search–; repeater–.

jamming. A countermeasure (q.v.) technique in which an attempt is made to block a communication or control channel to abort an enemy mission.

jamming. *Types of, see* accidental–; active–; barrage–; electronic–; off-target–; passive–; spot–; sweep–.

JAN. Joint Army-Navy.

JAN specification. Joint Army-Navy specification (q.v.).

J antenna. A half-wave antenna, end-fed by a parallel-wire, quarter-wave section having the configuration of a J.

japee (jaype). (Vernacular) A jet engine or a jet airplane.

Jato. *Jet-assisted take-off* (q.v.).

Jato cant point. The intersection of the Jato chamber axis and nozzle centerline.

Jato, reverse. *See* reverse Jato.

JB1. Ground-to-ground missile. Air Force cognizance.

Launched from a ramp with 5 solid fuel boosters. Turbojet engine propulsion (2 engines). Preset trajectory. Essentially a flying wing with thick body and vertical stabilizing rudder. Span: 30 ft.

Prime Contractor: Northrop Aircraft, Inc.

Program phased out.

JB1-A. Very similar to JB1 (q.v.).

Flying-wing type missile, no tail, radio-guided. Gross weight: approximately 6 tons.

Prime Contractor: Northrop Aircraft, Inc. Motor: Argus-Schmidt Resonance duct engine: Ford Motor Co.

Program phased out.

JB2. Designation for the ground-to-ground or ground-to-ship missile termed LOON (q.v.).

JB3. Air-to-air missile. Air Force cognizance.

Powered by a jet engine and guided by a homing head.

Prime Contractor: Northrop Aircraft, Inc.

Program phased out.

JB4. Air-to-ground missile. Air Force cognizance.

Pulsejet engine; remote control apparatus.

Prime contractor: Northrop Aircraft, Inc.

Program phased out.

JB10. Ground-to-ground flying bomb. Air Force cognizance.

Gross weight: 7200 lb; warhead: 400 lb; length: 12 ft; wing span: 29 ft; range: 185 miles; speed: 425 mph. Flying-wing type with short stubby body and a resonant duct engine. Larger than JB2 (q.v.). Gyro- and wing-stabilized; preset trajectory.

Prime Contractor: Northrop Aircraft, Inc. Engine: Ford Motor Co.

Program phased out.

JCS. Joint Chiefs of Staff (q.v.).

jerk. In kinematics, the *third derivative* of displacement, rate of change of acceleration. Jerk is useful in defining the nature of shock loads.

jet. *Types of, see* axial flow–; by pass–; centrifugal flow–; ducted fan–; thermal–.

jet-assisted take-off (Jato). An auxiliary rocket device for applying thrust to some structure or apparatus; usually providing a large thrust for a short time for heavy aircraft take-off or missile launching.

jetavators. Control devices used in rocket jet exhausts to provide a steering or rolling moment. A partial extension of the nozzle is turned to deflect the jet. Such a system is usually very nonlinear.

jet engine. *Types of, see* axial flow–; by-pass–; centrifugal flow–; ducted fan–; thermal–.

jet engine fuel. A liquid rocket propellant *fuel*. See Table 3, page 157, JP-4.

jet engines. Propulsive devices for guided missiles which impart thrust by the production of a high-velocity gas stream. Two general types are of major importance: (a) *thermal engines* (e.g., ramjet, pulsejet, turbojet, q.q.v.); (b) *rocket engines* (e.g., solid, liquid). *See* rocket engine. See Fig. 15, page 227; Figs. 19 and 20, page 240.

jet horsepower. The power of the exhaust jet equal to the product of thrust and effective jet velocity.

$$\text{thrust hp} = \frac{\text{thrust (lb)} \times \text{speed (mph)}}{375}$$

Statically 2.6 lb of thrust equal 1 hp.

jet nozzle. (1) A nozzle producing a jet of liquid or gas. (2) Specifically, an exhaust nozzle for the escape of gases on a jet engine or rocket.

jetomic. (*Jet* plus a*tomic*) Marked by the development of very high velocities and very great power, e.g., "the jetomic age."

jet power. (1) The power or thrust delivered by a jet engine, rocket engine, etc. (2) In a technical sense, the power or kinetic energy in a mass of controlled and accelerating gases. It is proportional to the weight of gas accelerated, multiplied by the difference of the squares of the gas velocities before and after acceleration.

$$\text{power} = \text{velocity} \times \text{thrust}$$

$$\text{thrust hp} = \frac{\text{thrust (lb)} \times \text{speed (fps)}}{550}$$

jet propulsion. Any method for propelling a body which employs as its propulsive thrust the reaction force produced by the discharge of matter from the propellant body; the discharged matter being in the form of a jet of fluid. Two general types of jet propulsion are utilized: (a) The jet consisting of highly heated, compressed, atmospheric air, admixed with the products of the combustion produced by burning a fuel in the air; the thermal energy of the fuel being employed to raise the air temperature to the desired value. A jet of this type is termed a *thermal jet. See* thermal jet engine. (b) The jet formed by generating large quantities of high-pressure, high-temperature gases by means of a chemical reaction which does not utilize atmospheric air. A gaseous jet produced in this manner is termed a *rocket jet. See* rocket engine.

jet steering. The use of fixed or movable gas jets on a space weapon, ballistic missile, or sounding rocket to steer it along a desired trajectory, during both propelled flight (main engines) and after main engine thrust cutoff. The jets may be supplied cold pressurized gas or hot gas obtained by burning propellants in a gas generator.

jet stream. (1) The stream of gas or fluid expelled by any reaction device (e.g., the stream of combustion products expelled from a jet engine, rocket engine, or rocket motor). (2) In meteorology, two circumpolar air currents moving in a highly irregular, periodically variable, east-to-west direction, marked by a narrow band of high-velocity wind, especially near the base of the stratosphere (q.v.) where the tropopause (q.v.) makes its greatest change in elevation. Their general location is about 35,000-55,000 ft above the Earth's surface, in middle-to-northern and middle-to-southern latitudes; thus the Northern Hemisphere jet stream passes over the United States and the Mediterranean, with loops much farther north. The jet stream in the Northern Hemisphere is farther south and stronger in winter than in summer. In winter it reaches maximum velocity off the east coasts of North America and Asia, and over Northern Africa. Velocities up to 450 mph have been recorded.

jet thrust. The thrust measured in pounds, developed by a jet engine, rocket engine, or the like, in reaction to its jet stream. It may be measured by use of strain gauges, thrust-balancing pistons, dynamometers, or spring scales, which are calibrated in pounds to represent the static weight moved by the engine.

$$\text{thrust} = \frac{\dot{w}}{g}\lambda V_j + (P_e + P_a)A_e$$

where $\dot{w}$ = mass flow of propellant, lb/sec; g = acceleration of gravity, fps²; λ = divergence coeff., exhaust nozzle exit angle (see Fig. 6, page 76); P_e = exit pressure, psia; P_a = ambient pressure, psia; A_e = exit area of nozzle; V_j = jet velocity, fps.

jettison device. (1) A mechanism for jettisoning a missile from a ship or launcher. (2) A mechanism for jettisoning a section of a missile in flight (e.g., at staging of a ballistic missile).

jettison weight. The weight of equipment and parts dropped at staging of a missile; the weight of a booster or other elements intentionally dropped or discarded at certain times.

jet vane. An aerodynamic vane made of high temperature-resisting material placed in the rocket engine exhaust stream for use in control of the thrust vector of a rocket by deflection of the stream.

jet vane controlled missile. A missile which is controlled by special vanes placed in the exhaust nozzle of the rocket or by some special jets acting normal to the missile centerline at a distance from the center of gravity to produce the necessary control moments.

jet vane stabilization. A means of controlling a missile by deflecting vanes in the exhaust stream of a (usually) rocket. Attitude stabilization only may be the objective (e.g., boost phase stabilization) or guidance and/or roll control may be obtained.

jet velocity. The velocity of a rocket jet stream, usually measured with respect to surrounding air.

$$V_j = gI_{sp} = \frac{Fg}{\dot{w}}$$

where V_j = jet velocity, fps; g = acceleration of gravity, fps^2; I_{sp} = specific impulse, lb sec/lb; F = thrust, lb; $\dot{w}$ = mass flow, lb/sec.

jet wash. The backwash or air turbulence caused by a jet engine, rocket engine, etc.

jitter. *Types of, see* beam–; commutator–.

JLC. Joint Logistics Committee.

JOC. Joint Operations Center.

Johnson noise. The noise generated by a resistor at a temperature above absolute zero. It is proportional to the absolute temperature and the bandwidth under consideration.

$$N = KTB$$

where N = noise power, watts; K = Boltzmann's constant; T = absolute temperature, °K; B = bandwidth, cps.

Joint Army-Navy specification. A part of the government system of general specifications. One agency is assigned cognizance of such specifications.

Joint Chiefs of Staff (JCS). A body within the Department of Defense consisting of the Chief of Staff, United States Army, the Chief of Naval Operations, the Chief of Staff, United States Air Force, and a chairman, serving as the principal military advisers to the President, the National Security Council, and the Secretary of Defense, and authorized to conduct certain military operations, such as those of continental air defense. The chairman presides over the JCS but does not vote.

jolt and jumble tests. Environmental tests (q.v.) used to evaluate equipment for adequacy for handling and shipment.

joule. A unit of work. The unit of work which is termed an *erg* (q.v.) is too small a unit for practical calculations, therefore, a larger unit, termed a *joule,* is generally used. A joule is equal to ten million (10^7) ergs. A *joule of work* is the amount accomplished by one watt of power acting for one second.

1 joule = 9.480×10^{-4} Btu = 0.23889 cal, gm = 0.00023889 cal, kg = 10^7 dyne-cm = 10^7 ergs = 0.73756 ft-lb = 10.197 gm-cm = 3.722×10^{-7} hphr = 2.7778×10^{-7} kwhr = 0.0002778 watt-hr = 1 watt-sec

1 joule-second = 1.5098×10^{33} Planck's constants

Joule's law. The principle that the quantity of heat generated by a steady electric current is proportional to the resistance of the conductor in which the heat is generated, to the square of the current, and to the time of its duration:

$$H = KRI^2t$$

If the resistance is in ohms, the current in amperes, the time in seconds, and the heat in calories, the constant K has the value 0.2390 calories/joule.

Joule-Thomson coefficient. The ratio of the change in temperature to the change in pressure when a gas expands at constant enthalpy to a lower pressure through a small aperture or porous plug.

Joule-Thompson effect. In passing a gas at high pressure through a porous plug or small aperture, a difference of temperature between the compressed and released gas may be noticed. Hydrogen and helium become warmer and all other gases cooler at ordinary temperatures and pressures. This phenomenon is termed the Joule-Thomson effect. It is due to the departure of real gases from the ideal gas laws. With a perfect gas no difference should be observed.

Joule-Thomson inversion temperature. The temperature, or one of the two possible temperatures, at which the Joule-Thomson coefficient (q.v.) changes its sign for a given gas.

JP-1, JP-2, JP-3, JP-4, JP-5, JP-6. Hydrocarbon fuels used in rockets and turbojets.

JP107A. A selected hydrocarbon *fuel* formerly used as a liquid rocket propellant. Similar to RP-1 (MIL-F-25576UAF).

JP fuels. Aircraft fuels used with turbojet-propelled aircraft and some rocket power plants (e.g., JP-4, JP-5).

JPL. Jet Propulsion Laboratory; California Institute of Technology.

JP-X. Rocket or turbojet *fuel* consisting of a mixture of RP-1, JP-4, or similar fuels and UDMH (q.v.).

JRDB. Joint Research and Development Board.

J-scope. A modified version of the A-scope (q.v.), with the range scale showing as a circular trace near the circumference of the screen, and the signal appearing as a deflection in the range scale.

JSPC. Joint Strategic Plans Group.

j-type (intrinsic) semiconductor. In solid state physics, a semiconductor in which the electrical properties are essentially not modified by impurities or imperfections within the crystal.

jump. *See* pressure jump.

jump resonance. Occurs in closed-loop saturated control systems which demonstrate a discontinuity in the frequency response. This phenomenon often has a hysteresis (q.v.) behavior such that the frequency jumps occur at two different frequencies depending on whether the frequency is increasing or decreasing.

junction. In a semiconductor device, a region of transition between semiconducting regions of different electrical properties.

junction. *Types of, see* collector–; hybrid–; –transistor.

junction diode. A semiconductor (q.v.) with good rectifying characteristics; generally less noisy than point contact types.

junction transistor. A solid-state device in which the emitter and collector connections are large surface contacts (low resistance). The emitter current is slightly larger than the collector current, and the base current is very small. It consists of two *p-n* junctions within a single semiconductor crystal. It can provide amplification and other functions performed by a vacuum-tube triode. Contrast with *point contact transistor* (q.v.).

JUNO I. Designation for the Army-launched Earth satellite using REDSTONE (q.v.) for the first stage. Also termed EXPLORER (q.v.). See Table 6, page 245.

JUNO II. Designation for the Army Moon rocket or Lunar probe. Employs JUPITER (q.v.) first stage. See Table 6, page 245.

JUPITER. Surface-to-surface Intermediate Range Ballistic Missile. Army cognizance.

Length: about 59 ft; body diameter: 100 in.; launching weight: about 100,000 lb; burnout speed: MACH 10; design range: 1500 miles. Liquid propellant rocket engine, 135,000-lb thrust. JUPITER C was a test version consisting of a REDSTONE missile (1st stage), four RECRUIT rockets (2nd stage), one RECRUIT rocket (3rd stage) (q.q.v.).

Systems Engineering: Army Ballistic Missile Agency. Prime Contractor: Chrysler Corp. Airframe: Chrysler. Engine: Rocketdyne, North American Aviation, Inc. Guidance system: inertial: Sperry and Ford Instrument Co. Radar: Motorola, Inc. Nose cone: Cook Electric Co. and General Electric Co.

JUPITER A. *See* REDSTONE.

K

K. (1) A symbol used by the Navy for "target drone version" in the designation of certain aircraft. (2) A Navy designation for "pilotless aircraft." (3) Knot or knots. (4) Kelvin scale. (5) A solid propellant rocket term; the ratio of burning propellant surface to nozzle throat area.

$$K = \frac{c_w P_c^{1-n}}{a\gamma_p}$$

where c_w = weight flow coefficient; P_e = chamber pressure, lb/sq in.; n = experimental constant, usually between 0.4 and 0.85; a = experimental constant, usually between 0.05 and 0.002; γ_p = specific weight of propellant, lb/cu in.

°K. Kelvin scale (q.v.).

KAN-2. Navy Bureau of Aeronautics designation for surface-to-air missile termed LITTLE JOE (q.v.).

Kantrowitz-Donaldson diffuser. A type of supersonic diffuser, which first contracts to a throat and then expands. Under proper conditions a normal shock occurs near the throat at decreased gas-stream velocity, thereby decreasing the shockwave strength and the pressure losses which would occur if the normal shock occurred at the lip of the diffuser.

KAPL. Knolls Atomic Power Laboratory.

Karman constant. An absolute constant introduced by von Karman in his similarity theory of turbulence. In turbulent boundary layers sufficiently close to the boundary, the rate of shear $\partial U/\partial y$ is related to distance from the boundary, y, by:

$$\frac{\partial U}{\partial y} = \left(\frac{r_o}{\rho}\right)^{1/2} \frac{1}{Ky}$$

where r_o = the shear stress at the wall; ρ = the fluid density; K = the Karman constant. The best available value of K is 0.41 ± 0.01.

Karman street of vortices. Beyond a critical flow Reynolds number (q.v.), the laminar wake of a long cylinder is unstable and develops into a double row of diffuser vortices, arranged alternately in two rows as are street-lamps. T. von Karman investigated the stability of a double row of line vortices in an inviscid fluid, and showed that only one alternating arrangement is stable, and that the computed ratio of spacing of the vortices to separation of the rows agrees well with observation.

Karnaugh map. Used in connection with Boolean algebra applications to provide a method for visualizing a function so that unnecessary terms can be identified and removed. The Karnaugh map differs from the Boolean matrix in that it is used to analyze *functions* rather than circuits.

katabatic wind. In meteorology, a cold air drainage downhill toward lower terrain. In desert ravines katabatic winds locally reach high velocities.

Katergol. A liquid monopropellant rocket engine system in which the monopropellant (q.v.) is decomposed by either a liquid or solid catalyst; e.g., hydrogen peroxide may be catalyzed by certain metals, etc.

KATIE. Surface-to-surface and anti-submarine missile. Navy cognizance.

A weapon system, like SUBROC (q.v.), aimed at extending the useful life of conventional naval ships in service. Reported to be a rocket with a nuclear fission warhead capable of utilizing regular 16-inch guns on Navy ships as launching tubes.

KATYDID. Target drone. Military designation KDD-1.

Length: 11.2 ft; span: 12.2 ft; speed: 200 mph. Launched by catapult or from the air. Resonance duct or ramjet engine. Gyroscope-stabilized and radio-controlled. Engines mounted on top of the body; two fins at the rear mounted in a V.

Prime Contractor: McDonnell Aircraft Corp.

K-band. A radio-frequency band of 11,000 to 33,000 mc/sec with a corresponding wavelength of 2.7 to 0.9 cm. See Fig. 8, page 105.

kc. Kilocycle.

K carrier system. A carrier system providing

telephone channels utilizing frequencies of approximately 60 kc.

KDA-1. Navy designation for the target and tactical missile termed FIREBEE (q.v.).

KDD-1. Military designation for the target drone termed KATYDID (q.v.).

KDM1. Designation for the Navy target drone or missile termed PLOVER (q.v.).

keep-alive anode. A holding or excitation anode.

Kelvin scale (°K). A temperature scale that uses Centigrade degrees, but makes the zero degree signify absolute zero. In this scale, water freezes at 273.16 degrees and boils at 373.16 degrees. Named after the first Baron Kelvin, English mathematical physicist and inventor. *See* temperature conversion formulas.

Kennelly-Heaviside layer. The E layer (q.v.).

Kepler's laws. The three laws of planetary motion formulated by Johann Kepler early in the 17th century on the basis of his analysis of Tycho Brahe's observations. They are: (1) The planets move in ellipses, with the Sun at one focus. (2) The Law of Areas: the line joining the Sun and a planet sweeps out equal areas in equal times. (3) The Harmonic law: the square of the time of revolution (in years) of any planet is equal to the cube of its mean distance from the Sun (in astronomical units). The Law of Areas enables changes in a planet's orbital speed to be calculated. From the Harmonic law we can obtain either the distance or period of revolution, provided the other is known from observation. The laws also apply to satellites, as the latter may be regarded as planets of their primary. It follows from the Harmonic law that artificial Earth satellites, whose mean distance will be very small, must have very short periods of revolution.

kern. In meteorology, a condensation nucleus.

kernel. In mathematics, a function of two sets of variables used to define an integral operator. If the integral operator so defined is the inverse of a differential operator, the kernel is known as the *Green's function* belonging to the differential operator.

kernel. *Types of, see* diffusion–; slowing-down–; Yukawa–.

kerosene. A liquid rocket propellant *fuel*.

keyer. An electronic device used in telemetering systems (q.v.) which, when triggered, produces

an outpulse for each trigger pulse. The duration of the output pulse depends on the amplitude of the voltage at the keyer input during the sampling interval.

K factor. An experimentally determined factor applied to telemetering calibration curves to adjust them to the actual initial conditions of the particular installation.

kill. The achievement of a desired effect against an enemy.

symbol	kill	definition
A	complete abortion	The enemy attack is less than 1% effective as compared with an unopposed successful attack.
B	partial abortion	The enemy's attack is thwarted so that its destructive effect is reduced, but not as much as for complete abortion.
C	complete denial	The enemy force or resource attacked is completely destroyed or made unavailable to him for use in further war activity.
D	partial denial	The enemy force or resource attacked cannot be used in further war activity unless repaired or replaced in part, or until after a lapse in time.

See abortion; attrition; K-kill.

kill measure (rank). The order of desirability of several kills.

kill parameter. A test situation, circumstance, or condition which requires that a test run be terminated immediately.

kill probability. (1) The chance that a target will be destroyed by a given operation. (2) The likelihood of producing the desired kill under the conditions specified.

$$P_{km} = 1 - (1 - P_k)^m$$

where P_{km} = cumulative kill probability; P_k = single-shot kill probability; m = number of shots.

kill switch. (Vernacular) A device for shutting down an experiment if something has gone wrong.

kilocycle. (1) One thousand cycles. (2) In radio, one thousand cycles per second, a measure of frequency.

kilogram. A unit of mass and weight measurement.

1 kilogram $= 0.80665 \times 10^5$ dynes $= 1000$ grams $= 35.27396$ oz (avoirdupois) $= 2.20462$ lb (avoirdupois) $= 0.001$ metric ton

kilogram-calorie. A unit of heat measurement equal to 1000 gram calories (q.v.). Also termed *large calorie.*

1 kilogram-calorie = 1000 gm-cal = 4.186 × 10^{10} ergs = 3087.4 ft-lb = 0.001559 hphr = 1.78005 × 10^{-7} hp-year = 4186 joules = 426.85 kg-meters = 0.001163 kwhr = 1.3274 × 10^{-7} kw-year = 1.163 watt-hr

kilogram-meter. A unit of work, being the work done by one kilogram of force when its point of application moves a distance of one meter in the direction of the force.

1 kilogram-meter = 0.009297 Btu = 2.3427 gm-cal = 0.0023427 kg-cal = 9.8067 × 10^7 ergs = 7.2330 ft-lb = 9.80665 joules

1 kilogram-meter/sec = 9.80665 watts

kiloliter. A unit of volume measurement.

1 kiloliter = 1.000027 × 10^6 cu cm = 35.316 cu ft = 1.000027 cu meters = 264.18 U.S. gal = 1000 liters

kilometer. A unit of length measurement; the common measure of distances.

1 kilometer = 10^5 cm = 3280.83 ft = 1000 meters = 0.62137 mile = 1093.6 yd

kiloton. (1) A weight equal to a thousand tons. (2) The explosive power of 1000 tons of TNT. Contrast with *megaton* (q.v.).

kilovolt. A unit of electromotive force measurement.

1 kilovolt = 1000 volts

kilowatt. A unit of power measurement.

1 kilowatt = 3413 Btu/hr = 56.884 Btu/min = 0.94807 Btu/sec = 14.333 kg-cal/min = 10^{10} ergs/sec = 2.6552 × 10^6 ft-lb/hr = 44,254 ft-lb/min = 737.56 ft-lb/sec = 1.341 hp = 3.6 × 10^6 joules/hr = 1000 watts

kilowatt-hour. A unit of energy equivalent to that transferred or expended in one hour by one kilowatt of power.

1 kilowatt-hour = 3413 Btu = 860 kg-cal = 2.6552 × 10^6 ft-lb = 1.341 hphr = 0.000153084 hp-yr = 3.6 × 10^6 joules = 0.000114155 kw-yr = 3.671 × 10^5 kg-meters = 1000 watt-hr

1 kilowatt year = 2.98958 × 10^7 Btu = 11,747.3 hphr = 1.34102 hp-yr = 3.1536 × 10^6 joules = 8760 kwhr

kinematics. The geometry of abstract motion without regard to forces or bodies of matter. The motion of a point is completely specified by writing the equations of motion of a body giving each of its three rectangular coordinates as a function of time. The kinematics of rigid bodies requires the introduction of a set of equations expressing the orientation relative to a set of coordinate axes established by the equations of motion of a point in the body as the origin and undergoing translation without rotation. *See also* mechanics.

kinetic energy. The energy of motion. Any moving body possesses kinetic energy in proportion to its mass and to the square of its velocity:

$$\text{kinetic energy} = \tfrac{1}{2}\text{ mass} \times \text{velocity}^2$$

kinetic friction. The friction (q.v.) when relative motion exists.

kinetic friction, limiting angle. *See* limiting angle of kinetic friction.

kinetic lead. The correction or allowance made for the relative motion of a target when computing the lead angle. Contrast with *ballistic lead* (q.v.).

kinetics. The branch of dynamics that treats of changes of motion produced by forces. *See* mechanics.

KINGFISHER. Target missile, Q-5. Army Ordnance cognizance.

Length: 38 ft; diameter: 20 in.; weight: 7600 lb; wing span: 10 ft. Parachute recovery. Usually air-launched (B-50). Airspeed: MACH 3.

kip. A thousand pounds of weight (used in the United States and Great Britain).

Kirchhoff's current law. A fundamental electrical law which states that: the sum of all currents flowing to a point in a circuit must be equal to the sum of all currents flowing away from that point.

Kirchhoff's voltage law. A fundamental electrical law which states that: the sum of all the voltage sources acting in a complete circuit must be equal to the sum of all the voltage drops in that same circuit.

kit. *Types of,* see adaptation–; conversion–.

K-kill. A standardized term which classifies the damage inflicted upon an aircraft target by a missile. For a K-kill the target must fall out of control without a reasonable doubt. It is a specialized case of the general A-kill which applies to all targets. *See* kill.

klystron. A vacuum tube for converting direct-current energy into radio-frequency energy by alternately slowing down and speeding up an electron beam, utilizing the transit time between two points to produce a velocity-modulated electron stream to deliver radio-frequency power to a cavity resonator. The term is applicable to an ultra-high-frequency amplifier, or generator, that combines the velocity-modulation principle with one or more cavity resonators to produce and/or utilize a velocity-modulated beam of electrons.

klystron, reflex. *See* reflex klystron.

km. Kilometer (q.v.).

knot. A nautical mile per hour; i.e., 1.1507 statute miles per hour. (For official reporting or recording purposes in the Air Force and Navy, miles-per-hour readings from airspeed indicators are often converted to knots; also, in Air Force and Navy meteorological practice, wind speeds are expressed in knots.)

$$1 \text{ knot} = 6076.103 \text{ ft/hr} = 1.688 \text{ fps} = 1 \text{ nautical mile/hr}$$
$$= 1.15078 \text{ statute miles/hr}$$

know-how. (Vernacular) Knowledge and ability.

Knudson number. The ratio of the mean free path of molecules (l) of a gas and the characteristic length (L) of a body in the fluid stream. Usual flow regime:

$$l/L \leq 0.01 \text{ gas dynamics}$$
$$l/L = 1 \quad \text{slip flow}$$
$$l/L \leq 10 \quad \text{free molecule flow}$$

Kollsman number. The number at which a pressure altimeter is set to correspond to the barometric pressure at a given point on the surface; the altimeter setting.

K-scope. A modified type of A-scope (q.v.), using a double lobe for scanning.

kt. Knot(s) (q.v.).

KUD-1. Designation for a kind of remote-controlled glide bomb, popularly termed the GARGOYLE (q.v.).

KUW-1. Designation for the ground-to-ground or ground-to-ship missile termed LOON (q.v.).

kva. Kilovolt ampere(s).

kw. Kilowatt (q.v.).

L

L. (1) Lift (q.v.), as used in aerodynamic formulas. (2) Launching, in Navy designations, of guided missiles used as test vehicles.

L*. Characteristic length (q.v.).

laboratory missile. A test vehicle; a complete missile, without propellant and armament, that is used to determine the physical and operational compatibility of a missile's mechanical, electrical, and electronic components and subsystems under laboratory conditions. It is used for parametric, off-design, and tolerance testing.

LACROSSE. Surface-to-surface guided missile. Army designation: SSM-A-12. Also used by the Marine Corps.

Length: 20 ft; body diameter: 20.5 in.; wing span: 108 in.; span of control surfaces: 5 in.; launching weight: over 2500 lb; range: up to 20 miles, irrespective of visibility. An all-weather support weapon for ground troops. Solid propellant rocket engine. Radar command guidance system.

Prime Contractor: The Martin Co., Orlando Div. Airframe: Martin. Engine: Thiokol Chemical Co., Redstone Div. Guidance: Federal Telecommunications Laboratories. Warhead, fuzing and arming: General Electric Co.

lag. In electricity and radio, short for *phase lag* (q.v.).

lag hinge. Drag hinge.

lag, phase. *See* phase lag.

LaGrange equations. Partial differential equations which describe the generalized coordinates of a system. For most systems the generalized coordinates are equal in number to the degrees of freedom of the system.

Lambert conformal projection. In cartography, a means for portraying the Earth's surface. A cone is placed over a sphere representing the Earth, with the axes of the cone and of the sphere in coincidence. The size of the cone is such that it cuts the surface of the sphere at the two parallels representing the parallels of latitude which have been selected as the stand-ard parallels of the projection. The meridians of the sphere are projected onto the cone and so determine the meridians of the chart. The land masses on the sphere are then projected onto the cone. In the Lambert conformal projection the area lying between the standard parallels is compressed and the area lying outside the standard parallels is expanded.

Standard parallels are arcs of concentric circles with the apex of the cone as a center. The area between the standard parallels may be further divided by swinging additional arcs for other parallels of latitude. The meridians are straight lines converging at the apex of the cone.

Advantages of Lambert conformal projection: (a) The distortion is comparatively minor. There is no distortion along the standard parallels. (b) The same distance scale may be used anywhere on the chart, with negligible error. (c) Meridians and parallels intersect at right angles and the angles formed by any two lines on the surface of the Earth are correctly represented on the chart. (d) A straight line on the chart closely approximates a great circle. The Lambert conformal projection thus also closely satisfies the requirements for missile guidance use.

lamina. (1) In meteorology, a layer of the atmosphere (q.v.) between designated altitudes. (2) In aerodynamics, any one of the separate sheets of airflow making up a laminar flow (q.v.).

laminar boundary layer. A boundary layer (q.v.) characterized by laminar flow (q.v.).

laminar flow. In aerodynamics, a particular type of streamline flow in which fluid in thin parallel layers tends to maintain uniform velocity. The term usually is applied to the flow of a viscous fluid near solid boundaries, when the flow is not turbulent.

laminar flow airfoil. An airfoil specially designed to maintain laminar flow about itself, especially at transonic or supersonic speeds, q.q.v. (e.g., a relatively thin airfoil with a sharp leading edge and maximum thickness approximately at the center of the choird).

laminar separation. Separation that exists when a laminar boundary layer (q.v.) leaves the surface of the airfoil and moves into the free fluid. This condition may arise when the airflow is decelerated to a point where slowly moving air near the surface is brought to rest. *See* stall; turbulent separation.

lanchester damper. A mechanical damper used in servos and mechanical systems in which the damping element is a flywheel; depending on the acceleration forces required to rotate the wheel for the damping. The wheel is sometimes submerged in oil for additional damping.

land fog. A fog occurring over the countryside. Land fog usually evaporates quickly, as its nuclei are normally only slightly hygroscopic.

landing rocket. A manned space vehicle operated to transfer passengers and cargo from a satellite (q.v.) or larger orbiting spaceship to the surface of a planet. A landing rocket must be provided with a means of reducing its velocity for a safe entry into the planet's atmosphere and the touchdown.

landing techniques. In space flight, when a spaceship reaches its destination it must, in order to land intact, destroy its velocity relative to the world on which it is to land. To do this in the absence of an atmosphere (q.v.), rocket motors must be used; but if there is a gaseous envelope it may be used to provide a frictional braking force. *See* braking ellipses. A powered landing requires almost exactly as much propellant as is needed to take off into space from the same place. The rocket has first to be oriented so that the thrust from its motors, when fired, is *away* from the landing point. A radar altimeter indicates height above ground and is coupled to a computer which controls the motors throughout the maneuver. Even in a manned rocket, the strain on the crew of the deceleration and the almost inevitably fatal consequences of a small error of judgment render manual control of the operation completely impracticable.

landline. A wire connection between transmitting and receiving station or stations. Specifically used to designate *non-RF link*.

land return. In radar, a ground return (q.v.).

Langmuir frequency. The term given to the resonant frequency (q.v.) in a plasma (q.v.) stream.

L antenna. A single-wire horizontal antenna, fed from one end, giving it an L-shaped appearance.

lapse rate. The rate of change in value of a meteorological phenomenon, usually the rate of decrease of pressure or temperature with elevation.

large calorie. *See* kilogram-calorie.

LARK. Surface-to-air missile. Military designation: CTV-N-9 and SAM-N-2.

Length: 14 ft plus booster (est. 4 ft); wing span: 6.3 ft; tail span: 4.0 ft; gross weight: 1210 lb. Launched from a ramp by a booster, radio-guided. Nitric acid and aniline fuel. Booster: 2 standard 1000-lb thrust Jato units in a large box-tail configuration. Used by the Army and Navy for training. Sometimes termed *U.S. guided missile trainer.*

Prime Contractor: Fairchild Engine and Airplane Co. and Consolidated-Vultee Aircraft Corp. (now Convair Division of General Dynamics Corp.).

Phased out; never operational.

LAT. Local Apparent Time (q.v.).

latch. A device designed to fasten a rocket in or on a launcher prior to firing.

late. A term describing armament which functions after the target has been passed and, therefore, cannot be damaged.

late bird. (Vernacular) A missile which arrives at the intersection of the missile-target trajectories after the arrival of the target.

latent heat of fusion. The quantity of heat required to change a unit amount of a solid into a liquid at the same temperature, usually at atmospheric pressure. Units: Btu per pound, cal per gram, etc.

lateral acceleration. Angular acceleration about the yaw axis. Looking down the yaw axis, positive acceleration is clockwise. *See* acceleration.

lateral attitude. The attitude of a vehicle with respect to its position about the longitudinal axis. The lateral attitude of a vehicle changes when it rolls.

lateral axis. The side-to-side axis of a vehicle, about which it revolves in pitching.

lateral control. (1) Control over the lateral attitude or movement of a vehicle. (2) The control surfaces, such as the ailerons, used for lateral control.

lateral oscillation. (1) The oscillation of a vehicle about its vertical axis. (2) Any periodic rolling or sideslipping motion.

lateral stability. In aerodynamics, stability of a missile with reference to disturbances about its longitudinal axis; i.e., disturbances involving rolling or sideslipping. The term *lateral* stability is sometimes used to include directional and lateral stability, since these cannot be entirely separated in flight.

lateral stability (and control) coefficients. *See* stability (and control) coefficients.

latitude. The angular distance, of any point, north or south of the equator; also, the angle at the Earth's center subtended by the arc of the meridian contained between the equator and the point. Latitude is measured numerically in degrees north or south of the equator.

latitude. *Types of, see* celestial–; co-latitude.

lattice. A pattern of fixed lines of position established by a system of radio or radar transmitters.

launch. To release or send forth, under its own power, a rocket, missile, or space vehicle (q.q.v.) from a special launcher (q.v.), rack, ramp, or other device or installation.

launch area. Launch base area (q.v.).

launch base area. For ground-launched missiles, a geographic area encompassing numerous command posts, launch stations and associated guidance stations, a control center, and a support base (q.q.v.).

launch complex. The facilities and equipment required for launching a missile including launcher, blockhouse, ground guidance (q.q.v.), launcher servicing, and other required ancillary equipment.

launch control operations. The minimum number of commands and system responses absolutely required to launch a missile from an advanced state of readiness or to hold-fire. System responses are limited to those commands sent to activate or actuate components or subsystems which are known to fail upon shutdown or activation (e.g., regulators) or which, upon malfunction, are known to cause hazardous conditions for subsequent operations.

launcher. A mechanical structure which constrains a missile to move in the desired direction of flight during initial motion but does not itself propel the missile.

launcher. *Types of, see* aircraft rocket–; gun–; rail-type–; retractable–; tower–; underground–; zero length–.

launcher adapter. A device that fits rigidly to an aircraft rocket launcher (q.v.) to adapt it to the firing of rockets of a different caliber than that for which the launcher was originally designed.

launcher and missile storage structure, surface or underground. A single structure combining the functions of the launcher and the missile storage structure.

launcher length. *See* effective launcher length.

launching. *Types of, see* retro–; zero-length–.

launching dispersion. The departure (usually, but not necessarily, random) from the desired flight path which a guided missile takes during the launching phase.

launching ramp. A ramp used for launching an aircraft or missile into the air.

launching rocket. *See* booster–; Jato.

launching silo. A type of underground launcher.

launching system. In naval usage, that part of a ship's installation designed and installed for the purpose of providing a means for launching a missile on a desired trajectory at a desired time. It may be either a *static type* with the missile providing its own ejection power or a *catapult type* in which the launcher powers or assists the missile take-off.

launch-latch. (1) A device which locks the safety and arming mechanism (q.v.) and which is released at missile take-off. (2) A device which restrains a missile until the proper conditions for its launching have been achieved.

launch pad. A specific (usually research and development) facility from which one missile at a time can be launched.

launch site. (1) A synonym for launch station (q.v.). (2) The location of a *launch complex* (q.v.).

launch station. One or more launchers with associated storage, assembly, and maintenance facilities.

launch station, augmented. *See* augmented launch station.

launch structure. *Types of, see* launch and missile storage–; sub-surface–.

lawn mower. (Vernacular) In electronics: (1) A kind of preamplifier used with a radar receiver to cut down the grass (q.v.) interference on a radar screen. (2) A machine used to cut chaff (q.v.) into various lengths.

law of gravitation. The principle that bodies are attracted to each other by a force which is directly proportional to their masses, and inversely proportional to the square of the distance between them. *See* inverse square law.

laws. *Types of, see* Bode's–; Buy-Ballot's–; Henry's–; Hooke's–; inverse square–; Joule's–; Kepler's–; Kirchhoff's current–; Kirchhoff's voltage–; law of gravitation; Pascal's–; Paschen's–; Newton's–; Ohm's–; scaling–; thermodynamics: first, second, and third–; Zeroth law of thermodynamics.

layer. *Types of, see* bifurcated–; boundary–; D layer; E layer; F layer; F_2 layer; friction–; G layer; Heaviside-Kennelly–; ionized–; ozone–; shock–.

layout. *See* one-line layout.

LAZY DOG. Air-to-surface anti-personnel missile. Air Force cognizance.

A steel dart approximately 2 in. long and resembling a small bomb. Penetration reported to be equal to that of a 45-caliber bullet. Designed to be dropped from low-flying aircraft against troop concentrations.

Developed by the Air Force at Eglin Air Force Base, Florida.

L-band. A radio-frequency band of 390 to 1550 mc/sec. with corresponding wavelengths of 77 to 19 cm. See Fig. 8, page 105.

LC **product.** A parameter used in circuit design. The inductance L in henries, multiplied by the capacitance C in farads.

LC **ratio.** A ratio used in circuit design. The inductance in henries, divided by the capacitance in farads.

LCS. Launch Control System.

L/D. Lift/drag or lift/drag ratio.

lead. (1) The action of aiming ahead of a moving target with a missile or rocket so as to hit the target, including whatever action is necessary to correct for deflection. (2) The lead angle (q.v.) (3) The distance between a moving target and the point at which a missile or rocket is aimed. *See* ballistic lead; kinetic lead.

lead angle. (1) The angle between the line-of-sight (q.v.) to a moving target and the line-of-sight to a point ahead of the target, at which point a missile is aimed so as to strike the target. It may include corrections for gravity and wind effects upon the missile, and also for other deflection effects if the launching device is also in motion, as well as for the motion of the target. However, a lead angle is not to be confused with a deflection angle (q.v.), which need not represent a lead. (2) A dropping angle.

lead angle. *Types of, see* intercept–; missile–.

lead azide. A sensitive explosive used especially as a warhead initiator (q.v.)

lead control. In servomechanisms, the control of the stability of feedback systems by use of lead networks.

lead-in. In electronics, a wire connecting the overhead part of an antenna to the transmitter or receiver.

leading edge. *Types of, see* pulse–; subsonic–.

leading edge pulse time. In electronics, the time at which the instantaneous amplitude first reaches a stated fraction of the peak pulse (q.v.) amplitude.

lead, kinetic. *See* kinetic lead.

lead prediction. The act of directing a missile (or projectile) ahead of a moving target, leading in aim, to a predicted collision point.

learning curve. A graphic representation of the increase in proficiency of personnel with increase in experience (e.g., for an 85% curve, the cost, or manhour requirement, is reduced 15% each time the number of articles is doubled).

Le Chatelier principle. A general law for physical systems: If a system is subjected to a constraint whereby the equilibrium is modified, a change takes place, if possible, which partially annuls the constraint.

Lecher oscillator. A device for producing a system of standing waves (q.v.) in two parallel wires called *Lecher wires;* used in measuring frequencies above 28 mc.

Lecher wires. Two parallel wires with a movable shunt that are connected to the output of a radio-frequency source and are used mainly to measure wavelengths shorter than about 10 meters (28 mc).

LEG. Logistical Expediting Group.

length. *Types of, see* characteristic–; Debye–; pulse–.

length/beam ratio. The ratio of the length of a vehicle fuselage or hull to its beam.

length-diameter ratio. The ratio of the length of the combustion chamber of a rocket motor to its diameter. Usually termed the *L/D ratio.*

lens. *Types of, see* antenna–; variable focus–; Zoomar–.

lenticular cloud. A cloud roughly shaped like a double convex lens, frequently stationary in position.

LEP. Lowest effective power.

lethality. The extent to which a given warhead can destroy a target or render it inoperable so that it eventually can be destroyed.

level. *Types of, see* confidence–; energy–; freezing–; pulse code modulation–; sea–.

LF. Low Frequency (q.v.) (30-300 kc/sec).

LF LORAN. Low Frequency LORAN.

LF/MF. Low Frequency/Medium Frequency.

LHA. Local Hour Angle (q.v.).

life characteristic of equipment. The relationship which holds between the failure rate (q.v.) of equipment and operating or test time. When the design provides adequate stress safety factors, the predominant failure characteristic will be a randomness which is inherent in the part reliability capabilities. This random failure characteristic yields an average failure rate for an equipment containing many parts which is constant for a reasonable period of time. The length of this constant failure rate period depends on the incidence of wearout and constitutes the normal operating period which follows debugging (q.v.).

life test. A test under controlled conditions and specified environment to determine life expectancy of an equipment. The test is designed to establish the failure probability for a given sample size.

lift. In aerodynamics, the force available to overcome gravity and/or maneuver a missile which results from the flow of air over a lifting surface or body.

$$\text{lift} = \tfrac{1}{2}\,\rho V^2 C_L S$$

where ρ = density of the air, slug/ft; V = velocity of the air, fps; C_L = coeff. of lift, a dimensionless parameter; S = a characteristic area, sq ft.

lift. *Types of, see* body–; center of–; dynamic–; negative–.

lift coefficient (C_L). A dimensionless parameter relating to the lift characteristics of a surface or body. Values may be derived from wind tunnel or full-scale flight tests.

$$C_L = \frac{\text{lift}}{S_w q}$$

where S_w = characteristic area, sq ft; q = dynamic pressure, $\tfrac{1}{2}\rho V^2$, lb/sq ft.

lift (due to) drag. *See* drag.

lifting surface. *See* aerodynamic lifting surface.

liftoff. Initial motion along the trajectory of a space weapon or ballistic missile as it rises from the stand under rocket propulsion; the take-off.

light. *Types of, see* ashen–; first–; zodiacal–.

light gas gun (mass accelerator). A test apparatus using light gases instead of power charges for propulsive energy. Projectiles at speeds of 10,000 mph to 20,000 mph may be obtained.

light year. The distance traveled in one year by light, which covers 186,284 miles in one second; equal to 5.88×10^{12} miles.

limit. *Types of, see* buffeting–; confidence–; elastic–; endurance–; load–; pressure–; production bandwidth–; range–.

limit cycle. In servo applications, an oscillation of fixed amplitude and period.

limit design. Plastic analysis of structures and structural elements with consideration of design for normal conditions and permanent deformation for loads which could occur with a very low probability. This is a weight-saving, economical design approach.

limited standard item. An item of supply or item of equipment that is not as satisfactory as a standard item, but usable as a substitute for the standard item and either in actual use or available for issue to meet demand.

limited storage. Storage for, or of, vehicles or equipment intended for use within *ninety days*.

limiter. In electronics, a circuit which limits the maximum positive or negative values of a waveform to some predetermined amount. (It is used in frequency modulation systems to eliminate unwanted variations of amplitude in received waves.)

limiting angle of kinetic friction. The angle at which a surface must be inclined to cause a body resting on that surface to slide at a uniform velocity. The tangent of this angle is equal to the coefficient of static friction.

limiting discriminator. The function of a discriminator unit which renders it insensitive to signal amplitude variation.

limiting link. In radar, that electronic linkage between an interrogator (q.v.) and a radar beacon (q.v.) which determines the reliable range of the beacon.

limit load. In stress analysis, the maximum value of a load expected during the life of a missile. It is usually multiplied by *one* to obtain design load.

limit load factors. In structural design, the maximum actual accelerations (in gravity units) anticipated during the life of a missile. Limit loads are obtained by multiplying the *unit* (one *g*) *loads* on the missile by the *limit load factor*.

line. *Types of, see* agonic–; butt–; datum–; delay–; DEW–; fiducial–; flexural–; geodesic–; hinge–; hot–; instability–; International date–; isoclinic–; isodynamic–; isogonic–; MACH–; squall–; transmission–; water–.

linear velocity. Velocity in a straight line.

line of departure. The direction of a rocket at the instant of launching.

line-of-flight. The line of movement, or the intended line of movement of a vehicle, guided missile, or projectile in the air. It may or may not be coincident with, or parallel to, the longitudinal axis of the body.

line of force. In electronics, a line whose direction at any point is the same as the direction of the force which would act on a small positive charge or pole placed at that point. A line of force is always considered as starting on a positive charge (pole) and ending on a negative charge (pole).

line-of-sight course. (1) A course in which a missile is guided so as to remain on the line joining the target and the point of control. (2) The distance to the horizon from an elevated point, including the effects of atmospheric refraction (q.v.). (3) The straight line from a transmitting radar antenna in the direction of the beam, especially toward a target.

line-of-sight distance. The distance to which radar scanning beams and certain other electronic beams are limited, owing to intersection of the beam by the horizon. (Under certain conditions the distance may be extended by atmospheric refraction (q.v.) of the beam or beams.) See Fig. 13, page 223.

line-of-sight range. The maximum distance over which microwaves can be transmitted. Refraction (q.v.) makes the distance somewhat greater than simple calculations of the Earth's curvature would suggest, but does not prevent that curvature from being the limiting factor. Therefore, the maximum range of microwave signals is limited to approximately 200 miles and this distance is possible only if the receiver or transmitter can be placed at a very high elevation.

liner. *Types of, see* ceramic–; inner–; outer–.

liner. In rocket engine applications, an inert material used on the inner surface of a solid rocket engine case to inhibit burning of the grain (q.v.) adjacent to the structural case wall. The grain is frequently bonded to the liner which in turn is bonded to the case. *See* inhibitor.

line squall. In meteorology, an extremely turbulent roll-type squall cloud usually found at the leading edge of squall lines associated with rapidly moving cold fronts.

link. *See* limiting link.

liquid hydrogen (H_2). A liquid rocket propellant *fuel*. See Table 3, page 157.

liquid oxygen. A liquid rocket propellant *oxidizer*. See Table 3, page 157.

liquid propellant. Liquid *fuel* which combines with a liquid *oxidizer* to provide a combustible mixture useful as a rocket propellant. See Table 3, page 157.

liquid propellant rocket engine. A rocket engine in which all of the propellants are in the liquid

state prior to their injection into the rocket motor. See Fig. 20, page 240.

liquid rocket propellant characteristics (desirable). A liquid rocket propellant desirably should have these properties: (a) high content of chemical energy (therefore high specific impulse and high combustion temperature); (b) high specific gravity; (c) low molecular weight; (d) low specific heat ratio; (e) high characteristic velocity; (f) low freezing point; (g) low hazard due to corrosion, explosion, fire, toxicity; (h) low hygroscopicity; (i) low vapor pressure; (j) small temperature variation; (k) low smoke formation; (l) availability at low costs.

Lissajous figures. A characteristic and useful portrayal of the combination of two sine waves.

list. *Types of, see* equipment component–; master equipment allowance–; Unit Property Record and Equipment Authorization–.

liter. A unit of measurement in the metric system (q.v.), defined as the volume of a kilogram of water at the temperature of its maximum density, 4°C, and under a pressure of 76 cm of mercury. The liter is slightly greater than the cubic decimeter (e.g., 1 liter = 1.000027 cubic decimeters).

$$1 \text{ liter} = 1000.027 \text{ cu cm} = 61.025 \text{ cu in.}$$
$$= 0.26418 \text{ gal} = 1000 \text{ ml} = 33.814 \text{ fluid}$$
$$\text{oz} = 1.0567 \text{ liquid qt}$$

lithium. A liquid metal used as a rocket propellant *fuel*.

lithium borohydride ($LiBH_4$) ammonia solution. A liquid rocket propellant *fuel*.

lithium perchlorate. A solid rocket propellant *oxidizer*.

LITTLE JOE. Surface-to-air missile. Navy Bureau of Aeronautics designation: KAN-2.

An earlier version of present day surface-to-air missiles.

Prime Contractor: McDonnell Aircraft Corp.

Status: obsolete.

LITTLE JOHN. Surface-to-surface "free" (unguided) rocket. Army designation: XM-47.

Length: 12 ft; body diameter: 12.5 in.; span: 33 in.; firing weight: 980 lb; maximum range: 18,000 yd. Solid propellant rocket engine. Similar to HONEST JOHN (q.v.), but much smaller. Missile is extremely mobile as an all-weather support of ground troops and can carry an atomic warhead.

Prime Contractor: Douglas Aircraft Co. and Emerson Electric Manufacturing Co. Airframe: Douglas and Emerson. Engine: Allegheny Ballistics Laboratory.

TABLE 3. Liquid propellant rocket combinations.

Fuel	Oxidizer	I_{sp} at 500 psi Pc	Bulk Density g/cc	lb/cu ft
Ammonia, NH_3	Bromine Pentafluoride, BrF_5	250	1.8	112.5
	Chlorine Trifluoride, ClF_3	243	1.26	78.7
	Fluorine, F_2	333	1.16	72.4
	Fluorine and Nitrogen Trifluoride, $F_2 + NF_3$	296	1.15	71.7
	Liquid Oxygen, O_2	260	0.88	55.0
	Oxygen Difluoride, OF_2	265	1.07	66.8
	RFNA (22% NO_2)	235	1.12	70.0
Butyl Mercaptan	Nitric Acid, HNO_3	225	1.28	80.0
Diborane	Fluorine, F_2	260	1.07	66.8
Diethylene triamine	Liquid Oxygen, O_2	263	1.06	66.2
Ethyl Alcohol (75%)	Liquid Oxygen, O_2	230	0.99	61.8
Ethyl Alcohol (92.5%)	Liquid Oxygen, O_2	237	0.98	61.2
Ethyl Silicate	Liquid Oxygen, O_2	224	1.05	65.6
Ethylene Diamine	Liquid Oxygen, O_2	255	1.04	65.0
Ethylene Oxide	Liquid Oxygen, O_2	220	0.99	61.8
Hydrazine, N_2H_4	Chlorine Trifluoride, ClF_3 (ST)	252	1.46	91.2
	Fluorine, F_2	286	1.3	81.2
	Hydrogen Peroxide, H_2O_2 (90%)	255	1.2	75
	Hydrogen Peroxide, H_2O_2 (99.6%)	268	1.24	77.5
	Nitrogen Tetroxide, N_2O_4 (ST)	263	1.2	75.0
	Liquid Oxygen, O_2	272	1.06	66.2
	Oxygen Difluoride, OF_2	262	1.23	76.8
	RFNA (15% NO_2)	252	1.26	78.7
	Tetranitromethane	233	1.29	80.6
	Perchloryl Fluoride, ClO_2F	258	—	—
Hydrogen, H_2 (Max $I_{sp} \times d$)	Fluorine, F_2	388	0.46	28.7
Hydrogen, H_2 (Max $I_{sp} \times d$)	Liquid Oxygen, O_2	367	0.43	26.9
Hydrogen, H_2 (Max I_{sp})	Fluorine, F_2	367	0.27	16.7
Hydrogen, H_2 (Max I_{sp})	Liquid Oxygen, O_2	355	0.26	16.2
Hydrogen, H_2	Liquid Ozone, O_3	393	—	—
Isopropyl Alcohol	Liquid Oxygen, O_2	224	0.98	61.2
JP-4	Fluorine, F_2	280	1.19	74.3
	Hydrogen Peroxide, H_2O_2 (99.6%)	243	1.28	80.0
C/H 6.85	Liquid Oxygen, O_2	245	0.98	61.2
C/H 6	Liquid Oxygen, O_2	252	0.98	61.2
	Liquid Oxygen (70%) and Ozone (30%), $O_2 + O_3$	257	1.04	65.0
	Liquid Oxygen (30%) and Ozone (70%), $O_2 + O_3$	262	1.08	67.7
	Liquid Ozone, O_3	266	1.14	71.2
	RFNA (22% NO_2)	233	1.3	81.2
Methyl Acetylene (propyne)	Liquid Oxygen, O_2	242	0.93	58.1
Methyl Alcohol	Liquid Oxygen, O_2	?	0.95	59.4
Methyl Cyclopentane	Liquid Oxygen, O_2	?	0.98	61.2
Methylamine	Liquid Oxygen, O_2	253	0.91	56.8
n-Octane	Liquid Oxygen, O_2	257	0.96	60.0
	Oxygen Difluoride	?	1.22	76.2
	RFNA (6.5% NO)	230	1.26	78.8
Nitroethane	Liquid Oxygen, O_2	220	1.09	68.1
Nitropropane	Liquid Oxygen, O_2	214	1.06	66.2
RP-1	Liquid Oxygen, O_2	266	1.04	64.8
Polyethylene	RFNA (22% NO_2)	?	1.4	87.5
Propylene Oxide	Liquid Oxygen, O_2	235	1	62.4
Propylene Oxide (69.5%) and Ethylene Oxide (30.5%)	Liquid Oxygen, O_2	?	1	62.4
Triethyl-Trithiophosphite	RFNA (22% NO_2)	235	1.43	71.4
Turpentine	Chlorine Heptoxide (85%) and Nitrogen Tetroxide (15%)	252	1.35	84.3
	Nitric Acid, HNO_3	249	1.32	82.5
	Liquid Oxygen, O_2	245	1.04	65.0
	RFNA (22% NO_2)	246	1.36	85.0
Unsymmetrical Dimethyl Hydrazine (UDMH); $(CH_3)_2NNH_2$	Liquid Oxygen, O_2	254	0.96	60.0
	RFNA (22% NO_2) (ST)	250	1.23	76.8
	Nitrogen Tetroxide, N_2O_4 (ST)	255	—	—
	ClO_3F	258	—	—

LME. Launch monitor equipment.

LMT. Local Mean Time (q.v.).

LN$_2$. Liquid Nitrogen.

load. *Types of, see* aerodynamic–; average–; basic–; design–; dummy–; gust–; limit–; off-load–; sand–; structural–; test-failure–; ultimate–; wind–; working–; yield–.

load cells. Strain gauges incorporated in the thrust mounts to weight a missile, and measure forces (e.g., wind, thrust) acting upon the vertical missile when in the test or launch stand.

load factor. In stress analysis, the ratio of the force acting on a mass to the weight of the mass. The net external force on the mass may be expressed in terms of *gravity units*. *Limit load factor* is maximum value of gravity units expected during the life of a missile.

loading. *Types of, see* beam–; wing–.

loading coil. In electricity, a coil attached to a circuit for adding inductance (q.v.) to the circuit.

load limit. The maximum allowable static or dynamic load that may be placed on or in a vehicle or part thereof under normal operating conditions.

loadmeter. In electricity, an aircraft instrument that measures and indicates, in percentages, the output or load of a generator.

loads report. A standard report used in structural design which includes the basic transportation, storage, stowage, handling, environmental, launcher, boost, flight and recovery loads; spanwise and chordwise pressure distributions on all important elements; inertia and gust loads for all important flight phases; pressure vessel loads; rotary and longitudinal acceleration factors, etc. Special and conventional design methods and techniques on which the design is based are included.

LOBBER. Ground-to-ground solid propellant rocket-propelled supply support missile. Army cognizance.

Length: 9 ft; diameter: 10 in.; range: 6-8 miles; payload: 50 lb; velocity: 1500 mph.

Prime Contractor: Convair, Division of General Dynamics Corp.

lobe. In electronics, one of the three-dimensional portions of the radiation pattern of a directional antenna.

lobe. *Types of, see* half–; side–.

lobe switching. A method of scanning or direction finding (q.q.v.) in which a lobe is periodically switched in two or more directions.

local apparent time (LAT). (1) Apparent time measured with reference to a given meridian. (2) In celestial navigation, the apparent time of the observer's meridian.

local civil time. Local mean time. *See* Greenwich mean time.

local control. The control of a radio transmitter or other electronic device directly at the transmitter or device, as distinguished from *remote control*.

local hour angle (LHA). The angle between the hour circle (q.v.) passing through a projection of the observer's position and the hour circle passing through any given celestial body, measured westward from 0 through 360 degrees.

local MACH number. The MACH number at some specified point on a moving body, as distinguished from the remote MACH number (q.v.).

local mean time (LMT). (1) Mean time measured with reference to any particular meridian. (2) Specifically, in celestial navigation, the mean time of the observer's meridian.

local oscillator. For microwave receivers: (1) An electronic device for generation of a reference frequency. It may be of the usual low-frequency, negative-grid type with the tuning circuits consisting of coaxial elements; or, more often, velocity-modulation tubes are used. (The latter type is practically the only suitable oscillator for receiver use above 4000 mc per sec.) (2) The oscillator in a superheterodyne receiver which supplies the frequency to the mixer necessary to heterodyne the original signal frequency down to the desired intermediate frequency. The elements for this oscillator may be in the same tube envelope as the mixer.

local oscillator tube. An electron tube in a heterodyne conversion transducer to provide the local heterodyning frequency for a mixer tube.

local shock. A suddenly applied force on an object which does not produce significant displacement except immediately adjacent to the point of application of the force.

local sidereal time. (1) The time of the sidereal day (q.v.), measured with reference to any particular meridian. (2) Specifically, in celestial navigation, the time of the sidereal day with reference to the observer's meridian.

lock. *Types of, see* gimbal–; phase–.

lockon. (Vernacular) The instant at which a radar is enabled automatically to track its target.

lockon, radar. *See* radar lockon.

lockon range. The range from a radar to its target at lockon (q.v.).

logarithm. Of a number, the power to which a second number, termed the *base*, must be raised in order to yield the original number. Bases in common use are 10 and ϵ (2.718).

logarithmic amplifier. In electronics, an amplifier whose output signal is a logarithmic function of the input signal.

logarithmic computer. A part of an electronic computing system that resolves problems in terms of logarithmic values, or as a logarithmic function.

logarithmic decrement. The natural logarithm of the ratio of two successive amplitudes of a decaying system. It is useful in determining the amount of damping in a system by measuring the rate of decay of oscillation.

The logarithmic decrement

$$\delta = \log \frac{X_1}{X_2} = \gamma \omega_n \tau$$

where $\gamma = C/C_c$ = damping factor; $\omega_n = \sqrt{k/m}$ $= C_c/2m$; x = displacement; τ = time for decay; m = mass; k = spring constant.

LOGBALNET. An Air Materiel Command network for the exclusive use of transmitting ballistic missiles logistical data via electrical media.

logic. *Types of, see* mathematical–; symbolic–.

logical design. A computer discipline in which the computational features and elements are logically grouped to provide an entity capable of handling a piece of data or to make a particular calculation.

logistic protection. In a guided missile system, that provision that insures the missile against functional degradation due to all the environmental factors encountered from the manufacturer's plant to operational expenditure. This environmental phase may be divided into two categories: (a) *transportation:* any movement, vertical or horizontal, of the missile; (b) *storage:* the time during which the missile is not being moved, and may be of short or extended duration.

logistics. The functions of supply and transport in support of the military establishment; i.e., those aspects of military operations that deal with: (a) design and development, acquisition, storage, movement, distribution, maintenance, evacuation, and disposition of materiel; (b) movement, evacuation, and hospitalization of personnel; (c) acquisition or construction, maintenance, operation, and disposition of fa-

cilities; and (d) acquisition or furnishing of services. It comprises both planning (including determination of requirements) and implementation.

logistics, air. *See* air logistics.

logistics concept. A general statement of approved military policy on logistics (q.v.) for a specified weapon system. The logistics concept establishes the overall logistics policies, objectives, assumptions, and requirements for the particular weapon system, based upon the weapon system requirements presented in the operations concept.

logistics plan. The plan based on the operations concept, operations plan, and guidance contained in the logistics concept (q.v.). It includes a general description of the materiel support system and specific guidance to the using of commands and subordinate command activities on actions to be taken and methods of supporting the weapon system.

logistics potential. The extent to which a nation can provide the physical means for the conduct of war, including materiel, manpower, and administration.

LOKI. Surface-to-air unguided missile.

One solid propellant rocket; diameter: 3 in.; fired in salvos.

Airframe: East Coast Aeronautics, Inc. Power plant: Grand Central Rocket Co.

Status: phased out.

long-delay fuze. A type of delay fuze (q.v.) in which the fuze action is delayed for a relatively long period of time, usually for any length of time from two minutes to five days.

longeron. In structural design, an element used to carry drag or compressive loads; also used to "break up" sheet panels to provide increased rigidity and load-carrying capacity. Typical use: semi-monocoque construction of missile airframes.

longitude. The angle between a place of interest and the Earth's prime meridian (q.v.) through Greenwich, England; measured numerically in degrees east or west of the prime meridian.

longitudinal acceleration. Forward and aft acceleration. Acceleration applied forward is positive. *See* acceleration.

longitudinal (antenna) fuze. An electronic fuze in which the sensitivity pattern is principally to the sides of a missile or other vehicle.

longitudinal attitude. The attitude of a vehicle with respect to its position about the vertical axis. (Longitudinal attitude changes when the vehicle yaws.)

longitudinal decalage. The difference between the angular settings of airfoils mounted one behind the other, as between a wing and a stabilizer. The angular setting is measured by the acute angle between the airfoil chord and the longitudinal axis of the vehicle, looked at from the side.

longitudinal oscillation. (1) Oscillation of a vehicle in the plane of symmetry (q.v.) about the lateral axis, consisting of pitching and the accompanying periodic climbing and diving motions, with consequent changes in flight speed. (2) The hunting or porpoising motion resulting from this oscillation, combined with forward motion.

longitudinal stability. In aerodynamics, stability of a missile with reference to disturbances in its plane of symmetry (q.v.); i.e., disturbances involving pitching and variation of the longitudinal and normal velocities.

long-term storage. Storage for, or of, vehicles for periods of over three years.

long wave. (1) In radio, an electromagnetic wave longer than those in the standard broadcast band. Long wave has been variously defined to mean a wave (a) longer than 545 meters, or (b) 600 meters long or longer. (2) In meteorology, a specific kind of atmospheric wave in the westerlies at high latitudes, associated with cyclogenesis.

LOON. Ground-to-ground or ground-to-ship missile. Air Force cognizance. Designation: JB2 and KUW-1.

Weight: 4370 lb; fuel weight: 1000 lb; warhead: 2200 lb; bomb load: 1540 lb; length: 25.5 ft; diameter: 2.7 ft; wing span: 19.1 ft; range: 100 to 150 miles; speed: 400 mph. Catapult-launched with a solid booster having a thrust of 4000 lb for 4 sec. Gyroscope-stabilized with wings; radio-controlled or preset trajectory.

Prime Contractor: Northrop Aircraft, Inc. Motor: Argus-Schmidt. Resonance duct by Ford Motor Co.

loop. (1) A series of interconnected components, accessories, assemblies, or subassemblies required to complete a specific function such as tracking, temperature control, antenna positioning, synchronizing, pressure control, etc., within a system. (2) In a standing wave, the variation of the measured quantity varies sinusoidally at each and every point. The points at which the variation is a maximum are termed *loops,* or *antinodes.*

loop. *Types of, see* closed–; dynamic hysteresis–; inner–; open–; outer–.

loop antenna. In electronics, a directional antenna (q.v.) consisting of one or more turns or loops of wire or other conductor. It may be in the shape of a circle, a rectangle, or any other convenient shape. It is normally bidirectional, but may be made unidirectional. *See* sense antenna.

loop gain. In feedback terminology, the gain around the feedback loop, numerically equal to the product of the forward gain and the gain of the feedback network. (The feedback network is also termed the β-network.)

loop ratio. The frequency response of the primary feedback to the actuating signal. Under linear conditions, the ratio is expressed as:

$$\frac{B}{E} = GH$$

where G = gain; H = feedback.

loop-type radio range. A radio using two separate loop antennas (q.v.) utilizing a single transmitter. The pattern of a loop-type radio range is similar to that of an Adcock radio range (q.v.), and is utilized for navigation in the same manner; most loop-type ranges, however, do not have simultaneous transmission of voice communication and radio-range signals. Loop-type ranges are designated in radio facility charts as *RL* (range, loop) for full-power ranges, *MRL* for medium power ranges, *ML* for low-power ranges. *See* Adcock radio range.

LOP. Line of Position.

LORAC. *Long range accuracy.* An accurate ship navigation system similar to LORAN (q.v.).

LORAN. *Long range navigation. See* hyperbolic navigation.

LORAN. *Types of, see* low-frequency–; sky-wave synchronized–.

LORAN chain. A system or combination of four or more LORAN stations, forming three or more pairs of stations for LORAN navigation. Contrast with LORAN triplet (q.v.).

LORAN triplet. A system or combination of three LORAN stations, providing two pairs of stations for LORAN navigation. One station in a LORAN triplet forms a pair with each of the others. Contrast with LORAN chain (q.v.).

LOS. Line Of Sight.

loss. *Types of, see* dielectric–; gravitational–; hysteresis–; insertion–; I^2R–; transducer insertion–; transmission–.

lossy. An adjective applied to a dielectric material which dissipates energy.

low. *See* cold low.

low-energy primary. Biologically dangerous cosmic ray particle which may be prevented from reaching the Earth by the heliocentric field. It constitutes a possible hazard to spaceflight.

lower atmosphere. (1) A term used to refer to any layer of the atmosphere (q.v.) relatively near the Earth. (2) Specifically, the troposphere (q.v.). See Fig. 1, page 21.

lower camber. The camber (q.v.) of the underside of an airfoil.

low explosive. Any nonatomic explosive characterized usually by deflagration rather than detonation, and used as a propellant in solid rockets.

low frequency (LF). In electronics, any frequency between 30 and 300 kc/sec.

low-frequency LORAN. A modification of standard LORAN, operating in a low-frequency range of approximately 180-200 kc/sec to increase range over land and during daytime. Often termed *LF LORAN*.

low-order detonation. An incomplete and relatively slow detonation (q.v.).

low pass filter. In electronics, a wave filter (q.v.) having a single transmission band extending from zero frequency up to some critical or cutoff frequency, not infinite. The value of the components may be selected as follows:

$$L = \frac{R}{\pi f_c} \quad \text{and} \quad C = \frac{1}{\pi f_c R}$$

The cutoff frequency is:

$$f_c = \frac{1}{\pi \sqrt{LC}}$$

where R = resistance; L = inductance; C = capacitance.

low-pressure area. In meteorology, an area of low atmospheric pressure. Sometimes termed a *low*.

low-tension ignition system. An ignition system in which the current is held at a low tension throughout most of the system, being stepped up by a transformer to a high tension prior to delivery to a spark plug. Low-tension systems are less subject to breakdown at high altitudes than other systems.

LOX. Liquid *ox*ygen. Sometimes *loxygen*. Industrial use of the term LOX means liquid oxygen explosive. The Air Force does not authorize use of the abbreviation. A liquid rocket propellant *oxidizer*.

loxing. (Vernacular) The task of loading liquid oxygen into the fuel tanks of a missile from a ground supply.

loxing time. The time needed to pump the required amount of liquid oxygen into missile lox tank or tanks and to reach a state of launch readiness.

loxodromic curve. In cartography, a *rhumb* line which spirals toward the poles.

LRPGD. Long Range Proving Ground Division.

L-scope. A kind of radarscope in which range is indicated by a vertical scale, with target displacement to right or left indicated by horizontal pulses from the vertical scale. The L-scope is a modification of the A-scope (q.v.).

LSE. Launch Sequencer Equipment; equipment that is used during automatic countdown and launching.

LTV. (Obsolete). Launching Test Vehicle.

lumen. The unit of luminous flux; the light emitted by a source of one international candle in a unit solid angle.

1 lumen = 0.07958 candlepower (spherical)
= 0.001496 watt

1 lumen/sq cm = 1 lambert

1 lumen/sq ft = 1 foot-candle = 0.001076 lambert

1 lumen/sq meter = 0.0929 foot-candle

luminous bands. Faint bands of luminosity which appear in the night airglow (q.v.). They may be caused by the impact of micrometeorites with the upper atmosphere. The height and origin of the phenomenon are in doubt, owing to the difficulty of making observations.

lumped constant elements. Distinct electrical elements, small compared to a wavelength (q.v.), which are calibrated and used in the control of voltage and current, and employed in conjunction with other electrical-electronic equipment.

lunar craters. The numerous walled formations scattered over the surface of the Moon. The largest are well over 150 miles in diameter, whereas the smallest are tiny pits below the limit of visibility.

lunar gravity. The attraction of particles and masses toward the gravitational center of the Moon.

Lunar Probe. A test vehicle designed to orbit, pass, or impact the Moon with the objective of gaining certain scientific knowledge. The first American (Air Force) attempt was at Cape Canaveral, Florida, at 0718 EST on August 17, 1958, using a THOR (q.v.) booster, VANGUARD (q.v.) second and third stages, and an 84-lb payload. The booster failed and the test was completely unsuccessful. The second American attempt was made at 0342 EST on October 11, 1958, using similar equipment. The payload was termed PIONEER I (q.v.); it ascended about 79,000 miles in space and was airborne approximately 43 hours and 20 minutes. The trajectory was about 3° in error and the 84-lb payload did not attain sufficient velocity to "escape." The third attempt, sponsored by the Air Force, was fired on November 7, 1958. Termed PIONEER II (q.v.); the third stage failed to ignite and the vehicle plunged to Earth. Same general configuration as PIONEER I. The first Army attempt was fired on December 6, 1958. Termed PIONEER III (q.v.) it aborted owing to a velocity and aiming error. An altitude of about 63,600 miles was achieved by the 13-lb payload. See Table 6, page 245.

lunar space. The space inside the lunar activity sphere with respect to the Earth.

Luneberg lens. An efficient electromagnetic energy reflector; sometimes a variable dielectric-constant device with a contour to focus an incident-plane electromagnetic wave to a point on the surface or to produce a plane wave from a point source (e.g., radar transmitter).

M

M. (1) MACH (q.v.). (2) MACH number (q.v.).

M-31. Army designation for the surface-to-surface unguided "free" ballistic missile termed HONEST JOHN (q.v.).

MAC. Mean Aerodynamic Chord (q.v.).

MACE. Surface-to-surface winged bomber. Air Force designation: TM-76A for ATRAN and TM-76B for inertial guidance.

Length: 45 ft; diameter: 4.5 ft; wing span: 22.9 ft; weight: 1000 lb; range: 650 nm; maximum speed: MACH 0.9. Turbojet sustainer engine, solid propellant rocket booster. Inertial or map-matching guidance system.

Prime Contractor: The Martin Co., Orlando. Guidance system: inertial: AC Sparkplug; map-matching (ATRAN): Goodyear. Engines: Allison J33A-41 turbojet sustainer; solid propellant rocket booster: Thiokol Chemical Co.

MACH. The speed of a relatively moving body or a part thereof, as measured by the speed of sound (q.v.) in the medium in which it moves, indicated by a number [as MACH 0.5 (a speed equal to one-half the speed of sound, MACH 1 (a speed equal to that of sound), MACH 1.33 (a speed one-third greater than the speed of sound)]. The speed of sound in dry air at 32°F, sea level, is about 1116 fps (760 mph); its speed in water at 8°C is about 4708 fps. At transonic speeds, a vehicle as a whole may have a speed less than MACH 1 at the same time that local points on the vehicle have speeds greater than MACH 1. (Named for the Austrian scientist, Ernst Mach.) *See* MACH number.

MACH angle. The angle between a MACH line (q.v.) and the path of a body moving with supersonic speed. The sine of this angle is the ratio of the local speed of sound to the missile velocity.

MACH cone. A hypothetical conical surface having at its apex a point source moving with supersonic speed; all of the shock disturbances remain inside the surface. Outside of the MACH cone the fluid is unaffected by the motion of the moving body. The MACH cone is bounded by a weak shock wave and a line drawn on the MACH cone from the vertex is known as a MACH *line* (q.v.).

MACH cone probe. A device for measuring the temperature of the upper atmosphere (q.v.). It uses sensing elements to determine the position of the shock wave (q.v.) from a slender cone mounted at the nose of a missile.

MACH diamond. A series of spaced, light areas in rocket exhausts caused by local equilibrium shifts.

MACH effect. A single effect, or a total effect, resulting from objects moving at transonic or supersonic speeds (q.q.v.). MACH effect may be considered in terms of: (a) the changes in the air brought on by a shock wave, i.e., changes in pressure, velocity, density, and temperature; (b) the fusion of shock waves in atomic explosions; (c) the changes in the drag coefficient, lift coefficient, or moment coefficient (q.q.v.) of a missile.

MACH line. An imaginary line drawn at an angle to the path of a rapidly moving body. It represents theoretically the shock wave (q.v.) which would be produced by a microscopic point moving with the speed of the body. The angles of very weak shock waves closely approximate the angle of the MACH line.

MACH meter. An instrument for sensing the MACH number of a missile in flight. (This parameter is often used to adjust the gain of the control system or engine thrust.)

MACH number. A fundamental aerodynamic parameter: the ratio of the velocity of a body to that of sound in the medium being considered. Thus, at sea level, in air at the *standard atmosphere* (q.v.), a body moving at a MACH number of *one* ($M = 1$) would have a velocity of approximately 1116.2 fps or 688 knots.

$$M = \frac{V}{a} = \frac{V}{\sqrt{gkRt}}$$

where a = local velocity of sound; t = local temperature, °F; g = gravity, fps²; k = ratio of specific heats; R = gas constant.

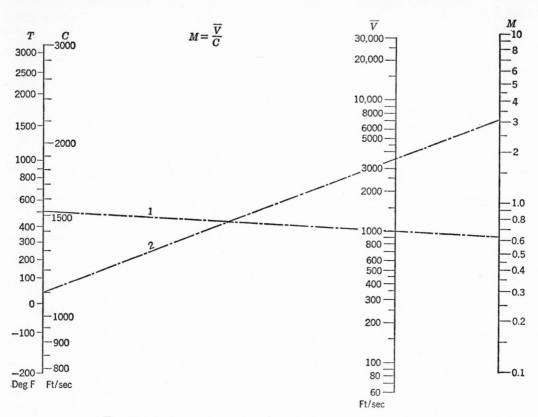

Fig. 12. MACH number nomogram. (J. G. Lowenstein, *Design News*)

a (mph) $= 33.44T^{\frac{1}{2}}$ (°R = °F + 460 = T)
a (mph) $= 44.86T^{\frac{1}{2}}$ (°K = °C + 273 = T)
a (knots) $= 29.04T^{\frac{1}{2}}$ (°R = °F + 460 = T)
a (knots) $= 38.96T^{\frac{1}{2}}$ (°K = °C + 273 = T)
See Fig. 12.

MACH number. *Types of, see* critical–; local–; remote–.

MACH wave. In supersonic aerodynamics, the limiting case of an infinitely weak shock wave (q.v.).

MAD AEC. Military Application Division of the Atomic Energy Commission.

MADW. Military Air Defense Warning net.
mae. mean absolute error (q.v.).

magic tee. In microwave techniques, a particular radar waveguide configuration, so-called because its physical aspect resembles a double letter "T". The use of this configuration permits the coupling of a radar transmitter and receiver to a common antenna without the use of a TR (transmit-receive) unit.

magnaflux testing. *See* magnetic testing.

magnesium perchlorate [Mg(ClO$_4$)$_2$]. A solid rocket propellant *oxidizer* with 34% available oxygen.

Magnesyn. In communications, a trade-mark name for a small electromagnetic device for transmitting a position signal. It is sometimes used in a repeater unit (e.g., gyro pickoff).

magnetic biasing coil. One of the coil windings on a saturable reactor used to establish a basic magnetization of the core in both polarity and magnitude.

magnetic dipole. In electronics, a pair of equal north and south magnetic poles spaced closely together.

magnetic equator. *See* isoclinic lines.

magnetic field. (1) Any space or region in which magnetic forces are present, as in the Earth's magnetic field, or in or about a piece of magnetized steel, or in or about an electrical current. (2) The magnetic forces present in such a space or region.

magnetic inclination. *See* dip.

magnetic meridian. Any line representing the horizontal component of the Earth's magnetic field that passes through the magnetic poles.

magnetic oscillograph. A recording instrument using as its sensitive element a galvanometer (D'Arsonval coil). Photographic recording is customary.

magnetic pole. Either of two small areas on the Earth's surface toward which the lines of force of the Earth's magnetic fields converge. The magnetic poles shift or move their positions constantly, but remain within limited areas, one in the far north, the other in the far south.

magnetic storm. A period of violent fluctuations in the Earth's magnetic field caused by solar flares. The fluctuations induce electric currents in the ionosphere (q.v.) and in long-distance cables and severely interrupt radio and telephone communications.

magnetic tape. (1) A means for storing information by varying the magnetic properties of a moving tape. (2) Tape impregnated with a ferromagnetic substance which undergoes varying magnetization corresponding to the magnitude of an applied current.

magnetic testing. A nondestructive means for testing ferromagnetic materials to determine variations in the physical and chemical properties, stress concentrations, structures, etc. In general, the tests are used to determine defects such as cracks, seams, voids, or inclusions, and consist of passing an electric current (AC or DC) through the part to create a magnetic field about the part, or through a coil surrounding the part to create a magnetic reaction within the part. Discontinuities in structure are flux leakage points and are easily located by use of appropriate instruments or equipment.

magnetic variation. The angular difference between magnetic north and true north, as in "the magnetic variation of x is 5° east." Also termed *magnetic declination,* though *magnetic variation* is the preferred term to avoid confusion with the term declination as used in astronomy.

magnetic wire. Wire capable of storing information by undergoing changes in magnetization conforming to the applied current representing the desired information.

magnetograph. An instrument for mapping the magnetic field of the Sun. Its action depends on the Zeeman effect. It scans the Sun in narrowly spaced lines and measures the Zeeman splitting of the spectral lines continuously. The measurements are recorded in a trace which wanders above or below the scanning line according to the sign and strength of the magnetic field at each point along the line.

magnetohydrodynamics. The science of controlling fluid flow. It deals with ultra-high altitude, high-speed flight; examines whether an electrically charged wing or aerodynamic body passing through a sea of ions can attract these charged particles on the one side and repel them on the other to produce lift. This opens the possibility of new forms of propulsion, new ways to protect high-speed aircraft from frictional heating, and new nuclear power plants. Other phases applied to this phenomenon are: *magnetofluid dynamics, magneto-gas dynamics, hydrodynamics, magneto-aerodynamics, gas dynamics.*

magnetometer. A device for measuring the Earth's magnetic field, notably magnetic anomalies.

magnetron. A high-vacuum thermionic tube capable of producing high output power in the microwave region of the frequency spectrum. The tube consists of a heater, cathode, usually a multisegment anode, and an external magnet (electro or permanent) for controlling the unidirectional current flow in the tube.

magnetron, cavity. *See* cavity magnetron.

magnetron strapping. In electronics, methods used to suppress undesired modes of oscillation.

magnification factor. For a flexibly supported object undergoing forced vibration, the magnification factor is a measure of the response of the object to the vibration and is the ratio between the magnitude of a particular characteristic of the vibration of the object and the same characteristic of the forcing vibration. Characteristics of particular concern are: *acceleration, displacement, force, velocity;* but *displacement* is usually meant unless otherwise indicated.

magnitude. In astronomy, the brightness of a star; first magnitude is the brightness of a candle flame at a distance of 1300 ft. Order of magnitude decreases from first to twentieth at a ratio of intensity of 2.5; the first magnitude is 100 times brighter than the sixth; stars of the first six magnitudes are visible to the naked eye.

magnitude. *Types of, see* bolometric–; order of–.

main bang. (Vernacular) In a radar set, the term applied to the transmitted pulse.

main control surface. Any one of the primary control surfaces (q.v.) used to change the direction of flight (e.g., an aileron, a movable wing).

main stage. That phase in the thrust buildup of a single rocket engine or a multiengine rocket powerplant when full thrust (at or above 90% of rated thrust) is obtained. With certain multi-stage designs, main stage defines the operation of rocket engines remaining on the vehicle after booster rockets have been expended and jetti-soned.

maintainability. A term indicating those quali-ties of an item which determine the relative effort necessary to sustain the item in a state of readiness to perform the function for which it was designed.

maintenance. All action taken to retain materiel in a serviceable condition or to restore it to serviceability. It includes inspection, testing, servicing, classification as to serviceability, re-pair, rebuilding, and reclamation.

maintenance. *Types of, see* depot level–; emer-gency–; engineering–; field level–; flight line–; organization–; precautionary–; preventive–.

maintenance depot. A military base where main-tenance is performed on materiel requiring major overhaul or a complete rebuilding of parts, sub-assemblies, assemblies, and end items. It per-forms the repair of parts, modifications, testing, and reclamation as required.

maintenance ground support equipment. *See* ground support equipment. In some instances, a maintenance function may be performed by support equipment intended primarily to per-form an operational function (e.g., missile checkout by means of the launch control equip-ment).

major subsystem. A large functional division of a weapon system (e.g., airframe, propulsion, guidance, radar, launcher, etc.).

major test point. A test point used to identify an overall function of a missile subsystem (q.v.).

"make and buy" structure. A composite listing of major parts and/or assemblies of an end item (q.v.) depicting those parts and/or assem-blies which will be made *on-site* and *off-site* in addition to research and development studies conducted in support thereof. Details of each "make and buy" structure vary depending upon the complexity of the end item being considered and are negotiated on an individual basis.

MAL. Materiel Allowance List.

malf-out. (Vernacular) Malfunction or failure of component.

mammatocumulus cloud. A small cumulus (q.v.) having large pouches or other protuber-ances hanging from its lower surface.

management. That part of administration con-cerned with the procedures, techniques, and processes employed in an operation; the per-sons concerned with these procedures, etc. The object of management is unified, economic, and coordinated effort. Those responsible for man-agement resolve, or attempt to resolve, prob-lems inherent in planning, deciding, organizing, measuring, communicating, etc.

management and administration personnel. Those individuals expending effort in the man-agement and administration area (including clerical and planning) in direction and support of all the other personnel categories. A typical breakdown would include such functions as in-dustrial relations, purchasing, the controller's office, and general management.

mandrel. A low-frequency jamming transmitter.

maneuver. (1) In space flight, a controlled change of orbit usually by means of thrust force (*impulse maneuver*), but possible also by uti-lizing a perturbation force (*perturbation maneu-ver*). (2) In missile trajectories, a controlled change in flight path in response to guidance system generated signals causing the control surfaces or thrust device to produce a maneuver.

maneuver. *Types of, see* capture–; correction–; escape–; impulse–; perturbation–.

maneuverability. (1) The ability of a missile to alter its flight path to meet tactical require-ments. (2) Specifically, that structural or aero-dynamic quality in a missile or aircraft which determines the magnitude and rate at which its attitude and direction of flight can be changed. Commonly expressed in g's.

man-hour. A unit of work representing the productive effort of one person in one hour. Used in cost and manpower analysis. In work-ing a man-hour, the person is assumed to lose no time in idleness, relaxation, or nonproductive effort. In practice about 85% of the actual man-hours are productive.

man-hours. *Types of, see* direct–; indirect–.

manifolding. A technique used in multiple rocket launching carriages to ensure equaliza-tion of chamber pressure and hence minimized thrust misalignment. A passageway connecting the head end of the several rockets provides for the required gas flow. *See* crossover tube.

manipulative deception. The manipulation of traffic in friendly communication channels with the intention of deceiving the enemy.

manned space vehicle. *See* space vehicle.

manual. *See* technical manual.

man-year. An effort equal to that of one person for one year. (It is equivalent to 2080 man-hours, (q.v.), that must be paid for. The somewhat lesser number of effective man-hours obtained from one man-year will depend upon local conditions and the type of personnel involved. The normal number of effective man-hours per man-year is approximately 1768.)

map matching. A guidance method in which a terrestrial reference is used. An airborne map obtained from photographic or radar reconnaissance is compared with actual terrain to obtain guidance information. Termed the *ATRAN system.*

mapping. *See* conformal mapping.

map, ultrasonic relief. *See* ultrasonic relief map.

margin. *Types of, see* gain–; phase–.

marginal testing. A procedure for system testing which indicates when some portion of the system has deteriorated to the point where there is a high probability of a resultant system failure during the next operating period (e.g., operation of a system with battery voltage reduced by a given percentage to determine whether the system will continue to perform satisfactorily at that reduced voltage). Thus, marginal testing is a form of prediction testing. It tests equipment under more severe conditions than are normally present and thus often will reveal a potential failure or intermittent malfunction by causing it to become a permanent failure.

margin of safety (MS). As used in missile design, the percentage by which the ultimate strength of a member exceeds the design load. The *design load* is the *applied load,* or *maximum probable load,* multiplied by a specified factor of safety. The use of the terms *margin of safety* and *design load* in the above sense is practically restricted to aeronautical engineering.

$$\text{MS} = \frac{\text{allowable load}}{\text{actual load}} - 1 = \frac{\text{allowable stress}}{\text{actual stress}} - 1$$

mark (MK). A designation, used with a numeral, for a model of equipment (e.g., Mark 52 fuze; Mark 51 gun director).

MARK 32. Ship-to-underwater missile. Navy cognizance.

Light-weight acoustic homing anti-submarine missile designed to replace torpedos.

Prime Contractor: Philco Corp.

MARK 43. Air-to-underwater missile. Navy cognizance.

Similar to the MARK 32 (q.v.), except that it can be launched from aircraft as well as from surface ships.

Prime Contractor: Clevite Corp.

marker flare. A pyrotechnic device employed in a missile in flight tests to mark an event of significance; the light or smoke emitted is photographically recorded.

marriage. (Vernacular) The process of physically uniting missile stages, or major subsystems.

MARS Probe. A test vehicle designed to orbit, pass, or impact Mars with the objective of gaining certain scientific knowledge.

MASER. *M*icrowave *a*mplification by *s*timulated *e*mission of *r*adiation (q.v.).

masking. The condition where a part of a missile structure blocks a portion of the warhead emission, fuze sensing area, or electromagnetic radiation area.

mass. In engineering units, mass is the *weight* of a body divided by the acceleration of gravity. The unit is the *slug. See* systems of measurement.

mass. *Types of, see* air–; initial–; polar air–; reduced–; tropical–.

mass accelerator. *See* light gas gun.

mass ratio. (1) The ratio of the initial mass of a rocket to the mass after final burnout (always greater than unity). (2) The ratio of the mass of a rocket after fuel burnout to the initial mass. Note that these commonly used definitions are reciprocals! (3) The ratio of propellant to the gross weight of a rocket (preferred meaning). Here the mass ratio determines the final velocity attainable by a rocket in terms of its exhaust velocity.

master equipment allowance list (MEAL). A publication that prescribes allowances of organizational equipment to be authorized to technical operation units through the medium of the unit mission equipment (q.v.) column of the Unit Authorization List (q.v.).

master indicator. In any system where more than one indicator is used (e.g., in a gyro flux-gate compass system), that indicator that is either considered the main one or is used as a transmitter to another.

master operational console (MOC). The central console and monitoring point for all missile launch station activities necessary for preflight checkout, countdown sequencing, firing, and post-firing deactivation.

master station. In a hyperbolic navigation system (q.v.), that station in a given pair of transmitting stations that controls the transmissions of the other station in the pair (the slave station) and maintains the time relationship between the pulses of the two stations.

master synchronization pulse. A pulse distinguished from other pulses by amplitude and/or duration, occurring at the end of every telemetering system commutator frame to indicate completion of frame.

MATADOR. Surface-to-surface winged bomber. Air Force designation: TM-61A, TM-61B, TM-61C.

Solid propellant rocket booster; turbojet sustainer. TM-61A and TM-61B have ground-controlled (MSQ1 ground system) and APW-11 airborne beacon guidance. TM-61C has hyperbolic radar; Shanticle system.

Prime Contractor: Martin Co., Baltimore. Airframe: Martin. Engine: Thiokol Chemical Corp. booster; Allison sustainer. Guidance system: Goodyear Aircraft Corp.; Fairchild Camera and Instrument Corp.

matching. In electrical circuitry, the connecting of two circuits in such a way that correct impedance exists in each circuit to insure maximum transfer of energy.

matching. *Types of, see* accelerometer–; impedance–; map–.

matching impedance. The technique of minimizing the standing-wave ratio when two devices having unlike impedances are coupled together. This process, at the same time, maximizes power flow between the two devices, assuming one to be a source and the other a sink. *See also* impedance matching.

material factor. A factor of safety (q.v.) included because of uncertainty of material strength or other physical property.

material-guaranteed minimums. Physical properties of materials which are expected by the producer to be minimum and therefore are guaranteed. *Tensile ultimate* and *yield* are usually the only guaranteed values—all others being on a *derived* basis.

material-90% probability values. Physical properties of materials which are expected to be obtained or exceeded by 90% of the material delivered by the producer. These are statistical values based on actual data for *tensile ultimate* and *yield* values; other properties are *derived*.

materials. *Types of, see* air target–; critical–.

material tests. Tests of the basic materials from which parts and components are made.

materiel. All items necessary for the equipment, maintenance, operation, and support of military activities without distinction as to their application for administrative or combat purposes.

materiel control. That phase of military logistics (q.v.) which embraces the act of managing, regulating, and directing the production, procurement, and distribution of materiel necessary to meet operating requirements.

mathematical logic. *See* symbolic logic.

mathematical model. A mathematical representation of a missile and/or its system and components which can be used to predict performance.

maximum ordinate. The distance from the center of the Earth to the apogee (q.v.) of a missile trajectory, or, preferably, this distance minus the radius of the Earth.

maximum sound pressure. *See* sound (acoustomotive) pressure.

maximum system bandwidth. This is equal to twice the maximum system deviation. Compare with frequency deviation (q.v.).

maximum system deviation. The greatest permissible frequency deviation. In the FM/FM telemetering system (q.v.) the value is set at $\pm 7.5\%$ of the subcarrier band center frequency for all bands below 20 kc. On the bands above 20 kc either $\pm 7.5\%$ or $\pm 15\%$ may be used.

MB. Munitions Board.

MB-1. Air Force designation for the air-to-air missile with a nuclear warhead termed GENIE (q.v.).

mc. Megacycle.

MCM. Surface-to-air missile. Air Force cognizance. Name is derived from *m*issile *c*arrying *m*issile. An experimental missile carrying several smaller target-seeking antiaircraft missiles at supersonic speed.

mcs. Megacycles per second.

MCW. Modulated Continuous Wave.

MDE. Monitor Display Equipment.

meaconing. In electronics, a system for receiving electromagnetic signals and rebroadcasting them with the same frequency so as, for instance, to confuse navigation (e.g., a confusion reflector such as chaff). *See* countermeasures; jamming; spoof.

MEAL. *M*aster *e*quipment *a*llowance *l*ist (q.v.).

mean. (1) A quantity representing the average of two or more other quantities, arrived at by adding the quantities together and dividing by their number. Also termed *arithmetic mean*. (2) In weather reporting, the average of the maximum and minimum temperatures is termed the *mean temperature*. (3) The *geometric mean* of two quantities is the square root of the product of the quantities.

mean absolute error (mae). In measurement theory, the arithmetic mean of all errors without regard to sign. Also termed the *average error*.

$$\text{mae} = \frac{\Sigma \, |X_i - \overline{X}|}{n} = 0.7979\sigma$$

where X_i = value of each measurement; $\overline{X}$ = mean value of measurements; n = number of measurements; σ = standard deviation.

mean aerodynamic chord (MAC). The chord of an assumed rectangular airfoil, representing the mean chord of an actual airfoil.

mean British thermal unit. A measurement, $\frac{1}{180}$ of the amount of heat required to raise one pound of water from 32°F to 212°F at a pressure of one atmosphere.

mean error. In measurement theory, the mean value of an error as contrasted to the spread of errors about that mean value. Also termed *arithmetic mean, algebraic average,* and *bias*.

mean free path. The distance the average molecule in a gas will travel before striking another molecule. At sea-level conditions the mean free path of a molecule is a very small fraction of an inch. As altitude increases, the atmospheric density drops because there are less molecules in a given volume of air. The criterion for *continuity* is the mean free path of a molecule.

mean gram-calorie. A measurement, $\frac{1}{100}$ of the amount of heat required to raise one gram of water from 0°C to 100°C at a pressure of one atmosphere (q.v.).

mean life. The arithmetical mean (average) of the operating time between failures.

mean mixture ratio. Ratio equal to the average oxidizer flow rate divided by the average fuel flow rate, within the 90 per-cent-of-rated thrust ordinates of a curve made of a complete firing of a rocket engine or gas generator.

mean solar day. A day of twenty-four hours, as reckoned by ordinary methods, measured from midnight to midnight and defined as the interval between two successive transits of a mean sun over the same meridian. Also termed a *civil day*. *See* Greenwich mean time.

mean sun. In its elliptical course around the Sun, the Earth accelerates as it moves toward the Sun and slows down as it recedes from it. This causes the Sun's apparent motion in the sky to vary throughout the year. The *mean sun* is an imaginary celestial body which moves through the sky with a constant speed equal to the average speed of the true Sun. The interval by which the true Sun is ahead of or behind the mean sun is termed the *equation of time*. It never exceeds seventeen minutes, and four times a year it is zero. It is tabulated in almanacs.

mean time between failure (mtbf). Of a complex system (in which failed parts are replaced with new parts of equal failure rate) is essentially the average time between outrages (q.v.) caused by catastrophic failures. It can be determined by dividing the product of the number of equipments tested (N) and the test time (t) by the number of failures (f) which occur during that time; i.e., mtbf or often just $m = Nt/f$; m is the reciprocal of λ, i.e., $m = 1/\lambda$, and is related to the probability of survival by the exponential failure law $P_s = e^{-t/m}$. The figure of merit m is convenient for use in determining if the reliability of an equipment is likely to be adequate for missions of specific lengths; m is sometimes expressed as $\overline{t}$.

measurement. *See* on-off measurement.

measurement systems. *Types of, see* cgs–; metric–; systems of measurement.

mechanical compliance. The reciprocal of stiffness. Compliance in a mechanical vibrating system is that coefficient which, when multiplied by 2π times the frequency, is the reciprocal of the negative imaginary part of the *mechanical impedance* (q.v.). The unit is the *centimeter per dyne*. *See* compliance.

mechanical equivalent of heat. The amount of work which is equivalent to a unit quantity of heat (e.g., 777.97 ft-lb = 1 Btu; 4.186×10^7 ergs = 1 cal).

mechanical filter. (1) A filter, which is usually sharply tuned, consisting of appropriately shaped metal rods which act as a series of coupled mechanical resonators. Electrical coupling into and out of the filter may be accomplished by piezoelectrical transducers. Since successful operation of these filters may be achieved up to several hundred kilocycles, the filters find frequent application in the intermediate-frequency amplifiers of "very selective" superheterodyne receivers. (2) Any mechanical device used as a band pass filter.

mechanical impedance. *See* mechanical rectilineal impedance.

mechanical injuries. Injuries caused by flying debris or fragments.

mechanical pilot. Automatic pilot (q.v.).

mechanical properties. Those properties that

reveal the reaction, elastic and inelastic, of a material to an applied force, or that involve the relationship between stress and strain (e.g., Young's modulus, tensile strength, fatigue limits). These properties have often been designated as *physical properties*, but the term *mechanical properties* is much to be preferred.

mechanical rectilineal impedance. An inertia-like quantity measured in terms of *mechanical ohms*. The impedance of a mass is proportional to the frequency of the system. Analogous to *electrical impedance* (q.v.).

mechanical rectilineal reactance (mechanical reactance). The component of the impedance (q.v.) of a mechanical system which is provided by the system compliance (q.v.). The unit is the *mechanical ohm*.

mechanical rectilineal resistance (mechanical resistance). The ratio of the applied force to the velocity at the point of application of the force. This is the part responsible for the dissipation of energy. The unit is the *mechanical ohm*.

mechanical rectilineal system. A system adapted for the transmission of linear vibrations and consisting of one or all of the following mechanical rectilineal elements: *resistance* (friction, inertia), *mass*, and *compliance* (q.q.v.).

mechanical rotational impedance. The complex quotient of the alternating torque applied to a system divided by the resulting angular velocity in the direction of the torque at its point of application. An inertia-like quantity measured in terms of the *rotational ohm*.

mechanical rotational reactance (rotational reactance). The component of the impedance (q.v.) of a rotational system which is provided by the system compliance (q.v.). The unit is the *rotational ohm*.

mechanical rotational resistance (rotational resistance). The ratio of the applied torque to the angular velocity. This is the part of the characteristic impedance (q.v.) responsible for the dissipation of energy. The unit is the *rotational ohm*.

mechanical rotational system. A system adapted for the transmission of rotational vibrations and consisting of one or all of the following mechanical rotational elements: *rotational resistance, moment of inertia,* and *rotational compliance.*

mechanical system. An aggregate of matter, devices, and elements which possesses mass and whose parts are capable of relative motion.

mechanical time fuze. A fuze (q.v.) whose time action is controlled by a clocklike mechanism.

mechanics. The branch of physics which deals with the effects of forces upon bodies at rest or in motion. The laws and phenomena of gases and liquids and solid bodies have a part in this subject, and it is one of the basic studies of engineering, physics, and astronomy. It is customary to divide mechanics into: (a) the study of liquids (*hydraulics, hydrodynamics,* and *hydrostatics*); (b) the study of the action of gases (*pneumatics*); and (c) the study of rigid or elastic particles or bodies in solid materials. It is to the latter field that the term mechanics is frequently restricted. For convenience it is further subdivided into *statics, kinematics,* and *kinetics. Statics* deals with bodies at rest, in equilibrium under the action of forces or of torques; *kinematics* deals with abstract motion; and *kinetics* treats of the effect of forces or of torques upon the motions of material bodies. Modern usage favors the term *dynamics,* reserving mechanics for the more practical phases of the field. *Fluid mechanics* is that branch of mechanics which deals with those fundamental laws which apply to all fluids (liquid or gases) at rest or in motion.

mechanics. *Types of, see* celestial–; fluid–.

mechanism. *See* safety and arming mechanism.

medium altitude. Any altitude considered in context to be neither low nor high. It depends for its meaning upon such factors as the equipment being flown and the highest altitudes being reached by recently developed equipment. Arbitrary limits, however, are sometimes indicated by the term as between 5000 and 13,500 ft, or between 8000 and 15,000 ft.

medium delay fuze. A type of delay fuze (q.v.) in which the fuze action is delayed for a period of time between that of short-delay fuzes and long-delay fuzes, normally 4 to 15 sec.

megacycle. One million cycles; a frequency used in the RF range—megacycles per second.

megaton. (1) One million tons. (2) The explosive power of one million tons of TNT, as in a "megaton thermonuclear warhead."

megmho. A unit of electric measurement.

1 megmho = 0.001 abmho = 10^6 mhos

megohm. A unit of electric measurement.

1 megohm = 10^{15} abohms = 10^{12} microhms
= 10^6 ohms = 1.113×10^{-6} statohm

memory unit. In computer usage, a memory device in which data required for computation are stored until needed.

Mercator projection. In cartography, a means

for portraying the Earth's surface. To obtain the proper proportion, the meridians are expanded in the same ratio as the parallels. As the latitude increases, the parallels expand on an increasing scale, and accordingly the meridians expand in proportion. To compensate for this error, different scales must be used on Mercator charts for measuring distances in different latitudes. The expansion of the latitude and longitude scales approximates the secant of the latitude for short distances.

Mercator projection. *Types of, see* inverse–; oblique–; track–; transverse–.

mercury fulminate. An explosive compound extremely sensitive to shock, spark, or friction, used to set off other explosives. It is a mercury salt of fulminic acid, $Hg(ONC)_2 \cdot \frac{1}{2} H_2O$.

MERCURY project. The National Aeronautics and Space Administration (q.v.) sponsored project to put a man in space. McDonnell Aircraft Corporation has the contract for the man-carrying capsule. The booster is planned to be either an ATLAS or TITAN (q.q.v.) rocket.

meridian. Great circles of the Earth which pass through its poles. The *prime* meridian is the meridian used as the origin of measurement of longitude. The meridian of the original site of the Royal Observatory at Greenwich, England, is used by nearly all of the countries in the world as the prime meridian.

meridian. *Types of, see* celestial–; Greenwich–; magnetic–; prime–; terminal–.

meru. *M*illi-*e*arth *r*ate *u*nit (q.v.).

meson. In physics, a particle with a mass approximately 200 times that of an electron, having either a negative or positive charge. Also termed a *mesotron* or *heavy electron.*

mesopause. That altitude (about 50 miles) at which the temperature profile changes. It separates the mesosphere (q.v.) and the thermosphere (q.v.) in the Chapman atmosphere. See Fig. 11, page 140.

mesosphere. That portion of the atmosphere extending from about 250 miles to 650 miles altitude (Gerson); or from about 15 miles to 50 miles altitude (Chapman temperature nomenclature). See Fig. 11, page 140.

mesotron. Synonymous with meson (q.v.).

metagalaxy. The entire material universe. The total of all the galaxies, including the particles, stars, and planets which make up the galaxies and are contained in the space between.

metal-ceramic. A substance consisting of a mixture of a metal in a ceramic such as metallic oxide, carbide, or nitride, which in general gives some ductility to the ceramic. Also termed *ceramet.*

metal parts. A generic term inclusively describing the parts of a solid propellant rocket, excepting the propellant charge, the inhibitor (inert liner), and the igniter. (Metal parts may comprise between 10% and 40% of the gross weight of a rocket.)

metal parts/weight ratio. A term used in solid propellant rocket design to ratio the weight of the metal parts to the total weight of the loaded rocket excluding special fittings and attachments. It equals unity *minus* the propellant/weight ratio.

metascope. A device for transforming invisible infrared rays into visible signals; used in communications where detection is guarded against.

metastable propulsion. Electrically neutral or charged molecules in an excited state are used to produce thrust. See Table 4, page 187.

METEOR. A manned satellite. METEOR stands for '*m*anned *E*arth-satellite *t*erminal *e*volving from *E*arth-to-*O*rbit ferry *r*ockets.'

Goodyear Aircraft Corporation has spent more than five years in the preliminary design investigation of the METEOR concept. The satellite could be used first as a research test vehicle, unmanned; then as a small, temporary, manned Earth satellite, as the basic unit for a permanent orbit in outer space and step by step to more advanced scientific ventures.

meteor. A transient celestial body that enters the Earth's atmosphere with great velocity, incandescent with heat generated by the resistance of the air.

meteor bumper. A thin shield, comparable in thickness with the diameter of the meteor to be intercepted, around a space vehicle and designed to dissipate thermally the energy of meteoritic particles. High impact velocity of the meteor leads to vaporization of the meteor and a part of the shield without penetration of any particles to the wall of the space vehicle.

METEOR JR. A Goodyear Aircraft Corporation proposal for the development of a space platform (q.v.). The ferry vehicle was proposed as a 3-stage, 500 ton rocket with a payload of 2000 lb and a crew of four. Stages are to be recoverable with turbojet power. Rocket propellants are 1:3 mixture of ammonia and liquid fluorine. Estimated I_{sp} (frozen) is 310 sec.

meteorite. A stony or metallic body that has fallen to the Earth from outer space.

meteorograph. An apparatus that measures two or more meteorological elements or characteristics, as air pressure, temperature, humidity, etc., and automatically either records these measurements on a sheet or, when airborne, transmits them by radio to ground observation stations. *See* radiosonde.

meteoroid. A small solid object in space.

meteorology. That branch of physics that treats of the atmosphere and its phenomena, especially heat and moisture changes, low and high pressures, or other such phenomena that affect the weather.

meter. A unit of length measurement.

1 meter = 10^{10} Å = 100 cm = 3.2808 ft
= 39.370 in. = 0.001 km = 10^6
microns = 1000 mm = 1.09361 yd

1 meter candle = 1 lumen/sq meter

meter. *Types of, see* driftmeter–; Frahm frequency–; inertial velocity–; MACH–; velocity–; yawmeter.

methane (CH_4). A liquid rocket propellant *fuel.*

methanol (CH_3OH). A liquid rocket propellant *fuel.*

method, *Types of, see* bump–; Didion-Bernoulli–; frequency response–; Gâvre retardation–; Monte Carlo–; Otto-Lardillon–; Rayleigh-Ritz–; Siacci–.

method of attributes. Method of measurement of quality which consists in noting the presence or absence of some characteristic (attribute) in each of the units in the group under consideration and counting how many do or do not possess it (e.g., go and not-go gaging of a dimension).

method of variables. Method of measurement of quality by measuring and recording the numerical magnitude of a quality characteristic for each of the units in the group under consideration. This involves reading a scale of some kind.

methyl acetylene (propyne). A liquid rocket propellant *fuel.* See Table 3, page 157.

methyl alcohol (CH_3CH). A liquid rocket propellant *fuel.* See Table 3, page 157.

methylamine (CH_3NH_2). A liquid rocket propellant *fuel.* See Table 3, page 157.

methyl cyclopentane. A liquid rocket propellant *fuel.* See Table 3, page 157.

metric data. The data which are obtained primarily for measurement purposes and from which a quantitative evaluation of missile performance may be made. *Metric film* is the film exposed for metric data purposes.

metric system. In the metric system of measurements, the principal units are: (a) the *meter* for length; (b) the *liter* for capacity or volume; (c) the *gram* for weight. Prefixes are used for subdivisions and multiples: (a) milli = 1/1000; (b) centi = 1/100; (c) deci = 1/10; (d) deca = 10; (e) hecto = 100; kilo = 1000; mega = 1,000,000. The most commonly used subdivisions and multiples are: (a) length = kilometer, meter, centimeter, and millimeter; (b) capacity or volume = cubic meter, cubic centimeter, and cubic millimeter; (c) weight = kilogram and gram. The U.S. customary lengths, areas, and cubic measures derived from the international meter are based on the relation 1 meter = 39.37 inches (exactly) or 1 yard = 0.9144018 meter. The U.S. customary weights derived from the international kilogram are based on the value 1 avoirdupois pound = 453.5924277 grams.

Linear measure
(length)

1 kilometer
= 1000 meters = 0.621 mile
1 meter (m)
= 100 centimeters (cm) = 39.37 inches
= 3.2808 feet = 1.0936 yards
1 centimeter (cm)
= 10 millimeters = 0.3937 inch
1 millimeter (mm)
= 1000 microns = 0.03937 inch
1 micron (μ)
= 10,000 Ångstroms (Å)
1 mile
= 1.609 kilometers
1 yard
= 0.9144 meter
1 foot
= 0.3048 meter = 304.8 millimeters
1 inch
= 2.54 centimeters = 25.4 millimeters

Cubic measure
(volume or capacity)

1 cubic meter
= 35.314 cubic feet = 1.308 cubic yards
= 264.2 U.S. gallons
1 cubic centimeter
= 0.061 cubic inch
1 liter (cubic decimeter)
= 0.0353 cubic foot = 61.023 cubic inches
= 0.2642 U.S. gallon = 1.0567 U.S. quarts
1 cubic yard
= 0.7645 cubic meter
1 cubic foot
= 0.02832 cubic meter = 28.317 liters
1 cubic inch
= 16.38716 cubic centimeters
1 U.S. gallon
= 3.785 liters
1 U.S. quart
= 0.946 liter

Weight measure

1 metric ton
  = 0.9842 ton (of 2240 pounds) = 2204.6 pounds
1 kilogram
  = 2.2046 pounds = 35.274 ounces avoirdupois
1 gram
  = 15.432 grains = 0.03527 ounce avoirdupois
  = 0.03215 ounce troy
1 ton (of 2240 pounds)
  = 1.016 metric tons = 1016 kilograms
1 pound
  = 0.4536 kilogram = 453.6 grams
1 ounce avoirdupois
  = 28.35 grams
1 ounce troy
  = 31.103 grams
1 grain
  = 0.0648 gram
1 kilogram/square millimeter
  = 1422.32 pounds/square inch
1 kilogram/square centimeter
  = 14.223 pounds/square inch
1 kilogram-meter
  = 7.233 foot-pounds
1 pound/square inch
  = 0.0703 kilogram/square centimeter

Heat measure

1 calorie (kilogram-calorie)
  = 3.968 Btu (British thermal unit)

See systems of measurement.

Mev. Million electron-volts.

MEW. Microwave Early Warning (q.v.).

MF. Medium Frequency (300-3000 kcs).

mho. A unit of electric measurement.

$$1 \text{ mho} = 10^{-9} \text{ abmho} = 10^{-6} \text{ megmho}$$
$$= 1 \text{ ohm}^{-1} = 8.988 \times 10^{11} \text{ statmhos}$$

Mickey. (Vernacular) A popular name applied to various airborne radar sets, radar range finders, and switch boxes. In full, *Mickey Mouse.*

microfarad. A unit of electric measurement.

$$1 \text{ microfarad} = 10^{-15} \text{ abfarad} = 10^{-6} \text{ farad}$$
$$= 8.988 \times 10^{5} \text{ statfarads}$$

microgram. A unit of mass measurement.

$$1 \text{ microgram} = 10^{-6} \text{ gram}$$

micro-H. An H-system bombing and navigational radar set which operates in the region of 10,000 mc/sec.

microhenry. A unit of electric measurement.

$$1 \text{ microhenry} = 1000 \text{ abhenrys} = 10^{-6} \text{ henry}$$
$$= 0.001 \text{ millihenry}$$
$$= 1.113 \times 10^{-18} \text{ stathenry}$$

microhm. A unit of electric measurement.

$$1 \text{ microhm} = 1000 \text{ abohms} = 10^{-12} \text{ megohm}$$
$$= 10^{-6} \text{ ohm} = 1.113 \times 10^{-18}$$
$$\text{statohm}$$

microlock. A phase lock-loop system for transmitting and receiving information. It may be used as a radar beacon for tracking, or to provide telemetering data. The system reduces bandwidth requirements.

micrometeorites. Small dust particles moving around the Sun; may be debris from the formation of the solar system or interstellar dust coming into the solar system; may cause erosion and destruction of optical and other surfaces on vehicles moving at high speeds.

micrometeorology. The study of the variations in meteorological conditions over very small areas, such as hillsides, forests, river basins, etc.

micromicron. A unit of length measurement.

$$1 \text{ micromicron} = 0.01 \text{ Å} = 10^{-10} \text{ cm}$$
$$= 10^{-6} \text{ micron}$$

microminiaturization. An extension of the state of the art in miniaturizing air- and space-borne equipment to reduce volume and weight. A technique used particularly for instrumentation carried by satellites (q.v.) and space probes (q.v.). *See also* miniaturization.

micron. A unit of length measurement.

$$1 \text{ micron} = 10,000 \text{ Å} = 0.0001 \text{ cm}$$
$$= 3.280833 \times 10^{-6} \text{ ft}$$
$$= 3.937 \times 10^{-5} \text{ in.} = 0.001 \text{ mm}$$
$$= 1000 \text{ millimicrons} = 0.03937 \text{ mil}$$
1 micron of mercury at 32°F
$$= 3.937 \times 10^{-5} \text{ in. of mercury at 32°F}$$
$$= 0.001 \text{ mm of mercury at 32°F}$$

microphonics. Unwanted noises and frequencies in an electronic circuit output caused by vibration of tube elements, bouncing switch contacts, etc. (e.g., output signals caused by the application of mechanical forces to a unit which is not supposed to respond to them).

microstrip. In electronics, a miniaturized transmission line technique used in the kilomegacycle range. It consists of a wire above a ground plane and is analogous to a two-wire line.

microvolt. A unit of electric measurement.

$$1 \text{ microvolt} = 100 \text{ abvolts} = 0.001 \text{ millivolt}$$
$$= 3.336 \times 10^{-9} \text{ statvolt} = 10^{-6}$$
$$\text{volt}$$
$$1 \text{ microvolt/meter} = 3.336 \times 10^{-11}$$
$$\text{statvolt/cm}$$
$$= 10^{-8} \text{ volt/cm}$$
$$= 2.540005 \times 10^{-8} \text{ volt/in.}$$

microwave. A subclassification of the electromagnetic spectrum. It generally covers the wavelength region from very high frequency (VHF) to extremely high frequency (EHF) (about 3 meters to 0.1 cm). See Fig. 8, page 105.

microwave amplification by stimulated emission of radiation (MASER). Devices made with gases or solids in which atoms or molecules can be raised to a high energy level at which they are unstable. A signal will cause them to radiate excess energy at a specific wavelength. Energy emitted greatly exceeds the incoming signal. Gaseous masses produce uniform and precise oscillations. Sometimes termed *molecular oscillators, versitrons, quantum-mechanical amplifiers.*

microwave discriminator. In electronics, a discriminator (q.v.) which converts a frequency-modulated microwave signal into an audio or video signal by using a tuned cavity in place of the tuned circuit present in ordinary discriminators.

microwave early warning (MEW). A high-power, long-range radar, giving high resolution and used for early warning of enemy craft.

microwave frequency filter. In electronics, resonant cavity sections (waveguide or coaxial line sections) built into microwave transmission lines to cause desired frequencies to be transmitted along the line and other frequencies to be rejected or absorbed.

microwave spectrum. A spectrum of wavelengths lying in the region between the far infrared and the conventional radio-frequency region. The boundaries of the microwave region have not been definitely fixed, but it is commonly regarded as extending from about 0.1 cm to 3 m in wavelength, representing about 8 octaves of the electromagnetic spectrum. See Fig. 8, page 105.

MIDAS (COTAR). A semiactive, omnidirectional, phase-comparison system used as an electronic equivalent of Askania theodolite (q.v.) to track any airborne target which transmits signals in the telemetry spectrum (200-260 mcs). It can track multiple targets simultaneously and, as a result, provide vector miss distance (q.v.), as well as test-control, range safety (q.v.), and target acquisition data (q.v.) in multiple-target tests.

midcourse. That phase of a guidance trajectory usually initiated at the end of the boost or launch phase and ending at the start of the terminal or homing phase. See Fig. 27, page 293.

midcourse guidance. The guidance applied to a missile between the termination of the launching phase and the start of the terminal phase of guidance.

MIG. Miniature Integrating Gyroscope.

Mighty Mouse. Air-to-air unguided rocket. Length: 48 in.; diameter: 2.75 in.; weight: 18.5 lb (warhead is 3.5 lb of this figure); thrust: 800-900 lb; speed: MACH 2.7. Uses a solid propellant power plant. Standard weapon for fighter aircraft. A T-110 rocket gun has been developed to fire this missile.

mil. (1) A unit of angular measurement. In artillery and guided missile usage, a mil is equal to 1/6400 of a circle. In infantry usage, a mil is the angle subtended by 1 yard at 1000 yards distance; 100 artillery mils equals 98.2 infantry mils. (2) A unit of linear measurement:

    1 mil = 0.001 in. = 0.00254 cm = 25.400 microns

mile. A unit of measurement of length or distance.

$$1 \text{ statute mile} = 80 \text{ chains} = 5280 \text{ ft}$$
$$= 1.60935 \text{ km} = 1609.35 \text{ meters}$$
$$= 0.86898 \text{ nm} = 1760 \text{ yd}$$

$$1 \text{ nautical mile} = 6076.103 \text{ ft} = \tfrac{1}{3} \text{ league}$$
$$= 1.15078 \text{ statute miles}$$

$$1 \text{ mile/hour} = 88 \text{ ft/min} = 1.4667 \text{ ft/sec}$$
$$= 0.86898 \text{ knot}$$

mile. *Types of, see* air–; nautical–; statute–.

milestone (milepost). An event or action within the research, development, test, production, and in-service life of a project. The milestone possesses a distinct, objectively identifiable terminal point, which can be used as a means of evaluating the progress of research and development in terms of its estimated schedule and as such, indicates the accomplishment of a significant step leading toward a broader, predetermined goal.

military characteristics. The performance requirements of equipment which must be satisfied by an over-all system intended to perform desired military functions. Military characteristics include *physical* and *operational* characteristics but not *technical* characteristics.

military phonetic alphabet. (obsolescent); *See* ICAO alphabet.

A Able	G George	N Nan	T Tare
B Baker	H Howe	O Oboe	U Uncle
C Charlie	I Item	P Peter	V Victor
D Dog	J Jig	Q Queen	W William
E Easy	K King	R Roger	X Xray
F Fox	L Love	S Sugar	Y Yoke
	M Mike		Z Zebra

military standard specification (MIL STD). A formal specification, coordinated and approved by the Army, Navy, and/or Air Force as appropriate. One of the services usually has cognizance of the specification. It is used to standardize procurement on a competitive basis.

Milky Way. The luminous belt stretching across the heavens consisting mostly of stars so faint that they cannot be seen individually. This belt defines the central plane of our galaxy. The galaxy itself is often loosely referred to as the Milky Way.

milliampere. A unit of electric current equal to one-thousandth of an ampere.

millibar. A unit of pressure equal to one-thousandth of a bar, a force equal to one thousand dynes per square centimeter. In measuring atmospheric pressure, a millibar is a unit of pressure equal to approximately 0.0295 inch of mercury at 32°F, under standard conditions of gravity.

milli-earth-rate unit (meru). A unit equal to 0.001 revolutions of the Earth per day.

milligram. A unit of weight measurement.

1 milligram = 0.001 gram

millihenry. A unit of electric measurement.

1 millihenry = 0.001 gram = 10^6 abhenrys
= 0.001 henry = 1000 microhenrys
= 1.113×10^{-15} stathenry

milliliter. A unit of volume measurement.

1 milliliter = 1.000027 cu cm = 0.061025 cu in. = 0.001 liter
= 0.03381 fluid oz

millimeter. A unit of length measurement in the metric system (q.v.).

1 millimeter = 0.1 cm = 0.03937 in. = 0.001 meter = 1000 microns
= 39.37 mils

millimicron. A unit of length measurement.

1 millimicron = 10^{-7} cm = 0.001 micron

milling. *See* chemical milling.

millisadic. A data processing system used to translate pulse width or analog data into digital form; a proprietary system marketed by Consolidated Electrodynamics Corp.

millivolt. A unit of electric measurement.

1 millivolt = 100,000 abvolts = 1000 microvolts = 3.336×10^{-6} statvolt
= 0.001 volt

1 millivolt/meter = 1000 abvolts/cm = 10^{-8} kv/cm = 1000 microvolts/meter
= 10^{-5} volt/cm = 2.540 $\times 10^{-5}$ volt/in.

mils. *Missile impact location system* (q.v.).

MIL STD. Military standard. *See* military standard specification.

miner's fuze. Synonymous with Bickford fuze (q.v.).

miniaturization. Usually, the reduction in size, weight, or both, of a system, package, component, or element by using very small parts and interconnections. Sometimes it denotes the addition of a capability, increased power, better performance, etc., for the same size or weight. *See* subminiaturization.

minitrack. An electronic interferometer (q.v.) measuring system which gives angular measurement by comparing phase of a signal received at two antennas on a short base line.

minor cycle. In a digital computer using serial transmission, the time required for the transmission of *one word*, including the space between words.

MINUTEMAN. Surface-to-surface three-stage Intercontinental Ballistic Missile. Air Force designation: for the weapon system: WS 133A; for the missile: SM-80.

Length: approximately 65 ft; maximum diameter: about 6 ft; launching weight: about 75,000 lb. Solid propellant rocket engines; swiveled nozzles for control; inertially guided.

Systems Engineering contractor: Space Technology Laboratories. Assembly and Test contractor: Boeing Airplane Co. Engine: Aerojet General Corp., Thiokol Chemical Co., Hercules Powder Co. Guidance and control: Autonetics Division, North American Aviation Co. Reentry vehicle (nose cone): AVCO.

MIRAN. *Mi*ssile *ran*ging (q.v.).

mirror. *Types of, see* Cassegrainian–; space–.

misalignment. *See* thrust misalignment.

misfire. An unsuccessful attempt to start a rocket motor; usually, but not always, a case where the igniter functions properly but where the propellant does not ignite (or does ignite but then goes out).

MIS program. *Man-in-s*pace. Follow-on to the Army's Project ADAM. *See* MERCURY project.

miss. *See* near miss.

miss distance. (1) The closest distance between two objects having relative motion (e.g., a guided missile intercepting a target). (2) The Great Circle Distance (q.v.) between the observed impact point and the intended impact point.

missile. A self-propelled, pilotless, airborne weapon.

missile. *Types of, see* antiaircraft–; antimissile–; ballistic–; bumper–; captive–; cluster–; composite–; contra-orbit–; cruise–; defensive–; experimental–; fleet ballistic–; flight–; flying–; glide–; ground–; guided–; guided aircraft–; interceptor–; intercontinental ballistic–; intermediate range ballistic–; jet vane controlled–; laboratory–; mock-up–; multiple stage–; one and a half stage–; operational–; parallel cluster–; readied–; single-stage–; static–; strategic–; sub–; tactical–; tandem–; two-stage–; winged–.

missile attitude. The position of a guided missile as determined by the inclination of its axes (roll, pitch, and yaw) in relation to another object, as to the Earth.

missile control and warning. A service or activity in which missiles are detected and tracked in flight and reported, followed by evaluation and plotting of the information obtained, which information is then used in a warning network and in the control of combative force.

missile impact location system (mils). A splash net system using hydrophones to locate impact areas of missiles.

missile lead-angle. The angle between the flight path of a missile on a collision course with a target and the interconnecting line-of-sight.

missile model types. *See* air-to-air–; air-to-ground–; air-to-surface–; air-to-underwater–; ground-to-air–; ground-to-ground–; surface-to-surface–; surface-to-underwater–; underwater-to-air–; underwater-to-surface–.

missile names. *See:* AEROBEE; AEROBEE HI; AEROSOUND; ALPHA DRACO; ARCON; ARCUS; ARS; ASP; ASROC; ATLANTIS; ATLAS; BDM; BETTY (MK90); BIG BROTHER; BIRD DOG; BLUE GOOSE; BOMARC; BULL DOG; BULL GOOSE; BULL PUP; BUMPER; BUMPER-WAC; CAJUN; COBRA; CORPORAL; CORVUS; CREE; CROSSBOW; DAN; DART; DEACON; DEACON-LOKI; DIAMONDBACK; DING-DONG; DOVE; DUCK; EAGLE; ESSO BEE; EX-8; FALCON; FAR SIDE PROJECT; FFAR; FIREBEE; FIREBIRD; GAPA; GAR-9; GENIE; GOOSE; GORGON; GREEN QUAIL; HASP; HAWK; HERMES; HIGH CARD; HOLY MOSES; HONEST JOHN; HOPI; HOUNDDOG; IRIS; KATIE; KATYDID; KINGFISHER; LACROSSE; LARK; LAZY DOG; LITTLE JOE; LITTLE JOHN; LOKI; LOON; MACE; MARK 32; MARK 43; MATADOR; MCM; MIGHTY MOUSE; MINUTEMAN; MX-774; NASTY; NATIV; NAVAHO; NEPTUNE; NIKE-AJAX; NIKE-ASP; NIKE-HERCULES; NIKE-ZEUS; OPERATION REDWING; ORIOLE; PERSHING; PETREL; PIED PIPER; PLATO; PLOVER; POGO; POLARIS; PRIVATE A; PRIVATE F; Q-5; RASCAL;

RAT; RAVEN; RECON; RECRUIT; REDEYE; REDSTONE; REGULUS I; REGULUS II; ROCKAIRE; ROCKOON; RP-77; SENTRY; SERGEANT; SHILLELAGH; SHRIKE; SIDEWINDER I; SNARK; SOLAR; SPAEROBEE; SPARROW I; SPARROW II; SPARROW III; SUBROC; TALOS; TARTAR; TEAL; TERRAPIN; TERRIER I; TERRIER II; THOR; TING-A-LING; TITAN; TRITON; VIKING; WAC CORPORAL; WAG TAIL; WASP; WHITE LANCE; WIZARD; WIZARD II; ZUNI.

missile quality (MQ). Superior quality in manufactured parts and assemblies to be used for missile applications.

missile ranging (MIRAN). A multi-station measuring system using pulse radar triangulation techniques for measurement of range.

missile retainer. *See* tail grab.

missile roll range. The angle through which a missile can be controlled in roll. For ballistic missiles, it determines the azimuth (q.v.) range of the targets that can be attacked without rotating the launcher.

missile safety system. Command destruct equipment which can destroy a missile remotely after launching in case of malfunction. It is powered by the emergency power supply and consists of command receivers, explosive elements, and initiators. Destruct impulses are initiated upon receipt of ground radio signals.

missile servicing tower. A superstructure providing personnel platforms for missile fueling and servicing.

missile stage. A flight separable section of the complete missile.

missile storage structure. The structure and facilities necessary to receive, support, store, and service one or more missiles.

missile stowage supports. In naval applications, supports provided within a missile magazine to secure the missile radially at the hard points and prevent excessive sway while being transported at sea.

missile system. The over-all terminology for a missile and its interconnected systems. This includes engines, airframe, control system, guidance system, nose cone, warhead, instrumentation, and telemetry (q.q.v.).

missile system. *Types of, see* fleet ballistic–; guided–.

missile test ranges. Test ranges operated by the Armed Services for missile development. *See* Atlantic Missile Range; Pacific Missile Range; White Sands Missile Range; AFMDC; AFFTC;

AEDC; RADC; NOTS; Wallops Island; WSPG.

missile test vehicle. *Types of, see* captive–; flight–; ground–; laboratory–; static–.

missilier. A person skilled in handling, launching, and directing guided missiles.

mission. The end objective of a military operation; the objective may be *tactical* or *strategic*.

mission system. The sum of several weapons and support systems invented to provide a mission capability.

Mitchell camera. A high-speed motion picture camera for recording rapidly occurring events during a missile flight test, particularly at launch and impact (q.q.v.).

mixed-flow compressor. A jet-engine compressor that provides for both axial-flow and radial-flow of the air or other fluid.

mixed force (concept). The concept of retaining a strategic air force as the major deterrent to enemy aggression while building up operational missiles (q.v.).

mixing ratio. The ratio of water vapor to dry air, used as a measure of humidity. Expressed in *grams of water per kilogram of dry air*.

mixture. *See* fuel-air mixture.

mixture ratio. The ratio of the weight of oxidizer used per unit of time to the weight of fuel used per unit of time in bipropellant (q.v.) rocket systems. Volume ratios are used also.

MK. Mark (q.v.).

ML. Medium loop. *See* loop-type radio range.

mm. Millimeter (q.v.).

moazagotl cloud. One or more stationary cloud banks, on the lee side of a mountain barrier or chain, and parallel to the mountains.

mobile stations. A missile launch complex (q.v.) designed for mobile use in forward combat areas for defense against aircraft or for attack on enemy ground targets.

mobility analogy. An acoustical-mechanical dynamical analogy in which velocity corresponds to a voltage and force corresponds to a current. *See* mechanical rectilineal impedance.

MOC. (1) Master Operational Controller, (2) Master Operational Console (q.v.).

mock firing. A test that simulates a complete flight test operation with the exception of firing the engine.

mock-up (MU). A structure or device which simulates an actual equipment or element of a missile system, thus enabling investigation of space relationships, physical fit, and human

operations problems. It may also be used for training.

mock-up, dynamic. *See* dynamic mock-up.

mock-up missile. A full-size representation of the actual article; normally required by the procurement agency; usually provided at the development engineering inspection (DEI), (q.v.).

mode. (1) In statistics, the value or number, in any large grouping, which appears most frequently. (2) In structural dynamics, the characteristic shape taken by a beam or structure when vibrated at a resonant frequency (usually the first 3 or 4 bending modes are most important). (3) A descriptive term applied to a particular methodology or sequence of performing one task of several possible tasks.

mode. *Types of, see* coupled–; failure–; free-free–; pi–; principal–; TE–; TEM–; $TEM_{0,1}$–.

model. *Types of, see* breadboard–; development–; mathematical–; production–; prototype–; preproduction–; research–; scale–.

model atmosphere. A hypothetical atmosphere based on the temperature function by layer. Each layer has a temperature gradient linear with geopotential altitude but whose first derivatives are discontinuous at the intersection of the layers. *See* ICAO standard atmosphere.

model designation. Formal designations for missiles as assigned by the government.

> *A typical system:*
> AAM   Air-to-air missile
> ASM   Air-to-surface missile
> AUM   Air-to-underwater missile
> GAM   Guided aircraft missile
> SAM   Surface-to-air missile
> SM   Strategic missile
> SSM   Surface-to-surface missile
> SUM   Surface-to-underwater missile
> UAM   Underwater-to-air missile
> USM   Underwater-to-surface missile
>
> Preceded by X for development missiles
> Preceded by Y for service test missiles
> Followed by -N for Navy missiles
>   -A for Air Force missiles
>   -G for Army missiles

See also guided missile.

model specification. A formal specification defining the characteristics of a particular missile, system, or subsystem model. The specification may be an equipment rather than performance type but will include design and test criteria. Usually prepared by the contractor as a contractual requirement.

moderator. A substance, such as graphite or heavy water, used in a reactor to slow down neutrons from the high energies at which they are released in fission to lower energies at which they cause fission more readily.

mode shape survey. A survey to determine the primary vibration modal shapes of a missile. It is usually limited to an experimental determination of the first three or four modes. *See* mode.

modification. A major or minor change in the design of an adopted item or materiel which is effected in order to correct a deficiency, facilitate production, increase reliability or performance, or to improve operational effectiveness.

modified double wedge (section) airfoil. An aerodynamic surface with a wedge leading and trailing cross section and a flat section between. The wave drag is:

$$C_{D_w} = \frac{6r^2}{\sqrt{M^2 - 1}} \quad \text{(flat = ⅓ chord)}$$

where $r =$ ratio of maximum thickness to chord of the cross section; $M =$ MACH number.

modulate. (1) To vary the amplitude, frequency, or phase of a radio or electric wave; to change a wave by varying its amplitude, frequency, or phase. (2) To vary the velocity of the electrons in an electron beam.

modulation. *Types of, see* amplitude–; balanced–; binary pulse code–; cross–; frequency–; phase–; pulse–; pulse duration–; pulse position–; pulse time–; pulse width–; velocity–.

modulation index. The ratio of the frequency deviation to the modulating frequency in a frequency-modulated (FM) system; usual value is 5.

$$m_f = \frac{f_d}{f_m} = \frac{f_\text{deviation in cps}}{f_\text{modulation in cps}}$$

modulator. *Types of, see* double-balanced–; reactance–; ring–.

module. (1) As used in the fields of automation and electronics, a single assembly of parts and/or components to form a larger component which meets a functional requirement by performing all of the resistive, inductive, and capacitive functions of a vacuum-tube circuit. (2) A combination of components within a package, or so arranged that they are common to one mounting, that provide a complete function or functions necessary for subsystem or system operation.

modulus. *Types of, see* bulk–; distance–; –of elasticity; Young's–.

modulus of elasticity. The ratio of stress to strain within the elastic range. When the modulus of elasticity, E, is determined from the slope of the stress-strain curve in a tension or compression test, it is often termed *Young's modulus*. Young's modulus for steels is approximately

30,000,000 lb per sq in., for magnesium alloys about 6,000,000 lb per sq in., and for aluminum alloys about 10,000,000 lb per sq in. The modulus of elasticity in shear is termed the *modulus of rigidity*. It is measured in a torsion test, and is the ratio of the unit shear stress to the displacement which it produces per unit specimen length in the elastic range. The shear modulus is:

$$G = \frac{E}{2(1 + \mu)}$$

where $\mu =$ Poisson's ratio, about 0.3 for most materials.

modulus of resilience. The energy stored in a cubic inch of an elastic material at the bottoming point of that material when under stress.

modulus of rigidity. *See* modulus of elasticity.

modulus of rupture. In metallurgy, a measure of the ultimate strength or the breaking load per unit area of a specimen as determined from a torsion, or, more commonly, from a bending, test. The modulus is calculated from the breaking load, assuming that the specimen remains elastic until rupture occurs, although this may not be the case. Its value will be intermediate between the ultimate tensile and compressive strengths.

moist adiabat. A pseudoadiabat (q.v.).

molectronics. *Mol*ecular *electronics*. A micro-miniaturization (q.v.) technique using solid state (q.v.) techniques to provide integrated circuit functions.

molecular beam tunnel. Used in the study of superaerodynamics. It operates at extremely low pressures—down to one ten-millionth of a sea-level atmosphere.

molecular oscillator. *See* microwave amplification by stimulated emission of radiation.

moment. In mechanics, the tendency of a force to produce motion about an axis or point. This tendency is a resultant of mass, force, velocity, or the like, and is measured by the product of one of these and the perpendicular distance (moment arm) from the point of application to the axis or point of rotation.

moment. *Types of, see* hinge–; induced rolling–; restoring–; rolling–.

moment coefficient. *See* aerodynamic forces and moments.

moment equilibrium. A system of forces is in moment equilibrium when the algebraic sum of the moments of the forces about any axis is equal to zero. Expressed mathematically as:

$$\Sigma M = 0$$

moment of area. About any axis the plane of the area is equal to the sum of the products of the component areas and their moment arms.

moment of inertia. A measure of the reluctance of a body to change its velocity of rotation about a given axis. The moment of inertia of a body is the product of its mass, acting at a point (often the center of gravity) times the square of the distance of that point from the axis of rotation.

momentum. The energy in a moving body that continues its motion without application of external force; the measure of this energy. Momentum is either angular or linear. Linear momentum is expressed as the product of the body's mass and its linear velocity.

momentum. *Types of, see* angular–; conservation of–.

monatomic gas. Gas having but one atom to the molecule—having the same valence as hydrogen, or unity.

monitor. To check a transmitted signal to ascertain correct functioning of the transmitting equipment.

monocoque. A type of airframe construction without framing, relying primarily for its rigidity upon the surface or skin which might be of sheet metal or of layers of veneer; a shell-like structure.

monoethylaniline ($C_2H_5C_6H_4NH_2$). A liquid rocket propellant *fuel.*

monogole. A monopropellant.

monomethyl hydrazine (MMH). A liquid rocket propellant *fuel.*

monopropellant. A rocket engine propellant (q.v.) which does not require an oxidizer and which decomposes to furnish its own oxidant and reductant.

monopulse radar. A radar in which directivity is achieved by an antenna having several precisely spaced apertures rather than by scanning. Phase comparison of the several signals yields direction.

Monroe effect. Reinforcement of explosive waves by each other to produce a stronger resultant wave. The concept is used in the design of shaped charges.

Monte Carlo method. A method of solution of a group of physical problems by means of a series of statistical experiments which are performed by applying mathematical operations to random numbers. This method applies most directly to stochastic problems.

Moon. Natural Earth satellite. Lunar atmos-phere may contain heavy gases and small amounts of xenon and krypton.

	Earth	Moon
Diameter	7,917	2,163
Value of g	1	0.16
Escape speed (mps)	7	1.5
Mass	1	0.0123
Mean density ($H_2O = 1$)	5.5	3.4
Average distance from Earth (miles)		238,854
Orbital period (days)		27.3

motion. *Types of, see* equation of–; proper–; retrograde–; shock–; transient–.

motor. *Types of, see* chemical fuel–; rocket–.

motor chamber. In solid propellant rocket usage, the pressure container or bottle containing the propellant grain (q.v.) to which is attached the nozzle. More properly termed an *engine chamber.*

motor head. The upper part of a liquid-fuel rocket engine, usually containing the propellant injection parts and the igniter.

mount. (1) A fabricated shock or vibration isolator, usually consisting of an elastic member and one or more relatively inelastic members, fastened between the equipment to be isolated and its supporting container or structure. (2) The support for a piece of equipment.

mount. *Types of, see* scanning antenna–; shock–; thrust–.

MOUSE. A particular satellite vehicle design, named for *M*inimal *O*rbital *U*nmanned *S*atellite of the *E*arth.

movable nozzle. *See* rotatable nozzle; swivel nozzle.

moving target indicator (MTI). A radar presentation which shows only targets which are in motion, thus improving their contrast to ground clutter. Signals from stationary targets are subtracted out of the return signal by the output of a suitable memory circuit. *See* Doppler radar.

MPI. Mean Point of Impact; also written M.P.I. and m.p.i.

MQ. Missile Quality (q.v.).

MRA. Medium Range Adcock. *See* Adcock radio range.

MRL. Multiple Rocket Launcher.

MS. Margin of Safety (q.v.).

MSA. Mutual Security Agency.

MSL. Mean Sea Level.

msl. Missile (q.v.).

MSP. Mutual Security Program.

MST. Mountain Standard Time. *See* standard time.

M storm. A magnetic storm, produced by disturbances on the Sun, identified by an indefinite beginning and ending and a fairly long period of duration.

mtbf. Mean time between failure (q.v.).

MTI. Moving target indicator (q.v.).

MU. Mock-Up (q.v.).

MUF. Maximum Usable Frequency.

multiple grain. An assembly of solid propellant tubular grains (q.v.) inside a rocket engine case; only exterior surfaces of the individual grains are burning surfaces. Total burning surface decreases as the combustion proceeds; the thrust-versus-duration curve is regressive (q.v.).

multiple hop. A radio transmission path, characterized by more than one reflection from the ionosphere (q.v.) and the Earth. Multiple path transmission can result from different depths of ionospheric penetration as well as from varying frequency of transmissions.

multiple-perforated single cylindrical grain. A solid propellant grain (q.v.) with several perforations parallel to its longitudinal axis; all of the burning surfaces are approximately the same distance apart. See Fig. 22, page 259.

multiple shock intake. In air-breathing engines, a means of increasing the total pressure recovery of a diffuser (q.v.) by reducing the losses encountered with a single normal shock. See Fig. 5, page 73.

multiple stage missile. A multistage vehicle, each stage containing a propulsion system, used as a missile.

multiple tropopause. The tropopause (q.v.) conceived as being at sharply different altitudes in different parts of the atmosphere (q.v.).

multiplex. *See* time-division multiplex.

multiplexer. A device by which simultaneous transmission of two or more signals may be made using a common carrier wave.

multiplexing ("time sharing" or commutation). Denotes the simultaneous transmission of several functions over one link without loss of detail of each function, e.g., amplitude, frequency, phase, or wave shape. Very high speed commutation that would satisfy these conditions could, in special instances, be correctly classified as multiplexing. However, to prevent confusion, the term *commutation* is still preferred whenever a switch is used.

multiplier-phototube. *See* electron-multiplier phototube.

multipropellant. A rocket propellant (q.v.) consisting of two or more unmixed chemicals fed into the combustion chamber (q.v.) separately. Contrast with *bipropellant* (q.v.).

multistage compressor. A centrifugal compressor (q.v.) that utilizes two or more impellers acting successively upon the flow of air or other fluid so as to increase pressure energy.

multistage rocket. A rocket or rocket missile having two or more thrust-producing units each used for different stages of the rocket's flight. (Normally, each unit of a multistage rocket is jettisoned when its fuel is consumed.)

multivibrator. A type of relaxation oscillator used to produce nonsinusoidal waves. It is usually an RC type.

Muraour's relationship. The relationship between the chamber pressure and the linear burning rate (q.q.v.) of a solid rocket propellant (q.v.).

mutual conductance. *See* transconductance.

mutual inductance. The inductance (q.v.) in a coil caused by a changing current in a separate adjacent coil.

mux. Multiplex.

MWO. Modification Work Order.

MX-774. Test missile. Air Force was cognizant service.

An early test vehicle for the ATLAS (q.v.). First U.S. rocket to use swiveling nozzles for control. Three were built and tested in 1949.

Prime Contractor: Consolidated-Vultee Aircraft (now Convair, a division of General Dynamics Corp.).

N

NAA. (1) National Aeronautical Association. (2) North American Aviation, Incorporated.

NACA. National Advisory Committee for Aeronautics (q.v.).

NaDevCen. Naval Air Development Center; Johnsville, Pa.

nadir. A point on the celestial sphere (q.v.) 180 degrees from the zenith; i.e., directly beneath the observer.

NAMTC. Naval Air Missile Test Center; Point Mugu, Calif.

NARTS. Naval Aeronautical Rocket Test Station (q.v.).

NASA. National Aeronautics and Space Administration (q.v.).

NASTY. Air-to-air missile. Air Force cognizance.

Prime Contractor: North American Aviation, Inc.

Status: phased out of development (was to be used as a defense against bombers).

National Advisory Committee for Aeronautics (NACA). A Government committee created by an act of Congress approved March 3, 1915, to direct and supervise study of the problems of flight and to direct and conduct aeronautical research and experiment. The NACA had seventeen members appointed by the President, including two representatives from the Department of the Air Force. The three principal aeronautical laboratories operated under the NACA were: the Langley Aeronautical Laboratory at Langley Field, Va.; the Ames Aeronautical Laboratory at Moffett Field, Calif.; and the Lewis Flight Propulsion Laboratory at Cleveland, Ohio. *See* National Aeronautics and Space Administration.

National Aeronautics and Space Administration (NASA). Successor in 1958 to the National Advisory Committee for Aeronautics (NACA) (q.v.). It controls the functions of research and development (q.v.) in the fields of aeronautics and space activities.

NATIV. Ground-to-ground research rocket. Air Force cognizance.

A part of the NAVAHO (q.v.) program. Developed for upper atmosphere and missile design research. Length: 14.5 ft; diameter: 1.5 ft; gross weight: 1235 lb. Oxygen-gasoline rocket engine. Four tail fins; supersonic; altitude attained: 10 miles.

Prime Contractor: North American Aviation.

natural frequency. That frequency at which a body will vibrate if displaced and allowed to oscillate freely. A tuning fork vibrates at its natural frequency. Most vibrating systems have many natural frequencies, usually harmonics of the fundamental.

natural horizon. The apparent horizon (q.v.).

natural mode of vibration. The set of amplitude ratios and phase differences in a system undergoing free vibrations at a single natural frequency.

nautical mile (nm). A unit of length equalling 6076.1033 ft, which is practically the length of a minute of arc of a great circle on the surface of the Earth. *See also* knot. Formerly, the nautical mile was equal to 6080.20 ft.

$$1 \text{ nautical mile} = 6076.103 \text{ ft} = \tfrac{1}{3} \text{ league}$$
$$= 1.15078 \text{ statute miles}$$

nautical mile, radar. *See* radar nautical mile.

nautical twilight. (1) That part of the twilight period that occurs, for computation purposes, when the Sun is between the horizon and a point about 12 degrees below the horizon, the latter measured at the middle of the Sun. (2) The light diffused or reflected during this period.

nautical units.

6076.1033 feet	= 1 nautical mile (nm)
	= 1.1507 statute mile
6 feet	= 1 fathom
120 fathoms	= 1 cable length
1 nautical mile per hr	= 1 knot
3 nautical miles	= 1 league
1 degree at the equator	= 60 nautical miles
	= 69.096 statute miles
360 degrees	= 21,600 nautical miles
	= 24,874.5 statute miles
	= circumference of Earth at the equator

Navaglobe. A particular kind of long-distance navigation system using one or more omni-directional radio ranges (q.v.) with the appropriate airborne equipment to furnish a vehicle with automatic azimuth (q.v.) and direction-finding indications in respect to a range station.

NAVAHO. Air-breathing surface-to-surface missile. Air Force designation: for the weapon system: WS104A; for the missile: XSM-64.

Guidance was inertial. Three 135,000-lb thrust engines (NAA) were used for booster and two C-W VR-J47 ramjets for cruise. The test vehicle was the X-10 (q.v.) powered by two P&WJ57 turbojets.

Prime Contractor: North American Aviation, Inc. Major subcontractors: Curtiss-Wright Corp., Walter Kidde & Co., Inc., Food Machinery & Chemical Corp., and Thomas Products, Inc.

Status: development cancelled July, 1957.

Naval Aeronautical Rocket Test Station (NARTS). A Government facility started in 1949 for the purpose of liquid rocket engine testing; located at Lake Denmark, N.J.

navigation. *Types of, see* automatic celestial–; celestial–; constant-bearing–; dead reckoning–; decca–; hyperbolic–; proportional–; short range–; star tracking–; tactical air–.

navigational planet. A term sometimes applied to Venus, Mars, Jupiter, or Saturn, the four planets commonly used in celestial navigation for obtaining lines of position.

navigation system. *See* inertial navigation system.

ND. Navy Department.

NDRC. National Defense Research Committee.

near miss. The strike of an explosive missile, near but not on the object of attack, and usually close enough to it to cause effective damage.

nearsonic. Approximating the speed of sound (q.v.).

nebulae. Galactic nebulae are clouds of interstellar matter whose presence is revealed either because they are illuminated by a bright star or because they noticeably weaken the light from stars in a particular region of the sky; unborn stars.

nebulae, galactic. *See* galactic nebulae.

need-to-know. A criterion used in security (q.v.) procedures that requires a person requesting classified information to establish his need to know such information in terms of his mission.

negative feedback. Feedback (q.v.) which decreases amplification, being 180° out of phase with the input signal.

negative lift. A force analogous to lift, which when exerted upon an airfoil causes it to go downward, e.g., the case of an aileron-wing combination moving downward when the trailing edge of the aileron is raised upward. *See* lift.

NEMA. National Electronic Manufacturing Association.

neoprene seal. A synthetic rubber seal used in fuel, oil, or hydraulic line connections. Neoprene is chosen for this purpose because of its resistance to deterioration from fuel, oil, or the like, and because of its chemical stability and nonflammability.

nephoscope. An instrument for determining the direction of cloud movement and, when used in conjunction with a timepiece, for determining the speed of such movement.

NEPTUNE. *See* viking.

net acceleration. The acceleration at take-off of a vertically launched rocket at sea level:

$$\frac{a}{g_0} = \frac{F_0}{W_0} - 1$$

where a/g_0 = take-off acceleration in multiples of sea-level gravitational acceleration; F_0/W_0 = thrust to weight ratio at take-off.

net jet thrust. The effective thrust of a jet engine, as measured by subtracting the ram drag from the gross thrust. *See* gross thrust; ram drag.

net positive suction head (NPSH). A parameter used in liquid rocket engine turbopump design to describe the effective inlet pressure conditions to the propellant pumps. The pressure head available at the pump suction flange is provided by tank pressure head, elevation, and acceleration forces (and is reduced by line friction and vapor pressure). NPSH is the head available to prevent pump cavitation.

net, SOFAR. *See* SOFAR net.

network. A group of parts or systems combined to provide a closed informational loop; i.e., one that provides for inquiry or command, interpretation, response, and interpretation of response in relation to inquiry or command.

network. *Types of, see* dividing–; isolation–; RC–; RL–; shaping–; signal shaping–.

neutral burning. A solid propellant rocket term denoting a burning condition which yields a constant pressure-time curve.

neutral point. In astronautics, that point on an imaginary line joining two celestial bodies at which their gravitational fields exactly balance.

neutral stability. In aerodynamics, that condition of a vehicle in which its reactions to a disturbing motion neither increase nor decrease in magnitude (e.g., a missile given a certain oscillating movement is in neutral stability if such movement is neither increased nor decreased).

neutron cross section. A measure of the ability of a material to interact with neutrons by *scattering, capturing,* or being *fissioned* by them.

neutron flux. A term used to express the intensity of neutron radiation, usually used in connection with the operation of a reactor (q.v.).

neutrons. Electrically neutral particles of atomic nuclei with approximately the mass of a hydrogen atom. Neutron radiation is highly penetrating. Free neutrons are often classified according to their speed or temperature, as *thermal, slow, intermediate,* and *fast.* This elementary nuclear particle has a mass of 1.00894 XMU (atomic mass unit). It is possible under certain conditions of excitation, for a neutron to break up into a *proton* and a *beta* particle. The neutron, however, is not merely a combination of a proton and electron; it is a distinct entity.

neutron source. Any material that emits neutrons (e.g., a mixture of radium and beryllium). A neutron source may be introduced into a nuclear reactor as part of the start-up procedure. The use of a neutron source is a safety measure to insure having at the outset a neutron flux large enough to be distinguished from background and measured quickly. Otherwise, as control rods are withdrawn, the reactor might reach a critical condition before its flux has risen high enough for the control system to operate. Especially if the reactor became *prompt-critical,* a rapid and uncontrolled increase in power to a harmful level then might result. When such a source is used, the control instruments show at an earlier stage the approach to critical conditions as safety and control rods are withdrawn. Also used in critical experiments.

newton. A unit of force measurement. That force which can accelerate one kilogram of mass at the rate of one meter per second per second.

1 newton = 10^5 dynes

Newton's laws of motion. (1) Every body continues in its state of rest or of uniform motion in a straight line except in so far as it may be compelled to change that state by the action of some outside force. (2) Change of motion is proportional to force applied and takes place in the direction of the line of force. (3) To every action there is always an equal and opposite reaction.

NIKE-AJAX. Surface-to-air, supersonic anti-aircraft guided missile. Army designation: SAM-A-25. Originally known as NIKE I.

Length: about 20 ft; diameter: about 1 ft; 2 sets of fins for guidance and steering. Missile and booster weight: more than a ton; range 10-20 miles; warhead weight: 300 lb. Guidance requires two radars, one to track the target, the other to track the missile. These are programmed into coincidence by a ground-based computer. Propellant is nitric acid and RP-4. Controlled in part by SAGE and Missile Master.

Prime Contractor: Bell Telephone Laboratories, Inc., Western Electric Co. Airframe: Douglas Aircraft Co. Engine: liquid propellant rocket sustainer: Bell Aircraft Corp.; solid propellant rocket booster: Hercules Powder Co. Guidance system: Western Electric Co.

NIKE-ASP. A research rocket using a NIKE booster and an ASP (Altitude Sounding Rocket) for the second stage. *See* NIKE and ASP.

NIKE-HERCULES. Surface-to-air missile. Army cognizance. An advanced version of the NIKE-AJAX (q.v.); formerly known as NIKE B.

Over-all length with booster: 41 ft 6 in.; length of basic missile: 27 ft; span: 74 in.; maximum body diameter: 32 in.; firing weight of missile without booster: 5000 lb; burnout speed: MACH 3.3; maximum slant range: 715 miles. Radar command guidance; 4 solid propellant rocket boosters, 1 solid propellant rocket sustainer. Nuclear warhead.

Prime Contractor: Western Electric Co. Airframe: Douglas Aircraft Co., N.C. Engines: solid propellant rocket boosters: Hercules Powder Co.; solid propellant rocket sustainer: Thiokol Chemical Co. Guidance system: Bell Telephone Laboratories, Western Electric Co.

NIKE-ZEUS. Surface-to-air missile to serve as an anti-missile missile against enemy Intercontinental Ballistic Missiles. Originally called NIKE II.

The mission of this project is to detect, intercept, and destroy an incoming enemy Intercontinental Ballistic Missile. Design altitude: 200 miles, but attempts will be made to increase this.

Prime Contractor: Bell Telephone Laboratories, Western Electric Co. Airframe: Douglas Aircraft Co. Guidance system: Bell Telephone Laboratories.

nimbostratus cloud. An extensive, thick, dark-gray layer of cloud, composed of ice crystals, occurring at altitudes between 6500 and 20,000 ft, and commonly accompanying precipitation.

NIT. In information theory, the choice among equiprobable events ($= 1.44$ bits).

nitric acid (HNO₃). A liquid rocket propellant *oxidizer*. See Table 3, page 157.

nitric oxide (NO). A liquid rocket propellant *oxidizer*.

nitrocellulose **[C₆H₇O₂(ONO₂)₃].** A solid rocket propellant organic nitrate *oxidizer*; basically an unstable compound and capable of oxidizing the organic material. It is used in double-base solid propellant rockets. See Table 5, page 214.

nitroethane. A liquid rocket propellant *fuel*. See Table 3, page 157.

nitrogen pentoxide (N₂O₅). A liquid rocket propellant *oxidizer*.

nitrogen tetroxide (N₂O₄). A liquid rocket propellant *oxidizer*. See Table 3, page 157.

nitrogen trifluoride (NF₃). A liquid rocket propellant *oxidizer*. See Table 3, page 157.

nitroglycerin **[C₃H₅(ONO₂)₃].** A solid rocket organic nitrate monopropellant; basically an unstable compound and capable of oxidizing the organic material. It is used in double-base solid propellant rockets. See Table 5, page 214.

nitroguanidine. An additive to rocket propellants used to reduce flashing. Also used for gas generator grains.

nitromethane (CH₃NO₂). A liquid rocket monopropellant (q.v.).

nitropropane. A liquid rocket propellant *fuel*. See Table 3, page 157.

nm. Nautical mile (q.v.).

NME. National Military Establishment.

***n*-octane.** A liquid rocket propellant *fuel*. See Table 3, page 157.

noctilucent cloud. High-altitude terrestrial cloud lying at an altitude of 50 miles in the temperature minimum layer. It appears only after sunset or before sunrise when contrasted against a dark sky; may consist of volcanic dust or interplanetary matter trapped by the temperature inversion.

nodal point. That point on a vibrating body having zero amplitude. The position of the nodal point varies depending on the particular frequency of the vibrating beam. *See* node.

node. (1) In a vibrating system, a particle which has zero amplitude by virtue of its posi-

tion in the system. (2) In physics, a line, point, or surface of a vibrating body which is relatively free from vibration. (3) In electricity and electronics: (a) a point on a conductor at which there is zero voltage or zero current; (b) a point in a radio wave or the like where amplitude is zero.

node. *Types of, see* orbit–; partial–.

noise. (1) Any unwanted disturbance within a dynamic electrical or mechanical system, e.g., undesired electromagnetic radiation in any transmission channel or device. (2) Uncontrolled random disturbances which arise in a guided missile system (q.v.) as a result of various physical phenomena.

noise. *Types of, see* delta–; galaxy–; impulse–; Johnson–; random–; solar–; target–; white–.

noise bandwidth. In a dynamic system or servomechanism, the frequency at which the open-loop gain equals unity defines the bandwidth effective in reducing system tracking error. It is frequently referred to as the *noise bandwidth* since below this frequency there is system *gain* (q.v.) and above there is *attenuation* (q.v.). This frequency is used in determining phase margin. In some instances the *asymptotic gain characteristic* may, without great error, be used in this connection in place of the *actual gain characteristic*.

noise figure. A figure, stated in decibels, that expresses the ratio of the actual noise output to the theoretical noise output that would result if only input impedance were contributing noise to the receiver. The higher the noise figure, the less efficient the performance of the receiver.

noise ratio (NR). The ratio of the *noise power* available at the output of a transducer (q.v.) divided by the *noise power* at the input.

NOL. Naval Ordnance Laboratory; White Oak, Md.

NOLC. Naval Ordnance Laboratory, Corona; Corona, Calif.

nolo flight. The flight of a drone without a human (safety) pilot aboard.

nomenclature system. See AN nomenclature system.

nominal bomb. A bomb whose energy release is equivalent to that of 20,000 tons of TNT, referred to as a 20-kt (kiloton) bomb. (Such a bomb was used against Hiroshima in World War II.)

nominal impact point. A fixed location in each impact area (q.v.), chosen for planning purposes in connection with instrumentation systems.

This point, when chosen, will remain fixed throughout a test program.

nonatmospheric control. Any device or system designed or set up to operate a guided rocket missile, rocket craft, etc., outside the atmosphere (q.v.) or in regions where the atmosphere is of such tenuity that it will not affect aerodynamic controls; the control provided by such devices or systems. Some of the systems used to accomplish nonatmospheric control incorporate vanes or fins directly in the jet stream; others are based on the swivelling or gimballing of the entire rocket motor, or the use of exhaust ports to direct the exhaust in such a manner as to change the course.

non-cooperative systems (instrumentation). Instrumentation systems characterized by transmission of data from airborne missile equipment to a ground station where the data are recorded (e.g., telemetry, photo-theodolites).

non-critical failure. A failure (q.v.) that judgment and experience indicate will not cause failure of the entire weapon system (q.v.).

non-cryogenic propellant. A generic classification usually applied to storable *oxidizers* which are liquid at standard pressure and temperature. Contrast with *cryogenic oxidizers*, e.g., liquid oxygen and liquid hydrogen, which are difficult to store because of their low boiling point.

nondelay fuze. An inertia-type impact fuze (q.v.) that functions quickly, before penetrating or glancing off the target. Distinguish from a *delay fuze*. However, its type of action is inherently slower than that of a *superquick fuze*.

nondirectional beacon. A radio beacon transmitting omnidirectional (q.v.) signals, usually serving as a homing beacon.

non-impinging injector. A liquid rocket engine injector in which the oxidizer and fuel do not impinge at a specific point but are mixed as a result of the combustion chamber turbulence.

nonisoelastic (anisoelastic) effects. A source of drift in gyroscopes caused by mass unbalance and nonlinearities resulting from a lack of isoelasticity in materials.

nonmateriel research. Research directed toward development or improvement of techniques, rather than toward the development of materiel. It includes such subjects as the application of psychology or of analytical and statistical methods to the study of military problems.

non-rotating earth. A mathematical artifice used in computing performance characteristics of long-range ballistic missiles (q.v.). The trajectory equations are simplified because of omission of the effects of Coriolis acceleration, Earth oblateness, and gravitational anomalies.

normal acceleration. *See* acceleration; vertical acceleration.

normal distribution (Gaussian). The distribution of random variables—found frequently in nature. The principal characteristics of the normal law are: (a) it is symmetrical—negative and positive deviations of equal magnitude are equally likely to occur; (b) it is a continuous function rather than a discrete function—it assigns a definite probability to every finite deviation—there are no excluded cases; (c) there is just one most probable result, identical with the first expectation of the variable.

normal lapse rate. In meteorology, the average rate of decrease in temperature with rise in altitude. The normal lapse rate is 3.3°F decrease per 1000 ft of altitude. *See* standard pressure lapse rate.

normal modes of vibration. *See* coupled modes.

normal shock. In aerodynamics, a shock wave (q.v.) generated by a flow compression which is perpendicular to the direction of supersonic flow. See Fig. 5, page 73.

normal shock diffuser. A supersonic diffuser with a plain inlet normal to the flow of air such that at supersonic velocities a single shock wave is formed. *See* pressure recovery and Fig. 5, page 73.

normal stress. *See* total stress.

north. *Types of, see* grid–; true–.

north magnetic pole. The magnetic pole located approximately at 71°N, 96°W, and at about 1140 nautical miles south of the North Pole.

nose cone. (1) A generic term for the separable payload portion of a long-range ballistic missile (q.v.). The nose cone includes the warhead, fuzing system, stabilization system, heat shield and supporting structure, and other equipment. (2) The payload of a research test vehicle. *Note: nose cone* is synonymous with *reentry vehicle*, which is the preferred terminology.

nose cone, ablating. *See* ablating nose cone.

nose fuze. A fuze (q.v.) assembled in the nose of a vehicle or reentry body (q.v.).

nose rib. A short rib between the front spar and the leading edge of an airfoil.

notch antenna. In electronics, an antenna in which the pattern is formed by a notch or slot in a radiating surface. Characteristics are similar to a properly proportioned conventional antenna and may be evaluated with similar techniques.

notch filter. Any band-rejection filter which produces a sharp "notch" in the transfer characteristic of a system.

NOTS. Naval Ordnance Test Station; China Lake, Calif.

NOTUS. A family of communication satellites sponsored by Advanced Research Projects Agency (ARPA) (q.v.). COURIER, a 24-hour satellite is part of this group.

nova. A star which undergoes a sudden and enormous increase in brightness; about 25 appear every year in our galaxy.

NOVA. A proposed Advanced Research Projects Agency (ARPA) (q.v.) 5-stage launching rocket for advanced satellite and deep space probe missions.

1st stage—cluster of 4 Rocketdyne 1.5 million lb thrust engines (CENTAUR (q.v.) 1st stage)
2nd stage—one 1.5 million lb thrust engine
3rd stage—liquid oxygen and hydrogen engine
4th stage—liquid oxygen and hydrogen engine
5th stage—storable liquid engine

Capable of sending 1 ton to the Moon and back; 7500 lb to Mars with 750 lb return load. *See* CENTAUR; SATURN; VEGA.

nozzle. A duct of varying cross section in which the fluid velocity is increased. Nozzles are usually converging-diverging, but may be uniformly diverging or converging.

nozzle. *Types of, see* canted–; canted rotatable–; exhaust–; exit–; fixed area exhaust–; jet–; movable–; overexpanded–; Prandtl–; RAO–; rotatable–; sonic–; subsonic–; supersonic–; swivel–; underexpanded–; variable area exhaust–.

nozzle area ratio. The ratio of the nozzle exit section area to the nozzle throat area.

nozzle box. A kind of collector ring surrounding the turbine wheel of a turbosupercharger, containing a series of nozzles through which the exhaust gases from the engine pass to drive the turbine wheel.

nozzle cant angle. The angle which a rocket booster nozzle axis makes with the rocket centerline.

nozzle diaphragm. In a turbojet engine, a kind of semipartition separating the combustion chambers from the turbine wheel, consisting of two circular bands one within the other with equally spaced blades between the bands, forming nozzles through which the gases pass from the combustion chambers to drive the turbine wheel.

nozzle screen. A filter screen installed immediately upstream of a fuel nozzle in a turbojet engine.

n-propyl nitrate ($C_3H_7NO_3$). A liquid rocket propellant *oxidizer*.

NPSH. Net Positive Suction Head (q.v.).

N-quadrant. The northernmost quadrant and its counterpart in an Adcock or loop-type radio range, in which the "N" signal is heard. *See* Adcock radio range.

NR. Noise Ratio (q.v.).

Ns. Nimbostratus (q.v.).

NSA. National Security Agency.

NSC. National Security Council.

N-scope. A combination of the type K and M scopes (q.q.v.).

NSS. National Stockpile Site.

n-type semiconductor. In solid-state physics, an extrinsic semiconductor in which the conduction-electron density exceeds the hole density.

nuclear disintegration energy. *See Q*-value.

nuclear energy. Stems in part from the transformation of matter into energy. The quantity of energy that can be obtained from the destruction of a given amount of matter is given by the equation:

$$\text{energy} = \text{mass} \times (\text{velocity of light})^2$$

nuclear fission. The division of a heavy nucleus into two approximately equal parts. For the heaviest nuclei the reaction is highly exothermic, the release of energy being about 170 mev per fission. A well-known example is the fission of the compound nucleus formed when U^{235} captures a slow neutron. Other examples are the fissions of U^{233} and Pu^{239} by the capture of slot neutrons. The approximate equality of the fission fragments distinguishes fission from such processes as *spallation,* in which relatively small fragments are ejected, leaving only one large residual nucleus. Fission has been induced by neutrons, charged particles, and photons. When induced by photons, it is termed *photofission. Spontaneous fission* is fission that occurs without particles or photons entering the nucleus from the outside. For this rare mode of radioactive decay which occurs only in the heaviest elements, the half-lives for decay are, without exception, very long. *Ternary fission* is the splitting of a nucleus into three nuclear fragments; there is disagreement as to whether this term should be used for the often-observed type of fission in which a small charged nuclear fragment (such as a proton, alpha particle, tritium, or Li^8 nucleus) is emitted during the process of split-

TABLE 4. Exotic fuels for propulsion, under optimum conditions

Fuel		Theoretical Max. I_{sp}, sec.
Nuclear fission	Solid reactor—H_2	200-3500
	Gaseous reactor—H_2	2500-5000
	Liquid reactor—H_2	1500-2500
	Controlled atomic bomb	Up to 1×10^6
Thermonuclear Fusion		5×10^5-3×10^6
Plasma Jet/Gun		700-20,000
	Solar—H_2	1000-1500
	Electric arc—H_2	1500-3500
Ions	Ionosphere ram	Up to ∞
	Accelerated	40,000-450,000
	Photons	3.057×10^7
Free radicals	$O_2 + H$	2225
	$H + H$	2140
	H (alone)	1360
	0.5 mol H_2 + 1 mol H	1100
	4 mol H_2 + 1 mol N	500
	4 mol H_2 + 1 mol H	540

SOURCE: *Aviation Week*, 1958.

ting into two massive fragments, or whether it should be reserved for splitting into three massive fragments, a process that has not been observed conclusively.

nuclear fusion. A type of nuclear transformation characterized by the combination of two light nuclei, e.g., tritium, as a result of tremendous pressures and heat. The transformation produces energy and a heavy nucleus.

nuclear propulsion. Propulsion by means of atomic energy. Nuclear propulsion utilizes atomic, or nuclear, energy to provide heat which in turn is converted, in one way or another, to mechanical energy. Instances of this propulsion are in the submarines Nautilus and Sea Wolf. See Table 4.

nuclear radiation. Any or all of the radiations emitted as a result of a nuclear transformation. The radiations include *gamma radiation* (of electromagnetic character) and *particle radiations* (alpha particles, positive and negative beta particles, and neutrons).

nuclear reactor. An apparatus in which nuclear fission may be sustained in a self-supporting chain reaction. It includes fissionable material (fuel) such as uranium or plutonium, and moderating material (unless it is a fast reactor) and usually includes a reflector to conserve escaping neutrons, provision for heat removal, and measuring ad control elements. The terms *pile* and *reactor* have been used interchangeably, with *reactor* now becoming more common. They usually are applied only to systems in which the reaction proceeds at a controlled rate, but they also have been applied to bombs. Reactors sometimes are designated according to the fuel used (e.g., graphite or beryllium reactor), or coolant (e.g., gas-cooled, liquid-metal cooled). The use of fusion in a reactor is speculative at this time.

nuclear rocket. A propulsion system (q.v.) using a controlled fission process as the source of heat. A heat exchanger transfers this heat from the reactor to a working medium, e.g., lithium hydride or high-pressure hydrogen. Estimated specific impulse varies from 600 to 2500 sec with a probable value of 600 to 800. The thrust-to-weight ratio is *very* low.

nuclear rocket engine. A rocket engine in which a nuclear reactor is used to accelerate a fluid contained in an independent circuit.

nucleonics. The science dealing with protons or neutrons in the nucleus of the atom; or, with all phenomena associated with the atom nucleus.

nucleus. The positively charged core of an atom that contains the major portion of its mass and the total positive electric charge. Its diameter is about 1/10,000 of the diameter of the atom; including its orbiting electrons.

nucleus, ice. *See* ice nucleus.

null. Zero, or without action; or, in the case of an instrument, without giving a reading.

null circle. A theoretical point in space where the gravitational attraction of one planet balances that of another planet; there can be no real null point, circle, or region because the solar system is dynamic—parts of it are always moving in relation to other parts.

number. *Types of,* see acceptance–; complex–; Knudson–; Kollsman–; MACH–; Péclet's–; performance–; rejection–; Reynolds–; Strouhal–.

number system. *See* binary number system.

nutation. A term describing a particular motion. (1) In the case of a spinning gyroscope, the inclination of the gyro's axis to the vertical will vary periodically between certain limiting angles. This motion is termed *nutation*. In general, a spinning top or gyroscope experiences both *nutation* and *precession*. (2) The oscillation of a gyroscope spin axis initiated by displacement of the base or frame (airframe). It continues with a definite frequency until the disturbance is dissipated and is least pronounced when the gimbals are at 90°. (3) A small oscillation or "wobble" in the Earth's axis in addition to precession with a cycle of 19 years. It is caused by the Moon's tendency to pull the Earth's equatorial bulge into line with its gravitational attraction.

Nyquist criterion. A useful parameter in servomechanism theory; it is the open-loop harmonic response function $Y_0 (j\omega)$, and is based upon the properties of functions of a complex variable. The technique is used for analyzing operating characteristics of closed-loop control systems.

O

O₃. Ozone (q.v.).

OAL. Ordnance Aerophysics Laboratory; Convair, Division of General Dynamics Corporation; Daingerfield, Texas.

objective. *Types of, see* design–; technical–; test–.

oblique approach chart. A target chart showing a perspective view of a target and target area from the air at a specified distance on a given heading, used in locating and identifying the target.

oblique Mercator. In cartography, a transverse Mercator (q.v.), the base line forming an oblique angle with the equator.

oblique shock. In supersonic aerodynamics, the flow condition occurring when air (or gas) flow is forced to turn in such a direction as to interfere with the flow of air in adjacent stream layers. See Fig. 5, page 73.

oblique shock diffuser. A means of improving the total pressure recovery of a diffuser by causing a series of oblique (really conical) shocks and then a normal shock. See Fig. 5, page 73.

oblique shock wave. A kind of shock wave forming an oblique angle with the line of flight greater than that of the MACH wave (q.v.). The velocity of air passing through the oblique shock wave drops more than the theoretical flow that passes through the MACH wave. See Fig. 5, page 73.

observational twilight. That part of the twilight period during which the horizon may be observed as a sharply defined line, and during which the navigational stars may be seen; the light diffused during this period. For computation purposes, this twilight begins or ends when the middle of the Sun is at a point about 10 degrees below the horizon. *See* twilight. Contrast with *nautical twilight* (q.v.).

obturation. In ordnance, the sealing of a chamber in a fuze (q.v.) to prevent the escape of gas in a particular direction.

occlusion. In meteorology, a frontal situation, (a) in which a cold air mass, having run a wedge

under a warm air mass, is itself underrun at its front by a colder air mass, or (b) in which a cold air mass overruns a colder air mass displacing upward a warm air mass—in either case, the warm air being occluded or shut off from the earth's surface.

OC curve. Operating characteristic curve for acceptance of sampling plans (q.v.).

OCLUS or OConUS. Outside Continental United States.

ocosphere. That portion of an atmosphere which will support life (e.g., oxygen supply). It extends to approximately 12,000 ft in the Earth's atmosphere.

octane (C_8H_{18}). A liquid rocket propellant *fuel.* See Table 3, page 157.

octave. The interval between two frequencies having a ratio of two to one. The interval, in octaves, between any two frequencies is the logarithm to the base two (3.322 times the logarithm to the base 10) of the frequency ratio.

octave filter. In electronics, a band pass filter (q.v.) which permits the passage of a range of frequencies from a lower limit to twice this value.

OD. Operations Directive.

oersted. In electronics, a measure of the magnetic field. One oersted of magnetic induction exists at the center of a long solenoid of any radius when $H = 4$ and $NI/10$ is equal to unity, where $I =$ measure in amperes and $N =$ number of turns per centimeter wound on the solenoid.

$$1 \text{ oersted} = 1 \text{ EM cgs unit of magnetizing force} = 2.998 \times 10^{10} \text{ ES cgs units of magnetizing force} = 2.988 \times 10^{10} \text{ stat-oersteds}$$

off-center PPI. A plan position indicator (q.v.) scope in which the sweep rotates about a point that may be offset from the center of the scope, or entirely off the scope, allowing expansion of a portion of the represented area and thus better resolution. Also termed *offset PPI.*

off-loading. Loading a propellant tank to less

than normal capacity to adjust gross weight or cg location.

offset-yield strength. The yield strength of a material determined by the departure of the actual stress-strain diagram from the initial straight-line relation of stress and strain (E). (Frequently taken as 0.002 in. per in.)

off-target jamming. The employment of a jammer (q.v.) at a point removed from the main units of the force, this being done to defeat the enemy's use of friendly jamming signals to his advantage.

ogive. A body of revolution whose contour is the arc of a circle. An ogive whose center of arc is in the plane of the base of the nose (thereby creating no break in the contour when attached to a cylinder at its base, that is, the surface joins the cylindrical surface on the tangent) is defined as a *tangent ogive*. An ogive generated by an arc not tangent, but intersecting at a small angle a segment which forms the cylindrical surface is a *secant ogive*. It may have any radius or curvature greater than that of the *tangent ogive* on up to an infinite radius of curvature (i.e., a straight, conical ogive) but, unless otherwise specified, a *secant ogive* has approximately twice the radius of curvature of a *tangent ogive*. An ogive generated by a line segment plus an arc of infinite radius is a *conical ogive* (i.e., a cone plus a cylinder).

ohm. The unit of resistance to the flow of an electric current. The international ohm has been defined as the resistance at zero degrees centigrade of a column of mercury of uniform cross section having a length of 106.300 centimeters and a mass of 14.4521 grams.

$$1 \text{ ohm} = 10^9 \text{ abohms} = 10^{-6} \text{ megohm}$$
$$= 10^6 \text{ microhms} = 1.113 \times 10^{-12}$$
$$\text{statohm}$$

Ohm's law. The principle that the current in an electric circuit is equal to the impressed electromotive force divided by the resistance.

$$I = \frac{E}{R}$$

oil burner. (Vernacular) A jet engine using kerosene or other like fuel, as distinguished from an engine that uses gasoline.

OJT. On-the-Job Training (q.v.).

omnibearing. A bearing toward an omnidirectional radio-range (q.v.) station, as given by the omnidirectional radio range.

omnidirectional antenna (or beacon). In electronics, an antenna having essentially uniform response in all directions.

omnidirectional radio range. A kind of radio range giving bearings in all directions from its transmitter; also, the equipment used to create such a range.

omnirange. *See* visual omnirange.

onboard guidance system. The system on missiles and spaceships which sends steering signals through the flight-control system during flight. The system may be self-contained (e.g., inertial guidance, q.v.) or may contain elements which require ground-based equipment to complete the guidance loop (e.g., beam rider, q.v.). Also termed the *airborne guidance system* and the *inflight guidance system*.

one and a half stage missile. A ballistic missile (q.v.) which stages (q.v.) part of the booster system but retains the basic tankage and other equipment. The main feature is that the sustainer engine is started on the ground (in contrast to a two-stage missile, q.v.). *See* ATLAS.

one atmosphere. The pressure of the atmosphere at sea level, used as a unit of measure (about 14.7 psi). *See* atmospheric pressure.

one-line layouts. Preliminary drawings or sketches depicting structural arrangements and locations in simple form.

ONI. Office of Naval Intelligence; Washington, D.C.

on-off measurement. Incremental frequency shift (q.v.).

ONR. Office of Naval Research; Washington, D.C.

on-the-job training (OJT). A training program that is usually given by a supervisor in the actual performance of work operations.

opacifier. A substance used to treat a solid rocket propellant so as to absorb light and heat and thus protect the propellant from deterioration until ready for use.

OpDevFor. *Op*erational *Dev*elopment *For*ces (q.v.).

open circuit. A circuit in which current cannot flow, or in which continuity is interrupted.

open-cycle turbine. A gas turbine in which the working gas is drawn in from the open, heated within the circulating system by the combustion of fuel, and discharged from the system after having completed its work. Contrast with *closed-cycle turbine* (q.v.).

open loop. A control system in which there is no self-correcting action for departure from the target value, as there is in a closed system (q.v.).

open loop operation. The operation of a system

or subsystem in which one or more of its inter-connections between the components of the system is broken. In some cases it is necessary to insert dummy loads at the break points of the open loop system to preserve nominal component operation.

open loop testing. A test technique character-ized by lack of a feedback path. *See* go-no-go testing.

open orbit. A circle or ellipse (q.v.) in a per-turbed field (with changing elements).

operating characteristic curve for acceptance sampling plan (OC curve). A curve showing the relation between the probability of acceptance and either lot quality or process average quality, whichever is applicable.

operation. *Types of, see* boot-strap–; check-out–; closed loop–; critical–; launch control–; open loop–; readiness monitoring–; subcritical–; supercritical–.

operational. A status of evolution of a system or weapon which permits its use by field forces for tactical or strategic applications. Generally, op-erational missiles are supplied from follow-on production to the development missiles.

operational capability. The extent to which a system or weapon can fulfill its assigned opera-tional mission.

operational characteristics. Those military char-acteristics which pertain primarily to the func-tions to be performed by equipment, either along with or in conjunction with other equip-ment; e.g., for electronic equipment, operational characteristics include such items as frequency coverage, channeling, type of modulation, and character of emission.

operational concept. A general over-all state-ment of approved military policy pertaining to a specified weapon system and containing the guidance necessary for the preparation of the logistics, installations, and personnel concepts and the operations plan for that weapon system. The operational concept contains such informa-tion as a general description of the weapon sys-tem and its application, the organizational struc-ture, the operational capabilities and the utiliza-tion of the system, the communications associ-ated with the system, and the theater deploy-ment for the system.

Operational Development Forces (OpDevFor). A naval force responsible for tactical evaluation of missiles, weapon systems, and other naval ordnance, under fleet operating conditions.

operational ground support equipment. Ground equipment which operates with a missile in the performance of the latter's mission as the major operational element of the weapon system (e.g., launcher, firing console). This category does not include *maintenance equipment.*

operational evaluation. The test and analysis of a specific end item (q.v.) or system, insofar as practicable under service operating conditions, in order to determine if quantity production is warranted considering (a) the increase in mili-tary effectiveness to be gained, and (b) its effec-tiveness as compared with currently available items or systems, consideration being given to personnel capabilities to maintain and operate the equipment; to size, weight, and location; and to enemy capabilities in the field.

operational missile. A missile that, in contrast to a research and development missile, can be used to attack an enemy target.

operational readiness. The probability that a system will perform satisfactorily at any point in calendar time. (Synonymous with *up-time.*)

operational readiness test (ORT). A test and inspection to determine or prove the extent of the overall operational readiness of an equip-ment. Such a test involves a simulated opera-tional situation.

operational requirements. The need of an armed service for a specified weapon system (q.v.).

operational research. Operations research (q.v.).

operational stockpile site. A support site at which the Atomic Energy Commission stores warheads and other operational nuclear or thermonuclear devices for issuance to the using commands.

operational suitability. A term descriptive of a weapon system (q.v.) which is capable of imple-menting an operations plan (q.v.).

operational system test facility (OSTF). An Air Force designation for a site used to test suita-bility of a weapon system (q.v.) for operational use.

operational system testing (OST). Operational system testing is performed by the development agency or the Air Proving Ground Command (APGC) and is conducted under actual or simulated combat and climatic conditions in co-ordination with the using activities. Usually the initial OST is performed by contractor person-nel.

OPERATION REDWING. *See* ASP.

operations (or operational) plan. An overall statement of approved military policy pertain-ing to a specified weapon system (q.v.) and containing methods for achieving the goals of the operational concept.

operations research. The scientific, qualitative, quantitative study of warfare by military agencies with the objective of improving the weapons, tactics, and strategy of future operations through analysis and evaluation of past operations and maneuvers and operations trials. Also known as *operational research, operations analysis,* and *operations evaluation.*

O Plan. Operation Plan.

OpNav. Office of the Chief of Naval Operations; Washington, D.C.

optical skyscreen. A vertical wire system used to determine "safe trajectory" limits. A pair of wires oriented at 90° are used to provide elevation and azimuth limits. Range limit is about 2000 ft.

optimization (optimilization). The approach to economically or technically perfect design or operation, accomplished primarily by analytical rather than "hit or miss" methods.

optimum expansion. The condition where the combustion-product stream passes through a supersonic nozzle and expands in the divergent portion of the nozzle with no reduction in exhaust velocity.

optimum height of burst. The calculated height of burst above the Earth's surface, or above a target, at which an atomic weapon should be detonated in order to produce a particular effect over the greatest possible area.

OpW. *Op*erating *w*eight.

orbit. The path in which a celestial body moves about the center of gravity of the system to which it belongs. Every orbit is basically in the shape of a conic section with the center of gravity at one focus. An orbit is completely described if six of its characteristics or elements are stated. The six elements usually given for planets are: (1) *eccentricity,* which determines the shape of the orbit, whether it is hyperbolic or elliptical, elongated or nearly circular; (2) *semi-major axis,* which fixes the size; (3) *inclination,* the angle between the plane of the orbit of the planet and the plane of the Earth's orbit, i.e., the ecliptic; (4) *longitude of ascending node,* which tells the direction of the point in which the planet crosses the ecliptic from south to north; (5) *longitude of perihelion,* which states how far around the orbit the point on it nearest to the Sun lies as measured from the ascending node. To find how a plane moves in this orbit it is necessary to know: (6) *time of perihelion passage* on any one occasion. This pro-

vides a starting point for reckoning based on Kepler's third law, from which is calculated the position and orbital speed of the planet at any other time, provided the mass of the Sun (or, more strictly, the mass of the entire solar system) is known. Failing this, a seventh element is required: (7) *period* or time taken to complete one circuit of the orbit.

orbit. *Types of, see* circumplanetary–; circumsolar–; closed–; comet–; conic–; disturbed–; Earth–; elliptical–; Hohmann–; open–; satellite–; stationary–; transfer–; twenty-four-hour–.

orbital bomber. *See* boost-glide bomber.

orbital decay. Diminution of the eccentricity of the elliptical orbit (q.v.) of an artificial satellite. The apogee (q.v.) of each successive revolution is closer to the Earth, until the ellipse becomes a circle which further decays into a spiral path. This brings the satellite into denser atmosphere where the heat produced by friction will vaporize it. Vaporization by aerodynamically generated heat is termed *burn-up.*

orbital energy. The sum of the potential and kinetic energies of a body revolving in an orbit (q.v.) about another body.

orbital nodes. Those points in an orbit (q.v.) where the plane of the ecliptic (q.v.) or the equator is crossed.

orbital period. (1) In astronomy, the length of time required by a celestial body to complete one revolution about its primary (q.v.). (2) In astronautics, the time required by an artificial satellite (q.v.) to circle the Earth or another celestial body.

orbital refueling. Suborbital technique analogous to inflight refueling of aircraft. It is designed to make possible high characteristic velocities without the penalty of impossibly high individual vehicle take-off weight. In practice, it might consist of sending a manned space vehicle into an orbit just outside the Earth's atmosphere and then replenishing its propellant supply from the payload of tanker rockets sent into the same orbit. These propellants would supply sufficient energy for the manned space vehicle to journey to the Moon and later to return to the terrestrial suborbit. More tanker rockets would carry propellants to the returning space vehicle for it to land back on the surface of the Earth.

orbital rocket. In astronautics, an *unmanned* rocket placed in orbit about the Earth. An artificial satellite.

orbital velocity. The velocity needed to keep a body moving in a closed orbit around the Sun, planet, or satellite. Orbital velocity is independent of the mass of the body, and the height uniquely determines velocity and period. It may be circular velocity or elliptical velocity and can vary over wide limits depending on the distance from the attracting force; orbital velocity of the Earth is 18.5 miles/sec.

$$V_0 = R \sqrt{\frac{g_R}{R + h}}$$

and for close in orbits

$$V_0 \simeq \sqrt{g_R R}$$

where R = radius of the Earth; g_R = gravitational force at Earth's surface; h = orbital altitude above the Earth.

orbit nodes. Points in an orbit where the orbit crosses a reference plane, such as the ecliptic or the equatorial plane.

orbits. Paths described by celestial bodies. Most of the minor planets revolve at distances from the Sun intermediate between those of Mars and Jupiter. The average orbital eccentricity is 0.15, but some particular members exceed this greatly [e.g., Albert (0.54) and Hidalgo (0.65)]. The inclinations also show a wide range from 43° (Hidalgo) down to almost nil. No minor planet with retrograde motion has been discovered.

ORD. Operational Ready Date.

ord. Ordnance.

ORDCIT. *O*rdnance *R*esearch and *D*evelopment, *C*alifornia *I*nstitute of *T*echnology; Pasadena, Calif.

order of magnitude. A factor of ten. Two orders of magnitude are a factor of 100, etc.

ordinate. *See* maximum ordinate.

ordnance. (1) Military weapons, ammunition, explosives, combat vehicles, and battle materiel collectively, together with the necessary maintenance tools and equipment. (2) *Capitalized,* an organization or activity that stores, issues, or maintains such materiel. (In Air Force usage, the word "ordnance" is commonly applied to aircraft cannon and machine guns, ammunition, bombs, rockets, rocket launchers, and explosives, together with the appropriate repair tools and equipment. Chemical warfare weapons and the like, although falling within the broad meaning of "ordnance" are not usually considered as such.)

organizational maintenance. That maintenance authorized for, the responsibility of, and performed by a using organization on its assigned equipment. Organizational maintenance will normally consist of preflight, post-flight, and periodic inspection of missiles, daily or minor inspection of other materiel, servicing, preventive

maintenance, calibration of systems, and removal and replacement of components.

organ pipe resonance. A resonant organ note produced in a jet engine diffuser tail pipe under certain conditions of gas flow. It is often accompanied by overheating and therefore to be avoided. The fundamental frequency is:

$$f = \frac{c}{2l}$$

where c = velocity of sound, fps; l = length of pipe, ft; f = frequency, cps.

ORI. Operational Readiness Inspection.

ORIOLE. Air-to-air missile. Navy Bureau of Aeronautics designation: XAAM-N-4.

Prime contractor: The Martin Co.

Status: phased out of production.

ORT. Operational Readiness Test (q.v.).

orthicon. A more complex development of the iconoscope (q.v.), having improved light sensitivity. Also termed *orthiconoscope.*

orthogonal. The property of being at right angles, or more generally, independent (e.g., the X, Y, and Z directions, or the R, o, and O directions in polar coordinates are orthogonal. Functions represented by the electric intensities of two radio signals, the ratio of whose frequencies is irrational, are orthogonal).

orthographic projection. A map projection made so that features of the globe are presented as they actually would appear if viewed from a point in space. An orthographic projection is made with the point of vision at a great distance (mathematical infinity), so that light rays coming from the globe could be considered parallel. A *polar orthographic projection* is a type of orthographic projection of the globe with the North or South pole at the center, the parallels being presented as a series of concentric circles, getting closer together toward the circumference of the projection, and with the meridians being shown as straight lines radiating from the pole, with distances greatly compressed along them near the equator. Because of this crowding of parallels and compression of meridians, distortion increases toward the circumference of the orthographic projection, but perspective is maintained.

orthotoluidine. A liquid propellant *fuel.*

oscillation. A periodic phenomenon. (1) A periodic moving or swinging from one extreme position or attitude to another, each time passing a mean or meridian position or attitude. (a) Any such swinging back and forth by a vehicle about one of its axes, as in pitching up and down. (b) Any such movement in an elastic surface (e.g., flutter). (2) In servomechanisms, a periodic change of the controlled variable from one value to another. (3) A single swing in this movement from one extreme position to the other. (4) In electricity; (a) a recurring periodic disturbance in the flow of electricity; (b) an alternating current.

oscillation. *Types of, see* free–; lateral–; longitudinal–; parasitic–; stable–; steady-state–; unstable–.

oscillator. (1) Any mechanical or electrical device designed to set up and maintain oscillations of a frequency determined by its physical constants (e.g., vacuum tubes, crystals, arc generators). (2) In a superheterodyne receiver, that stage which generates a radio-frequency signal of the correct frequency to mix with the incoming signal and produce the intermediate-frequency of the receiver. (3) In a transmitter, the stage that generates the carrier frequency or a frequency equal to some definite multiple of the carrier frequency. (4) A test instrument that can be set to generate an unmodulated or tone-modulated radio-frequency signal at any frequency needed for aligning or servicing radio receivers and amplifiers. (5) A test instrument for generating an audio-frequency signal, at any desired frequency for test purposes. (6) In early radio, a form of generator or radio transmitter. (7) In the very high and ultra-high frequencies, a generator that is coupled to some form of radiator, as a transmitter.

oscillator. *Types of, see* backward wave–; beat frequency–; blocking–; coherent–; crystal–; crystal controlled–; Lecher–; local–; molecular–; push-pull–; relaxation–; resistance controlled–; saturable reactor controlled–; self-excited–; subcarrier–; variable inductance–; very stable–; voltage controlled–.

oscillograph. A device whose visual output is a representation of the electrical wave form applied to the input. Electromechanical recording oscillographs are commonly used to translate the electrical output of a telemeter ground station into permanent visual records.

oscillograph. *Types of, see* direct writing–; magnetic–.

oscilloscope. An electronic or mechanical-electrical device for detecting and portraying visually the changes occurring in an electric voltage or current. The mechanical-electric type of oscilloscope utilizes electromagnets, filaments carrying the current to be observed, and mirrors to portray the wave form of the current. The usual type of oscilloscope, however, utilizes a

cathode-ray tube (q.v.). A recording oscilloscope is termed an *oscillograph.*

oscilloscope. *Types of, see* cathode-ray–; wamoscope.

OSN. Office of the Secretary of the Navy; Washington, D.C.

OSRD. Office of Scientific Research and Development.

OSS. (1) Office of Strategic Service. (2) Operational Stockpile Site. (3) Operational Storage Site.

OST. Operational Suitability (q.v.) Testing.

OSTF. (1) Operational Suitability Test Facility (2) Operational System Test Facility (q.v.).

Oswatitsch (Ferri or spike) diffuser. A type of supersonic diffuser for ramjets, with an inner body projecting forward of the diffuser lip designed to permit pressures to be raised gradually through a series of conical shocks. The pressure recovery possible with this type of diffuser operating at high MACH numbers is considerably greater than could be obtained by a diffuser designed for single normal shock. See Fig. 5, page 73.

Otto-Lardillon method. A method of computing ballistic trajectories (q.v.) which gives exact solutions to the equations of motion. The only approximation is the assumption that the drag is proportional to the square of the velocity. Numerical integration of the trajectory is performed. Results are more accurate than those obtained by Didion-Bernoulli method (q.v.).

OTU. Operational Training Unit.

ounce. A unit of weight measurement.

1 ounce (avoirdupois) = 16 drams (avoirdupois) = 437.5 grains = 28.3495 grams = $\frac{1}{16}$ lb (avoirdupois)

1 ounce (fluid) = 29.5737 cu cm = 1.80469 cu in. = 8 drams (fluid) = $\frac{1}{16}$ pint (liquid)

outage. In a (usually ballistic) missile, the propellant remaining in the tankage which cannot be used (e.g., converted into useful energy).

outer liner. The outer casing of a combustion chamber (q.v.) in a turbojet engine.

outer loop. A term describing the control loop including the missile and its guidance dynamics. This loop is outside the normal control system feedback loop which includes the aerodynamics of the missile. See Fig. 3, page 49.

outer space. (1) Space beyond the Earth's atmosphere. (2) Space beyond the solar system. *See also* space.

output. (1) The quantity of something that is

generated, especially the power or energy delivered by an energy-producing device. (2) In electricity, the electric power, current, or voltage delivered by any form of electrical device or circuit (e.g., a battery, radio transmitter, receiver, etc.).

output. *Types of, see* counter–; thrust–.

output drift. A change of the initial balanced conditions with respect to time.

output impedance. The impedance (q.v.) exhibited by a circuit when looking at it through its output terminals before the load impedance is added.

outside burning. In ramjet applications, the technique of creating the proper pressure field for thrust by causing combustion to occur in the regime aft of the injector but in such a way as to act as though a tail pipe or combustion chamber existed.

over-all efficiency. The efficiency of a jet engine, rocket engine, or rocket motor in converting the total heat energy of its fuel—first into available energy for the engine, then into effective driving energy. Over-all efficiency is expressed as a percentage of the total heat energy of the fuel. It is a product of thermal efficiency and propulsive efficiency.

over-all specific impulse. In rocketry, the impulse per unit total weight of system.

$$I_o = \frac{Ft}{W_o}, \quad \frac{\text{lb sec}}{\text{lb}}$$

where F = thrust, lb; t = time, sec; W_o = total weight of the system, lb.

overcast. A term descriptive of the sky when it is more than nine-tenths covered with clouds. Viewed from on top (aircraft view) it is said to be undercast.

overexpanded nozzle. A nozzle in which the working fluid is expanded to a lower pressure than the external pressure (i.e., exit area is too large).

overlap. *See* valve overlap.

overpressure. The destructive pressure in the blast wave from an explosion, usually expressed in pounds per square inch above atmospheric pressure. During some period of the passage of the wave past a point, the overpressure may be negative; that is, the absolute pressure at that point may be less than atmospheric pressure.

overpressure, peak. *See* peak overpressure.

overshoot. The travel beyond the expected position or value of an object or function when responding to a stimulus (e.g., a spike occurring at the leading edge of a rectangular pulse that is produced by overshoot of the sensing or amplifying device).

overshoot factors. Aerodynamic factors which define the load applied to a surface or body as the result of maneuvers. A missile overshoots the desired angle of attack owing to control system and aerodynamic damping characteristics.

overtime (labor cost). Refers to hours worked in excess of eight hours per day per shift, or forty hours per week per shift (whichever is greater). In overseas areas, hours worked in excess of eight hours per day or forty hours per week are not considered as overtime providing such hours do not exceed the standard workday or workweek for the geographical area and are not subject to a premium pay rate.

overtone. (1) A physical component of a complex sound having a frequency higher than that of the basic frequency (q.v.). (2) A component of a complex tone having a pitch higher than that of the fundamental pitch. (3) the term *overtone* has frequently been used in place of *harmonic*, the *n*th harmonic being called the $(n-1)$st *overtone*. There is, however, ambiguity sometimes in the numbering of components of a complex sound when the word *overtone* is employed. Moreover, the word *tone* has many different meanings so that it is preferable to employ terms which do not involve *tone* wherever possible.

OWI. Office of War Information.

OX. *Ox*idizer (q.v.).

oxidizer. That portion of a rocket propellant which provides the oxygen for combustion (e.g., liquid oxygen, nitric acid).

oxygen bifluoride (OF_2). A liquid rocket propellant *oxidizer*. See Table 3, page 157.

oxygen fluoride (OF_2). A liquid rocket propellant *oxidizer*. See Table 3, page 157.

ozone (O_3). An allotropic form of oxygen; a liquid rocket propellant *oxidizer*. See Table 3, page 157.

ozone layer. A layer in the atmosphere about twenty miles above sea level which strongly absorbs solar ultraviolet radiation; absorption of energy not only converts molecular atmospheric oxygen into ozone but heats the atmosphere and produces a high-temperature layer, a little above the ozone layer.

ozonosphere. A region in the stratosphere (q.v.) having a relatively high concentration of ozone (q.v.), occurring at a height between 15 and 22 miles, and important chiefly for its absorption of solar radiation. Sometimes termed the *ozone layer* or *ozone stratum*.

P

P. P-band (q.v.) frequency (225–390 mc/sec). See Fig. 8, page 105.

Pacific Missile Range (PMR). The Navy operated missile test range which includes the Naval Air Missile Test Center (NAMTC) (q.v.) at Point Mugu, California and the range associated with Vandenberg Air Force Base at Lompoc, California.

package. (Vernacular) A component, system, "black box," or other element capable of being handled separately.

packaging. (1) *Commercial:* the art or operations required in the preparation of goods for shipment, storage, and delivery to the consumer. Packaging involves protection against deterioration, mechanical damage, and pilferage; requires the use of container materials, and facilities for the production and handling of packages, and consideration of distribution and merchandising aspects. (2) *Military:* application or use of appropriate wrappings, cushioning, interior containers, and complete identification markings up to, but not including, the shipping container. (3) *Guided missile usage:* (a) the assembly of parts, pieces, and subassemblies into a package, taking into consideration the environment, heat dissipation, maintenance, handling; (b) the orderly assembly of "boxes" or equipment into the missile; (c) the preparation for shipment.

pad. (1) A permanent or semipermanent load-bearing surface, constructed or laid on the ground, upon which a permanent or mobile catapult or launcher can be placed. (2) A non-adjustable attenuator (q.v.). (3) A resistance network used in coupling two impedances. Use of resistance rather than impedance results in a power loss, but gives coupling independent of frequency. (4) A disc, usually of some high-permeability alloy placed near the face of an E-coil to vary the reluctance by changing the air gap. (5) "To pad"—changing capacity for the purpose of adjusting frequency.

padding capacitors. Capacitors used to "pad" or tune an oscillator to a frequency, by adding or subtracting the capacitors to the tank circuit.

paint. (Vernacular) The image on a radarscope; to show an image on a radarscope; said of radar equipment.

pair. *See* twisted pair.

PAM. Pulse Amplitude Modulation telemetering (q.v.).

panel. *Types of, see* control–; patch–; rack–.

panel flutter. In aerodynamics, dynamic instability of a panel subjected to airflow parallel to its equilibrium midplane.

panic button. (Vernacular) A control button or switch for use in some emergency.

panoramic. Of a radarscope, displaying simultaneously all of the signals received at different frequencies.

PAR. Precision Approach Radar.

parabola of escape. Critical orbit in a central force field. Orbits of bodies moving in a gravitational field were shown by Newton to be conic sections. Ellipses and hyperbolas are common orbits. The parabolic orbit is such that a body has escape velocity (q.v.) at every point along it.

parabolic trajectory. The path of a body if the energy exactly equals escape energy when it is released tangentially. The body will never return to the Earth.

parabolic velocity. The velocity which a particle must possess in order to describe a parabolic orbit in the gravitational field of another body. This is a boundary case: a slightly lower velocity causes the particle to move in a closed ellipse (q.v.), while a slightly greater speed gives it a hyperbolic orbit (q.v.) in which it never returns to the same vicinity. Parabolic velocity is the minimum escape velocity.

paraboloid reflector. A hollow reflector used for radar antennas having an inner surface shaped as if by the rotation of a parabola about its axis. It is so shaped that all rays emanating from a single point on the axis, the focus, will be reflected in a direction parallel to the axis. Also termed *parabolic reflector.*

parallax. The apparent displacement of an object, or the apparent difference in its direction of motion, if viewed first from one standpoint, then from another.

parallax correction. A correction required if the location of a gun director or tracking radar is remote from the gun or missile launcher. It is also required for missile guidance systems which determine position at the end of launch on the basis of ballistic information.

parallel circuit. In electricity, an arrangement in which all the positive poles, electrodes, terminals, etc., are connected to one conductor, and all the negative components to another conductor.

parallel cluster missile. A descriptive term applied to missiles in which the sustainer and booster stages are side by side, contrasted to a *tandem* (q.v.) arrangement.

parameter. An arbitrary constant, as distinguished from a fixed or absolute constant (e.g., missile gross weight). Any desired numerical value may be given to a parameter.

parameter. *Types of, see* hold–; kill–.

parametric excitation. In a control system, the process of causing instability by varying a system parameter.

parametric studies. A systematic approach to the evaluation of effects of independent and dependent variables or parameters on the design and performance of a missile.

paraphase amplifier. An electronic device sometimes used in place of transformers to operate push-pull (q.v.) circuits; essentially a combination amplifier and phase inverter.

parasite drag. That part of the total drag caused by the skin friction and shape of the non-lifting surfaces of a vehicle. Parasite drag is the total drag minus the induced drag and the profile drag. Sometimes termed *structural drag*. *See* profile drag.

parasitic oscillation. An unintended, self-sustaining oscillation at a frequency different from the operating frequency. It occurs chiefly in vacuum-tube circuits.

pardop. A passive instrumentation or measurement system utilizing the Doppler principle (without an airborne transponder) and depending on reflection of a continuous signal. *See* Doppler.

parity. A symmetry property of a wave function; the parity is 1 (or even) if the wave function is unchanged by an inversion (reflection in the origin) of the coordinate system, and −1 (or odd) if the wave function is changed only

in sign. All non-degenerate stationary states have a definite parity.

parsec. A unit of distance with which astronomers compare stars on the basis of absolute magnitude, or the brightness of stars as if they were all at a distance of 10 parsecs and photographic magnitude, or the brightness as it appears on a photographic plate. It is equal to 19,150,000,000,000 miles or nearly 3.26 light years. The word "parsec" is a contraction of *parallax second*, i.e., the distance at which the mean radius of the Earth's orbit would subtend an angle of one second of arc. Our galaxy has a diameter of approximately 30,000 parsecs.

part. The smallest article; a piece of equipment which cannot be broken down without losing its identity (e.g., transistors, resistors, capacitors, nuts, bolts, etc.).

part failure rate (λ_p or r_p). The ratio of the number of component parts which fail to the number tested over a given period of time under a controlled and specified set of operating conditions. The failure rate may vary with the age of the parts as a function of the inherent life characteristics.

partial component failure. A malfunction of a component which reduces the normal accuracy of a missile rather than causing a direct and complete failure of the missile.

partial node. In a vibrating system, a particle which has a lesser amplitude than any nearby particle.

particle. *Types of, see* alpha–; beta–.

parts. *Types of, see* fit and function–; metal–.

Pascal's law. The principle that a fluid exerts pressure equally in all directions, or that a fluid not acted upon by external forces has internal pressure the same at all points. (Named after Blaise Pascal, French mathematician.)

Paschen series. A sequence of lines in the infrared region of the hydrogen spectrum.

Paschen's law. The principle that the sparking potential of a gas is a function only of the product of the sparking distance and the gas pressure. (Minimum sparking potential for air $\simeq 340$ volts.)

pass band (of a filter). That band of frequencies which are passed with little or no attenuation (q.v.).

passive detection. The detection of a target or other object by means that do not reveal the position of the detecting instrument or detector. Instruments sensitive to noise or infrared light provide means of passive detection; likewise instruments for detecting radar signals.

passive electronic countermeasures. Electronic countermeasures (q.v.) involving actions taken which are of such nature that their employment is not detectable by the enemy.

passive homing guidance. A system of homing guidance (q.v.) wherein the receiver in a missile utilizes natural radiations from the target.

passive jamming. The utilization of confusion reflectors (q.v.) to return spurious and confusing signals to the transmitting radar set.

patching. The process of connecting incoming electrical lines to one of the outgoing lines with a plug-in cord or patchcord.

patch panel. A panel of electrical connectors some of which represent incoming lines, and the remainder of which represent outgoing lines. A patch panel is used to permit flexible cross connections of systems, instrumentation, etc.

pathfinder. A warhead or beacon delivered into a target area by superlative guidance to help guide less accurate missiles into the target area.

Patrick AFB. Patrick Air Force Base, Cocoa Beach, Florida.

pattern. *Types of, see* antenna–; field strength–; radiation–; warhead–; wind flow–.

payload. (1) That portion of missile weight which is carried by the vehicle for the purpose of inflicting damage on the target. In the case of research and test vehicles, this includes instrumentation equipment for taking data and transmitting or recovering it. (2) Weight of everything in a rocket or missile that can be described as "useful cargo," e.g., scientific instruments, passengers, supplies, or, in the case of weapons, the warhead; usually less than a tenth of the total weight of the missile with full propellant tanks. In a step rocket, the payload of each step but the last consists of the succeeding steps.

payload ratio. A figure of merit ratio used in missile design. In rocket applications, it is defined as the ratio of the payload mass to the initial mass of the rocket (stage).

PBAA (polybutadiene-acrylic acid) ammonium perchlorate. A solid rocket propellant copolymer *fuel* of the synthetic rubber type.

P-band. A radio-frequency band of 225 to 390 mc/sec with wavelengths of 133 to 77 cm, respectively. See Fig. 8, page 105.

PCM. Pulse Code Modulation telemetering (q.v.).

PDA. Pump Drive Assembly (q.v.).

PDM. Pulse Duration Modulation telemetering (q.v.).

p.e. Probable error (q.v.).

peak inverse voltage. In electronics, the maximum instantaneous voltage occurring across an operating rectifier in the direction opposite to that which will produce current flow through it.

peak overpressure. The maximum overpressure caused by a nuclear explosion at any given distance from ground zero (q.v.).

peak pulse power, carrier frequency. The power averaged over that carrier-frequency cycle which occurs at the maximum of the pulse of power (usually one-half the maximum instantaneous power).

peak sound pressure. *See* sound (acoustomotive) pressure.

peak-to-peak amplitude. The algebraic difference of the positive and negative magnitudes of maximum deviation from the rest condition; also termed *double amplitude.*

pea soup. Any heavy fog, but especially the local fog occurring in and near the city of London.

pebble bed heater. An air preheater used in connection with high-speed wind tunnels. Refractory materials contain an alumina pebble bed which is gas or electric heated. Air is then forced through the bed and into the working section of the wind tunnel.

Péclet's number. The product σR, where $R =$ Reynolds number and $\sigma =$ Prandtl number.

PEI. Preliminary Engineering Inspection (q.v.).

Peltier effect. The heat developed at the junction of two electrical conductors as the result of a current flow. It is a function of the absolute temperature of the junction and the thermoelectric powers of the conductors.

pencil beam. A radar beam nearly round about its axis, and equally sharp in all planes that pass through its axis.

pendulous gyroscope accelerometer. An instrument in which the force generator is a gyroscope (q.v.) element.

pendulous integrating gyroscope (PIG). A constrained pendulum accelerometer based on the HIG (q.v.) construction. The seismic mass is a pendulum, and the force generator is the torque generator.

pendulum. *Types of, see* physical or compound–; reversible–; simple–.

penetration ballistics. A branch of terminal ballistics (q.v.) concerned with the motion and behavior of a missile after penetrating a target.

pentaborane. High-energy rocket or ramjet fuel; a boron derivative.

pentode. A vacuum tube with five electrodes; usually: the cathode, control grid, screen grid, suppressor grid, and anode.

peptizer. A substance added to another substance to bring it into colloidal solution. It is used in cold weather as a fuel additive.

perchlorial fluoride (ClO_3F). A storable liquid rocket propellant *oxidizer*.

perchloric acid ($HClO_4$). A liquid rocket propellant *oxidizer*.

perforated inlet diffuser. An intake designed to reduce spillover of approaching supersonic air by causing some of the air entering the diffuser to flow through appropriately located perforations owing to the differential pressure. The effect is to move the shock wave closer to the diffuser intake.

performance. The characteristic(s) desired or expected from a system; a description of what the system is supposed to do. Contrast with *reliability* (q.v.) which is the probability that the system will have this performance when called upon.

performance index. *See* specific fuel consumption.

performance number. A number which, when applied to a given substance or thing, indicates its performance rating by reference to an arbitrary standard. It is applied specially to fuels. Thus, the number 100/130, when applied to an aviation gasoline, indicates that the lean-mixture power performance of the gasoline is the same as that of 100 octane gasoline, and that its rich-mixture power performance is 1.3 times that of 100 octane gasoline.

performance specification. A document which defines the performance of a guided missile system as contrasted with its design requirements. *Translation to performance specification:* Once an operational requirement has been established for a guided missile it is then necessary to formulate a corresponding performance specification. This is a task for the materiel commands, since such a specification will form the basis of a development contract. Actually, the prospective contractor often participates in this task, depending upon circumstances. Predicted performance is derived from an operational analysis of the proposed missile and is tempered by prior experience with similar missile developments. Sometimes it is determined that per-formance fully meeting the operational requirement cannot be attained under the current state of the art. In such cases lesser performance is generally accepted by the operational command as an interim goal.

perigee. The point in a satellite or space ship orbit at which it is closest to Earth (usually refers to elliptical braking orbits).

perihelion. The point of orbit (q.v.) closest to the Sun when the Sun is the body being orbited (i.e., the primary). *See* perigee.

period. The time between each repetition of a complete vibratory phenomenon; i.e., between successive passages in the same direction across the position of rest. Mathematically, the *period* is the reciprocal of *frequency*.

period. *Types of, see* Earth rotation–; preproduction–; production–; sidereal–.

periodic inspection. An inspection (q.v.) repeated either at regular intervals of calendar time or, in reference to certain equipment, after a device has been used for a given number of hours.

period of revolution of a satellite in a circular orbit about the Earth.

Height above the Earth (miles)	Approximate Period
200	90 minutes
1,000	2 hours
22,000	1 day
235,000	1 lunar month

permafrost. In arctic regions, a mixture of earth and water solidly frozen together and not subject to seasonal thawing; also ground unmixed with water that remains at a temperature below freezing. (The permafrost stratum is nearly always below the ground surface. Above the permafrost is the active layer.)

permanent echo. An electronic echo received by ground-based radar as a result of radar beams striking mountains, cliffs, bridges, buildings, or similar fixed objects.

permanent emplacement. In weapon system usage, a missile launching site with permanent features (e.g., antiaircraft sites to protect United States cities, NIKE; ICBM sites in Zone of Interior (Z.I.); coast protection; etc.).

permanent set. A measure of the inability of a material to return to its original dimensions after removal of stress; normally determined after sufficient stress is applied to produce a 0.2% permanent set or strain.

permanent sites. Guided missile sites used for launching very large missiles, usually from the continental United States [Zone of Interior (Z.I.), q.v.].

permeability. The ratio of magnetic induction (B) to magnetizing force (H). *Maximum permeability* is the slope of the *B-H* curve at its steepest point. Dynamic or a-c permeability is the slope of a line drawn through the tips of an AC hysteresis loop (B_{Tip}/H_{Tip}).

permeance. The susceptibility of a material to magnetic flow; the reciprocal of *reluctance* (q.v.).

per second per second. Of a rate of acceleration, changing by so much *per* second *every* second (e.g., an object accelerating from rest at the rate of 20 ft per second per second would travel 20 ft in the first second, 40 ft in the second, 60 ft in the third, etc. At the end of 3 seconds, it would have travelled 120 ft).

PERSHING. Surface-to-surface solid-fuel ballistic missile. Army cognizance.

Designed to replace, eventually, the REDSTONE (q.v.), which is liquid fueled. It will be smaller, lighter, and more mobile than the REDSTONE. Inertial guidance; two-stage solid propellant rocket engines.

Development: Army Ballistic Missile Agency, Redstone Arsenal. Prime Contractor: The Martin Co., Orlando Division. Airframe: essentially the solid rocket engine casing plus some transition sections provided by the Martin Co. Engines: Thiokol Chemical Corp. Guidance: Bendix Eclipse-Pioneer Division. Fuzing and arming: Bulova Watch Co.

personnel. *Types of, see* engineering support–; management and administration–; product support–; scientific and engineering–; shop and production–.

perturbation. (1) The effect of gravitational pull of one body upon the orbit of another; a satellite moving around the Earth is disturbed by the gravitational fields of the Sun and the Moon and by the Earth's bulge. (2) In space flight, the disturbance of an orbit by gravitational or other (e.g., drag) effects.

perturbation maneuver. *See* maneuver.

perturbation theory. The study of the effect of small disturbances on the behavior of a system.

perturbative force. In space flight, the resultant of all forces causing a disturbance of the orbit.

perveance. The saturation current which can flow in a vacuum tube. This current is proportional to the 3/2 power of the applied potential.

PET. Production Environmental Testing (q.v.).

petal catchers. (Vernacular) Devices used in shock tubes, pneumatic and hydraulic systems to capture burst diaphragm elements after rupture to avoid damage to the downstream system.

PETREL. Air-to-surface; air-to-underwater. Navy Bureau of Ordnance cognizance. Evolved from the GREBE and KINGFISHER (q.v.) projects. Prime Contractor: Fairchild Engine and Airplane Corp.

Phased out of production in 1957 after it had been operational.

PF. (1) Preflight. (2) Proximity Fuze (q.v.).

PFRT. PreFlight Rating Test (q.v.).

P-funds. In procurement The Air Force designation for various types of procurement funds:

P-130	Supply or production money for complete missiles
P-150	Industrial facilities and equipment money
P-240	Development program support money (ground handling equipment)
P-300	Military construction money
P-600	Research and development money
P-160	Support and spares money
P-440	Training equipment and aids money

PGC. Proving Ground Command.

phanastron. A circuit used for producing a rectangular pulse of known short duration.

phantastron. (1) A monostable multivibrator used to generate very short pulses and linear sweeps. (2) A certain type of one-tube relaxation oscillator employing Miller feedback to generate a linear timing waveform. This class of circuits has been termed *sanatron* or *sanaphant*.

phantom accelerations. The acceleration which a missile in flight experiences (a) because the Earth is not a perfect sphere and (b) from the Coriolis effect (q.v.).

phase. *Types of, see* terminal–; trajectory–.

phase coherent carrier system. A communication system involving the transmission of a continuous wave (CW) signal to and/or from a vehicle so as to receive information in the form of phase changes with respect to the original carrier. The standard of coherence is the frequency and phase of the carrier.

phase lag. In radio or electricity, a delay expressed in degrees, in which one wave reaches its maximum and minimum values later than another reaches its maximum and minimum values.

phase lock. A type of detection for recovery of phase-coherent signals in the presence of wideband noise. Signal-to-noise ratios are improved by using *a priori* information to reduce the bandwidth.

phase locked demodulation. A synchronous detection scheme for demodulation; not used to improve signal-to-noise ratio but to prevent the ratio from being damaged by threshold noise.

phase margin. The result of the phase magnitude at the frequency corresponding to unity gain, subtracted from 180 degrees.

phase modulation (PM). A method of modulating a carrier-frequency current by causing the phase of the modulated signal (with respect to the unmodulated carrier) to vary from instant to instant in accordance with the audio frequency or other modulation signal. As in frequency modulation, the power output of the transmitter is constant at all times.

phase plane (method). A technique for analyzing *servo* (q.v.) performance. The response of a servo is plotted as a function of velocity vs. displacement (instead of displacement vs. time), for a variety of step amplitudes to provide a *phase portrait* in the phase plane. *Note: phase* does not relate to *phase angle* or *phase shift* associated with linear servo frequency. Stability of the servo is determined from the *phase portrait*.

phase shift. The retardation of a wave with respect to time or another measure, measured in electrical degrees (e.g., phase shift of the voltage wave with respect to the current wave). It denotes a time difference between the input and output signal of a control unit or system.

phase shifter. *See* waveguide phase shifter.

phase-shift omnidirectional radio range. A kind of omnidirectional radio range used to indicate the azimuthal position of a vehicle by use of two carrier waves or signals, one of which is subject to a continuous phase shift, and is in phase with the other only along a reference line (usually north).

phase splitting circuit. A circuit that produces from the same input waveform two output waveforms that differ in phase from each other.

phase velocity. The velocity at which a point of given phase moves in a travelling wave (mechanical, electrical, or acoustic).

phasing. *See* system phasing.

phasitron. The name of a specialized electronic vacuum tube designed to provide phase-modulation detection.

phosphor. A substance applied to the inner face of a cathode-ray tube which fluoresces during bombardment by electrons, and phosphoresces after bombardment.

photoelectric. Of or pertaining to (a) the emission of electrons by certain substances when struck by light of suitable wavelengths, or (b) the change in current of certain devices when exposed to light of certain wavelengths.

photoelectron-multiplier tube. *See* electron-multiplier phototube.

photofission. *See* nuclear fission.

photogrammetric instrumentation (P-I). Any instrumentation that utilizes *photographs* for determining the position of an object, utilizing ballistic, cinetheodolite, or ribbon frame cameras.

photon. A quantum; a corpuscle of radiant energy which has energy equal to h times the frequency; h is the Planck constant: 6.547×10^{-27} erg sec.

photon propulsion. Conversion of matter to light energy based on the conversion of mass to energy relative to Einstein's theory:

$$E = mc^2$$

(energy is equal to mass times speed of light squared).

photon rocket. An "ideal" momentum-type propulsion concept proposed by Saenger in which "light" is used as the working medium. It uses the photon momentum (e.g., from a nuclear reactor) under controlled conditions to provide I_{sp} of about 10^7 sec. The thrust/weight ratio is *very* small and the engine could be used only in gravitationless fields.

photorecorder. A photographic device for recording the readings of instruments, especially of flight-test instruments or of instruments sent to high altitudes in rockets.

photosphere. That layer of the Sun's surface normally seen from the Earth. A turbulent region on which most of the visible solar features appear, such as sunspots and solar flares.

phototheodolite. Range instrumentation equipment used to track missiles optically. The missile image and angular coordinates are recorded against time (2 to 4 frames per sec).

phototheodolite, Askania. *See* Askania phototheodolite.

phototube. *See* electron-multiplier phototube.

phugoid oscillation. A long-period oscillation characteristic of the disturbed longitudinal motion of a missile.

physical or compound pendulum. A pendulum which is a rigid body with no restriction on size, shape, or composition. When suspended from a fixed axis passing through the body, it undergoes oscillations.

physical properties (materials). *See* mechanical properties.

physical units and constants.

Acceleration is rate of increase of velocity; the change of velocity per unit time (e.g., as centimeters per second per second). The usual form for writing the units is: ft/sec^2 or cm sec^{-2}. A negative acceleration is a *retardation*.

Density of a substance is its mass per unit volume.

Energy is the ability to do work. It is measured in the same units as work.

Force is that which tends to alter the uniform motion (or rest) of a body. Force is stated in terms of the weight that exerts an equal force (e.g., a force of: pounds weight or of grams weight). The unit of force defined dynamically is the *dyne* (q.v.); the megadyne is one million dynes. The unit of force defined by gravity is the *kilogram-force* $= 980 \times 10^3$ dynes approximately.

Force can also be measured by the acceleration it can produce: a force of 1 dyne will accelerate a mass of 1 gram by 1 centimeter per second per second.

The *pound force* is the force required to support the *standard pound body* (q.v.) against gravity, *in vacuo*, in the standard locality; or, it is the force which, if applied to the standard pound body, supposed free to move, would give that body the *standard acceleration*.

The *kilogram force* is the force required to support the standard kilogram against gravity, *in vacuo*, in the standard locality; or, it is the force which, if applied to the standard kilogram body, supposed free to move, would give that body the *standard acceleration*. The most desirable terminology for the units is: *kilogram force* and *kilogram mass*, respectively.

Heat is measured in calories. One calorie is the amount of heat required to raise the temperature of one gram of water by one degree centigrade (from 14.5° to 15.5°); also termed *gram-calorie* or *small calorie*. The *kilogram-calorie* or *large calorie* is equal to 1000 gram calories. One degree centigrade is one hundredth of the difference of temperature between melting ice and boiling water (at normal pressure).

temperature = heat per unit mass

Power is the rate of doing work. It is measured in units of work per unit time (e.g., gm-cm/sec or ft-lb/sec).

1 horsepower = 550 ft-lb/sec
1 poncelet = 100 kg-m/sec
1 cheval-vapeur = 75 kg-m/sec

1 watt = 1 joule/sec = 10,000,000 dyne-cm/sec
1 kilowatt = 1000 watts = 10^{10} dyne-cm/sec

Pressure is force per unit area (e.g., lb/sq in.). It is also stated in *millibars* (1000 dynes/sq cm) or as the height of a column of mercury which exerts such a pressure. *Normal atmospheric pressure* = 760 mm of mercury = 14.79 lb/sq in. = 1013.4 millibars.

Speed is the distance covered in any direction per unit time; it can never be negative. It is expressed in cm/sec or miles per hour (mph) or any equivalent combination.

Velocity is speed in a given direction. It is measured in the same units as speed, but a motion in a direction opposite to the given direction has *negative velocity*.

Work is done when a force moves its point of application. It is expressed as the product of the force and distance through which it has moved its point of application without diminishing or getting stronger (e.g., ft-lb, gm-cm, or ergs).

1 erg = 1 dyne-cm
1 joule = 10^7 ergs = 10,000,000 dyne-cm
1 kilowatt-hour = 3,600,000 joules = 3600 × 10^{10} dyne-cm

See cgs system–; metric system–; systems of measurement.

EARTH MEASUREMENT CONSTANTS:

Equatorial radius $a = 3963.35$ miles
Polar radius $b = 3950.01$ miles
Flattening $c = (a - b)/a = 1/297.0$
Acceleration due to gravity $g = 32.17$ ft/sec^2 = 981 cm/sec^2 (45° latitude)
Mass of the Earth = 6.6×10^{21} tons
Velocity of escape from the Earth = 6.94 miles per sec

EARTH ORBITAL MOTION CONSTANTS:

Solar parallax = 8.79″
Constant of aberration = 20.47″
Annual general precession = 50.26″
Obliquity of ecliptic = 23°26′50″
Orbital velocity = 18.5 miles/sec = 29.8 km/sec
Parabolic velocity at earth = 26.2 miles/sec

GALACTIC SYSTEM:

North pole of the galactic plane = R.A. 12 hours, 40 minutes, Dec. +28°
Center, 325° galactic longitude = R.A. 17 hours, 24 minutes, Dec. −30°
Distance to center = 30,000 light years
Diameter = 100,000 light years
Rotational velocity (at Sun) = 163.1 miles/sec
Rotational period (at Sun) = 2.2×10^8 years
Mass = 2×10^{11} solar masses

LENGTH UNITS:

1 Ångstrom unit	$= 10^{-8}$ cm
1 micron	$= 10^{-4}$ cm $= 0.001$ mm
1 centimeter	$= 0.3937$ inch
1 inch	$= 2.54$ centimeters
1 meter	$= 10^2$ cm $= 3.28084$ ft
1 kilometer	$= 10^5$ cm $= 0.62137$ miles
1 mile	$= 1.60935 \times 10^5$ cm $= 1.60935$ km $= 5280$ ft
1 astronomical unit	$= 1.49678 \times 10^{13}$ cm $= 93,005,000$ miles
1 light year	$= 9.463 \times 10^{17}$ cm $= 5.880 \times 10^{12}$ miles $= 63,300$ astronomical units

MISCELLANEOUS UNITS:

Constant of gravitation	$g = 6.670 \times 10^{-8}$ C.G.S. units
Mass of the electron	$m = 9.035 \times 10^{-28}$ gm
Mass of the proton	$m = 1.662 \times 10^{-24}$ gm

1 radian $= 57.2958° = 3437.75' = 206,265''$
$\pi = 3.141,592,654$
No. of square degrees in the sky $= 41,253$

NAUTICAL UNITS:

6076.1033 feet	$= 1$ nautical mile (NM) $= 1.1507$ statute mile
6 feet	$= 1$ fathom
120 fathoms	$= 1$ cable length
1 nautical mile per hr	$= 1$ knot
3 nautical miles	$= 1$ league
1 degree at the equator	$= 60$ nautical miles $= 69.096$ statute miles
360 degrees	$= 21,600$ nautical miles $= 24,874.5$ statute miles $=$ circumference of Earth at the equator.

RADIATION CONSTANTS:

Velocity of light $= 299,774$ km/sec $= 186,271$ miles/sec
Solar constant $= 1.93$ gram calories/sq cm/min
Light ratio for 1 magnitude $= 2.512$
Log ratio $= 0.4000$
Radiation from a star (zero apparent magnitude) $= 3 \times 10^{-6}$ meter candles
Total energy emitted by a star (zero absolute magnitude) $= 5 \times 10^{25}$ horsepower

SOLAR MOTION CONSTANTS:

Solar apex R.A. 18 hours 4 minutes; Dec. $+31°$
Speed relative to neighboring stars $= 12.2$ miles/sec $= 20$ km/sec

TIME UNITS:

Sidereal day	$= 23$ hours, 56 minutes, 04.09 seconds of mean solar time
Mean solar day	$= 86,400$ seconds $= 1,440$ minutes $= 24$ hours
Synodical month	$= 29$ days, 12 hours, 44 minutes
Sidereal month	$= 27$ days, 7 hours, 43 minutes
Tropical year	$= 365$ days, 5 hours, 48 minutes, 46 seconds $= 31,556,926$ seconds
Sidereal year	$= 365$ days, 6 hours, 9 minutes, 10 seconds $= 31,558,150$ seconds
Eclipse year	$= 346$ days, 14 hours, 53 minutes.

physiological atmosphere. The ecosphere (q.v.).

P-I. Photogrammetric Instrumentation (q.v.).

piccolo. A code name for a kind of jammer (q.v.) using a series of high-power magnetrons.

picket. A radar beacon set up in a peripheral area. See radar picket.

pickoff. A device for converting mechanical motion into an electric signal proportional to the mechanical motion.

pickoff, gyroscope position. See gyroscope position pickoff.

pickup. In instrumentation, a sensing instrument that measures a varying quantity, e.g., air pressure, temperature, vibration, etc. Vernacular for *transducer* or *end instrument*.

pickup. *Types of, see* absolute pressure–; angular position–; differential pressure–; pressure–; stopped–; telemetering–; variable reluctance–; velocity–; vented pressure–; vibration–.

picric acid [$C_6H_2(NO_2)_3OH$]. A liquid monopropellant.

PIED PIPER. See SENTRY.

piezoelectric. The property of certain crystals in developing electrical charge or potential difference across certain crystal faces when subjected to a strain by mechanical forces, or conversely to produce a mechanical force when a voltage is applied across the material (e.g., quartz, tourmaline, Rochelle salts, and certain ceramics).

PIG. Pendulous Integrating Gyroscope (q.v.).

piggy-back control. (Vernacular) Cascade control (q.v.).

pigtail. In electricity: (1) A short, coiled connecting wire, or a short bundle of connecting wires (e.g., an igniter connector for rockets). (2) A short, flexible connecting wire between two parts having slight relative motion.

pilot. *Types of, see* automatic–; gyropilot; mechanical–.

pilotless aircraft. (1) Obsolescent term for a guided missile (q.v.). (2) An aircraft which is equipped to function without a human pilot aboard. (3) Sometimes the term is used to describe a drone (q.v.).

pi mode. In a magnetron, the mode of resonance oscillation in which the phase difference between any two adjacent anode segments is π radians.

$$\pi \text{ mode} = \frac{N}{2}$$

where N = number of cavities.

pinch effect. When a large electrical current flows through ionized gas, the current filaments attract each other, which causes the gas column to constrict. The result is termed the *pinch effect*.

pint. A unit of capacity measurement.

1 pint (dry) = 33.600 cu in. = $\frac{1}{2}$ qt (dry)
1 pint (liquid) = 28.875 cu in. = 0.4732 liter
= 16 fluid oz = $\frac{1}{2}$ liquid qt

PIONEER I. The first Lunar Probe. Air Force had cognizance. Stage I: THOR (q.v.) booster; Stage II: modified VANGUARD (q.v.) second stage, 7500-lb thrust; Stage III: solid propellant ABL rocket, 2500-lb thrust; Stage IV: solid propellant Grand Central rocket; 85-lb payload: Space Technology Laboratories. Owing to a thrust vector deviation the objective was not achieved, but the 85-lb payload reached an altitude of about 79,120 miles and had a flight period of about 43 hours and 20 minutes. See Table 6, page 245.

PIONEER II. The third attempt to launch a Lunar Probe. The launching occurred on November 7, 1958, at Cape Canaveral, Florida. The size and configuration of the rocket was the same as PIONEER I (q.v.). The third-stage rocket failed to ignite and the mission aborted. See Table 6, page 245.

PIONEER III. The first Army attempt at a Lunar Probe. Stage I: JUNO II (modified JUPITER IRBM, q.v.); Stage II: 11 SERGEANT (q.v.) solid propellant rockets; Stage III: 3 SERGEANT rockets; Stage IV: 1 SERGEANT rocket; payload: Jet Propulsion Laboratory. Owing to 3.7-sec

early cutoff of the booster engine the terminal velocity was 24,000 instead of the desired 24,990 mph. This and a 3° aiming error aborted the mission, but the 13-lb payload achieved an altitude of about 66,600 miles and a flight time of about 26 hours and 15 minutes. See Table 6, page 245.

pip. (Vernacular) The figure presented on the oscilloscope of a radar caused by the echo from the target. Also termed *blip*.

pitch. In aerodynamics, an angular displacement about an axis parallel to the lateral axis of an airframe.

pitch. *Types of, see* angle of–; experimental mean–.

pitch programmer. A device used to provide initial pitch or tiltover guidance to a vertically launched missile to put it "on target." The device may be airborne or ground-based with a radio link.

pitot tube. (1) A tube that measures the impact pressure of a moving fluid. (2) Short for pitot-static tube (q.v.).

pitot-static tube (pitot tube). A tube arrangement which, when inserted into a moving fluid, such as air, measures *impact pressure* and *static pressure*. Essentially it consists of two tubes, one inside the other or one parallel to the other. One of these (the pitot tube) points into the fluid flow and measures impact pressure (including static pressure). The other is a static tube, which measures static pressure by having the opening normal to the airstream. The difference between the two pressures is termed the *pressure difference. See* static tube.

plan. *Types of, see* controlled materials–; installations–; logistics–; operations (or operational)–.

plane. *Types of, see* phase–; principal–; range–; vertical–.

plane of polarization of a radio wave. A term which defines the orientation of energy in an electromagnetic wave; determined by convention to be the direction of the electric field with respect to the Earth's surface.

plane of symmetry. A vertical plane containing the longitudinal axis of a symmetrical object, and on either side of which both halves of the object are symmetrical. The vertical plane is taken when the object is in its assumed upright position.

planet. A mass of matter moving in an elliptical orbit (q.v.) which has the Sun as one of the foci. The nine planets listed in the table, along

Planet	Mean distance to Sun	Astro. units	Revolution around Sun	Rotation on axis	Diameter	Mass (Earth = 1)	Escape velocity	Moons	Surface gravity (Earth = 1)
Mercury	36,000,000 miles	0.387	88 days	88 days	3100 miles	$\sim$0.04	2.2 mps	none	$\sim$0.27
Venus	67,300,000 miles	0.723	225 days	30 hrs	7700 miles	0.8	6.3 mps	none	0.86
Earth	92,870,000 miles	1.0	365 days	24 hrs	7927 miles	1.00	7.0 mps	1	1.00
Mars	141,700,000 miles	1.524	687 days	24h37m	4300 miles	0.11	3.1 mps	2	0.37
Jupiter	483,900,000 miles	5.203	4333 days	9h55m	88,770 miles	317.0	37.0 mps	12	?
Saturn	886,100,000 miles	9.539	29.458 years	10h38m	71,000 miles	95.0	22.0 mps	9	?
Uranus	1,785,000,000 miles	19.182	84.015 years	10h45m	32,400 miles	14.7	13.0 mps	5	?
Neptune	2,797,000,000 miles	30.057	164.788 years	15h50m	30,900 miles	17.2	14.0 mps	2	?
Pluto	3,670,000,000 miles	39.518	247.697 years	?	7900 miles	0.7	14.5 mps	none	?

with the comets, planetoids, and meteors, comprise our solar system.

planet. *Types of, see* inferior–; navigational–; superior–.

planetary space. The region of close vicinity to the respective planet, in the same sense as defined for terrestrial space (q.v.).

planetoid. One of the several hundred small planets revolving between the orbits of Mars and Jupiter. (A body resembling a planet.) *See* asteroid.

plane wave tube. An acoustical environmental test device used to produce high-energy sound waves.

plan position indicator (PPI). A radar display in which targets are positioned in terms of azimuth (q.v.) and distance.

plasma. A partially ionized jet; a mixture of gas and electrically charged particles (e.g., ions, electrons) at high temperatures.

plasma jet. An electrical discharge used to heat air to extremely high temperatures.

plastic deformation. The permanent change in size or shape of a ductile material under stress. The deformation occurs along the slip planes of the crystals, and anything that tends to interfere with this slippage or to resist the deformation will result in an increase in tensile strength.

plasticizer. A material which is added to a solid rocket propellant to increase plasticity, workability, or to extend physical properties.

plastic, thermoset. *See* thermoset plastic.

plate. The common name for the principal anode of a vacuum tube.

plate circuit. A circuit including the plate voltage source and all other parts connected between the cathode and plate terminals of a vacuum tube.

platform. *Types of, see* gyroscope-stabilized–; space–; stabilized–.

PLATO. Anti-missile missile study program. Army and Air Force cognizance. Similar to NIKE-ZEUS and WIZARD (q.q.v.).

Prime Contractor: Sylvania Electric Co.

playback. Playing back of a magnetic tape recording for the purpose of reconstructing the original electrical signals as faithfully as possible.

playback, telemetry. *See* telemetry playback.

plenum chamber. (1) Any chamber used as a reservoir or accumulator. (2) An air chamber opening into the compressor chamber on certain turbojet or turboprop engines, and in which air is collected for the compressor.

plotting board. A device used to record the function of a variable, usually in real time. (In missile applications, it is used to monitor range, target bearing, missile position, etc., by automatically plotting such variables as azimuth, altitude, range.)

PLOVER. Missile or target drone. Navy cognizance. Designation: KDM1.

A GORGON IV converted to a target drone by use of a jet engine. Motor: Marquardt RJ30MA6 ramjet; length: 7 ft; diameter: 1.75 in.; weight: 175 lb; thrust: 1400 lb. Radio guided, airlaunched with electronic fire control system.

Prime Contractor: The Martin Co.

Status: phased out.

PLOWSHARE project. An Atomic Energy Commission designation for the project for the peaceful use of nuclear explosives—untamed, but put to such jobs as blasting, flood control, production of power and radioisotopes.

plug. *Types of, see* glow–; umbilical–.

plug-in. A unit or device which may be plugged into a receptacle to afford ease of installation and/or replacement.

plumbing. (Vernacular) In missile and radar usage: (1) The designation for waveguides, coaxial lines, and other equipment used for transmission of RF energy. (2) The piping, lines, and connections associated with an engine and its control system. (3) The piping, lines, and connections associated with the hydraulic system.

PLUTO project. An Atomic Energy Commission project designation for application of nuclear energy to rocket propulsion.

plutonium reactor. A nuclear reactor in which plutonium is the principal fissionable material.

PM. (1) Pulse Modulation (q.v.). (2) Phase Modulation (q.v.).

PMR. Pacific Missile Range (q.v.).

pneudraulic. Of, or pertaining to, mechanisms or devices that work by both pneumatic and hydraulic action (e.g., pneudraulic shock strut).

pneumatics. The study of the action of gases. *See* mechanics.

POC. Productional Operational Capability. *See* IOC.

POGO. Target drone. Navy Bureau of Ordnance cognizance.

Airframe is 14 ft in length, uses a solid rocket sustainer and a solid rocket booster. Has a very high altitude capability and is used for target applications.

point. *Types of, see* burble–; burnout–; control–; cutoff–; dew–; equigravitational–; fire–; flash–; hard–; image–; impact–; Jato cant–; major test–; nodal–; subastral–; sublunar–;

subpoint–; subsolar–; substellar–; transition–; triple–; Trojan–; yield–.

Point Arguello. A portion of the Pacific Missile Range (q.v.); the southern (Navy) area of Vandenberg Air Force Base near Lompoc, California.

point contact transistor. A solid state device in which the emitter and collector connections are point contact (high resistance). The collector current is larger than the emitter current. Contrast with *junction transistor* (q.v.).

point impedance. In electronics, the ratio of the maximum E-field to the maximum H-field observed at a given point in a waveguide or transmission line because of the energy flow under consideration.

point target. A precise target of small dimensions. Distinguish from an *area target*.

point-to-point wiring. A production technique for wiring electronic chassis in which the connections between components or parts are made without intermediate supports.

Poisson's probability distribution. A mathematical expression of the distribution of random quantities often found in nature.

polar air. The air in an air mass (q.v.) having its origin in a subpolar anticyclone and in regions somewhat south of the regions in which arctic air originates. Polar air is divided and classified into two types: *polar continental air* (q.v.) and *polar maritime air*.

polar concept. A concept of the world in which air movement, strategy, and planning are considered in the knowledge that the region of either pole offers a shorter practical route between certain points than that offered by other latitudes.

polar continental air. Polar air that originates over a continent and remains relatively stable and dry as it moves over a continental area.

polar day. A synthetic temperature vs. altitude profile used for performance calculations. Characteristics are shown in Fig. 25, page 267.

polar front. A front or frontal surface between polar air masses and warmer air masses to the south.

polar gnomonic projection. In cartography, a method of portraying the Earth's surface. If the pole is chosen as the point of tangency for a gnomonic projection (q.v.), the meridians appear as radial lines and the parallels of latitude appear as concentric circles. Also termed polar gnomonic chart.

polar grid. A special kind of grid (q.v.) used

with an aeronautical chart in polar air navigation set up in accordance with a G-system (q.v.).

POLARIS. Two-stage Intermediate Range Ballistic Missile launched from a submarine. Also termed fleet ballistic missile (FBM) (q.v.). Navy Bureau of Ordnance cognizance.

Length: 40 to 50 ft; diameter: 60 in.; range: up to 1500 miles. Solid propellant rocket engines. Inertial guidance. Jetavators are used for control.

Systems Engineering: Special Projects Office (SP), Navy Bureau of Ordnance. Prime Contractor: Lockheed Aircraft Corp., Missile Systems Division. Airframe: Lockheed. Engines: Aerojet-General Corp. Guidance system: General Electric Co. Reentry vehicle: Lockheed.

polarity. In electricity, a characteristic or quality of point or poles in an electric or magnetic circuit or field with respect to the flow of electrons or of magnetic lines of force; the quality of having opposite charges, one positive and one negative, or of having opposing magnetic poles. *Positive polarity:* the characteristic of a point toward which negative particles flow. *Negative polarity:* the characteristic of a point away from which the flow occurs.

polarization. (1) In physics, the act or process of affecting light waves or electromagnetic waves so that they are made to vibrate in a certain given direction. (2) In electricity, the formation or accumulation of gas or some substance on the electrodes of an electric cell as a result of the passage of current; the condition arising from such formation or accumulation.

polarization, vertical and horizontal. *See* vertical and horizontal polarization.

polar trough. In meteorology, a trough (q.v.) associated with a polar front, which extends from high latitudes to the middle and lower latitudes.

pole. *Types of, see* celestial–; geographic–; magnetic–; north magnetic–; south magnetic–; terrestrial–.

polyconic projection. In cartography, a method of portraying the Earth's surface. The projection is made on a series of cones tangent to the Earth. Meridians, except the central one, are represented as curved lines. Parallels of latitude are nonconcentric circles, but having their centers along the central meridians, usually beyond the limit of the map. There is no distortion along the central meridian and, unless the spread in longitude is great, maximum distortion is small. The polyconic projection is not suitable

for navigational purposes because both direction and distance are difficult to measure accurately and both rhumb lines and great circles are curves.

polyethylene. A liquid rocket propellant *fuel.* See Table 3, page 157.

polysulfide. A solid rocket propellant *fuel* of the synthetic rubber type.

polyurethane. A solid rocket propellant *fuel* of the synthetic rubber type. See Table 5, page 214.

porous reactor. A nuclear reactor (q.v.) composed of a porous material or an aggregate of small particles with coolant or fluid fuel flowing through the pores.

port area. In rocketry, the cross-sectional area perpendicular to the longitudinal axis of a rocket propellant grain available for free gas flow.

port-to-throat ratio. In solid propellant rocket design, the ratio of the grain porting or void area to the area of the nozzle throat.

position. *Types of, see* geographic–; present–.

position data. Successive data defining the position of a target being tracked by radar or other means.

position feedback. A type of feedback in control systems in which position of the controlled device is used as the reference (e.g., position of a wing, swivelled thrust chamber, radar dish, etc.).

positive displacement. (1) The displacement of an aerodynamic control surface that causes the airfoil either to rise or to move to the right. (2) Mechanical displacement contrasted to obtaining movement by induced means.

positive displacement compressor or pump. A compressor or pump so constructed as to compress the working fluid by displacing it mechanically, as with a piston or two gears acting as a gear pump.

positive feedback. Feedback which increases amplification, being in phase with the original signal. Contrast with *negative feedback* (q.v.).

positron. *Posit*ive plus elec*tron.* A positively charged particle having the same mass and ionizing power as an electron. The positron was first discovered in 1932 in cosmic rays. Positrons also are emitted from radioactive substances, and are sometimes termed *positive electrons.*

post aircraft rocket launcher. A type of aircraft rocket launcher (q.v.) carrying the rocket on a post or posts fitted to the rocket motor.

potassium nitrate (KNO₃). A solid rocket propellant inorganic *oxidizer* with 40% available oxygen. See Table 5, page 214.

potassium perchlorate (KCIO₄) A solid rocket propellant *oxidizer* with 46% available oxygen. See Table 5, page 214.

potential. *Types of, see* ground–; logistics–.

potential energy. A body has potential energy by virtue of its position relative to a force that is acting upon it.

potential instability. Convective instability (q.v.).

potential temperature. In meteorology, the temperature which a particular parcel of air would have if it had a pressure of 1000 millibars.

potentiometer. A device for translating a quantitative motion (angular or linear) into a proportional electrical resistance; it measures by comparing the difference between known and unknown electrical potentials.

potting. The process of imbedding an electronic circuit component or assembly in a (usually) plastic material to reduce susceptibility to deleterious environments, simplify maintenance, etc. Sometimes used as a structural element (e.g., to carry compressive loads).

pound. A unit of weight measurement.

$$\begin{aligned} \text{1 pound (avoirdupois)} &= 256 \text{ avoirdupois drams} \\ &= 4.4482 \times 10^5 \text{ dynes} \\ &= 7000 \text{ grains} \\ &= 453.5924 \text{ grams} \\ &= 16 \text{ oz(avoirdupois)} \\ &= 32.174 \text{ poundals} \end{aligned}$$

$$\begin{aligned} \text{1 pound/sq ft} &= 0.01414 \text{ in. of mercury at } 32°\text{F} \\ &= 0.01602 \text{ ft of water at } 39.2°\text{F} \end{aligned}$$

$$\begin{aligned} \text{1 pound/sq in.} &= 2.036 \text{ in. of mercury at } 32°\text{F} \\ &= 27.673 \text{ in. of water at } 39.2°\text{F} \\ &= 144 \text{ lb/sq ft} \end{aligned}$$

poundal. The force which, if applied to the standard pound body (q.v.), would give that body an acceleration of 1 fps²; that is, 1 poundal = 1/32.1740 of a pound force.

1 poundal = 1.3825×10^4 dynes = 0.031081 lb

powder. *See* double-base powder.

power. (1) The time rate of doing work (of utilizing or creating energy). (2) The time rate at which energy is transmitted from one point to another.

$$\text{power} = F\frac{ds}{dt} = Fv = \text{force times velocity}$$

See physical units and constants.

power. *Types of, see* atomic–; emissive–; half–; jet–; secondary nuclear auxiliary–.

power and heat measurements.

1 horsepower-hour	= 0.746 kilowatt-hour
	= 1,980,000 foot-pounds
	= 2545 Btu (British thermal units)
	= 2.64 pounds of water evaporated at 212°F
	= 17 pounds of water raised from 62° to 212°F
1 kilowatt-hour	= 1000 watt-hours
	= 1.34 horsepower-hour
	= 2,655,200 foot-pounds
	= 3,600,000 joules
	= 3415 Btu
	= 3.54 pounds of water evaporated at 212°F
	= 22.8 pounds of water raised from 62° to 212°F
1 horsepower	= 746 watts = 0.746 kilowatt
	= 33,000 foot-pounds/minute
	= 550 foot-pounds/second
	= 2545 Btu/hour
	= 42.4 Btu/minute
	= 0.71 Btu/second
	= 2.64 lb of water evaporated per hour at 212°F
1 kilowatt	= 1000 watts = 1.34 horsepower
	= 2,655,200 foot-pounds/hour
	= 44,200 foot-pounds/minute
	= 737 foot-pounds/second
	= 3415 Btu/hour = 57 Btu/minute
	= 0.95 Btu/second
	= 3.54 pounds of water evaporated per hour at 212°F
1 watt	= 1 joule/second
	= 0.00134 horsepower
	= 0.001 kilowatt = 3.42 Btu/hour
	= 44.22 foot-pounds/minute
	= 0.74 foot-pound/second
	= 0.0035 pound of water evaporated per hour at 212°F
1 Btu (British thermal unit)	= 1054.8 watt-seconds
	= 778 foot-pounds
	= 0.252 kilogram-calorie
	= 0.000292 kilowatt-hour
	= 0.000393 horsepower-hour
	= 0.00104 pound of water evaporated at 212°F
1 foot-pound	= 1.36 joule
	= 0.00000377 kilowatt-hour
	= 0.00129 Btu
	= 0.0000005 horsepower-hour
1 joule	= 1 watt-second
	= 0.000000278 kilowatt-hour
	= 0.00095 Btu = 0.74 foot-pound

powered flight trajectory. In a ballistic, glide, or skip missile (q.q.v.) trajectory, that part which includes flight while under power from booster, sustainer, or vernier engines (q.q.v.). During this period, azimuth, elevation and velocity adjustments may be made in terms of intended target coordinates. See Fig. 27, page 293.

power factor. The ratio of the power passing through a circuit to the product of the voltage and amperage, or the cosine of the phase angle between the current and the impressed electromotive force.

$$\text{power factor} = \cos\theta = \frac{P}{EI}$$

where θ = phase angle; E = impressed electromotive force; I = current.

For an alternating current, the power in watts is:

$$P = EI \cos\theta$$

For a direct current, the power in watts is:

$$P = EI = I^2R$$

where E = electromotive force in volts; I = current in amperes; R = resistance in ohms.

power plant. The hardware associated with various types of propulsion (q.v.) including ramjets, turbojets, pulsejets, or rockets (q.q.v.) or other propulsive devices used to propel a missile. Synonymous with *engine*.

power spectral density (PSD). Limiting mean square acceleration (velocity, displacement, stress, or other random variable) per unit bandwidth (e.g., the limit of the mean square acceleration in a given rectangular bandwidth, divided by the bandwidth as the bandwidth approaches zero). The intensity for a 1-cycle bandwidth is:

$$\text{PSD} = \frac{g^2}{\Delta f}; \qquad g = \sqrt{\tfrac{1}{2}\Sigma A}$$

where Δf = bandwidth; g = rms gravity; A = maximum amplitude of acceleration for each frequency in the bandwidth.

power standing ratio. *See* standing wave ratio.

power supply. *Types of, see* accessory–; emergency–; internal–; static–.

PPI. (1) Plan Position Indicator (q.v.). (2) Present Position Indicator (q.v.).

PPM. Pulse Position Modulation (q.v.).

PPS. Pulse Per Second.

practice rocket. A rocket used in practice or training having either an uncharged head, or a head containing a spotting charge, but having the same kind of motor as the corresponding service rocket.

Prandtl-Meyer expansion. The character of supersonic flow around a corner. It describes, on the basis of two-dimensional theory, the acceleration and flow characteristics.

Prandtl nozzle. A highly efficient bell-shaped nozzle used in solid propellant rockets operating at vacuum altitudes. Most of the jet's kinetic energy is converted into thrust with a minimum of frictional loss.

preamplifier (preamp). An extra stage of amplification at the front end of an amplifier or receiver used to increase signal strength.

precautionary maintenance. A procedure of reconditioning a product before failure in order to prevent failures in service. (This procedure is not based upon specific instructions and scheduling.)

precession. (1) A change in the orientation of the axis of a rotating body, e.g., a spinning projectile or gyroscope, the effect of which is to rotate this axis (axis of spin) about a line (axis of precession) perpendicular to its original direction and to the axis (axis of torque) of the moment producing that change. See Fig. 21, page 254. (2) A slow change in the direction in space of the Earth's axis of rotation. It arises from the tendency of the gravitational attraction of the Sun and the Moon to pull the Earth's equatorial bulge into line with this attraction. The Earth behaves like a spinning top whose axis is tilted to the vertical at a fixed angle throughout its "wobble." As a result of precession, the poles of the celestial sphere describe circles among the stars; a complete cycle requires nearly 26,000 years.

Angular velocity of precession:

$$\Omega = \frac{T}{\omega I}$$

where T = torque; ω = angular velocity; I = moment of inertia.

precession. *Types of, see* apparent–; axis of–; gyroscope–; true–.

precipitation. In meteorology: (1) The act or process by which moisture in the air condenses and falls. (2) The condensed droplets or particles of moisture that fall on the Earth's surface. Precipitation includes: rain, sleet, snow, hail, and mist. Dew, fog, frost, and other forms of moisture that do not fall to the Earth are not ordinarily considered precipitation, although moisture struck by a vehicle in flight is sometimes so considered.

precipitation static. In radio, static resulting from the precipitation of snow, rain, etc., from the impact of dust particles on a receiving antenna, or from particles in the atmosphere striking the surfaces of a flying vehicle.

precooling. *See* cooling.

prediction. *See* radar prediction.

predictor. *Types of, see* deck motion–; impact–.

preflight rating test (PFRT). In engine test

programs, a series of tests performed during development to establish design adequacy and ability to withstand design level performance for limited periods. The completion of PFRT usually permits use of the engine for research and development missile tests.

preflight system calibration. The process of determining the response characteristics of a device by recording the change in a data signal received by the ground station when the transducer (q.v.) associated with that data channel is stimulated with or replaced with an electrical signal.

prefrontal thunderstorm. A squall-line thunderstorm.

pre-launch console. A display panel and control panel housed in a blockhouse (q.v.) that will automatically monitor or checkout a missile during a time interval prior to actual launch.

pre-launch tests. Tests of missile and/or ground equipment to determine readiness to launch. May include a countdown (q.v.) and a flight readiness firing (q.v.) with all launch complex (q.v.) equipment operating, but not including actual launching of the missile.

preliminary design. That design phase which has for its objective the establishment of the basic configuration and resultant performance of the missile and/or its auxiliary equipments.

preliminary engineering inspection (PEI). An unofficial product or system inspection not covered by military regulations. Precedes the Development Engineering Inspection (DEI) (q.v.), and is essentially a three-dimensional mock-up of the product or system. Frequently, alternate designs are evaluated.

premature. A detonation of the warhead prior to the time that the safety and arming (S and A) (q.v.) was to arm the system.

preproduction period. The time between beginning work in preparation for production and completion of the first article.

preprototype. A device, article, assembly, or system which precedes the actual prototype (q.v.). In terms of time, the preprototype usually follows the breadboard (q.v.) and is functionally correct in about the right package and proportion. Generally the device, *et al.*, has not been designed for environment, maintenance, and other features usually found in a prototype article.

presented target area. The projection of the target upon the perpendicular plane used in defining the dispersion area; used to analyze the performance requirements of an armament system.

present position. A technical term indicating the position of a moving target the instant it is fired at or indicated by a display system (e.g., radarscope).

present position indicator (PPI). A device or system with computational features used to establish, for fire control or guidance systems, an indication of the present position of a missile target.

preset guidance. A technique of missile guidance wherein a predetermined path is set into the guidance and control mechanism of a vehicle and cannot be adjusted after launching. A missile using preset guidance is not a *true* guided missile.

pressure. (p) Force (q.v.) per unit area. The pressure caused by a force F distributed uniformly over an area A:

$$p = F/A$$

Pressure is measured in pounds per square inch (psi), dynes per square centimeter, etc., or by the height of the column of water or mercury which it will support (in feet, inches, or centimeters).

pressure. *Types of, see* absolute–; acoustomotive–; atmospheric–; base–; blast–; chamber–; dynamic–; effective chamber–; equilibrium–; gage–; impact–; injection–; peak sound–; ram–; rated operating–; reference–; reflected–; sound–; static–; static air–; temperature sensitivity of–; working–.

pressure altimeter. An altimeter (q.v.) that measures and indicates altitude by means of differences in atmospheric pressure. A pressure altimeter uses an aneroid barometer as its sensing and actuating element.

pressure altitude. (1) Generally, altitude above the standard datum plane, as determined by applying the standard pressure lapse rate to the atmospheric pressure at altitude. (2) Either indicated pressure altitude or calibrated pressure altitude. (3) A simulated pressure altitude inside a low-pressure chamber.

pressure altitude variation. The difference in feet between the standard datum plane (29.92 in. of mercury) and the datum plane above which altitude is measured.

pressure anomaly. The difference between the actual pressure lapse rate and the arbitrary standard pressure lapse rate for which an altimeter (q.v.) is designed.

pressure feed system. In liquid rocket engines,

a stored or generated gas system used to cause the propellants to flow to the combustion chamber.

pressure difference. In determining the pressure of air on a vehicle due to movement alone, the difference between *impact* pressure and *static* pressure (q.q.v.). *See* pitot-static tube.

pressure front. Shock front (q.v.).

pressure gas. In a liquid-fuel rocket, a gas fed under pressure into the propellant tanks to force the propellants into the combustion chamber.

pressure gradient. In meteorology, the rate of pressure increase or decrease on any atmospheric plane, usually a horizontal plane, for any given distance.

pressure jump. In meteorology, an abrupt change in atmospheric pressure across a narrow zone.

pressure level. *See* sound pressure level.

pressure limits. The upper and lower chamber pressure limit within which a *solid rocket propellant* (q.v.) will operate satisfactorily.

pressure measurement.

1 pound/square inch	= 144 pounds/square foot
	= 0.068 atmosphere
	= 2.042 inches of mercury at 62°F
	= 27.7 inches of water at 62°F
	= 2.31 feet of water at 62°F
1 atmosphere	= 30 inches of mercury at 62°F
	= 14.7 pounds/square inch
	= 2116.3 pounds/square foot
	= 33.95 feet of water at 62°F
1 foot of water at 62°F	= 62.355 pounds/square foot
	= 0.433 pound/square inch
1 inch of mercury at 62°F	= 1.132 feet of water
	= 13.58 inches of water
	= 0.491 pound/square inch

pressure pickup. A device used in telemetering (q.v.) which converts changes of gas or liquid pressure into corresponding changes of an analog quantity, such as a change of inductance or resistance.

pressure pickup response. The measure of the ability of a pressure gage or telemetering pickup to respond to various rates of change of pressure.

pressure ratio. A ratio between two pressures (e.g., the ratio between the inlet and outlet pressure in a compressor or between chamber pressure and nozzle pressure in a rocket).

pressure recovery (diffuser). The measure of the kinetic energy of the air to pressure head in a diffuser. For a normal shock diffuser (q.v.) the pressure recovery is:

$$\frac{p_2}{p_o} = \left(\frac{7 + \eta}{6}\right)M_o^2$$

where p_2 = pressure at the completion of diffusion; p_o = free stream overpressure; η = diffuser efficiency; typical values are 0.6 to 0.75; M_o = free stream MACH number.

pressure sensitivity. The ratio of the maximum pressure frequency minus the minimum pressure frequency, divided by the mean of these two frequencies.

$$\frac{\text{pressure}}{\text{sensitivity}} = \left(\frac{f_{\text{max pressure}} - f_{\text{min pressure}}}{f_{\text{max pressure}} + f_{\text{min pressure}}}\right)/2$$

pressure thrust. The product of the cross-sectional area of the exhaust jet leaving a vehicle and the difference between the exhaust pressure and the fluid pressure; that part of the thrust of a rocket resulting from the pressure difference as compared to the velocity thrust (q.v.).

$$\text{pressure thrust} = (p_e - p_a)A_e$$

where p_e = pressure at nozzle exit; p_a = ambient pressure; A_e = nozzle area at exit.

pressurize (pressurization). In pressure-fed propellant systems, that phase of operation in which the pressurizing gas is applied to the propellant to cause it to feed to the pumps or combustion chamber, or to prevent boiloff or vaporization.

prestage. A phase in starting liquid rocket engines in which combustion is initiated and combustion chamber pressure is developed to a predetermined level at which time *main stage* (q.v.) is initiated.

prevailing westerlies. In meteorology, winds that blow toward the poles from the horse latitudes. They are not as steady as the trade winds in the Northern Hemisphere, but they are more constant in the Southern Hemisphere, where they are known as the *roaring forties*.

preventive maintenance. A procedure of inspecting, testing, and reconditioning a product at regular intervals and according to specific instructions, in order to prevent failures in service and to retard deterioration.

PRF. Pulse Repetition Frequency. *See* radar pulse repetition frequencies.

primacord. An explosive charge, shaped like a rope (used in flight missiles to sever structure for flight termination purposes. Also used to sever control links, booster assemblies, etc.).

primary. The most massive body in any system of bodies which revolve about their common center of gravity. The Earth is the Moon's primary; every planet is the primary of its satellites. The primary is the body about which an orbit takes place.

primary battery. A self-contained source of electrical energy which is characterized by the need to renew the chemically reacting parts (e.g., dry cell).

primary structure. The main framework, including fittings and attachments. Any structural member, the failure of which would seriously impair the safety of the missile, is a part of the primary structure.

prime contractor. A contractor having a contract directly with the Government or other funding agency. Contrast with a *subcontractor* who has a contract with a prime contractor.

prime meridian. The arbitrary zero of longitude on the Earth's surface. It is defined as the meridian passing through the Airy transit circle at the Royal Observatory, Greenwich, England.

primer. The first sensitive explosive element in an explosive chain which is initiated by the low-level fuze output signals.

principal modes. *See* coupled modes.

principal planes. The three mutually perpendicular planes through a point in a stressed body on which the stresses are purely normal; i.e., tension or compression. Of these principal stresses, one is a *maximum* and one is a *minimum*. When one principal stress is zero, a state of *plane stress* exists; when two are zero, a state of *uniaxial stress* exists.

printed circuit. Any circuit formed by depositing a conducting material on the surface of an insulating sheet. This may be achieved by the use of electrically conducting ink, electroplating, etc.

printed circuitry. A generic classification for fabricated wiring which may be obtained by: metal to plastic laminate etching, silk screening, photo-offset printing, plating, stamping, electro-forming, embossing, spraying.

PRIVATE A. Research rocket. This rocket was one of the first experimental programs used for research. Its altitude was about 11 miles.

PRIVATE F. Research rocket. A modification of PRIVATE A. No longer in use.

probability. The chance that a certain result will occur under a defined set of circumstances.

probability. *Types of, see* cumulative kill–; failure–; hit–; kill–; single-shot–; survival–; thermodynamic–.

probable error (p.e.). In a measurement system, the chance that fifty per cent of the errors have absolute magnitude greater than the probable error.

probe. *Types of, see* Lunar–; MACH cone–; Mars–; Venus–.

processing. *See* data processing.

process water. Water required for deflector cooling, fire fighting, and washdown at engine or missile test or launch stand facilities. This water usually is filtered but not pure.

procurability. A relative term pertaining to those characteristics of a military item which determine the degree to which integration of technical development and production capability has been provided to achieve optimum materiel satisfaction at minimum cost.

procurement lead time. The time elapsing between the initiation of procurement action and the receipt into the system of materiel purchased as a result of such actions. Procurement lead time is applicable to materiel to be obtained from any source outside the procuring department or by manufacture within that department, and is composed of three distinct elements: (a) The time elapsing between the initiation of procurement action and letting of contract or placing of order; (b) The time elapsing between letting of contract or placing of order and completion of manufacture; (c) The time elapsing between completion of manufacture and receipt of materiel into the system.

producer's and consumer's risk. A concept used in reliability and test activities to avoid having either the consumer or the producer accept most of the risk for the acceptability of the product. The concept is based on the probability that the consumer will accept a defective product so many times and that he will reject a good product so many times; also that the producer will deliver with a certain probability a defective product or that he will reject a good product.

producer's risk. The probability of risk of rejecting a lot, for a given lot quality or process quality, whichever is applicable. The term is usually applied only to quality values that are relatively good.

producibility. A relative term describing those inherent design characteristics of an item which determine the factors of production (both kind and quantity) necessary to produce it.

product. *Types of, see* end–; fission–; *LC*–.

product engineering. Translation of the development design into one suitable for efficient manufacture in the desired quantities and for the conditions of specified usage, handling, and life; the development and preparation of functional ordnance designs and/or specifications which are not only sufficiently clear and complete to represent the requirements and intent of research, but are also prepared in such manner as to facilitate efficient manufacture with the minimum of modification. Product engineering includes such liaison with and direction over production engineering as to insure that the end product is suitable for service use, including all environmental considerations, and preparation of classification of defects.

production. The manufacture of a finished device, built to definite specifications; the translation of the product engineering design into the desired quantity of the end product. Skilled engineering is frequently required during production to correct defects in design, to improve operating characteristics, or to increase rate of production. However, such engineering changes are based on the fundamental design created by development, which in turn was based on the facts discovered by research. The term production may be divided into the two following categories: (a) *experimental production* (including pilot line operation); (b) *mass production* (which includes the usual high production manufacturing operations).

production bandwidth limits. The sum of the maximum and minimum frequency deviations which a device is intended to achieve in production with the application of full range stimulus. This is always less than the maximum bandwidth and takes into account the maximum intelligence frequency to be transmitted, the inherent instability of the device, the precision of production test equipment, and the tuning tolerance of the installer or assembler.

production engineering. Consultation with product engineering on prototype (q.v.) or functional developments and designs and specifications, and the making of recommendations that will promote maximum efficiency and economy in manufacture. It includes participation in an advisory or consulting capacity in the preparation of detailed manufacturing drawings and specifications from which a missile can be most efficiently manufactured, having in mind not only the limited production required in time of peace but also the high rate of production with unskilled workers which is required in time of war. It may involve the performance of the engineering function incident to efficient manufacture, e.g., tool and gage engineering, methods engineering, process engineering, production research, job standards. Participation in the preparation of *classification of defects* (q.v.) for quality control (q.v.) purposes may also be indicated by the term.

production environmental testing (PET). A test technique to check workmanship in which the article or system is subjected to a reduced intensity environmental test (compared to the design requirement).

production lead time. The time elapsing between *establishment* of a requirement and *delivery* by a contractor. Contrast with *procurement lead time* (q.v.).

production method change. Any change in the method of producing an article or item which does not alter the physical characteristics of the end product.

production model. Equipment in its final mechanical and electrical form, of final production design and made by production tools, jigs, fixtures, and methods.

production period. A period of time spent in production. Two production periods are recognized: (a) *initial production period,* the time between completion of the first article and the attainment of the peak rate of production; (b) *peak-rate production period,* the period of time between the time the peak rate is reached and the time at which production is slowed down or discontinued.

production-to-target environment. The physical conditions existing at each step described in the production-to-target sequence (q.v.); they are given in terms of temperature range, pressure, humidity, shock, vibration, acceleration, etc., with the time duration of each condition usually included.

production-to-target sequence. A chart or table showing all of the steps involved in manufacture, transport, storage, maintenance in storage, withdrawal from storage, assembly prior to launch, check-out prior to launch, launch, flight, and reentry or termination.

production type test. Verification tests performed on early production equipment to establish conformance to design requirements.

product rule. The rule that the reliability of a system with n independent components can be calculated by multiplying the individual reliabilities together, e.g.:

$$R = R_1 \times R_2 \times \ldots R_n$$

product support personnel. Includes those direct labor personnel involved in service engineering, overhaul, storage, receipt, packaging, and reshipment of equipment that has been returned by operational units of personnel at test sites.

The indirect labor portion includes the personnel involved in these areas but not involved in the actual overhaul or supply functions.

profile. *Types of, see* Sissenwine–; wind–.

profile drag. That part of the airfoil drag that results from the skin friction and the shape of the airfoil as indicated by the airfoil profile. (Profile drag, strictly speaking, does not include the parasite drag (q.v.) resulting from objects attached to the wing, but is sometimes interpreted to include such drag.)

program. (1) An entity; a definable portion of work; a scheduled development including study, design, fabrication and/or test phases. (2) A pre-established and preset series of functions, maneuvers, or operations (e.g., roll program, tilt over, gain change, etc.).

program. *Types of, see* BMTS–; crash–.

programmed turn. The automatically controlled turn of a ballistic missile from the vertical direction, maintained after liftoff, into the curved path that will lead to the correct velocity vector at thrust cutoff for the final portion of the trajectory, the coasting flight that will impact on the target. See Fig. 27, page 293.

programmer. A device, either airborne or ground-based, used to control missile motion in accordance with a predetermined plan.

programmer, pitch. *See* pitch programmer.

programming. *See* thrust programming.

progressive burning. Burning of a solid propellant rocket grain characterized by an increasing pressure with time.

progressivity ratio. In solid rocket grain design, a ratio indicating the degree of neutrality of the pressure-time curve.

$$PR = \frac{\text{area of final propellant surface}}{\text{area of initial propellant surface}}$$

projectile. A body which is accelerated to a velocity by the application of mechanical forces and which continues its motion along a ballistic trajectory. The mechanical forces may be generated by propellant gases in a rocket propulsion system as well as in a tube or gun barrel.

projectile. *Types of, see* fin-stabilized–; spin stabilized–.

projection. *Types of, see* chart–; conformal–; equidistant azimuthal–; gnomonic–; Lambert conformal–; Mercator–; orthographic–; polar gnomonic–; polyconic–; transverse Mercator–.

prominences (solar). Masses of glowing gas projected above the solar chromosphere.

proof stress. The load per unit area which a material is capable of withstanding without experiencing a permanent deformation of more than a specified amount per unit of gage length after complete release of load; i.e., the stress that will produce a very small permanent deformation, generally specified as 0.01% of the original gage length. Because this is difficult to determine by the alternate loading and releasing which is generally prescribed, the *offset method* is frequently employed.

proof test. (1) An acceptance test for materials or parts in which a specified stress level must be sustained without deformation in excess of a specified amount. (2) In a general sense, any kind of a test of a device at some working condition (e.g., vibration test of a component to the same intensity as nominally expected in flight).

propagation. The manner in which an emission travels outward from its source.

propagation. *Types of, see* flame–; velocity of radio–.

propagation anomalies. Irregularities introduced into an electromagnetic or other sensing device by discontinuities in the medium of propagation.

propane (C_3H_8). A liquid rocket propellant *fuel.*

propellant. The oxidant and fuel utilized in a rocket to obtain propulsion. When the oxidant and fuel are combined in a single substance, this substance is termed a *monopropellant.* See Table 5 and Table 3, page 157.

TABLE 5. Solid propellant rocket combinations

Fuel	*Oxidizer*	I_{sp}	*Weight,* (lb/cu in.)
Castable Composite			
Polyester styrene	Potassium perchlorate, $KClO_4$	178	0.068
Polyurethane	Ammonium perchlorate, NH_4ClO_4	238	0.062
Cellulose acetate	Ammonium nitrate, NH_4NO_3	171	0.056
Polyurethane	Ammonium perchlorate Potassium nitrate	236	0.063
Extruded Double-Base			
Nitroglycerin	Nitrocellulose	160-220	0.057 (avg.)
Asphalt Base Thermoplastic			
Potassium perchlorate	Asphalt	180-195	0.063

propellant. *Types of, see* auto-igniting–; bi-propellant; composite–; double-base–; en-trapped–; free radical–; heterogeneous–; homogeneous–; hypergolic–; liquid–; monopro-pellant–; multipropellant–; non-cryogenic–; re-stricted–; rocket engine–; single-base–; solid–; storable–; trapped–; unrestricted–.

propellant charge. The solid stage oxidizer and fuel used in solid propellant rockets. The charge usually includes the inhibitor (q.v.) which does not contribute to the total impulse. See Table 5, and Fig. 22, page 259.

propellant cutback. In the manufacture of solid propellant rocket grains (q.v.), the finishing (cutting) operation in which the length of the grain (q.v.) is adjusted to provide the proper weight of the propellant.

propellant loading ratio (y_k). (1) The ratio of propellant loaded on a missile to the gross weight of the missile (preferred). (2) The ratio of the propellant loaded on a missile to the dry weight of the missile. *Note:* these commonly used definitions are quite different from each other.

propellant mass fraction. In solid rocket usage, the ratio of the propellant weight used during burning time to this same weight plus the inert engine weight including case, nozzles, liners, sliverage, ignition material.

$$M_p = \frac{W_p}{W_p + W_i}$$

propellant utilization system. A measuring sys-tem used in long-range rockets to insure that the fuel and oxidizer are consumed in the proper ratio so that a minimum residual propellant remains at the end of powered flight.

proper fuze. A fuze function which occurs within plus or minus three standard deviations of the normal distribution for fuze function.

proper motion. The continuous movement on the celestial sphere (q.v.) of a star, as seen from the Sun.

properties. *See* mechanical properties.

property. *Types of, see* contractor-furnished–; Government-furnished–.

prop-jet. *See* turboprop.

proportional control. Control in which the cor-rective control applied to a missile is made proportional to the error signal.

proportional navigation. A homing guidance (q.v.) technique in which missile turn rate is directly proportional to the turn rate in space of the line-of-sight (q.v.); the seeker tracks the target semi-independently from the missile maneuver.

propulsion. *Types of, see* ion–; jet–; meta-stable–; nuclear–; photon–; reaction–; rocket–.

propulsion system. The entire system whose function is to provide thrust, which is normally used to propel a vehicle through all phases of powered flight, but also may be used for attitude control purposes; includes the engine, acces-sories such as pumps and turbines, pressurization system, tankage (unless part of the primary structure), and all related equipment to insure satisfactory operation of the engine either on the ground or in flight.

propylene oxide. A liquid rocket propellant *fuel*. See Table 3, page 157.

propyne. A liquid rocket propellant *fuel*.

protection. *Types of, see* environmental–; logis-tic–.

proton. An elementary particle having a posi-tive charge equivalent to the negative charge of the electron but possessing a mass approximately 1845 times as great (1.00758 amu). The proton is in effect the positive nucleus of the hydrogen atom and is a constituent of all nuclei.

prototype. A model (of a guided missile or other equipment) that is suitable for complete evaluation of form, design, and performance. A prototype model utilizes approved parts and is representative of the final equipment. It follows an *experimental model* and precedes the *produc-tion model.*

prototype equipment. New equipment devel-oped and produced to evaluate in service its suitability for establishing standards for produc-tion models (q.v.).

prototype preproduction model. A model suita-ble for evaluation of mechanical and electrical form, design, and performance. It approaches final mechanical and electrical form, employs approved parts, or reasonable equivalent, and is representative of final equipment.

proximity detector. A sensing device that pro-duces an electrical signal when passing near an object or prior to impact.

proximity fuze (PF). A fuze which initiates the warhead as a consequence of a determination that a target is within some specified region near the fuze, but not by contact with the tar-get.

pseudoadiabat. The process in which saturated air is rising in the atmosphere and losing its water vapor by condensation and precipitation.

The mean slope of a pseudoadiabat is approximately 1.77°C per 1000 ft as compared with that of 3.4°C per 1000 ft of an adiabat (q.v.).

pseudoadiabatic chart. A chart containing a series of diagonal lines, termed *pseudoadiabats* (q.v.) showing graphically the cooling or heating which theoretically takes place in a series of ascending or descending parcels of moisture-saturated air. Moisture in saturated air condenses as it cools, thereby releasing heat.

pseudo-integration. A means of determining the occurrence of a given minimum value of the time integral of acceleration.

PSF ratio. Payload/Structure/Fuel (weight) ratio; applied especially to rockets.

PST. Pacific Standard Time. *See* Standard time.

psychrometer. A kind of hygrometer (q.v.) that measures humidity by a differential temperature reading between two thermometers, one of which is moistened. If the air has a heavy humidity, the thermometers will register the same temperature; if the air is relatively dry, however, the moistened thermometer will indicate a lower temperature than the other. Humidity is then determined by reference to prepared tables.

PTM. Pulse Time Modulation telemetering (q.v.).

***p*-type semiconductor.** In solid-state physics, an extrinsic semiconductor in which the hole density exceeds the conduction-electron density.

pulse. The high-power, short duration output of a pulse radar system (e.g., a sinusoidal voltage of VHF to EHF—100 to 30,000 mc, 3 m to 1 cm—is transmitted for a period of, typically, 1 microsecond).

pulse. *Types of, see* dunking–; fruit–; gate-closing–; gate-opening–; information–; master synchronization–; radio-frequency–; reset–; shock–.

pulse amplitude-modulation telemetering (PAM). A telemetering system in which signal sources are sequentially sampled; an amplitude-modulated pulse is transmitted for each data point. This series of pulses is then used to frequency-modulate the subcarrier. The entire system usually is PAM/FM/FM.

pulse averaging discriminator. A subcarrier discriminator employing resistive and capacitive tuning components and deriving its output by averaging pulse width.

pulse code. (1) The modulation imposed on a pulse train to convey information. (2) Loosely, a code consisting of pulses, such as *Morse code, Baudot code, binary code.*

pulse code modulation level. In electronics, the number by which a given subrange of a quantized signal may be identified.

pulse code modulation telemetering (PCM). A time division multiplexing system used for telemetering. Data are serially sampled at a high rate and encoded (usually) into a binary system prior to transmission. Advantages are high accuracy and capacity and efficient use of bandwidth. The PCM signals may be used to modulate an RF link (PCM/FM).

pulsed altimeter. A radar altimeter that emits pulses of radio-frequency energy.

pulse decay time. In electronics, the time required for the instantaneous amplitude to decay from 90 per cent to 10 per cent of the peak value.

pulse duration modulation telemetering (PDM). A telemetering system in which time division multiplexing is used. A large number of channels of information can be handled, but the frequency response is reduced in comparison to the subcarrier bands of the FM/FM system. The RF carrier may be modulated by either *frequency modulation (PDM/FM)* or *phase modulation (PDM/PM). See* pulse width modulation telemetering (PWM).

pulsejet. A compressorless jet-propulsion device which produces thrust intermittently with an operating frequency determined by the acoustic resonance of the engine. It consists of a pulsating or intermittent inlet-valve system, a combustion chamber, and a discharge nozzle. Owing to the partial vacuum created for a short time in each cycle by the pulsating nature of the combustion and exhaust, this device can take in air and produce thrust even under static conditions.

$$\text{frequency of pulses} = \frac{\text{velocity of sound}}{4 \times \text{length of tailpipe}}$$

pulse leading edge. The major portion of the rise of a pulse of electrical energy.

pulse length. The time duration of the transmission of a pulse of electrical energy, usually measured in microseconds or in the equivalent distance in yards, miles, etc., represented by the pulse signal on a radarscope. (Short pulses of from 0.1 to 1 microsecond are usual for accurate radar work; longer pulses up to about 10 microseconds are used for less accurate work at greater ranges.)

pulse length error. An error caused by pulse length, which makes certain targets appear longer or broader than they actually are in the direction of the radar beam.

pulse modulation (PM). A method of modulating an RF carrier by pulsing it periodically by one or more pulses.

pulse position modulation (PPM). A form of pulse time modulation (q.v.) in which the instantaneous sample of a modulating wave controls the time position of a pulse in relation to the timing of a recurring reference pulse.

pulse radar. A radar which employs a transmitter that emits pulses of energy of very short duration. By measuring the time interval between transmission of a pulse and the reception of an echo pulse, the range can be determined. Pulse radars can measure distances and survey several targets simultaneously.

pulse rate. The frequency with which pulses occur per unit of time. Also termed the *pulse recurrence frequency, pulse recurrence rate, pulse repetition frequency.*

pulse repetition frequency. The pulse repetition rate (q.v.) of a periodic pulse train (q.v.).

pulse repetition rate. The average number of pulses per unit of time.

pulse selector. A device for selecting the proper pulse. In a decommutator (q.v.) it is referred to as a *single counter stage.*

pulse stretcher. A special video detector which converts a train of video pulses into a DC voltage upon which is superimposed an AC signal proportional to the modulation envelope of the pulse train. The AC component contains the angle information. The DC component is a function of average pulse amplitude and is used to control the receiver gain.

pulse synthesizer. An electronic flywheel supplying counter stepping pulses in the absence of an input signal.

pulse time. *Types of, see* leading edge–; trailing edge–.

pulse time modulation (PTM). A method of modulating an RF carrier by pulsing it periodically with a reference pulse followed by timed pulses to convey information.

pulse train. A series of pulses in digital representation of data.

pulse width. The time duration of any single electrical wave of an impulse type measured at a specific level. (In practice, the base pulse width is measured at ten per cent of normal amplitude and the peak pulse width is measured at ninety per cent of normal amplitude.)

pulse width modulation telemetering (PWM). In PWM telemetering systems, a voltage-generating end instrument is sampled briefly to determine its instantaneous level. This level is converted, by appropriate circuitry, into a pulse whose duration is a measure of its original voltage level. Sometimes termed *pulse duration modulation (PDM).*

pump drive assembly (PDA). An assembly used in liquid rocket propulsion systems consisting of the turbine, propellant pumps, gear boxes, power take-offs, and housing.

pump, positive displacement. *See* positive displacement pump.

purging system. The system which introduces a non-combustible gas, (e.g.) carbon dioxide or nitrogen, into the space above propellants to sweep out any toxic or combustible propellants when draining propellant tanks (e.g., after an unsuccessful attempt to launch a missile).

pursuit course. A homing guidance system (q.v.) in which a missile is directed along a flight path whose tangent coincides with the line-of-sight (q.v.) from missile seeker to target or deviates from it by a predetermined fixed angle.

pushover. *See* tilt angle.

push-pull amplifier. An amplifier employing two vacuum tubes working in opposite phase to one another.

push-pull circuit. A two-tube amplifier circuit in which the grid and plate of one tube are operating 180° out of phase with the grid and plate of the other tube, as against parallel operation in which the grids are connected together and the plates are connected together. Push-pull operation generally results in higher output efficiency. Even-order (2nd, 4th, etc.) harmonics are cancelled out. Hum in the plate supply circuits is used at both audio and radio frequencies.

push-pull oscillator. A vacuum-tube oscillator containing two tubes or a double-section tube connected in a phase relation similar to that of a push-pull amplifier (q.v.).

push-pull parallel circuit. A vacuum-tube circuit consisting of four tubes (or two double-section tubes) wherein the tubes are paired off in two's and grid and plates connected in parallel and then treated as two single tubes connected in push-pull. This circuit is mostly used in high-powered amplifiers.

push-pull transformer. An iron-core AF transformer designed for use in a push-pull amplifier (q.v.) circuit. If it is the input transformer, it will have a center-tapped secondary winding. If it is the output transformer, it will have a center-tapped primary winding.

push-push circuit. A two-tube amplifier circuit in which the grid of one tube operates 180° out of phase with the grid of the other tube, but the plates are connected together. It is noted for fairly high efficiency when used for frequency-doubling in radio-frequency power amplifiers.

PU system. Propellant Utilization system (q.v.).

PWM. Pulse Width Modulation telemetering (q.v.). *See also* pulse duration modulation telemetering.

Pyroceram. An extremely hard, fine-grained crystalline material (formed from glass) used for radomes (q.v.) or high-speed missiles.

"pyrogen" igniter (fire-generating). An ignition system consisting of a small rocket engine located in the head end of a larger rocket engine. It exhausts its products onto the main chamber grain to cause ignition. A small, conventional initiator starts the "pyrogen."

pyrophoric fuel. A fuel which ignites spontaneously in air.

pyrotechnic. A mixture of oxidant and reductant designed to produce light, heat, or perform some other non-propulsive function.

Q

Q. (1) A rating applied to coils, capacitors, and resonant electrical circuits, equal to reactance divided by resistance. (2) The ratio of energy stored to energy dissipated per cycle in mechanical or electrical systems.

$$Q = 2\pi \left(\frac{\text{average energy stored}}{\text{energy dissipated per half cycle}} \right)$$

(3) In structural applications, the reciprocal of structural damping.

$$Q = \left(\frac{1}{2c/c_c} \right)$$

where c = damping; c_c = critical damping.
(4) A dimensionless parameter equal to the ratio, at the resonance frequency, of mass reactance $(2\pi fm)$ to mechanical resistance (c) for a simple mechanical resonator or for a mass exhibiting some dissipation of energy under vibration; or the ratio of spring reactance $(k/2\pi f)$ to mechanical resistance for a spring.

q. Dynamic pressure (q.v.).

Q*. A figure of merit for effective heat-absorbing capacity per pound of a material (Btu/lb); essentially the *specific heat* when considering only the solid state.

Q-2. Military designation for the target and tactical missile termed FIREBEE (q.v.).

Q-5. Military designation for target missile termed KINGFISHER (q.v.).
Supersonic winged target missile; length: 39 ft; weight: 7600 lb.
Prime Contractor: Lockheed Aircraft Corp.

QA. Quality Assurance (q.v.).

QB-17. Target drone used to test the NIKE (q.v.) at 30,000 ft. Also used to test the FALCON (q.v.). A surplus B17 bomber converted for remote control. Range: 17 miles.

Q-band. A radio-frequency band of 36,000-46,000 mc with wavelengths of 0.8 to 0.6 cm, respectively. See Fig. 8, page 105.

QC. Quality Control (q.v.).

Q factor. In bombing, a factor representing the ratio of the velocity of the differential ballistic wind (q.v.) to the velocity of the wind at release altitude.

QM. A code or symbol for DECCA navigation system.

QOR. Qualitative Operational Requirement (q.v.).

QPRI. Qualitative Personnel Requirements Information (q.v.).

QRC. Quick Reaction Capability (q.v.).

quadrant. *Types of, see* elevation–; N-quadrant.

quadrature. Displaced 90° in phase angle. This is expressed by use of the letter j, which may be considered as an operator producing a rotation of 90° counterclockwise. Since j equals the square root of minus one, the square of j equals minus one. Thus two such operations would result in rotation of 180° or from plus to minus. An additional rotation of 90° (total 270°) results in minus j.

qualification tests. (1) A series of tests designed to establish adequacy of a product to meet specified requirements. They are sometimes termed *type tests* and are destructive in the sense that the article cannot be used for its intended function since qualification tests, by definition, are made to specification extremes or environmental performance. (2) A test of an item of materiel to determine its suitability or qualifications for service use. This test is normally conducted prior to the awarding of a contract and at the request of a manufacturer seeking to establish his concern as an approved source for supply of the item. (3) A final series of tests, especially on engines or rockets, in which the article is qualified for its intended service function. Life tests and off-design value tests are required.

qualified component. A component (part, assembly) which has successfully passed a set of predetermined performance and environmental tests.

qualitative operational requirement (QOR). A

formal statement of an essential operational need of an Air Force activity, including the broad characteristics of the item, system, technique needed to enable the Air Force to carry out its assigned mission more effectively.

qualitative personnel requirements information (QPRI). Essential information about operational and position requirements from which qualitative personnel requirements (QPR) can be formulated. QPR consists of the specifications for human capabilities in a system and the characteristics whereby such capabilities can be obtained by means of position structure, selection, training, training devices, operating procedures, handbooks of instructions, and other printed material.

qualitative requirement. A requirement expressed or regarded in terms of kinds or quality of the required materials or services, rather than in terms of quantity.

quality assurance (QA). With the greatly increasing proportion of inspectors in precision factories, the inspection organizations have become so large that their reporting to top management does not alone assure that a "Quality Control" group (under the same top supervision) will impartially patrol their own organization. In some cases management has considered the inspection as a function analogous to production, and established an organizationally separate group reporting to top (corporate) management, known as "Quality Assurance," for the purpose of impartially "auditing" the quality function (e.g., the A.E.C. has contracted to a Sandia "Quality Assurance Department" the responsibility to police all inspection practices in their area; even Sandia's own Inspection Department). The area generating the quality assurance action will vary with the organizational breakdown concerned, but the basic distinction is that it refers to an *organizational concept* of quality enforcement, not to any specific improved inspection technique. From the contractor's point of view, the Air Force inspectors are a Quality Assurance group.

quality characteristics. The properties of a product which the operation intended to produce and which must meet specified tolerance limits (e.g., dimensions, strengths, weights, voltages, etc.). They are basic building blocks of quality control.

quality control (QC). That function which enforces compliance with engineering instructions, whether given by drawing, specification, or other method. This includes responsibility for the proper execution of the following functions,

with line authority varying according to company setup: (a) receiving inspection—technical or functional; (b) in-process inspection; (c) process control—worker qualification; (d) final inspection—non-functional; (e) functional inspection; (f) material review—salvage or scrap.

Quality Control is the agency to implement the requirements of the Engineering Department and Management on quality by establishing sample sizes, inspection intervals, detail acceptable limits, etc., from Engineering's more general specifications.

quality control, statistical. *See* statistical quality control.

quality level, acceptable. *See* acceptable quality level.

quality of conformance. The adherence of a product to the design as it comes off the production lines. *Note:* Improving the quality of conformance usually *lowers* production costs.

quality of design. The inherent value of the product that is designed into it. *Note:* Improving the quality of design usually increases production and engineering costs but may under some circumstances reduce these costs.

quantitative requirement. A requirement expressed or regarded in terms of the quantity of the required materiel or services, rather than in terms of quality.

quantity-distance tables. The distance from a certain location (e.g., an inhabited building, public railway, magazine, or operating building) required to protect that location against substantial structural damage from the ignition or explosion of a *definite* quantity of a *specific class* of explosives. *See* class II explosive; class IX explosive.

quantum-mechanical amplifier. *See* microwave amplification by stimulated emission of radiation (MASER).

quantum theory. In physics, a theory that atoms or molecules emit or absorb energy by a process that takes place in a series of steps, each step being the emission or absorption of an amount of energy termed the *quantum.*

quart. A unit of volume measurement.

1 dry quart $= 67.2006$ cu in. $= \frac{1}{8}$ peck
$= 2$ pt (dry)

1 liquid quart $= 946.3596$ cu cm $= 57.75$ cu in. $= \frac{1}{4}$ gal $=$ 0.94633 liter $= 32$ fluid oz $= 2$ pt (liquid)

quasi-stationary front. In meteorology, the ideal

stationary front is seldom found in nature, but it often occurs that the frontal movement is such that no appreciable displacement takes place. The front is then said to be *quasi-stationary*.

quenching circuit. A circuit which diminishes, suppresses, or reverses the voltage applied to a counter tube in order to inhibit multiple discharges from a single ionizing event.

quick-look data. The reduction of the first raw or unreduced data available for inspection on an expedited basis to permit review of test results for the purpose of preliminary test evaluation. Data includes: (a) plotting board records of radar tracking data; (b) oscillograph and direct-writing recorder analog records of the demodulated subcarrier telemetry signals; (c) photographic film or prints.

quick-look telemetry. A telemetry display that furnishes a real-time, permanent record which is available for inspection during or shortly after the test period. Quick-look data usually are not linearized.

quick reaction capability (QRC). Ability to develop a rapid counterattack.

Q-value. The energy, Q, released or absorbed in a nuclear reaction. A synonym for *nuclear disintegration energy*.

R

RA. Range, Adcock. *See* Adcock radio range.

rabal. *R*adiosonde *bal*loon. Sounding method of obtaining speed and direction of winds aloft. Radiosonde ascent is observed optically with a theodolite (q.v.) to determine azimuth (q.v.) and elevation angles; altitudes are computed from information telemetered back to the surface by the radiosonde.

RACE. Rapid Automatic Checkout Equipment; a proprietary system.

rack panel. A standard metal or non-metal panel upon which is mounted electronic equipment. It fits into relay or rack cabinets. (Standard width is 19 in.; available in various heights which are always multiples of 1¾ in.). Mounting notches are standard, to fit multiple-drilled racks and cabinets.

racon. *R*adar bea*con* (q.v.).

rada. *R*adi*o*active.

radar. *R*adio *d*etection *a*nd *r*anging; the principle of locating reflecting targets or objects by measurement of reflections of radio-frequency energy from the targets. The term is applied to devices which make use of the radar principle.

radar. *Types of, see* acquisition–; airborne early warning–; airborne interception–; air intercept–; bistatic–; continuous wave–; C-W Doppler–; defensive–; diversity–; Doppler–; FM–; gap-filler–; homing–; monopulse–; pulse–; scan–; search–; tracking–; V-beam–.

radar altimeter. An absolute altimeter (q.v.) that by measuring the time lapse between transmission and return of a pulse of radio energy establishes distance from the surface. Also termed a *radio altimeter*.

radar beacon. Generally an omnidirectional radiating device, containing an automatic radar receiver and transmitter, that receives pulses (interrogations) from a radar and returns similar pulses or sets of pulses (responses). The beacon response may be on the same frequency as the radar, or may be on a different frequency.

radar beam. The characteristic pattern of the emission of a radar antenna in which a target can be detected effectively and/or tracked. Its boundary is defined by custom as the locus of a point, measured radially from the beam center, at which the power has decreased to one-half.

radar calibration. The process of determining the extent and accuracy of the radar coverage of a given radar installation, especially of an aircraft-warning or tactical air control radar installation. It includes the making of computations to determine the theoretical coverage of the radar installation, the making of flights to check the coverage of the radar, the preparing of charts, diagrams, and overlays.

radar clutter. In radar, the visual evidence on the radar indicator screen of sea return or ground return which tends to obscure the target indication.

radar control. Guidance, direction, or employment exercised over a missile by means of, or with the aid of, radar; the area or airspace in which radar control is exercised.

radar countermeasures (RCM). Any electronic countermeasure against radar. *See* electronic countermeasure and radio countermeasures.

radar cross section. An echo area (q.v.) considered as a cross section of the target. See Fig. 7, page 83.

radar deception. Deception of the enemy by electronic countermeasures against his radar. *See* electronic deception.

radar dish. The reflector of the radar antenna; a parabolic-shaped device usually placed behind the dipole for the purpose of shaping and directing the radar beam.

radar dome. *See* radome.

radar drift. (1) The drift of a vehicle as determined by a timed series of bearings taken on a fixed radar target. (2) The drift of the servo (q.v.) controlling the movement of the antenna.

radar fence. A network of radar warning stations surrounding a protected area. *See* DEW line.

radar frequencies. *See* frequency spectrum.

radar homing. A method of missile guidance wherein a missile-borne radar provides the required intelligence. *See* homing guidance; homing active guidance; homing passive guidance; semi-active guidance.

radar horizon. The lowest elevation angle at which a radar can operate effectively owing to its line-of-sight (q.v.) propagation and the Earth's curvature.

radar illumination. (1) The use of a radar beam to illuminate a target. (2) A method of missile guidance wherein a radar external to the missile but aimed at the target causes the target to emit echoes suitable for homing (q.v.).

radar lockon. That condition of radar operation where it becomes possible to track a target by automatic rather than manual means. Sometimes termed *autotrack*.

radar nautical mile. The time interval, approximately 12.4 microseconds, required for radio-frequency energy used in radar to travel one nautical mile (q.v.) and return.

radar picket. A ship or aircraft equipped with early warning radar, that operates in a peripheral area so as to extend the range of radar detection.

radar prediction. A graphic representation of what may be expected to show on a radar screen when an actual radar scan is made; used to increase ease of recognition.

radar/radio horizon. The locus of the Earth's surface beyond which high-frequency electromagnetic signals from a given source cannot be propagated. This limitation arises from the inability of such signals to propagate in other than a straight line and due to the curvature of the Earth including consideration of diffraction. See Fig. 13.

radar pulse repetition frequency. The pulse repetition rates which are used in radar transmitters. They vary from approximately 200 to 2000 per sec. The ratio

$$\frac{\text{pulse duration}}{\text{total period from start of one pulse to the next}}$$

is termed the *duty cycle* (q.v.) and in most installations lies between approximately 0.0005 and 0.002.

radar range. The theoretical maximum free-space range, R, of a radar using an isotropic common receiving and transmitting antenna, lossless transmission line, and a perfect receiver, may be found as follows:

If λ = wavelength; A_t = effective area of transmitting aerial; A_r = effective area of receiving aerial; A_e = effective radar or echoing area of the target; G = power gain of transmitting aerial; $k = G\lambda^2/A_t$—a constant for the particular type of transmitter aerial; P_t = peak transmitted power; P_m = minimum power required for detection; transmitted pulse energy = P_t (in peak watts) $\times \tau$ (in sec); energy incident on target = $P_t\tau/A\pi R^2$ per unit area; energy returned to an-

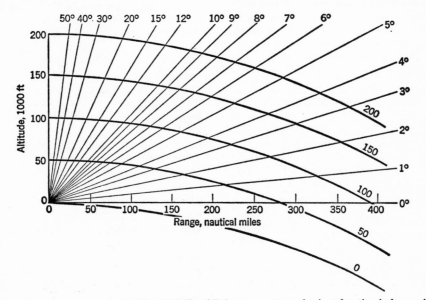

Note that the curves are corrected for "4/3 Earth" (average atmospheric refractive index variation).

Fig. 13. Radio/radar range to horizon. (ITE Circuit Breaker Co.)

tenna $= P_t \tau A_e/(4\pi R^2)^2$ per unit area; energy at receiver input $= P_t \tau A_e \lambda^2/(4\pi)^3 R^4$; receiver input noise energy $= KT = 4.11 \times 10^{21}$ joules; and assuming that the receiver adds no noise, and that the signal is visible on the indicator when signal and noise energies are equal, the maximum range, R, is found to be:

$$R = \left[\frac{P_t \tau A_e \lambda^2}{(4\pi)^3 KT}\right]^{1/4} = \left[\frac{P_t K A_t A_r A_e}{P_m (4\pi)^2 \lambda^2}\right]^{1/4}$$

$$= \left[\frac{P_t G A_e A_r}{P_m (4\pi)^2}\right]^{1/4}$$

Thus: (i) Range is proportional to the fourth root of transmitter power. (ii) Doubling P_t increases range by only about 20 per cent. (iii) To double the range, P_t must be increased 16 times. (iv) Range is increased by decreasing the wavelength. This is because the beam becomes narrower, and G is consequently increased.

Range measurement in air:

1   microsecond corresponds to 149.85 meters or 163.88 yards

6.673   microseconds correspond to 1 kilometer

10.739 microseconds correspond to 1 statute mile

12.35   microseconds correspond to 1 nautical mile (6076 ft)

radar reflection interval. The length of time required for a radar pulse to travel from the source to the target and return to the source, taking the velocity of radio propagation to be equal to the velocity of light, 2.998×10^8 m/sec, or 299.8 m/micro-sec. Since the pulse must travel, in all, twice the distance to the target (out and back), the apparent velocities obtained are only one-half of the true velocity of the pulse. Likewise, the reflection intervals are just twice as great when target ranges are considered.

radar repeat-back guidance. A guidance system for guided missiles using a search radar in the missile which transmits information to the point of control.

radar resolution. The ability of a radar to distinguish between a desired target and its surroundings.

radar scan. A mode of radar operation wherein the beam direction is systematically changed in order to search for or track more effectively (e.g., *circular, conical, spiral, helical,* or *rectangular*).

A-scan: An indicator with a horizontal or vertical sweep, giving range only. Signals appear as deflections on the time scale.

B-scan: Type of presentation in which signal appears as a bright spot with azimuth angle as the horizontal coordinate and range as the vertical coordinate.

C-scan: Type of presentation in which signal appears as a bright spot with azimuth angle as the horizontal coordinate and elevation angle as the vertical coordinate.

D-scan: Presentation combining B and C types. The signal appears as a bright spot with azimuth angle as the horizontal coordinate and elevation angle as the vertical coordinate. Horizontal trace is expanded vertically by a compressed time sweep to facilitate separation of signal from noise and give a rough range indication.

E-scan: A modification of B-scan. Signal appears as a bright spot with range as horizontal and elevation as vertical coordinate.

F-scan: A single signal only, appearing as a bright spot. Azimuth error angle (relative bearing) appears as the horizontal coordinate, elevation angle as the vertical coordinate.

G-scan: A single signal only, appearing as a bright spot on which wings grow as the distance to the target is diminished. Azimuth angle appears as the horizontal and elevation angle as the vertical coordinate. This has been referred to as *Mark VI* indication.

H-scan: A modification of B-scan. Signal appears as a bright line the slope of which is proportional to the sine of the angle of elevation. Azimuth appears as the horizontal coordinate, and range as the vertical coordinate.

J-scan: A modification of type A in which the time sweep produces a circular range scale near the circumference of the CRT face. The signal appears as a radial deflection of the time trace. No bearing indication is given.

radar shadow. An area behind a hill, cloud, or other obstruction in the path of a radar beam, within which radar waves are absent or weak; a blank area on a radar screen resulting from this phenomenon.

radar storm detection. The detection of certain storms or stormy conditions by means of radar. In radar storm detection, liquid or frozen water drops within the storm reflect radar echoes. Storms not accompanied by precipitation are not ordinarily detectable.

radar target. Any radio-frequency reflecting object of particular interest in the path of a radar beam.

radar wind (rawin). Wind of which the movement, speed, and direction are observed or determined by radar tracking of a balloon carrying a radiosonde, a radio transmitter, or a radar reflector. *See* rawin.

RADC. Rome Air Development Center; Griffis Air Force Base, Rome, New York. Responsible for research and development on ground-based electronic equipment, and tests under operational conditions. A part of Air Research and Development Command (ARDC).

RADCM. Radar countermeasures and deception.

radiac. *Ra*diation *d*etection, *i*dentification, *a*nd *c*omputation. (1) The act or process of detecting, identifying, and measuring the intensity of nuclear radiation in an area. (2) Short for *radiac instrument* (e.g., dosimeter, q.v.).

radial-flow compressor. A centrifugal compressor (q.v.) in which air is drawn into a rotating impeller axially, being discharged radially at the circumference of the impeller at high velocity into a diffuser, where velocity is reduced—resulting in conversion of kinetic energy into pressure energy. Distinguish from an *axial flow compressor* (q.v.).

radial G. A *g* force (acceleration force) resulting from radial acceleration.

radial hole. In solid propellant rocketry, a hole bored through the wall of a tubular grain (q.v.).

radial velocity. The speed of approach or recession of a body from the point of observation with respect to the Earth; it can be determined by measuring the Doppler shift (q.v.) between lines of the same elements in the spectra of the star and of a point on the Earth.

radian. In mathematics, an angle at the center of a circle, subtending an arc of the circle equal in length to the radius.

   radian = 57.29578 degrees = 57°17′44.8″

radiant energy. The energy inherent in electromagnetic waves (e.g., radiated energy of the Sun).

radiant heat. Electromagnetic radiation at wavelengths between those of infrared and the shortest radio waves.

radiation. *Types of, see* atomic–; Cerenkov–; electromagnetic–; gamma–; nuclear–; solar–; thermal–.

radiation constants. *See* physical units and constants.

radiation fog. A fog that develops in nocturnally cooled air in contact with a cool surface. Radiation fog forms over land and not over water because water surfaces do not appreciably change their temperature during hours of darkness.

radiation pattern. The directivity pattern of a radiating device (e.g., radiation pattern of an antenna); a plot of relative field strength at a given distance with various angles with respect to the antenna installation. It usually is plotted on polar coordinate paper.

radio deception. The employment of radio to deceive the enemy; it includes sending false dispatches, using deceptive headings, employing enemy call signals, etc.

radio frequency (RF). The frequencies of electromagnetic radiation used for the transmission of radio signals through space, generally ranging from between 15,000 cps in long-wave transmission, to 36,000 mc/sec in short-wave transmission. Specifically, it includes that part of the general frequency spectrum between audio sound and infrared light (about 20 kc to 10,000,000 mc). Generally, it refers to an alternating-current frequency whose electromagnetic field can be radiated over great distances.

Radio frequencies are designated by the FCC as follows: *very low frequency,* 10-30 kc; *low frequency,* 30-300 kc; *medium frequency,* 300-3000 kc; *high frequency,* 3000-30,000 kc; *very high frequency,* 30-300 mc; *ultra-high frequency,* 300-3000 mc; *super-high frequency,* 3000-30,000 mc. *See also* extremely high frequency. See Fig. 8, page 105.

radio-frequency pulse. A radio-frequency carrier, amplitude-modulated by a pulse. The amplitude of the modulated carrier is zero before and after the pulse. Coherence of the carrier (with itself) is not implied.

radio fuze. A fuze activated by a radio device; a radio proximity fuze (q.v.).

radio horizon. The distance to the radio horizon for a given antenna height. The effect of the Earth's curvature can be taken into account, approximately, by assuming the radius of the Earth to be $4/3$ its actual value. For radio horizons over water the Earth's radius should be doubled. See Fig. 13, page 223.

radio inertial guidance (RIG). A command type of guidance system (q.v.) consisting essentially of: (a) a radar tracking unit, comprised of radar equipment on the ground, one or more transponders in the missile, and necessary communication links to the guidance station; (b) a computer that accepts missile position and velocity information from the tracking system, and furnishes appropriate signals to the command link to steer the missile; (c) a command link which consists of a transmitter on the ground and an antenna and receiver on the missile (actually, the command link is built into the tracking unit); (d) an inertial system for

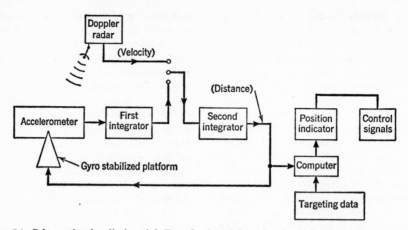

Fig. 14. Schematic of radio inertial, Doppler inertial, and radar inertial guidance systems.

partial guidance in event of radio guidance failure or to provide more "up-to-date" data for correcting the radar guidance information. See Fig. 14.

radiometer. Any device for measuring the flux density of infrared radiation from total radiant power falling on it. Radiometers usually comprise a sensitive detector (e.g., a thermocouple); an optical system (e.g., a paraboloidal mirror aluminized on its front surface, to form an image of an object or a selected area on the thermocouple); and some means of measuring the thermocouple voltage (e.g., a galvanometer or an ultrasensitive voltmeter).

radio navigation guidance. The guidance or control of a guided missile in which the missile flies along a course established by external radio transmitters. *See* hyperbolic guidance.

radio-noise interference. The same as *electro interference* (q.v.), except for restrictions in frequencies considered (generally 150 kc minimum) and types of equipment (usually electronic only).

radio-noise interference test. A test to determine and correct the effect of any undesired electrical phenomenon which is created by, or which adversely affects, any device whose normal functioning requires the utilization of electrical phenomena. Colloquially termed *radio and electrical noise or interference, hash, jitter, grass, hunting, ambiguity, cross-modulation, TV interference (TVI), hum,* etc. The word *interference* alone may be used in reference to some manifestations of electro-interference.

radio propagation. *See* velocity of radio propagation.

radio proximity fuze. A proximity fuze that uses an RF system for intelligence, the echoes triggering detonation at the desired instant.

radio range. *See* radio horizon.

radio range. *Types of, see* Adcock–; aural–; loop-type–; omnidirectional–; phase-shift omnidirectional–; visual-aural–; visual-aural VHF–.

radiosonde. An instrument which fulfills the same function as the aerometeorograph but to much greater altitudes. A pilot balloon carries the instrument aloft; a parachute lowers it to Earth again when the balloon bursts in the upper atmosphere. By means of a clockwork motor and very light-weight radio-transmitting set, the indications of instruments sensitive to pressure, temperature, and humidity are automatically transmitted at regular intervals during the flight. The signals from the radiosonde are received and recorded on a special receiver on the ground, and are then translated into readings of pressure, temperature, and humidity at the various altitudes. Sometimes the instrument is tracked by radar to verify altitude.

radio spectrum. (1) That part of the electromagnetic spectrum lying above the spectrum of audible frequencies but below that of infrared frequencies. (2) The range of useful radio frequencies in this spectrum. The upper limit of the radio spectrum is fixed by the state of the art. The limits fixed by the Federal Communication Commission are about 10,000 kc to about 30,000 mc. *See* frequency spectrum. See Fig. 8, page 105.

radio telemetry. A method used for transmission of large quantities of data over long distances on a modulated carrier. This method is used to link a test missile with remote ground receiving and recording equipment.

radio tracking. *See* celestial radio tracking.

radio wave plane of polarization. In a propagated electromagnetic wave, the direction of the electric field with respect to the Earth's surface. *Vertically polarized:* electrical field is vertical. *Horizontally polarized:* electrical field is horizontal. *Circularly polarized, elliptically polarized:* electrical field is caused to rotate during propagation.

radio wave scattering. Occurs when a radio wave strikes a surface too rough to support specular (or mirrorlike) reflection. Scattering may occur when a wave passes through a non-homogeneous medium. Anomalies of the index of refraction of the Earth's atmosphere produce some scattering. Scattering also occurs when a radio wave strikes raindrops, fog, hail, or snow in the Earth's atmosphere. Condensed water and other forms of precipitation are capable of both scattering the incident radiation and absorbing energy from the radio waves. The amount of energy which is lost by scattering is a function of the radio frequency and the size, shape, distribution, and index of refraction of the particles in the atmosphere.

radius, damage. *See* damage radius.

radius of gyration. The square root of the ratio of the moment of inertia to the mass. If the mass of a body were concentrated at one point while preserving the same moment of inertia about an axis of rotation, the distance from this point to the axis of rotation would be the *radius of gyration.*

radix. In communication theory, the total number of distinct marks or basic elements in a number system (e.g., binary system: 2; decimal system: 10).

radl. Radiological.

Radlab. Berkeley Radiation Laboratory; University of California, Berkeley, Calif.

radlwar. *R*adiological *war*fare.

radnos. A transposition of *no radio* plus *s*. A particular radio fadeout, especially in arctic regions, considered to be caused by solar explosion, sunspots, or aurora borealis.

radome. *R*adar *dome*. The housing for a radar antenna, essentially transparent to radio frequency.

rail aircraft rocket launcher. An aircraft rocket launcher (q.v.) carrying the rocket on rails (i.e., not zero length, but with some guided travel).

railing. (Vernacular) The jamming of radar transmissions by transmitters at a pulse rate of 50 to 150 kcs, causing images resembling fence railings to appear on radar screens.

rail-type launcher. A structure supporting a set of rails which in turn support a missile-Jato

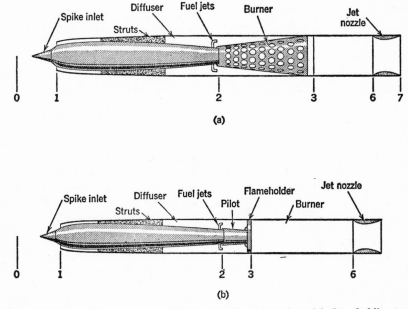

Fig. 15. (a) Ramjet engine with can-type combustor. (b) Ramjet engine with flameholding-type combustor. (Bonney, Zucrow & Besserer, *Aerodynamics, Propulsion, Structures & Design Practice*, D. Van Nostrand)

combination. The rails provide orientation and control during the early portion of the launching phase.

rain. Liquid water drops in the atmosphere ranging in diameter from 0.5 mm to approximately 5.0 mm, usually falling with velocities ranging from 3 m/sec to 8 m/sec. Rain is the most common type of precipitation.

ram. (1) The forward motion of an air scoop or air inlet through the air. (2) A ram effect (q.v.). (3) Capitalized, a popular name for a large aircraft rocket with a shaped charge.

ram drag. The induced drag (q.v.) in thermal jet engines (q.v.) resulting from flow of the air required for combustion.

$$D_r = \frac{\dot{w}V}{g}$$

where $\dot{w}$ = weight flow of air; V = vehicle velocity; g = acceleration of gravity.

ram effect. The increased air pressure in a jet engine due to ram (q.v.). Essentially it results from the compression of air due to rapid movement of an air scoop. See Fig. 16.

ramjet. A compressorless jet-propulsion engine which depends for its operation on the air compression accomplished by the forward motion of the engine. Compared with turbojet engines, the ramjet engine offers (in its flight regime) certain advantages: (a) the ramjet can produce a larger thrust per unit of maximum frontal area; (b) because of the absence of rotating machinery, the ramjet engine can produce a larger thrust per unit of engine weight; (c) the ramjet engine can be operated with a higher maximum temperature in its thermodynamic cycle. See Fig. 15, page 227.

ramjet, solid propellant. *See* solid propellant ramjet.

ramp. *See* launching ramp.

ram pressure. The dynamic pressure or pressure at the inlet of an air-breathing engine resulting from its velocity through the air. It is the function of the air inlet and diffuser to decelerate the air entering the engine and transform a large portion of the kinetic energy of the air into a pressure rise. See Fig. 16.

The ram pressure ratio is as follows:

MACH No.	Ram Pressure Ratio
0	1.0
1	1.9
2	7.8
3	37.0
4	157.0

ram recovery. A measure of the pressure re-

covery of a diffuser; the conversion of the kinetic energy into pressure head. See Fig. 16.

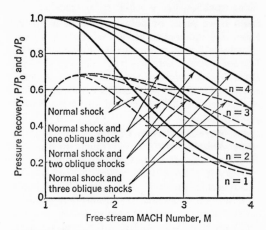

Solid line: maximum possible pressure (total) after n shocks expressed as ratio of the maximum pressure possible behind the last shock to the total, or reservoir, pressure of the free stream, P/P_0.

Dashed line: maximum possible static pressure recovery after n shocks expressed as ratio of maximum possible static pressure to free-stream total pressure p/P_0 with p measured behind last shock.

Fig. 16. Ratios P/P_0 and p/P_0 as a function of the free-steam MACH number for conical shock supersonic diffusers with different numbers of shocks. (Bonney, Zucrow & Besserer, *Aerodynamics, Propulsion, Structures & Design Practice*, D. Van Nostrand)

ram-rocket. (1) An integral Jato-ramjet combination in which the rocket is utilized for obtaining operating speed for the ramjet. (2) A solid-fuel ramjet (q.v.).

R and D. Research and Development.

random error. An error which varies in a random fashion during a missile test (e.g., instrument internal noise or film reading error).

random noise (or fluctuation). Noise characterized by a large number of overlapping transient disturbances occurring at random.

random noise testing. A test technique in which the applied forcing function (e.g., a driving signal to a shaker) is a complex wave of varying frequencies and amplitudes—usually, but not always, assumed to have a normal distribution in each octave. The complex forcing function may be obtained from an experimental source (e.g., a missile telemetering record) or may be made from a signal generator.

range. *Types of, see* actual–; aural–; aural type VHF–; down–; flying–; frequency–; fuze–; homing–; line-of-sight–; lockon–; missile roll–;

omnidirectional radio–; radar–; radio–; slant–; transonic–; true–; useful–.

range instrumentation (and range safety equipment). Equipment used to obtain data from a test and/or to provide for flight termination. Such equipment normally is not part of an operational weapon system but may be included in modified or reduced capacity form for confidence firings. Two categories are used: (a) *active*—airborne and ground equipment required; (b) *passive*—non-specialized airborne and standard ground equipment required.

range limits. Lines plotted on the range-plotting board by range safety personnel to establish safety areas. These limits take into consideration instantaneous impact prediction (IIP), characteristics of test vehicle, objectives, etc.

range plane. In missile testing, the plane, fixed in respect to the Earth and vertical at the launch point, that contains the initial portion of the nominal powered flight trajectory of a missile.

range safety. Equipment, on the surface of the Earth, that monitors a missile trajectory and remotely directs missile destruction or engine shutdown to prevent improper flight or a hazard to range facilities, civilian installations, and personnel.

range safety equipment. *See* range instrumentation.

range safety systems. Systems which gather and present trajectory-position data of an airborne missile, and provide means of terminating missile flight in accordance with range safety regulations at the test field.

range time. In missile testing, a time interval during which range flight facilities are required for a specific operation.

ranging. *See* missile ranging.

Rankine scale. A temperature scale that uses Fahrenheit degrees, but makes the zero degree signify absolute zero (q.v.). In this scale, water freezes at 491.69 degrees, and boils at 671.69 degrees. (Named after J. M. Rankine, Scottish physicist.) Compare with Kelvin scale (q.v.). *See also* temperature conversion formulas.

RAO nozzle. A modified bell-shaped rocket exhaust nozzle designed to optimize expansion at vacuum altitudes.

RaOb. *Ra*diosonde *ob*servation.

rapid scanning. In radar, scanning (q.v.) with a narrow beam at the rate of ten sweeps per second or more, used especially in tracking fast-moving targets.

rarefaction. In an atomic bomb explosion, a condition existing at the center of the explosion, in which the pressure, after a rise induced by the explosion, drops below that which existed prior to the explosion.

rarefaction wave. A pressure wave or rush of air or water induced by rarefaction (q.v.). The rarefaction wave (also termed a *suction wave*) travels in the opposite direction to that of the shock wave (q.v.) directly following a nuclear explosion.

rarefied atmosphere. Thin, tenuous atmosphere as encountered at high altitudes.

RASCAL. Air-to-surface, rocket-powered robot bomber. Air Force designation: GAM-63.

Length: 32 ft; wing span: 25 ft; launching weight: 13,000 lb; speed: MACH 1.6; maximum range: 100 miles; thrust: 18,000 lb. Uses a three-barrel liquid propellant rocket engine for cruise propulsion. Command and inertial guidance system.

Prime Contractor: Bell Aircraft Corporation. Airframe: Bell. Engine: Bell. Guidance system: command: Bell; inertial: Federal Telecommunications Laboratories.

RAT. Surface ship-to-underwater ballistic missile. Navy Bureau of Ordnance cognizance. Name is derived from *R*ocket *A*ssisted *T*orpedo.

A cross between the standard torpedo and a ballistic missile, this 16-ft weapon can search out and destroy an enemy submarine. The missile is launched from a standard five-inch gun mount. The torpedo is fired from the ship by rocket, lowered into the water by a parachute, and then seeks out the target automatically. Approximate diameter: 1.20 ft. Acoustical homing guidance; solid propellant rocket.

Prime Contractor: Naval Ordnance Test Station. Engine: Allegheny Ballistics Laboratory.

rate. *Types of,* see erosive burning–; failure–; lapse–; normal lapse–; part failure–; pulse–; pulse repetition–; repetition–; standard pressure lapse–.

rate action. In servomechanisms, a type of control action in which the rate of correction is made in proportion to how fast the condition has gone out of control. Also termed *derivative action.*

rated operating pressure. The pressure at which working stresses are encountered; usually measured under steady-state conditions.

rate gyroscope. A gyroscope with a single gimbal mounting, such that rotation about an axis perpendicular to the axis of the gimbal and to the axis of the gyroscope produces a precessional torque proportional to the rate of rotation. See Fig. 17.

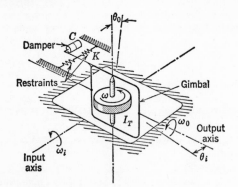

Fig. 17. Simplified diagram of rate gyroscope. (A. S. Locke, *Guidance*, D. Van Nostrand)

ratio. *Types of, see* actuating signal–; area–; aspect–; augmented thrust–; blip-scan–; charge/weight–; contraction–; control–; damping–; deviation–; diffuser area–; drag-weight–; effective aspect–; equivalence–; error–; exchange–; expansion–; fineness–; frequency–; front-to-back–; front-to-rear–; fuel-air–; fuel weight–; impulse-weight–; *LC*–; length/beam–; length-diameter–; loop–; mass–; mean mixture–; metal parts/weight–; mixing–; mixture–; noise–; nozzle area–; payload–; port-to-throat–; pressure–; progressivity–; propellant loading–; PSF–; reactant–; signal-to-noise–; slenderness–; standard wave–; stiffness-weight–; thrust-to-weight–; trim–; viscous damping–.

rational horizon. A plane that passes through the center of the Earth, perpendicular to the zenith-nadir axis (q.v.) of an observer; also, the circle on the celestial sphere made by the intersection of the sphere with this plane. Contrast with *celestial horizon* (q.v.).

Rato (bottle or unit). *Rocket-assisted take-off.* A rocket engine used especially to assist a vehicle in take-off, so-called because of its resemblance to a bottle.

ratrace. A particular type of radar waveguide configuration which serves the same purpose as the *magic tee* (q.v.) but allows the handling of greater power.

RAVEN. Air-to-surface missile. Navy Bureau of Aeronautics designation: ASM-N-7.

Standoff missile.

raw data. Data which are unprocessed; data obtained directly from telemetering transmitters,

range instrumentation, etc., which have not been calibrated, adjusted, compensated, or otherwise reworked.

rawin. *R*adar (or *r*adio) *win*d. (1) Wind tracked either by radar or radio direction-finding. (2) The action of determining the movement and velocity of winds. A radiosonde, radiosonde balloon, or other specially equipped balloon is used for this purpose. (3) Wind information gathered by means of radar tracking or radio direction-finding of a specially equipped balloon.

rawinsonde. A balloon-borne transponder which is tracked as it rises for the purpose of determination of winds aloft.

Rayleigh distribution. A mathematical statement of the distribution of random variables which occur often in nature. See Fig. 18.

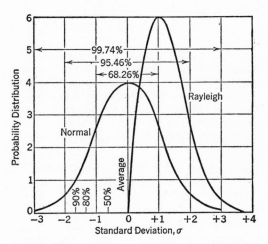

Fig. 18. Normal frequency curve and Rayleigh distribution.

$$\sigma = \sqrt{\frac{\Sigma X}{N}}$$

where X = deviation of individual values; N = number of data. Area under the probability curve for intercepts equal to:

$1\sigma = 68.26\%$	$50\% = 0.675$
$2\sigma = 95.46\%$	$80\% = 1.282$
$3\sigma = 99.74\%$	$90\% = 1.645$
$4\sigma = 99.994\%$	
$5\sigma = 99.999578\%$	$(1 - P = 4.22 \times 10^{-6})$
$6\sigma = 99.99, 99, 99, 9145\%$	$(1 - P = 8.55 \times 10^{-10})$

(C. W. Besserer, *Missile Engineering Handbook*, D. Van Nostrand)

Rayleigh pitot equation. In aerodynamics, the ratio of stagnation to static pressure in air.

Rayleigh-Ritz method. In mathematics, a variational principle for the solution of the eigenvalue equation $A\psi = \lambda B\psi$ (A, B are operators) based on taking as a trial function a linear combination of a complete set of functions, with coefficients which are to be varied to give the correct solution. (Used in aeroelasticity for computation of mode shapes and frequencies.)

rays. *Types of, see* cosmic–; crepuscular–; direct–.

RC constant. The time constant of a resistor-capacitor circuit.

$$t = RC, \text{ in sec}$$

RCM. Radar CounterMeasures (q.v.).

RC network. An electrical network of resistors and capacitors used in circuit design for capacitive-differential systems. Frequently the circuit time constant is such as to reduce the transient effect on the total response, and the circuit response is essentially steady state.

Current and voltage transients:

Charging	*Discharging*
$i = \dfrac{E}{R}\,\epsilon^{-t/RC}$	$i = \dfrac{E}{R}\,\epsilon^{-t/RC}$
$V_c = E(1 - \epsilon^{-t/RC})$	$V_c = E\epsilon^{-t/RC}$

where i = current, amp; E = voltage; V_c = reactive volts across a capacitance; R = resistance, ohms; t = time, sec; c = capacitance, farads.

RDB. Research and Development Board (now disbanded).

RDF. (1) Radio Direction Finder (or Finding). (2) Reflection Direction Finding.

RDX. *See* cyclonite.

Re. Rejection number (q.v.).

reactance. That component of the impedance (q.v.) of an electrical circuit which is provided by the inductance (or capacitance) (q.v.); it varies directly as the frequency of the exciting current. It is analogous to *moment of inertia* in a rotational mechanical system.

reactance. *Types of, see* acoustical–; electrical–; inductive–; mechanical rectilineal–; mechanical rotational–.

reactance modulator. A vacuum-tube circuit which converts changes of input voltage into corresponding changes of reactance; i.e., its output usually acts the same as a variable capacitor.

reactant ratio. The ratio of the weight of oxidizer flow to fuel flow in a rocket.

reaction. *Types of, see* chain–; thermonuclear–.

reaction engine. An engine that derives thrust by expelling its gases of combustion to the rear. A reaction engine moves forward in accordance with the third of Newton's laws of motion: "every action produces an equal and opposite reaction" (e.g., jet engines and rocket engines).

reaction propelled. In propulsion, propelled by means of reaction to a jet of gas or fluid projected rearward (e.g., jet engine, rocket engine).

reaction turbine. A turbine which develops its power by the use of a high-pressure low-velocity gas flow through the rotor blades. The pressure energy is converted to kinetic energy within the rotor blade passages.

reactor. *Types of, see* atomic–; breeder–; heterogeneous–; high-flux–; homogeneous–; nuclear–; plutonium–; porous–; saturable–; thermal–.

readied missile. A missile which has been tested, fueled, warmed up, supplied with firing data, and is prepared in all respects for activation of its firing sequence.

readiness monitoring operations. The monitoring of the status of those portions of a weapon system which must be in a pre-established condition to enter the launch control operation and for which it is known that performance degrades with "on time" (e.g., uncaged gyroscopes) or for which there is a specific operational requirement (e.g., target assignment).

readiness time. The length of time required to obtain a stabilized system ready to perform its intended function. (Readiness time includes warm-up time.) The time is measured from the point when the system is unassembled or uninstalled to such time as it can be expected to perform as accurately as at any later time. *Maintenance activity time* is excluded from readiness time.

read-out. The transfer of information from an information processing system (e.g., a computer) to an output device (e.g., a printer, plotter, etc.).

ready storage. Missile storage adjacent to the launcher or in such location that it is available to the handling equipment which will place it on the launcher. *Tactical storage, testing,* and *ready storage* conceivably may be in a single confined area and comprise one general operation if the circumstances so warrant.

real time. (1) A term applied to the simulation of a guided missile operation on the same time scale as the actual operation. (2) The presentation of data on the same time scale as the actual events.

real-time data. Data presented and/or recorded which can be immediately observed as events are taking place.

Rebecca-Eureka system. A vehicle radar homing system in which an airborne interrogator-responser (Rebecca) homes on a ground radar beacon (Eureka) that has been dropped or set up in advance. This system also allows range measurement by the Rebecca radar to the Eureka beacon.

receiver. *Types of, see* antitransmitter–; cut-off–; superheterodyne–.

receiver bandwidth. The band of frequencies a receiver will pass with a uniform or prescribed attenuation with the receiver tuning fixed.

receiver sensitivity. The lower limit of useful signal input to the receiver; set by the *signal-to-noise* (S/N) ratio (q.v.) at the output.

receiving station. An installation to receive and record a telemetering (or other) signal.

receiving station error. The error in intelligence introduced by a data system receiving station between signal input to the receiver and the discriminator.

reception. *See* diversity reception.

reciprocating compressor. A positive-displacement compressor that employs the action of a piston to compress air or other fluid.

reciprocity theorem, electric network. An equivalence theorem of value in electric network analysis. In an electric network composed of passive bilateral linear impedances, the ratio of an electromotive force introduced in any branch to the current measured in any other branch, called the *transfer impedance,* is equal in magnitude and phase to the ratio that would be observed if the positions of the electromotive force and the current were interchanged. When altering the location of an electromotive force in a network, the branch into which the electromotive force is to be introduced must be opened, while the branch from which it has been removed must be closed.

reckoning. *See* dead reckoning.

recommended ground zero (RGZ). That point, with relation to the Earth's surface, where it is recommended that a nuclear detonation take place in order to accomplish the desired effect.

RECON. Reconnaissance drone vehicle. Army cognizance.

Used to transmit television view of enemy targets to helicopter for relay to ground forces.

recorder. A device for storing information for use at a later time. There are several types of recorders, for example: (a) *tape recorder* which stores information magnetically, (b) *oscillograph*

recorder which stores information visually on sensitized film or paper.

recorder. *Types of, see* intercept ground optical–; oscillograph–; photorecorder–; strip chart–; tape–; telescopic photographic–; VG–.

recording optical tracking instrument (Mk I & Mk II) (ROTI). Field instrumentation equipment for recording missile position in space by means of two, long focal length, large aperture telescopes. Cameras record the missile image and azimuth and elevation dials versus time. A missile tracking instrument using a modified 90-mm M2A1 gun turret. A 70-mm camera is mounted on a 24-in. diameter, 100-in. focal length telescope. Tracking rate is about 10° per sec and range coverage up to about 175,000 ft is attainable.

recovery. A generic term covering the means whereby a missile or a valuable part thereof can be recovered for analytical study and/or reuse. (The principal techniques are landing on wheels on a skid strip, lowering by parachute, recovery of a ruggedized data casette.)

recovery. *Types of, see* diffuser–; pressure–; ram–.

RECRUIT. A small solid propellant rocket developed by Grand Central and used for advance stages on Army Ballistic Missile Agency (ABMA) satellite and lunar tests.

rectifier. An electrical device that conducts in one (the forward) direction and is an insulator in the opposite direction.

rectifier. *Types of, see* full-wave–; half-wave–.

REDEYE. Surface-to-surface anti-tank missile. Army cognizance.

A small missile, guided by a simple infrared system. Intended for operations against armored vehicles and similar targets, and low-flying aircraft.

Developed by Convair, Pomona.

redox. Acronym for *re*duction-*ox*idation chemical rocket propellant systems in which the fuel is oxidized and the oxidizer is reduced.

REDSTONE. Surface-to-surface ballistic missile. Military designation: SSM-A-14. Termed JUPITER A.

Length (excluding the nose probe): 63 ft; body diameter: 72 in.; fin span: 12 ft; launching weight: 40,000 lb; burnout speed: MACH 5; maximum range: over 200 miles. Control is by means of jet vanes in the rocket exhaust. Liquid propellant rocket, one 75,000-lb thrust engine. Inertial guidance. Warhead will accommodate an atomic or conventional payload.

Systems Engineering: Army Ballistic Missile Agency. Prime Contractor: Chrysler Corp. Airframe: Chrysler. Engine: North American Aviation, Inc., Rocketdyne Div. Guidance system: Ford Instrument Co.

reduced mass. In treating any two-body problem, the most absolute coordinate frame in which the laws of motion may be applied is an inertial system (e.g., a system which is not accelerated with respect to the fixed stars). The center of mass system of two bodies, having masses M and m and acted on only by mutual forces, is such an inertial system. When the equations of motion are transformed to center of mass coordinates, it is found that they are identical with equations in a system having its origin fixed at M if the mass m is replaced by the reduced mass, $\mu = Mm/(M+m)$. If $M \gg m$, the reduced mass is closely approximated by m, the reduced mass is closely approximated by M.

reduced velocity. In flutter analysis, the ratio of airspeed to oscillation frequency of an aerodynamic surface.

reduction of area (per cent). In a material subjected to a breaking stress, the difference between the original cross-sectional area and that of the smallest area at the point of rupture. It is usually stated as a percentage of the original area; also termed *contraction of area*. The *reduction of area* is a satisfactory physical characteristic to describe ductility or degree of brittleness in a material.

redundancy. The employment of multiple devices, structural elements, parts, or mechanisms in combination (where each is capable of performing the same function) for the purpose of increasing the probability of occurrence and the reliability of the particular function or operation. It allows the adoption of more than one path in achieving a desired effect.

reentry. That point in the trajectory of a body (ballistic missile, nose cone, space weapon, or bomb from a satellite bomber) where it first contacts the sensible atmosphere (q.v.). The reentry phase (reentry point to impact) is the portion of the terminal trajectory where thermal heating becomes critical. See Fig. 27, page 293.

reentry body. That portion of a space-traversing missile which usefully reenters the atmosphere. In a long-range ballistic missile, the separable reentry body contains the heat shield, warhead, attitude stabilizing and fuzing equipments needed to reenter the Earth's atmosphere without self-destruction from a very high velocity and altitude, reduce the dispersion, and explode the warhead.

reentry vehicle (R/V). That stage of a missile which contains the warhead and terminal guidance equipment. Sometimes termed *nose cone*, though reentry vehicle (or body) is the preferred terminology.

reference angle. In radar, the acute angle between the centerline of a radar beam striking a reflecting surface and a line perpendicular to the reflecting surface.

reference area. Any arbitrary area on a body taken as a coefficient in equations for determining an aerodynamic force acting upon the body (e.g., an equivalent flat-plate area, q.v.).

reference ellipsoid. The figure or geometric shape of the Earth arbitrarily defined as an oblate spheroid. The Army Map Service "best fit ellipsoid" gives an Earth radius of 6378.26 km and a flattening at the poles of 1/297 (about 25 km).

reference frequency. (1) A frequency standard, highly stable and accurate, used to calibrate test equipment. (2) A source of AC used as a phase standard in any system where phase reference is important.

reference pressure. The pressure standard used in the sealed chamber of differential gauges (e.g., one atmosphere, q.v.).

reference stimulus. Any reference quantity applied to a telemetering system (e.g., reference voltage, pressure, etc.).

reference temperature. A standard temperature source used for a reference in some high-temperature measuring devices.

reference trajectory. A performance trajectory based on nominal engine and guidance characteristics. It is used as a specification and/or a point of reference for tradeoff studies, design trajectories, etc. For ballistic missiles, reference trajectories usually are two-dimensional and based on a spherical, non-rotating earth.

reference voltage. Any one of several standard voltage sources used for comparison to other voltages for purposes of identification or phasing in FM work.

reflected pressure. The pressure from an explosion, which is reflected back from a solid object or surface, rather than dissipated in the air.

reflected shock wave. A shock wave resulting from an explosion or other supersonic wave which is reflected from a surface or object.

reflected wave. In electronics, an electromagnetic wave (radio or radar wave) that is reflected from a surface or object.

reflecting target. In radar, a target that reflects radar waves.

reflection interval. In radar, the time interval between the transmission of a radar pulse or wave and the reception of the reflected wave at the point of transmission.

reflective code. *See* Gray code.

reflector. In electronics, a surface or object that reflects radio-frequency energy or a flow of electrons: (a) a metallic device in a directional antenna system that reflects radio-frequency energy from a feed or radiator and directs it in a desired direction or directions; (b) a metallic object placed near a radiator in an antenna assembly, used to block radiation in an undesired direction and reinforce it in a desired direction; (c) a repeller (q.v.).

reflector. *Types of, see* complex–; confusion–; corner–; paraboloid–.

reflex circuit. A circuit in which the signal is amplified, both before and after detection, in the same amplifier tube or tubes.

reflex klystron. A klystron (q.v.) in which the two resonant circuits of a conventional klystron are confined into a single resonant cavity, which now acts also as anode. As an oscillator, the reflex klystron possesses the advantage of having only one tuned circuit to be adjusted. Also it is possible to make small adjustments to the frequency by altering the voltage on the repeller. (The tuning range obtainable in this way is small, of the order of about one per cent.)

refraction. In radio, the bending of a radio or radar wave, caused by striking the ionosphere (q.v.). *See* Fig. 13, page 223.

refueling. *See* orbital refueling.

regeneration. A method of securing increased output from an RF amplifier by feeding part of the output back to the amplifier input in such a way that reinforcement of the input signal is obtained. With this arrangement, a signal may pass through the same amplifier over and over again, with a resultant increase in amplitude. Regeneration causes oscillation when carried to extremes.

regenerative cooling. A method of cooling engines in which incoming fuel is circulated around hot areas, serving to cool the combustor, tailpipe or thrust chamber; the fuel is then fed into the engine, and the heat absorbed is available for thermodynamic processes resulting in increased thermal efficiency. In rockets, the fuel is circulated around the combustion chamber and nozzles, and serves to prevent burning of these parts, while returning the heat back to the combustion chamber as the fuel is burned.

regenerative engine. A jet or rocket engine that utilizes the heat of combustion to preheat air or fuel entering the combustion chamber.

region. *Types of, see* Fraunhofer–; isothermal–; stagnation–; subsonic–; supersonic–.

regressive burning. Burning of a solid propellant rocket grain characterized by a decreasing pressure versus time characteristic.

REGULUS I. Surface-to-surface missile. Navy Bureau of Ordnance designation: SSM-N-8A.

Length: 33 ft; height: 9.5 ft; diameter: 4.5 ft; span: 21 ft; total weight: 14,520 lb. Designed to be launched from submarines, surface ships, and shore bases by the Marine Corps, as well as the Navy, against sea and land targets. Launched from a steam-driven catapult or two solid propellant 1000-lb thrust rockets. Uses turbojet delivering 4600 lb of thrust. Speed is 600 mph.

Prime Contractor: Chance-Vought Aircraft Corp. Airframe: Chance-Vought. Engine: solid propellant rocket booster: Aerojet-General Corp.; turbojet sustainer: Allison Division, General Motors Corp. Guidance system: radio-controlled: Stavid Engineering, Bendix; autopilot stabilized: Sperry Gyroscope Co.; ATRAN may be adapted: Goodyear; another alternate guidance system is inertial: Sperry or Bendix.

REGULUS II. Surface-to-surface guided missile. Navy Bureau of Aeronautics designation: SSM-N-9.

Length: 57 ft; span: 20 ft; launching weight: 23,000 lb; cruising speed: MACH 1.9; ultimate range: 1000 miles (with drop tanks). One J-79 turbojet cruise engine; two solid propellant rocket boosters. Inertial guidance. Used on the Halibut, nuclear-propelled submarine, as well as the submarines Grayback, Growler, and Firestone.

Prime Contractor: Chance-Vought Aircraft Corp. Airframe: Chance-Vought. Engine: turbojet: General Electric Co.; boosters: Aerojet-General Corp. Guidance system: Sperry Gyroscope Co.

Program cancelled Dec., 1958.

reheating. The heating of gases between stages in certain types of turbines in a turbojet engine to increase the efficiency of the engine. In reheating, the gases leave the combustion chamber and expand through a number of stages of the turbine, then enter another combustion chamber where fuel is again burned, raising the temperature of the gases, which expand through more turbine stages and then escape through the exhaust nozzle. Reheating is different from *afterburning* (q.v.) in that in the latter the gases do not pass through any additional turbine stages after the second combustion process.

reinsertion of carrier. The combining of an incoming suppressed-carrier type signal with a locally generated carrier signal in the receiver.

rejection, image. *See* image rejection.

rejection number. The smallest number of defectives (or defects) in the sample or samples under consideration that will not prevent the acceptance of the inspection lot. For a fixed plan the rejection number (Re) and the acceptance number (Ac) have the relation $Re = Ac + 1$.

relative error. An error relative to a quantity of the same dimension (e.g., a relative error of 1 part in 1000).

relative humidity. The ratio of the amount of water vapor in the air to the maximum amount which air at any given temperature can retain without precipitation. Relative humidity is usually expressed in terms of per cent. The temperature at which relative humidity is measured is necessary to give meaning to the measurement. *See also* humidity.

relative velocity. (1) The velocity of relative motion, especially in regard to a vehicle and the airstream. (2) The velocity of one moving object as compared with that of another moving object.

relative wind. The velocity and direction of the air with reference to a body moving in it. It is usually determined from measurements made at such a distance from the body that the disturbing effect of the body upon the air is negligible.

relaxation oscillator. (1) Generally, an oscillator having a decidedly nonsinusoidal output, resulting from abrupt transitions from one unstable state to another. (2) An oscillator in which the frequency is controlled by the charge or discharge of an inductor or capacitor through a resistor. (3) A multi-vibrator oscillator circuit employing two tubes (or a double section tube) with resistance-capacitance coupling between the tubes to feed the output back and forth between them. It is used in television circuits to generate sweep voltages for cathode-ray tubes.

relaxation time. The time period for equilibrium of molecular action in a flow field; about 0.0001 sec for oxygen and 0.00002 sec for nitrogen.

relay. An electromagnetic switch employing an armature to open or close contractors. A small current through the coil actuating the armature

thus can control a heavy-duty circuit at the contacts; an electro-mechanical circuit element.

relay, time-delay. *See* time-delay relay.

reliability. The probability of a device performing its purpose adequately when requested for the period of time intended under the operating conditions encountered. If the product rule is used, the *over-all reliability* is based on the product of the individual reliability of each element (e.g., 100 components—if independent—with a 99% reliability each, will have an over-all reliability of 36.5%).

$$\text{over-all reliability} = q_1 \cdot q_2 \cdot q_3 \cdot q_4 \ldots q_n$$

where $q_1 = (1 - p_1)^n$, etc.; $p_1 =$ probability of component failure at some random time; $q_1 =$ probability that component will not fail at this random time; $n =$ number of such components in series. *See* functional reliability.

reliability. *Types of, see* cumulative–; functional–; system–.

reliability index. A quantitative figure of merit related mathematically to the reliability of the equipment; for example: (a) the number of failures per 100 (1000) operations; (b) the number of failures per 1, 10, 100, 1000, or 10,000 equipment operating hours as may be appropriate to the equipment application; (c) the mean time between failure (q.v.) in equipment operating hours.

reliability level. *See* acceptable reliability level.

reliability tests. Tests and analyses in addition to other kinds of tests which are designed to evaluate the level and uniformity of reliability in a product, part, or system and the dependability or stability of this level with time and use under various environmental conditions.

relief valve. An hydraulic or pneumatic system element designed to limit the pressure to a maximum safe value by relieving or venting the working medium to reduce the pressure.

reluctance. (1) The resistance of a material to magnetic flow; the reciprocal of *permeance* (q.v.). (2) In electricity, the opposition in a magnetic circuit to the passage of magnetic lines of force.

remanence. The residual induction, B_r, when the magnetizing field is reduced to zero after saturation.

remote MACH number. The MACH number of a moving object taken as a whole. Contrast with local MACH number (q.v.).

remote velocity. The velocity of an object taken as a whole, as distinguished from the local velocity of any of its parts. In transonic flow, the remote velocity of a vehicle may be less than MACH 1, whereas the velocity of a local point on the vehicle may be MACH 1 or greater.

reoperative system. A rocket engine (or other system) designed for repeated operation.

repair time. The time actually required for the replacement of defective items. This time must be indicated in terms of the number of men and their calendar hours of active maintenance. In addition, the type of supply support should be indicated; that is, it should be stated whether spare components or spare parts were furnished.

repeater jammer. A device that serves to confuse or deceive the enemy by causing his equipment to present false information; this is accomplished by a system that intercepts and reradiates a signal on the frequency of the enemy equipment, the reradiated signal being so modified as to cause the enemy equipment to present erroneous data on azimuth, range, number of targets, etc.

repeller. In electronics, an electrode in certain oscillators that reverses the flow of electrons in the oscillator tube.

repetition rate. In communications and electronics, the rate at which recurrent signals are transmitted; a pulse rate. *See* pulse repetition rate.

report. *Types of, see* aerodynamic–; loads–; stress analysis–; structural test–; weights–.

reproducibility. (1) In instrument work, the exactness with which a measurement of a given value can be duplicated. (2) In manufacturing, the degree to which parts, assemblies, etc., can be duplicated.

request for alteration (RFA). A formal request for a study, design change, mockup change, etc. It results usually from a development engineering inspection (DEI) (q.v.) or other formal inspection of a vehicle, subsystem, weapon system, etc.

request for proposal (RFP). A document requesting the competitive submittal of a design, plan, technique, mode of operation, etc., for assessment and selection by the procuring agency.

requirements. *Types of, see* force–; operational–; qualitative–; qualitative operational–; qualitative personnel–; quantitative–; vectoring–.

research. A continued process of scientific investigation prior to and during development. It has for its aim the discovery of new scientific facts, techniques, and natural laws.

research. *Types of, see* applied–; background–; basic–; nonmateriel–; operations–; scientific–.

Research and Development Board (RDB). A board established by the National Security Act of 1947 "to advise the Secretary of Defense as to the status of scientific research relative to the national security, and to assist him in assuring adequate provision for research and development on scientific problems relating to the national security." The Research and Development Board was composed of a civilian chairman appointed by the President, and two representatives each from the Departments of the Army, Navy, and Air Force. This board was abolished in 1953 by the Reorganization Plan No. 6; its functions were taken over by an Assistant Secretary of Defense.

research and development facility. That part of an establishment which may include land, structures, equipment, or combinations thereof, used operationally in the pursuit of research, development, or tests and evaluation incidental thereto, and which physically occupies a single geographical location (e.g., wind tunnels, test stands, ballistic laboratories, climatic laboratories, etc.).

research and development project. A project that involves basic research in some form or other, especially directed at discovering new principles, methods, or facts, but one that is also directed at applying newly discovered or already known principles, facts, or methods to the production of some object, plan, system, or situation that will serve a practical purpose.

research model. An early (in time) model of a concept, device, or system usually embodying only those features associated with performance and seldom, if ever, having engineering features. Includes any or all of the following: breadboard model, development model, mathematical model (q.q.v.).

reserve battery. A self-contained source of electrical energy which is characterized by long shelf life in an unenergized state. Electrolyte is added when battery power is desired.

reset pulse. Stimulus in the form of a pulse serving to force a counter into a prescribed operating condition at the beginning of every frame.

residual contamination. Nuclear radiation remaining after an atomic warhead detonation. It usually refers to radiation from the cloud or from fission products deposited on the ground.

resilience. *See* modulus of resilience.

resistance. In electricity, the opposition to the flow of current in a conductor caused by the physical nature and condition of the conductor.

$$R = E/I$$

where E = voltage; I = current, amp.

resistance. *Types of, see* air–; head–; mechanical rectilineal–; mechanical rotational–.

resistance bridge. A special arrangement of connections for four or more resistors which allows accurate measurement of one of the resistors using the other known resistance values. It is sometimes operated in a balance whereby a small change of resistance of one or more of the legs produces an unbalance that is used as an indication of the amount of change of one of the legs.

resistance calibrator. A special bridge-type circuit which facilitates calibrating resistance bridges (q.v.).

resistance-controlled oscillator. A phase-shift oscillator utilizing RC circuits as the frequency controlling elements. One type uses a resistance bridge as a part of the phase-shift circuit. A variation of the resistance of the legs of the bridge varies the frequency of the oscillator.

resistance derivative. In aerodynamics, one of various quantities that form the experimental basis of the theory of stability and express the variation of moments and forces due to the disturbance of steady motion of a vehicle. Resistance derivatives are classified as *lateral, longitudinal, rotary,* and *translational,* treating of lateral, longitudinal, rotational, and translational motions, respectively.

resistor. An electrical part which offers resistance to the flow of electric current. Its electrical size is specified in ohms or megohms (one megohm equals 1,000,000 ohms). A resistor also has a power-handling rating in watts, indicating the amount of power which can be safely dissipated as heat by the resistor.

resistor. *Types of, see* thermistor–; variable–.

resnatron. A high-power, high-efficiency, *cavity-resonator tetrode* designed to operate in the VHF region. Principle of operation is similar to that of a class C oscillator, with careful attention to beam focusing playing a large part in the high efficiencies achieved.

resojet. *See* pulsejet.

resolution. The capability or property of a radar or optical system to distinguish between objects closely adjacent either in azimuth or range, and to display or present them as separate images; the capability of such a system to present well-defined objects. The measuring unit of resolution is *lines per millimeter.*

resolution, radar. *See* radar resolution.

resonance (resonant frequency). (1) That frequency at which the magnification factor is at a maximum. It normally occurs when the natural frequency of the item and the forcing frequency are the same. (2) In electricity, the condition existing in a circuit when inductive and capacitive reactance balance each other, leaving only circuit resistance to oppose current flow; the intensification of waves that results. (3) In physics, the condition existing in a body when the period or frequency of an applied vibration equals the natural frequency of the body.

resonance. *Types of, see* combustion–; jump–; organ pipe–; velocity–.

resonant burning. In solid rocket design, the phenomenon of unstable combustion vibration resulting in acoustical resonance. (More commonly termed *chugging* or *screaming.*)

resonant frequency. *See* resonance.

resonant jet. A pulsejet engine, so-called because of the intensification of power under the rhythm of explosions and compression waves within the engine. *See* pulsejet.

resonator. *Types of, see* cavity–; klystron–.

responder. That part of a transponder (q.v.) that automatically transmits a reply to the interrogator-responser. Also termed *responder beacon* when its function as a beacon is emphasized. *See* beacon.

response. Of a device or system, a quantitative expression of the output as a function of the input under conditions which must be explicitly stated. The response characteristic, often presented graphically, gives the response as a function of some independent variable, such as frequency or direction. Modifying phrases must be prefixed to the term "response" to indicate explicitly what measure of the output or of the input is being utilized.

response. *Types of, see* frequency–; pressure pickup–; thermal–; time–.

responser. That component of an interrogator-responser (q.v.) that receives and displays the reply from the responder (q.v.) beacon.

response time. Of a system or element, the time required for the output first to reach a specified value after the application of a step input or disturbance.

resting frequency. The initial frequency of a frequency-modulated carrier wave before modulation. Also termed *center frequency.*

restoring moment. A righting moment.

RESTRICTED. Formerly used to designate classified information, material, or matter other than that classified TOP SECRET, SECRET, or CONFIDENTIAL, which required some degree of security protection. "RESTRICTED" designated the least sensitive type of security material. It is no longer used as a security classification.

RESTRICTED area. A security or classified area to which access is controlled.

restricted burning grain. A solid propellant rocket grain in which the burning surface is restricted or inhibited to provide particular pressure-time characteristics.

RESTRICTED DATA. A security classification for all data concerning the manufacture or utilization of atomic weapons, the production of fissionable material, or the use of fissionable material in the production of power, but not including any data which the Atomic Energy Commission from time to time determines may be published without adversely affecting the common defense and security.

restricted propellant. A solid rocket propellant system in which combustion takes place perpendicular to the longitudinal axis of the grain ("cigarette" fashion). Often termed *end burner* or *end burning grain.* See Fig. 22, page 259.

resultant. In physics, a force or vector that combines two or more forces acting on an object.

retainer. *See* missile retainer.

RETMA. *R*adio, *E*lectronics, and *T*elevision *M*anufacturers *A*ssociation.

retractable launcher. A launcher designed to carry a missile in one position and extend it to a new position for launching.

retrofit (backfit). A modification of a missile or other equipment to incorporate changes made in later production of a similar piece of equipment. Retrofitting may be done in the factory or field.

retrograde motion. Orbital motion within the solar system in a direction opposite to that of the planets; i.e., clockwise as seen from north of the ecliptic.

retro-launching. Launching a missile backward relative to its parent airplane.

retro rockets. Rocket units, usually solid propellant type, used to retard one body relative to another (e.g., fired opposite to main power units to separate burned out stages of a multistage missile).

return. In radar, a radar echo appearing on a radar screen. *See* background return.

return. *Types of, see* ground–; land–.

reverse Jato. A Jato unit or units mounted or turned backward so that their force can be opposed to the forward movement of a vehicle, thereby acting as a brake. *See* retro rockets.

reversible pendulum. A pendulum which is used for accurate determinations of the acceleration of gravity. By measuring the period corresponding to two different suspension lengths, there is no need for a measurement of the moment of inertia. The acceleration of gravity is given by:

$$g = \frac{4\pi^2(l_A^2 - l_B^2)}{l_A P_A^2 - l_B P_B^2}$$

where l_A, l_B = two different lengths of suspension to center of mass; P_A, P_B = periods corresponding to the above lengths.

revolution. (1) A single turn; a procedure or course as in a circuit back to a starting point. (2) In mechanics: (a) a turning round or rotating, as on an axis; (b) a moving in a circular or curving course (e.g., about a central point); (c) a single cycle in such a course. (3) In astronomy: (a) the action or fact of going round in an orbit; (b) a single course of such movement; (c) an apparent movement around the Earth.

    1 revolution = 360 degrees = 6.2832, or 2π
                    radians
    1 revolution/min = 6 degrees/sec = 0.104720
                    radian/sec

Reynolds number. A correction factor applied to analysis of the fluid flow about scale models in wind tunnel tests to determine the results to be expected of the flow about full-scale models. The Reynolds number corrects for the scale effect resulting from the difference in size between the scale model and its full-scale prototype.

$$\text{Reynolds No.} = \frac{\rho V L}{\mu}$$

where ρ = density; V = velocity; L = characteristic length; μ = viscosity.

RF. Radio Frequency (q.v.).

RFA. Request For Alteration (q.v.).

RF energy. In electronics, alternating current generated at radio frequencies (q.v.).

RF head. A unit consisting of a radar transmitter and part of a radar receiver, the two contained in a package for ready installation and removal.

RFNA (red fuming nitric acid: $HNO_3 + NO_2 + H_2O$). A liquid rocket propellant *oxidizer.* See Table 3, page 157.

RFP. Request For Proposal (q.v.).

RGZ. Recommended Ground Zero (q.v.).

rheostat. In electricity, a variable resistor used to regulate the current in a circuit.

RHI. Range Height Indicator.

rhumbatron. A resonant cavity (used instead of circuits) consisting of lumped inductance and capacitance, to act as an oscillator capable of giving several kilowatts output at frequencies of several thousands of megacycles.

rhumb line distance. Distance measured along a rhumb line; i.e., a line on the surface of the Earth making the same angle with all meridians.

RI. Radio Inertial (guidance system).

rib. *See* nose rib.

riffle cloud. A cloud made up of wavy masses or riffles, occurring near a mountain over a leeward plain or valley, and paralleling a crest cloud.

RIFI. (1) Radio Interference Field Intensity. (2) Radio Interference Free Instrument.

right ascension. In air navigation, the arc of the celestial equator (q.v.), or the angle at the celestial pole (q.v.), measured eastward from the hour circle (q.v.) of the vernal equinox to the hour circle of a given celestial body, either through 24 hours or 360 degrees.

rigidity. *See* modulus of rigidity.

RIGS. Radio Inertial Guidance System (q.v.).

rime (ice). In meteorology, a rough or feathery coating of ice deposited by fog on terrestrial objects.

RIME. Radio Inertial Monitoring Equipment.

ring. *Types of, see* adapter–; burner–; collector–.

ringing. *See* circuit ringing.

ring modulator. A rectifier modulator (demodulator) employing four diode elements connected in series to form a ring. The diodes are connected with a polarity which will readily permit current flow around the ring in one direction. Appropriate input and output connections are made to the four nodal points of the ring. The ring modulator is also termed the *double-balanced modulator*. It can serve as a balanced modulator as well as a phase-sensitive detector or demodulator.

ringtime. In radar, the time interval between the beginning of a radar pulse and the instant at which the energy reradiated from an echo box falls below the minimum required to produce an indication in a radar receiver.

ripple. The alternating-current component present in the output of a direct-current generator, rectifier system, or power supply.

ripple fire. The launching of guided missiles in short succession.

RISE project. Research In Supersonic Environment project carried out by North American Aviation Company using NAVAHO (q.v.) missiles to obtain data for the B-70 bomber project. Cancelled November, 1958.

rise time. The shortest time in which the output function of a pickup will register a change of stimulus which takes place at an infinitely rapid rate.

risk. The probability of making an incorrect decision.

risk. *Types of, see* calculated–; consumer's–; producer's–.

RL. (1) Rocket Launcher. (2) Full-power loop range. *See* loop-type radio range.

RL constant. The time constant of a resistor-inductance circuit.

$$t = \frac{L}{R}, \text{ in sec}$$

where L = inductance, henries; R = resistance, ohms.

RL network. An electrical network of resistances and inductances.

Current and voltage transients:

Charging	*Discharging*
$i = \dfrac{E}{R}(1 - \epsilon^{-t/(L/R)})$	$i = \dfrac{E}{R}\epsilon^{-t/(L/R)}$
$V_L = E\epsilon^{-t/(L/R)}$	$V_L = E\epsilon^{-t/(L/R)}$

where i = current; E = voltage; V_L = reactive volts across an inductance; t = time; L = inductance, henries; R = resistance, ohms.

robot pilot. Automatic pilot (q.v.).

ROCKAIRE. A DEACON (q.v.) launched from an aircraft which has assumed a vertical position.

rocket. A thrust-producing system which derives its thrust from ejection of hot gases generated from material carried in the system, not requiring intake of any outside oxidizing agent. *See* rocket engine; rocket propulsion. See Figs. 19 and 20, page 240.

rocket. *Types of, see* aircraft–; bazooka–; booster–; braking–; chemical–; circumsolar–; dawn–; ducted solid propellant–; dusk–; ferry–; free–; guided–; guided aircraft–; high velocity aircraft–; hybrid–; ideal–; ion–; landing–; launching–; multistage–; nuclear–; photon–; practice–; ram–; retro–; separation–; solid–;

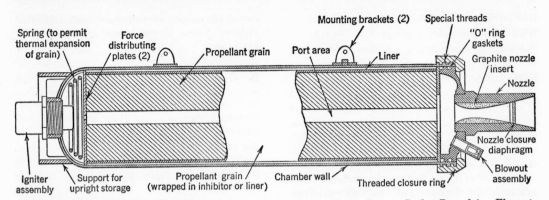

Fig. 19. Sectional view of typical solid-propellant rocket booster. (G. P. Sutton, *Rocket Propulsion Elements*, John Wiley & Sons)

solid-liquid–; sounding–; spinner–; staging–; step–; thermonuclear–.

rocketeer. One whose specialty is rocketry; a person who uses or operates rockets.

rocket engine. (1) A type of propulsive device which develops thrust independently of the medium in which it operates. The classes are: (a) liquid propellant rocket engine, see Fig. 20; (b) solid propellant rocket engine, see Fig. 19; (c) nuclear rocket engine; (d) photon rocket engine (q.q.v.). (2) A propulsive component of a guided missile. In rocket usage, that part of the propulsive system which actually produces the thrust. A liquid rocket engine includes auxiliary pumps and drives and is a self-contained unit but does not include the tankage, pressurization, or control systems.

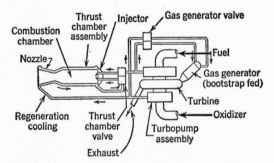

Fig. 20. Components of liquid-propellant rocket engine with turbine-driven pump system for propellant pressurization. (U. S. Air Force, *Air University Quarterly Review*, Vol. IX, No. 3, Summer 1957)

rocket engine. *Types of, see* liquid propellant–; nuclear–; photon–; solid propellant–.

rocket engine propellant. Material, consisting of fuel and oxidizer, either separate or together, liquid or solid, in a mixture or compound which, when suitably ignited, changes into a large volume of hot gases which, upon ejection through a nozzle, impart momentum to a rocket or missile. See Table 3, page 157; and Table 5, page 214.

rocket engine system (or propulsion system). A complete power plant consisting of one or more thrust chambers and related pumping, pressurization, and control equipment.

rocket motor. A generic (and improper) term for a solid propellant rocket consisting of the assembled propellant, case, ignition system, nozzle, and appurtenances. See Fig. 19.

rocket propulsion. The means whereby thrust is developed by a rocket engine; i.e., the fundamental principle upon which all propulsion prime movers operate is based on Newton's third law: "for every action there is an equal and opposite reaction." Upon combustion of the propellants in the burning chamber, the gases expand through the nozzle at a high velocity, the internal pressure at the nozzle end is relieved, causing an unbalanced pressure at the other end which tends to move the chamber and vehicle to which it is mounted in the direction opposite to the issuing jet. Propulsion is dependent upon internal conditions alone and not the effect of the jet "pushing" against the surrounding air.

rocketry. (1) The science or study of rockets, embracing theory, research, development, and experimentation. (2) The art and science of using rockets either on the ground or in the air.

rocket ship. (1) An aircraft or other flying vehicle using rocket propulsion for its main or only source of motive power. The rocket ship also may be controlled by the use of rocket jet streams. (2) A sea-going vessel equipped with rocket launchers and rocket ammunition.

rocket sled. A sled propelled along a fixed track by rockets to permit acceleration, deceleration, and/or high-speed tests (e.g., SMART, SNORT q.q.v.).

ROCKOON. Research missile. Navy cognizance. The ROCKOON is a DEACON (q.v.) launched from a balloon. Length: 12.3 ft; diameter: 6.6 in.; weight: 218 lb; solid propellant; design altitude: 700 miles.

Prime Contractor: Douglas Aircraft Co.

roentgen. The absolute unit of X- or gamma-ray dosage used for measuring radiation exposure; that quantity of X-ray or gamma radiation which produces 109 ion pairs/cu cm of air or, in the body, the production of 10^{12} ion pairs/gm of tissue.

roll. An angular displacement about the longitudinal axis of an airframe from its prelaunch attitude. Looking forward, clockwise roll is positive.

roll. *Types of,* see angle of–; induced–.

roll acceleration. Angular acceleration about the longitudinal axis. Looking forward, clockwise acceleration is positive.

roll capture. Missile flight paths which do not require initial roll stabilization may require a period of time to roll stabilize. Proper roll orientation, which permits guidance signal decoding, is termed *roll capture.*

roll control. Missiles are stabilized in appropriate axes to permit resolution of guidance signals. *Intelligence* is obtained from a reference system such as a gyroscope (free, rate, or in combination with networks) and *control* is obtained from aerodynamic surfaces (separate rollerons, differential motion of wing or tail superimposed on P and Y motions), or from gimballed rocket engines operating differentially.

roll cumulus. Stratocumulus cloud (q.v.).

rolling moments. Moments on a missile airframe created by roll control surfaces, misalignments, induced rolling moments due to coupling, etc. These are reacted by the roll moment of inertia and the roll damping. *See* induced rolling moments.

roll off. (1) The characteristic reduction in amplitude response of a servomechanism as a function of frequency. Roll off may be designed into a system in lieu of a cutoff filter. (2) The attenuation of a "white noise" spectrum as a function of frequency.

ROMOTAR. Similar to DORAN; a measuring system using fewer modulating frequencies than DORAN. It obtains direct slant range by employing a ground station receiver located at the same point as the transmitter.

Ronchi technique. A method of evaluating schlieren photographs utilizing a grating with opaque lines.

rope. Reflectors of electromagnetic radiation consisting of long strips of metal foil. A small parachute or other device may be attached to each strip to reduce the rate of fall. *See* confusion reflector.

Rosebud. A kind of airborne radar beacon used in radar control and identification, friend or foe (IFF) (q.v.).

rotatable nozzle (canted). A thrust vector steering control system used on solid propellant rocket engines. The nozzle exit cone is canted to a small angle and the entire assembly made to rotate about the uncanted nozzle throat centerline to provide thrust control. Contrast with *swivel nozzle* (q.v.).

rotational compliance. In a mechanical rotational system, a measure of its responsiveness to periodic torque; the mechanical element which opposes a change in applied torque. The unit is the *radian per foot per pound.*

rotational impedance. *See* mechanical rotational impedance.

ROTI. Recording Optical Tracking Instrument (q.v.).

rough burning. Severe pressure fluctuations frequently observed at the onset of burning, but which can occur at any time at the combustion limits of a ramjet or rocket.

round. Artillery terminology for a single projectile or missile.

Routh's stability criterion. A method used in feedback control analysis to establish whether a system is stable by determining the number of roots with real positive parts in the characteristic equation. The criterion does *not* establish how stable a system is or what can be done to improve system stability.

ROVER project. The Atomic Energy Commission designation for the project for application of nuclear energy to rocket propulsion.

RP-1. A liquid rocket propellant *fuel.* It closely resembles fuels complying with MIL-F-25576 (USAF); similar to kerosene. See Table 3, page 157.

RP-71. Reconnaissance drone. Army Signal Corps cognizance.

Length: 12 ft; wing span: 12 ft; speed: more

than 200 mph. Jet-launched from a catapult. A photo-reconnaissance version is the Q-19 target drone. Contains still and motion picture cameras in order to take aerial photos from a low altitude of a few hundred feet to a high altitude of four miles. It is recovered by ground guidance and a parachute system. Can operate in all types of weather.

Prime Contractor: Radioplane. Power plant: McCulloch Motors Corp.

RP-77. Target drone and aerial reconnaissance.

Can be used for several purposes such as aerial reconnaissance of enemy land or water areas, nuclear detection, weather reconnaissance, or training for missile crews. Can be recovered by a parachute and ground guidance.

Prime Contractor: Radioplane. Power plant: Turbojet.

RRU. Remington Rand Univac.

RSDS. Range Safety Destruct System.

RSO. Range Safety Officer.

RT switch. A switch device that prevents radar echoes from feeding into a radar transmitter. *See* gate.

RTV. (1) Reentry Test Vehicle. (2) Ramjet Test Vehicle (obsolete). (3) Rocket Test Vehicle (obsolete).

ruggedizing. A technique used to improve the ability of a device or equipment to withstand a severe environment.

running rabbits. A type of interference on a radar screen caused by other nearby radar sets, consisting of random spots drifting across the screen.

rupture. *See* modulus of rupture.

R/V. Reentry Vehicle (q.v.).

R-W. The Ramo-Wooldridge Corporation; Los Angeles, Calif. Succeeded by the Thompson-Ramo-Wooldridge Corporation; Los Angeles, Calif., and Cleveland, Ohio.

S

S. S-band frequency (1550-5200 mc/sec). See Fig. 8, page 105.

SAAM-N-7. Navy Bureau of Ordnance designation for air-to-air guided missile termed SIDE-WINDER I (q.v.).

SAB. Scientific Advisory Board (q.v.).

sabin. In acoustics, a unit of equivalent absorption equal in its absorbing effect to one sq ft of a completely absorbing surface; that is, one that does not reflect sound waves.

sabot. A thrust transmitting attachment which serves as a gas seal for the propellant gas and positions and drives a projectile in the bore of a gun or launcher.

SAC. Strategic Air Command; Headquarters, Offutt Air Force Base, Omaha, Nebr.

SAC-Mike (SAC Missiles). Strategic Air Command Ballistic Missile Staff; Ballistic Missile Division; Inglewood, Calif.

SAF. (1) Secretary of the Air Force. (2) Strategic Air Force.

safe-time. The time during which the safety and arming mechanism (S and A) (q.v.) is in the unarmed condition, i.e., prevents warhead detonation by fuze action. Safe-time is the period during which warhead detonation cannot occur by fuze action.

safety. *Types of, see* factor of–; margin of–; range–.

safety and arming mechanism (S and A). A device to interrupt the functional path between fuze and warhead until after proper launching has taken place and until the missile has passed beyond nearby friendly forces; arming consists of completing the functional path at the proper time.

safety factor. (1) Any margin, factor, or element that insures safety, or a degree of safety, in an operation. (2) In structural design, the ratio of *ultimate load* (q.v.) to *limit load* (q.v.). (3) The extent of a unit's capacity to withstand loads or other inputs in excess of those normally expected to be applied. *See also* factor of safety.

safety fuse. Bickford fuse (q.v.).

safety system. *See* missile safety system.

SAGE. semi-*automatic* *ground* *environment* (q.v.).

salvo fire. The launching of guided missiles simultaneously in groups.

SAM. *Surface-to-air missile* (q.v.); a model designation (q.v.).

SAM-A-7. Designation for the surface-to-air missile termed NIKE (q.v.).

SAM-A-25. Army designation for surface-to-air supersonic anti-aircraft guided missile termed NIKE-AJAX (q.v.).

SAM-N-2. Military designation for the ground-to-air missile termed LARK (q.v.).

SAM-N-6. Navy Bureau of Ordnance designation for surface ship-to-air guided missile termed TALOS (q.v.).

SAM-N-7. Navy Bureau of Ordnance designation for surface ship-to-air guided missile termed TERRIER I (q.v.).

sampling. *Types of, see* double–; single–.

sanaphant. Phanastron (q.v.).

sanatron. Phantastron (q.v.).

S and A. Safety and Arming mechanism (q.v.).

Sandia Base. The Sandia Corporation, Division of Western Electric; Albuquerque, N.M.

sand load. In radio, an attenuator (q.v.) which is a mixture of sand and graphite, used as a terminating section to dissipate power in radio-frequency lines, as in a coaxial cable. Also termed a *dry load*.

SARAH. An electronic communication system using a coded beacon. Originally designed for distress signal purposes.

satellite. A smaller body revolving around another, generally a planet.

satellite. *Types of, see* artificial–; communication–; selenoid–; synodic–; twenty-four hour–.

satellite code names. *See* Alpha 57-1; Alpha 58-1; Beta 57-1; Beta 58; Gamma 58; Gamma 58-1; Delta 58-1 and 2; Epsilon 58-1; Zeta 58. See Table 6, page 245.

satellite lifetimes.

(Circular orbits)

Initial Height of Orbit (miles)	Approximate Lifetime
300	Nearly a year
200	About 15 days
100	Less than 1 hour

satellite orbit. A closed orbit about a celestial body as the center of attraction.

satellites and satellite launchers. *See:* ATLAS-ABLE; ATLAS-HUSTLER; CENTAUR; DELTA; DISCOVERER; EXPLORER; JUNO I; JUNO II; JUNO V; MERCURY; METEOR; METEOR JR.; NOVA; SATURN; SCORE; SCOUT; THOR-ABLE; THOR-HUSTLER; VANGUARD; VEGA.

satellite vehicle. A vehicle made to revolve about the Earth in order to gather scientific data. The orbit is such that its velocity and direction create a radial force equal and opposite to its attraction to the Earth. See Table 6.

satellite velocity. For a circular trajectory, the velocity of a satellite must be sufficient to balance the Earth's gravitational field by means of its centrifugal force:

$$V_e = R_e \sqrt{\frac{g_o}{R_e + h}}$$

where g_o = gravity at the Earth's surface; R_e = radius of the Earth; h = altitude. Note that this velocity is $\sqrt{2}$ or 1.4 less than the escape velocity. The velocity at which a body in any gravitational field will maintain a stable satellite orbit around the generator of the field if the velocity is tangent to the surface of the generating planet is the satellite velocity.

satelloid. (1) A satellite vehicle usually intended to be kept in its orbit by low-thrust motors. (2) A proposed satellite at about 80 miles altitude. Weakly powered in order to maintain itself at this altitude, it would fire small powder rockets intermittently. It would be manned and recoverable by gliding back to Earth. A propellant weight of 3400 lb after being established in orbit would have a time aloft of about 1 week. It is proposed to be shaped like a plane with 500 sq ft of wing surface to reduce temperature and aerodynamic heating to a reasonable level. Weight: 5 tons empty; it would carry one man. Orbital circuit time: 1.44 hr at 80 miles. It was proposed by Dr. Krafft Ehricke.

saturable reactor. A special type of passive variable inductance which has two or more coil windings. It converts changes of current into changes in inductance. Changing current in the control coil varies the magnetization of the core, which then varies the inductance of the output winding. It is possible for very small changes to produce relatively large inductance changes thereby resulting in amplification through the device.

saturable reactor controlled oscillator. An oscillator (q.v.) with a saturable reactor in its tuning circuit to control the output frequency.

saturate. (1) To overwhelm defensive firepower by sheer numbers of weapons. (2) To overwhelm any automatic device by excessive inputs.

SATURN. An Advanced Research Projects Administration (ARPA) (q.v.) sponsored 4-stage launching rocket for advanced satellite and deep Space Probe missions. The first stage is based on the 1.5 million lb thrust Rocketdyne cluster developed by Army Ballistic Missile Agency (ABMA) (q.v.) for National Aeronautics and Space Administration (NASA) (q.v.). The second stage is a modified TITAN (q.v.). The third stage is a CENTAUR (q.v.) second stage. A storable liquid rocket engine is used for the fourth stage. Capable of sending 20,000 lb to the Moon. See CENTAUR; NOVA; VEGA.

saw-tooth generator. A neon or thyratron relaxation oscillator or a vacuum-tube oscillator providing an alternating voltage characterized by a *saw-tooth* wave form.

S-band. A radio-frequency band of 1550 to 5200 mc/sec with wavelengths of 19.35 to 5.77 cm, respectively. See Fig. 8, page 105.

scalar. (1) An entity representing that which has a magnitude without direction. Distinguish from *vector* (q.v.). (2) Of a quantity, having magnitude but not direction.

scale. *Types of,* see Kelvin–; Rankine–.

scale effect. An effect in fluid flow, that results from changing the scale, but not the shape, of a body around which the flow passes. Correction of this effect is by application of the Reynolds number (q.v.).

scale factor. (1) In analog computing, a proportionality factor which relates the magnitude of a variable to its representation within a computer. (2) In digital computing, the arbitrary factor which may be associated with numbers in a computer to adjust the position of the radix (q.v.) so that the significant digits occupy specified columns. (3) A measure of the sensitivity or merit of an instrument (e.g., a galvanometer or similar device where it is the rate of the current through, or the voltage across, the terminals to the deflection).

scale model. A model of something built to a smaller or larger scale but duplicating the shape in all essential details.

TABLE 6. Earth satellite summary

Probe or Satellite	Mission	IGY Designation	Launching Date/Place	Weight In Orbit (lb)	Geometry and Size	Period (min)	Apogee (mi)	Perigee (mi)	Estimated Life	Status
SPUTNIK I	Satellite	1957 Alpha I	4 Oct. 1957 Russia	184 (+4 tons)	Sphere 22.8 Dia	96.2	588 (Vel 16,000 mph)	145 (Vel 18,000 mph)	——	Burned up 4 Jan. 58
SPUTNIK II	Satellite	1957 Beta	3 Nov. 1957 Russia	1120 (+3000)	Cone 19″ × 59″ Base Dia	103.7	1,056 (Vel 15,000 mph)	150 (Vel 18,000 mph)		Burned up 14 April 58
EXPLORER I (Army)	Satellite	1958 Alpha	31 Jan. 1958 2255 EST AMR*	18.13 (+12.7)	Cylinder 80″ × 6″ Dia	114.95	1,573	223	3-5 yr	
VANGUARD I TV-4 (Navy)	Satellite	1958 Beta	17 Mar. 1958 0726 EST	3.25 (+50)	Sphere 6.4″ Dia	135	2,553	409	>200 yr	
EXPLORER III (Army)	Satellite	1958 Gamma	26 Mar. 1958 1238 EST AMR*	18.56 (+12.4)	Cylinder 80″ × 6″ Dia	115.8	1,741	117	——	Burned up 27 June 58
SPUTNIK III	Satellite	1958 Delta	15 May 1958 Russia	2919 (+4100)	12′ × 68″	106	1,168 (Vel 14,640 mph)	140 (Vel 18,800 mph)	15 mo	
EXPLORER IV (Army)	Satellite	1958 Epsilon	26 July 1958 1106 EST AMR*	25.80 (+12.6)	Cylinder 80″ × 6″ Dia	110	1,375	163	4 yr	
PIONEER I (Air Force)	Lunar Probe	(See Note 10)	11 Oct. 1958 0342 EST AMR*	75.3 39.6 (+44.8)	Toroidal 30″ × 29″ Dia	——	70,700	——	43.3 hr	
PIONEER III (Air Force)	Lunar Probe	(See Note 12)	6 Dec. 1958	13	Conical	——	63,600	——	38.1 hr	
SCORE (ATLAS) (Air Force)	Satellite (Communication)		18 Dec. 1958 1802 EST AMR*	150 (8700)	Cylinder (entire ATLAS missile except booster engines 85′ × 10′ Dia)	101	920	110		Burned up 21 Jan. '59
MECHTA or LUNIK (3 stages)	Space Probe-Heliocentric Orbit		2 Jan. 1959 Russia	797 (+2449)						Believed to be orbiting the Sun on a 15 mo cycle.
VANGUARD II (Navy)	Satellite (weather eye)		17 Feb. 1959 1055 EST AMR*	20.74	20″ Dia	125.9	2,064	347	>10 yr	Wobbling motion
DISCOVERER I (Mod. THOR-HUSTLER) (Air Force)	Satellite		28 Feb. 1959 1349 PST PMR**	245 (+1050)	Cylinder 19.2′ × 5′ Dia	95.9	100	605		Burned up 5 Mar. 59
PIONEER IV (Air Force)	Lunar Probe	(See Note 15)	3 Mar. 1959 AMR*	13.4	20″ × 9″ Dia		106.1	91.7		
DISCOVERER II (Mod. THOR-HUSTLER) (Air Force)	Satellite		13 April 59 PMR**	440 (+1170)		90.5	220	150		Burned up 26 April 59

Notes:

1. VANGUARD (TV-3) 6 December 1957. First stage pressurization failed 4″ off the pad.
2. VANGUARD (TV-3 backup) 5 February 1958. Hard over deflection of control system caused structural failure at 57 sec.
3. EXPLORER II was launched 5 March 1958, but failed to orbit when final stage rocket failed to fire. 823 sec flight.
4. VANGUARD (TV-5) 28 April 1958, third stage failed to ignite. Altitude 340 mi, range 1500 mi.
5. VANGUARD (SLV-1) failed 27 May 1958. Peak altitude 2200 mi. Travelled 7500 mi in 20 min flight.
6. VANGUARD (SLV-2) 26 June 1958. Failed to orbit. Second stage malfunction.
7. Lunar Probe No. 1 launched at 0718 EST on 17 August 1958, failed at 77 sec when first stage blew up.
8. EXPLORER V launched at 0118 EST on 24 August 1958, failed to orbit owing to failure of second stage to separate properly from the first stage. All stages burned full duration, but had the wrong angle.
9. VANGUARD (SLV-3) launched on 26 September 1958, but failed owing to low performance of second stage. May have orbited the Earth one time.
10. Intended to be a Lunar Probe, PIONEER I reached an altitude of approximately 70,700 mi. Its course was slightly deflected and the fourth stage was not fired. First stage: THOR IRBM; second stage: VANGUARD second stage (Aerojet); third stage: 1 ABL solid rocket.
11. PIONEER II, an Air Force Lunar Probe was launched on 8 November 1958, but the mission failed when the third stage failed to ignite. Altitude: 963 mi.
12. PIONEER II failed in its mission to pass the Moon due to 3.7 sec early cutoff of the booster (24,000 instead of 24,990 mph) and a 3° aiming error. First stage: JUNO II (modified JUPITER); second stage: eleven SERGEANT solid propellant rockets; third stage: 3 SERGEANT solid propellant rockets; fourth stage: 1 Grand Central solid propellant rocket—used for orbital injection.
13. VANGUARD (SLV-5) fired 13 April 1959. Failed owing to second stage malfunction. Flight time 500 sec.
14. DISCOVERER I & II were placed in a north-south (polar) orbit.
15. PIONEER IV passed within 37,000 mi of the Moon on 4 March 1959 at 4490 mph. Perihelion of 91.7 million mi reached on 17 March and aphelion of 106.1 million mi on 1 October 1959. Injection velocity was 24,790 mph (188 mph too low).
   * AMR—Atlantic Missile Range, Cape Canaveral, Florida.
   ** PMR—Pacific Missile Range, Vandenberg Air Force Base, Lompoc, California.

scaling law. A formula which permits the calculation of some property for a given article based on data obtained from a similar, but different size, article (e.g., crater size, nuclear radiation, etc., for a nuclear warhead of any yield from the known values for another yield).

scan. In radar, to traverse or sweep an airspace or region with a succession of directed beams emanating from a radar antenna. *See* radar scan.

scan. *Types of, see* helical–; linear–; radar–; sector–; spiral–; track-while-scan.

scanning. (1) In radar, the motion, usually periodic, given to the major lobe of an antenna. (2) The process of directing a radio-frequency beam successively over all points in a given region of space.

scanning. *Types of, see* circular–; conical–; rapid–.

scanning antenna mount. A mechanical support for an antenna which provides mechanical means for scanning or tracking with the antenna, and means for readout information for indication and control.

scanning loss. A loss in radar sensitivity due to scanning across a target, as compared to the sensitivity when the beam is directed constantly at the target.

scarf cloud. A thin, halo-like cloud that mantles the head, and sometimes the sides, of a cumulus (q.v.). Sometimes termed a *cap cloud* or *false cirrus* (q.v.).

scatter. *See* forward scatter.

scattering. The phenomenon of deflection and dispersion in all directions of light which falls on a small particle. Blue light is scattered more readily than red. The particles must be of small diameter compared with the wavelength of light—of the order of 1/100,000 of an inch.

scattering. *Types of, see* back-scattering; radio wave–.

scattering cross section. A radar cross section that returns scattered echoes.

SCEL. Department of the Army; *S*ignal *C*orps *E*ngineering Laboratories; Ft. Monmouth, N.J.

schematic diagram. A diagrammatic presentation of the element-by-element relationship of all parts of a system.

schematic drawing. A line drawing showing the interconnections of the various elements and circuits within a component or system using conventional symbols to represent the detail parts.

schlieren. A photographic technique used to record high-speed gas density discontinuities; gradients or variations in gas density, or striae (from the German word). Schlieren are made visible by an optical system which either cuts off or passes a large change in light intensity owing to the slight refraction of the light passing through the gas. This system is often used in wind tunnels, making visible turbulence and weak shock waves by showing the first derivatives of gas density directly.

schmoo plotting. Plots which show the operating margins when the component under test is varied between its upper and lower "end of life" limits while all other components are at the worst end of the initial acceptance tolerances.

Schottky effect. Lowering of the surface barrier by an electric field; the lowering of the work function due to an applied accelerating field. It is responsible for a noticeable increase in emission current as the applied voltage is increased.

Schuler pendulum. *See* Earth pendulum.

Scientific Advisory Board (SAB). A civilian board that advises the Chief of Staff, United States Air Force, upon scientific matters.

scientific and engineering personnel. Those persons engaged in scientific or technical duties which require formal education or its equivalent (e.g., aerodynamicists, physicists, chemists, electrical engineers, mathematicians, mechanical engineers, metallurgists, thermodynamicists, etc.).

scientific research. (1) Research in a field of science. It usually connotes either basic or applied research (q.q.v.). (2) Research done by employing methods and techniques considered to reflect a high degree of exactness in the results. It need not be in a field of science.

scintillation counter. A device consisting of several transparent phosphors together with a photo-multiplier tube, which detects ionizing particles or radiation by means of the light flash emitted when the radiation is absorbed in the phosphors.

scintillation, target. *See* target scintillation.

SCN. Specification Change Notice.

scope. (1) A cathode-ray screen. (2) A cathode-ray tube. (3) Short for oscilloscope.

scope. *Types of, see* A-scope; azel–; B-scope; C-scope; E-scope; expanded–; F-scope; G-scope; H-scope; J-scope; K-scope; L-scope; N-scope.

scope dope. (Vernacular) A radar watcher.

scopodromic. *On the target* course; homing, or heading in the sighted direction.

score. *Types of, see* signal–; z-score; Z-score.

SCORE Project. Advanced Research Projects Agency (ARPA) project to orbit the ATLAS (q.v.) intercontinental ballistic missile (ICBM) for the purpose of experimenting on signal communications by orbiting relay equipment. *See also* ATLAS satellite.

Scorsby table. A two degree of freedom random motion table used for testing gyroscope drift.

SCOUT. An Air Force 'workhorse' 4-stage satellite launching rocket.

    1st stage—modified POLARIS (q.v.) first stage.
    2nd stage—two modified SERGEANT (q.v.) solid propellant rockets.
    3rd stage—VANGUARD (q.v.) third stage with additional propellant.
    4th stage—VANGUARD third stage.
Payload: about 150 lb. Used for communication and weather satellites.

scramble. In electronics, (1) to alter transmitted radio or telephonic frequencies in order to make them unintelligible unless unscrambled; (2) to transmit a message with altered frequencies.

screaming combustion. A combustion instability in jet engines producing relatively high-frequency pressure oscillations and auditory effects.

screen, nozzle. *See* nozzle screen.

screen grid. In electronics, an electrode placed between the control grid and the plate of certain vacuum tubes to reduce interelectrode capacitance.

screening. A screen or sheet-metal wall or partition intended to protect a space or instrument from undesirable radiation. Wire screens guard against radio waves; gamma rays and cosmic rays can be absorbed by lead.

scrub. (Vernacular) The act of cancelling or backing out of a countdown or launching sequence because of an unacceptable hold or the breakdown of an essential component of the missile or support equipment.

scud. Fragments of loose clouds driven by wind; fractonimbus (q.v.).

scupper. (Vernacular) An opening used for drainage.

SdRng. *Sound ranging.*

sea fog. An advection fog (q.v.) formed over an open body of water when warm, moist air moves over a colder water current. Sea fog retains its name even when it moves over land.

sea level. The zero altitude coordinate taken as the level of mean high-tide.

search radar. Radar or a radar set designed especially for searching out objects, as distinguished from radar designed primarily for other purposes (e.g., navigation, bombing, or altitude measurement). It ordinarily determines only the range and azimuth of objects within its area of detection. It is used for early warning, in connection with ground-controlled approach (GCA), ground-controlled interception, etc.

sea return. In radar, echoes from the surface of a body of water that tend to clutter the radar screen.

second. A unit of measurement.

    second (angle) = 0.00027778 degree = $\frac{1}{60}$ min
                      = 4.84814×10^{-6} rad
    second (time) = 0.00027787 hr = $\frac{1}{60}$ min

secondary battery. A self-contained source of electrical energy which is characterized by reversible electro-chemical processes. The chemically reacting parts are restored after partial or complete discharge by reversing the direction of current flow through the battery (e.g., wet cell).

secondary front. In meteorology, a second front of similar nature to and following fairly closely behind a primary front. A disturbance connected therewith is called a *secondary disturbance*.

secondary nuclear auxiliary power (SNAP). An Air Force project to develop a low-weight power source for satellite or space vehicle application.

SECOR. A range instrumentation system designed to provide distance and position information. A missile-borne transponder is interrogated by a ground station and the answer received by several stations to provide distance data. Angle measurement is provided by phase comparison techniques. The system was developed by the Cubic Corporation.

SECRET. Of classified material: having such status that unauthorized disclosure would endanger national security, cause serious injury to the interests or prestige of the United States, or be of great advantage to a foreign nation with respect to the United States. *See* CONFIDENTIAL, a lower security classification, and TOP SECRET, a higher security classification.

section. *Types of, see* airfoil–; instrumentation–; neutron cross–.

sector scan. A radar scan (q.v.) through a limited angle, either in azimuth or depth, as distinguished from a scan that rotates fully.

security. Methods and means for preserving secrecy, including access to classified information.

security classification. The classification given a document, piece of equipment, etc., that indicates the degree of danger to the nation if information within or about it is revealed or compromised. The usual classifications are CONFIDENTIAL, SECRET, and TOP SECRET (q.q.v.).

security clearance. A clearance given to a person permitting him access to classified material, equipment, or information up to and including a given classification, provided he can establish a need-to-know (q.v.).

security, transmission. *See* transmission security.

seeker. Any moving object, especially a missile, that seeks its direction through a device attracted to light, heat, radio waves, sound, emitted by the target; the device used in such an object.

seeker. *Types of, see* heat–; target–.

selector. *See* pulse selector.

selenoid satellite. A Moon satellite.

self-destruction. Desired actuation of destructive agents to destroy a missile in the event of a target miss or other abortion (q.v.) of the particular mission.

self-destruction equipment. Some type of explosive in a circuit such that the equipment may be exploded by: (a) a time-delay mechanism; (b) a radio-command link; (c) an automatic trip mechanism actuated by engine cutoff, loss of a signal, etc.

self-destruction system. A system within a missile that will destroy the missile, or a prescribed section of it, upon activation by external command or by automatic internal initiation when certain predetermined factors occur. A separate demolition charge is considered only as a component of the self-destruction system.

self-destruct signal. *See* command-destruct signal.

self-excited oscillator. A vacuum-tube oscillator (q.v.) that operates without external excitation and solely by the direct voltages applied to the electrodes.

self-guided. (1) In missilery, a vehicle directed along a course by use of self-contained devices (e.g., by use of present mechanisms, a radio set, or a self-reacting device). (2) In a more restricted sense, directed in response to built-in self-reacting devices only.

self-inductance. In electronics, inductance within a circuit induced by the circuit itself.

self-piloting ignition. The continuous ignition of

a ramjet's fuel-air mixture by means of the flame in the combustion chamber.

self-reacting device. A device that works as desired in response to some environmental influence other than direct or remote control.

SELSYN. *Self syn*chronous. A General Electric Company trade name for a synchro (q.v.).

semi-active homing. *See* radar illumination.

semi-active homing guidance. A system of homing guidance (q.v.) wherein the receiver in a missile utilizes radiations from a target which has been illuminated from a source other than the missile.

semi-automatic aircraft rocket launcher. An aircraft rocket launcher (q.v.) requiring operation of both feeding and firing switch.

semi-automatic ground environment (SAGE). A defense system providing instantaneous information needed for control of missiles and aircraft used to wage air battles; a Massachusetts Institute of Technology Lincoln Laboratory development.

semiconductor. An electrical conductor with resistivity in the range between metals and insulators, in which the electrical charge carrier concentration increases with increasing temperature over some temperature range.

semiconductor. *Types of, see* j-type–; n-type–; p-type–.

semi-monocoque. A structure in which sheet and stringers are used in conjunction to provide a stiff, load carrying cell. The longerons divide the sheet into small panels with corresponding buckling resistance.

SENL. Standard Equipment Nomenclature List.

sense antenna. In electronics, a receiving antenna, used with a directional receiving antenna, that distinguishes the direction of a signal.

sensible atmosphere. Arbitrarily assumed to exist to an altitude of 250,000 ft. Properties at this altitude are: temperature, $-105.3°F$; pressure, 3.38×10^{-4} psi.

sensible horizon. A plane that passes through the eye of an observer, at right angles to the vertical and parallel to the rational horizon (q.v.). Because it is always tangent to the Earth, or tangent to a spherical surface parallel to the Earth, the sensible horizon is actually a succession of planes for a moving observer.

sensing device. A device that reacts in some particular way when stimulated by electronic or other forcing function emanating or reflected from an object or other source.

sensitivity. (1) The property of an explosive that relates to the quickness of its reaction to the igniting action. (2) The property of an electrical or electronic piece of equipment to respond quickly and clearly to a signal, sometimes measured by its response to a minimum signal. (3) That characteristic of a radio receiver which determines the minimum strength of signal output. (4) In a telemeter pickup, full-range sensitivity is the input required to give attained bandwidth.

sensitivity. *Types of, see* deviation–; frequency–; pressure–; receiver–; temperature–; temperature sensitivity of pressure.

sensitivity time control (STC). In electronics, reduction in the sensitivity of a radar receiver while nearby echo signals are being received, thus allowing receiver gain to build up to full sensitivity for more distant targets.

SENTRY. Reconnaissance satellite. Air Force designation: WS 117L. Also known as PIED PIPER, BIG BROTHER, ARS.

Will be used for reconnaissance, target location, and intelligence. This satellite is designed to carry television cameras and radar scanning systems, and to orbit between 300 and 1000 miles altitude. The initial version is unmanned. Prime Contractor: Lockheed Aircraft Corp., Missile Systems Division.

separation. (1) The phenomenon in which the boundary layer of the flow over a body placed in a moving stream of fluid separates from the surface of the body, allowing a condition of low-energy turbulent air to exist in the region between the body and the smooth flow. (2) Regarding multistage missiles, the action time or place at which a burned-out stage is discarded and the remaining missile continues on its way.

separation. *Types of, see* laminar–; turbulent–.

separation rockets. Relatively small rockets, usually solid propellant type, installed in groups of two or more on a second or higher stage to be operated when the stage needs additional thrust to accelerate away, at separation, from the preceding stage. They are not to be confused with *retro rockets* (q.v.) which are vectored to retard a used stage rather than to give positive acceleration. *See* stage, sense (2)

separator. *See* four-channel separator.

sequence-checker. A device for monitoring a partially or completely automatic process.

sequence, production-to-target. *See* production-to-target sequence.

sequence valve. A valve that automatically opens or shuts in response to a particular preceding event.

SERGEANT. Surface-to-surface ballistic missile. Army designation: FAGMS-S.

Replaces the CORPORAL (q.v.). Overall length: 32 ft; body diameter: 36 in.; fin span: 110 in.; launching weight: 40,000 lb; burnout speed: MACH 5; maximum range: more than 200 miles. Solid propellant rocket engine. Carries an atomic warhead. Engines used in the X-17 (q.v.) reentry research program. Inertial guidance.

Development: Jet Propulsion Laboratory. Prime Contractor: Sperry Gyroscope Co. Airframe: Douglas Aircraft Co. Engine: Thiokol Chemical Corp. Guidance system: Sperry.

series. *Types of, see* Fourier–; Paschen–.

series circuit. In electricity, an arrangement in which the parts of a circuit are placed end to end to form a single path for the current. Contrast with *parallel circuit* (q.v.).

serviceability. The degree to which a missile or equipment is susceptible to use by armed forces personnel. It involves simplicity of design and consequent absence of superfluous members or components, specification of adequate and reliable elements for trouble-free service life, accessibility of critical components, and use of standard parts where possible. Ease of maintenance, readiness with which adjustments can be made, ease of accurate alignment of parts, ease of handling and loading, and many similar criteria are also included.

service test. (1) A test, under simulated or actual conditions, to determine the characteristics, capabilities, and limitations of a given piece of equipment or material. (2) A similar test made of a plan, method of doing something, or organization. (3) An operational suitability test (OST) (q.v.), especially when used as an attribute (e.g., service test guided missile). (4) A test made at any point in the development of a piece of equipment or material, with the object of predetermining, if possible, ultimate capability and serviceability; i.e., any test made during the research and development stage, or a test to see if a contractor has complied with specifications, or a test on refined or modified material.

servo. A combination of devices for controlling a source of power in which the output (or some function thereof) is fed back and compared to some reference at the input, the difference of this comparison being an error signal used to effect the desired control.

servo. *Types of, see* stable–; unstable–; velocity limiting–.

servo corner frequency. (1) The frequency at which the break in the slope of an open-loop characteristic curve occurs. (2) The frequency at which full amplitude motion cannot be attained.

servodyne. A power unit used in a servo system (q.v.).

servomechanism. A servo (q.v.) used to control a mechanical function.

servo order. Classes of servos:

First. A servo with a zero static error, but a finite steady following error to a step velocity input.

Second. A servo with a zero steady following error for a step velocity input. It has one time lag in the loop. Termed *zero velocity error servo.*

Third. Similar to a second-order servo with two time lags in the loop.

servo system. An error-reducing closed-cycle automatic-control system so designed that the output element or output quantity follows as closely as desired the input to the system. The output is caused to follow the input by the action of the servo-controller upon the output element in such a way as to cause the instantaneous error, or difference between output and input to approach zero. All servo systems are dynamic systems containing at least one feedback loop which provides an input signal proportional to the deviation of the actual output from the desired output; this property distinguishes servosystems from ordinary automatic-control systems. In general, servomechanisms exhibit the following properties: (a) include power amplification; (b) are "error sensitive" in operation; (c) are capable of following rapid variations of input.

servo table. A precision test table, servo driven at a rate to eliminate the effect of the Earth's rotation when properly aligned, and used to evaluate drift rates of a gyroscope (q.v.).

settling time. Of a system or element, the time required for the absolute value of the difference between the output and its final value to become and remain less than a specified amount, following the application of a step input or disturbance. The specified amount is often expressed in terms of per cent of the final value.

seven-o-one calculator. Normally written *701 calculator.* An electronic digital, binary type computer built by International Business Machines (IBM), and used for the solution of complicated or lengthy mathematical problems.

SFB. Structural Feedback.

SHA. Sidereal Hour Angle (q.v.).

shadow. *See* radar shadow.

shaker. A vibration device for generating controlled force of variable amplitude and frequency.

shaped-charge. A type of warhead (q.v.) based on the Munroe effect, which focuses explosive forces into very sharp beams of high gain.

shaping network. An equalizing network.

shear. The tendency of one portion of a body to slide past an adjacent part of the body.

shear center. In structures, the point through which a shear force acts to produce "pure" or torsion-free bending of a beam.

shear flow. In structures, the shear force acting per unit of length of a thin wall element.

$$q = s_s t$$

where s_s = shear stress; t = thickness of material.

shearing stress. A stress between two contiguous parts of a body that tends to make one slide against the other in a direction parallel to their plane of contact. This stress results from applied forces.

shear lag. In box and wide flange beams, the difference in shear from that predicted by elementary theory. Flange bending stresses on a wide flange beam may not be constant along a line parallel to the neutral axis. The shear stresses, which are related to the bending stresses, will not correspond to those predicted by elementary theory—this is the *shear lag.*

shear web. In structures, a web subjected to pure shear stresses.

$$q = \frac{s}{h}$$

where q = shear flow; s = total shear force; h = height of web.

shear, wind. *See* wind shear.

sheet stiffener (sheet stringer). In airframe construction, the combination of thin cover or surface plates or skin reinforced by longitudinal stiffeners running in the direction of the compressive load.

shelf life. The in-service capacity of equipment while standing unused.

SHERWOOD Project. The Atomic Energy Commission's over-all name for the Controlled Thermonuclear Research Program—the effort to "tame the H-bomb."

SHF. Super High Frequency (q.v.) (3000-30,-000 mc/sec). See Fig. 8, page 105.

shield. *Types of, see* flame–; heat–.

shielded pair. In electronics, a two-wire electrical transmission line surrounded by a metallic sheath.

shift. *Types of, see* Doppler–; phase–.

shifting equilibrium. A rocket performance term pertaining to characteristics of the combustion process in the nozzle. Calculation of specific impulse takes into consideration the heat released due to chemical action of the products of combustion as they move through the nozzle. Because of the short *stay* time, the gases may not come to equilibrium. Compared to *frozen equilibrium* (q.v.) conditions, the I_{sp} is 3% to 10% higher. Actual engines usually perform somewhere between these extremes.

SHILLELAGH. Antitank missile. Solid propellant beam rider, infrared guidance. Airborne guidance: Aeronutronics; Fire control: Raytheon.

ships. *See* guided missile ships.

shock. A suddenly applied force or a sudden change in direction of a motion or a sudden change in velocity of a motion. A shock can be specified in terms of the envelope of spectra for measured shocks (assuming no narrow frequency bands).

shock. *Types of, see* attached–; detached–; ground–; local–; normal–; oblique–; swallowed–; velocity–.

shock excitation. (1) Initiation of oscillations in a resonant circuit of a vacuum-tube oscillator by a pulse due to application of electrode voltages. (2) The reception of signals, on an antenna not designed for the frequency of the signals, and due solely to the power of the initial radiation plus the proximity of the receiving antenna. Also termed *shock reception*. (3) The complex excitation of a mechanical device or structure when subjected to a shock wave (q.v.) or impact.

shock front (pressure front). In supersonic aerodynamics, the initial part of the shock wave (q.v.) in which the pressure rises from zero up to its peak value. The shock front is generally assumed to be infinitely thin and a mathematical discontinuity, but is actually of finite thickness. This front is not in equilibrium; it is a transition region between equilibrium conditions in the air ahead of the shock and the changed gas mixture behind it.

shock layer. In supersonic aerodynamics, the region between the shock front (q.v.) and the boundary layer (q.v.); assumed to be an inviscid flow (q.v.). Radiation from the shock layer to the nose cone of high-speed missiles is one of the causes of skin heating.

shock layer composition. The composition of air is changed by its passage through the shock (q.v.) and into the shock layer (q.v.) where it reaches some sort of thermodynamic equilibrium. Instead of the familiar mixture of about four-fifths nitrogen, one-fifth oxygen, and traces of rare gases, the air in the shock layer of a MACH 20 missile is about one-half atomic nitrogen, one-quarter molecular nitrogen, and one-quarter atomic oxygen. Nitric oxide will also be present to some extent.

shock motion. (1) A sudden transient motion with significant relative displacement. (2) In packaging, a sudden change in the velocity of an object (e.g., from rest to motion or vice versa), a condition also termed *velocity shock*. *See* shock; velocity shock.

shock mount. A mount for sensitive equipment that reduces or prevents transmission of shock or some vibration frequencies to the equipment.

shock pulse. The complete description of a shock (q.v.), that is, either the force-time relationship of the shock or the displacement-time relationship of the object.

shock spectrum. An equivalent measure of what a shock (q.v.) does to a complex elastic device. The value at any frequency, f, of the shock spectrum is the maximum acceleration which is experienced by a mass supported by an essentially undamped spring with linear elasticity whose natural frequency is f and which is excited by the shock motion. Velocity or displacement may be used in place of acceleration. Shock spectra may also be specified with stated amounts of damping.

shock test. An environmental test intended to subject the test article to a sharp-edged representation of design requirements. Characteristics of the test may be varied depending on the wave shape desired.

shock tube. A test device consisting of a controlled-atmosphere tube in which a shock wave (q.v.) is used as a driving force to produce a high MACH number of very short duration (order of milliseconds).

shock tube (tunnel). An experimental device used to obtain very high MACH numbers. Usually it is a straight tube containing the gas (e.g., air) to be studied and the driver gas (e.g., helium). The latter is released from a high pressure state to move the gas specimen through a nozzle at a controlled but high speed.

shock tunnel. An intermittent blowdown type of wind tunnel (q.v.) with the driving medium being the high-pressure, high-temperature gas pocket produced in the shock tube (q.v.). By expanding the hot gas pocket through a supersonic nozzle it is possible to extend the useful range of a shock tube to a more accurate simulation of hypersonic flight.

shock wave. In aerodynamics, an extremely thin wave, or layer of gas, generated by the relative supersonic movement of the gas stream and a body, or generated by an explosion. Free-stream gas, upon passing through this wave, experiences abrupt and discontinuous changes in pressure, density, velocity, temperature, and entropy. These changes are irreversible owing to some of the pressure energy being lost to heat. Shock waves are commonly termed *compression waves,* and may be either normal or oblique to the gas-stream direction. The stream upon passing through a normal shock always has its velocity reduced from supersonic to subsonic (q.v.). In passing through an oblique shock, the velocity is reduced but is still supersonic. In the case of shock waves ahead of blunt bodies of revolution, wherein a normal shock blends into an oblique shock pattern, there will be a *sonic line* dividing the flow behind the shock wave into regions of subsonic and supersonic flow. In such cases the total stagnation pressure is reduced, while the density, static pressure, and free-stream temperature are increased in the gas stream.

shock wave. *Types of, see* oblique–; reflected–.

shop and production personnel. Includes those persons engaged in fabrication, assembly, test, checkout, acceptance, and other manufacturing operations (e.g., flashing, annealing, heat treating, baking, refrigeration, anodizing, plating, painting, and packaging). The manufacturing support functions of tooling and tool manufacturing are also included.

SHORAN. *Short range navigation* (q.v.).

short range navigation (SHORAN). A precision position-fixing system using a pulse transmitter and receiver and two transponder beacons at fixed points. *See* hyperbolic navigation.

shot effect. The noise produced by the random emission of electrons from a vacuum-tube cathode. It is considerably reduced or "smoothed" by space charge effects.

SHRIKE. *See* RASCAL.

shutdown. Process by which the thrust of a rocket engine is brought from its steady-state value to a zero value.

SI. (1) Shipping Instructions (sometimes ASI —Amended Shipping Instructions). (2) Strategic Information (q.v.).

Siacci method. A method of computing ballistic trajectories (q.v.) for rockets in which the burnout velocity is greater than 800 ft/sec. It takes into account the drag law of the particular body of interest. Essentially the Gâvre function (q.v.).

sideband(s). (1) The frequency bands on both sides of a carrier frequency within which fall the frequencies of the wave produced by the process of modulation. (2) The frequency components lying within such bands. In the process of amplitude modulation with a sine-wave carrier, the *upper sideband* includes the sum (carrier plus modulating) frequencies; the *lower sideband* includes the difference (carrier minus modulating) frequencies. When only one of these is employed the modulation is said to be *single sideband.*

sideband, vestigial. *See* vestigial side band.

side lobe. A portion of the radiation from a radar antenna outside the main beam, and usually of substantially smaller intensity. A side lobe is a region between two minima in the pattern.

sidereal day. A day as measured by sidereal time (q.v.). A sidereal day begins and ends when the first point of Aries is directly over the reference meridian. Owing to the motion of the Earth around the Sun, a sidereal day is almost 8 minutes shorter than the mean solar day (q.v.).

sidereal hour angle (SHA). The angular distance between an hour circle passing through the first point of Aries to the hour circle passing through a given celestial body, measured westward from 0 through 360 degrees.

sidereal period. The time between two successive passages of a planet or satellite through the same point on its orbit. It is also termed the *period of revolution* or simply the *period.*

sidereal table. A test device with a servo-driven table which is used to cancel out Earth's rotation. The axis of the table is aligned for the particular latitude of the location. Single degree of freedom gyroscope tests are made by connecting the gyroscope sensitive axis to the table servo. At the end of 24 hours, any difference in position from the start is a measure of the gyroscope drift rate, etc.

sidereal time. Time measured by the rotation of the Earth with respect to the stars. A sidereal day is approximately 8 minutes shorter than a solar day. Length of day: sidereal—23 hr, 56 min, 4.091 sec; mean solar—24 hr, 3 min, 56.555 sec.

SIDEWINDER I. Air-to-air guided missile. Navy Bureau of Ordnance designation: SAAM-N-7. Air Force designation: GAR-8.

Length: 9 ft; diameter: 4½ in.; speed: MACH 2.5; range: 18,000 ft; altitude: 50,000 ft; firing weight: 155 lb. Uses a solid sustainer motor; infrared homing guidance. Two more advanced versions of this missile. SIDEWINDER II and SIDE-WINDER III, are included in the family.

Prime Contractor: Philco Corp. Airframe: Philco and General Electric Co. Engine: Norris-Thermador Corp., Hunter-Douglas Aluminum Corp. Guidance system: Avion, Division of ACF Industries; General Electric Co.

sighting. *See* bore sighting.

sigma score. Denotes the number of standard deviations below or above the mean.

signal. A detectable physical quantity which conveys useful information (e.g., information relayed from one point in a control system to another).

signal. *Types of, see* arming–; command-destruct–; error–; feedback–; ghost–; self-destruct–; spurious–.

signal conditioner. In instrumentation, a device used to shape or adapt a signal to the requirements of the data transmission link.

signal generator. A test instrument that generates an unmodulated or tone-modulated radiofrequency signal at any frequency needed for aligning or servicing electronic equipment. Also termed an *all-wave signal generator, oscillator,* or *test oscillator.*

signaling. *See* closed circuit signaling.

signal shaping network. An equalizer network.

signal strength. (1) A measure of the power output of a radio transmitter at a particular location; usually expressed as millivolts per meter of effective height of the receiving antenna employed. (2) The amplitude of a transmitted signal in microvolts appearing at the antenna terminals of a receiver.

signal-to-noise (S/N) ratio. In an electrical system or device for conveying intelligence, the ratio of the value of the signal to that of the noise. This ratio is usually in terms of peak values in the case of impulse noise (q.v.) and in terms of the root-mean-square values in the case of the random noise (q.v.). Where there is a possibility of ambiguity, suitable definitions of

the signal and noise should be associated with the term; for example: *peak-signal to peak-noise ratio; root-mean-square signal to root-mean-square noise ratio; peak-to-peak signal to peak-to-peak noise ratio,* etc. This ratio is often expressed in decibels. This ratio may be a function of the bandwidth of the transmission system. The term is sometimes used analogously in servomechanisms.

silo (missile launcher). A launching scheme in which the missile is housed and fired from a hole in the ground. Usually used to provide a hardened launcher. The MINUTEMAN (q.v.) weapon system utilizes this scheme. Contrast with *silo lift* (q.v.).

silo lift (missile launcher). A launching scheme in which the missile is housed on an elevator in a hole in the ground. Used to provide a hardened storage area but with launching being accomplished by raising the missile to ground level on an elevator prior to liftoff (q.v.). The TITAN (q.v.) weapon system utilizes this scheme. Contrast with *silo* (q.v.).

silver thaw. After a period of cold weather and below-freezing temperature, a mass of warm air passing over the region will cause frost or glaze to form on objects that are still at a low temperature. This condition is known as a *silver thaw,* and usually lasts only a few hours, as the warm air soon warms all exposed objects above 32°F.

similarity. *See* dynamical similarity.

simple pendulum. A mechanical oscillator (q.v.) which consists of a weight suspended from a fixed point by an inextensible member of negligible mass. The weight and suspension are free to perform circular motion about the fixed point. The resulting motion is *simple harmonic* with a period of:

$$p = 2\pi \sqrt{\frac{l}{g}}$$

where l = length of suspension; g = acceleration of gravity.

simplex. A method of operation which permits performing two independent functions alternately as an effective means of simultaneous operation (e.g., alternate firing from several launchers with the same guidance radar). Contrast with *duplex* (q.v.).

simulated altitude. A controlled body of air, as in a decompression chamber, in which the conditions of any given altitude may be simulated. In simulating a given altitude, the particular barometric pressure and temperature of that altitude in a standard atmosphere constitute the principal conditions sought after.

simulation. A technique for studying a guided missile operation by its simulation in the laboratory. Both physical environment and dynamic behavior can be simulated to varying degrees. Simulation is the imitation of the behavior of the actual missile system by the behavior of some *other device*. This *other device* can be made more flexible than the final "hardware"; changes in it can be accomplished with relative ease and at low cost, and it can be subjected to performance tests under controlled conditions. In its most basic form this simulator may simply set up the equations governing the behavior of the guided missile.

simulation, gravity. *See* gravity simulation.

simulator. Concerning missiles, a device which solves a problem by use of components which obey the same equations as the system being studied. Frequently, an electrical analog or rotation instead of translation is used for mechanical problems. In general, a simulator is an alternative means of determining the effects of changing each of several design parameters at much less expense than building and testing complete missiles or systems. A simulator which operates only in the yaw (pitch) plane is termed a *yaw* (or *pitch*) simulator. The missile is assumed to be completely roll-stabilized and the problem is solved in a single plane.

single-base propellant. A nitrocellulose rocket propellant.

single degree of freedom gyroscope. A gyroscope with *two* rotational axes but a *single* gimbal axis. The geometric position at any instant is expressed by *one* number. If the restraint on the gimbal is a spring, the unit is classed as a *rate* gyroscope (q.v.). If the restraint is viscous, the unit is classed as an *integrating* or *displacement* gyroscope (q.v.). See Fig. 17, page 230, and Fig. 21.

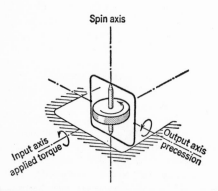

Fig. 21. Single degree of freedom or single axis free gyroscope. (A. S. Locke, *Guidance*, D. Van Nostrand)

single-drift correction course. A single heading course in which the factor of drift is applied but once.

single hop. Refers to the relatively long range spanned by a radio wave departing from its transmitter at a small angle to the horizontal. This type of wave penetrates only a relatively short distance into the ionosphere (q.v.) before it is reflected back to the Earth's surface. There is a definite maximum range that can be spanned by "single hop" transmission. This is the distance covered by a ray departing horizontally. It is about 1500 miles in the case of E-layer (q.v.) transmissions.

single sampling. Sampling inspection in which a decision to accept or to reject is reached after the inspection of a single sample.

single-shot probability. A factor that measures the probability of a single missile striking a specified target point or area.

single sideband transmission. A mode of radio transmission in which the RF carrier and one of the two sidebands produced by amplitude-modulated signals are suppressed at the transmitter. The one sideband carries all of the intelligence. It is used in radio and trans-ocean telephony.

single-stage compressor. A compressor so constructed as to use only one set of impeller vanes, either on a single-faced or double-faced wheel. Distinguish from a *multistage compressor* (q.v.).

single-stage missile. A missile with a single propulsion system and no separable stages. *See* multistage rocket.

single-stage turbine. A jet engine turbine having only one row of stator blades next to one row of rotor blades.

Sissenwine profile. A unique wind profile, promulgated by Norman Sissenwine of Cambridge Air Development Center. This profile is superseded in the literature by the ARDC model atmosphere (q.v.).

site. *See* permanent site.

sizing. A term describing the selection of significant design parameters—particularly those relating to over-all configuration and weight of a system or missile.

skid strip. (1) A longitudinal strip on the fuselage of a pilotless aircraft upon which it can be launched and/or landed. (2) A landing strip on which missiles are recovered.

skin drag. Drag which occurs because of the motion between different layers of air near a moving body; the air immediately in contact with the surface moves with the body.

skin friction. *See* drag.

skin stressed. In missilery, structures designed so the skin bears the primary stresses in the fuselage. *See* monocoque.

skip-glide vehicle. A winged vehicle that is boosted above the atmosphere by large rocket-powered stages and turned into a somewhat circular orbit before thrust is cut off. From this point, the extraterrestrial vehicle follows an undulating trajectory, glancing or skipping off the upper regions of the atmosphere as it travels around the Earth. *See* boost-glide vehicle.

skip trajectory. A long-range missile trajectory in which the initial powered flight is followed by a reentry skip and glide path using the upper portion of the atmosphere to aerodynamically support the missile on successive ballistic type reentries. *See* skip vehicle.

skip vehicle. A hypersonic vehicle with a power boost similar to a long-range ballistic missile (q.v.) but with lifting surfaces to provide reentry control. Contrast with *glide vehicle* (q.v.). *See also* skip trajectory.

skip zone (skip distance). The area within the range of a radio transmitting station in which that station's signals are heard poorly or not at all—affected area determined by operating frequency of station and height of ionized layers in ionosphere.

sky condition. The state of the cloud cover in the sky. In terms of tenths of sky covered, airways' observers in the United States recognize four sky conditions:

Clear sky	—less than $\frac{1}{10}$ cover of clouds
Scattered clouds	—$\frac{1}{10}$ to $\frac{5}{10}$ cover
Broken clouds	—more than $\frac{5}{10}$ but not more than $\frac{9}{10}$ cover
Overcast	—more than $\frac{9}{10}$ cover

International practice and observations made for synoptic charts in North America recognize ten states of the sky. They are indicated by code numbers as follows:

0—no clouds
1—less than $\frac{1}{10}$
2—$\frac{1}{10}$
3—$\frac{2}{10}$ to $\frac{3}{10}$
4—$\frac{4}{10}$ to $\frac{5}{10}$
5—$\frac{7}{10}$ to $\frac{8}{10}$
6—$\frac{9}{10}$
7—more than $\frac{9}{10}$ but with openings
8—$\frac{10}{10}$
9—sky obscured by fog, dust, snow, etc.

skyscreen. *See* optical skyscreen.

sky wave. In electronics, a radio wave which travels upward into space and may or may not be returned to Earth by reflection from the ionosphere (q.v.).

sky wave synchronized LORAN (SS LORAN). A kind of LORAN in which range is extended, and transmitting stations synchronized, by signals reflected from the ionosphere (q.v.).

slant range. (1) The line-of-sight (q.v.) distance from the measuring point to the target, especially an aerial target. (2) The direct distance between an explosion and any given point.

slat. A movable auxiliary airfoil running along the leading edge of a wing. It remains against the leading edge in normal flight conditions, but lifts away from the wing to form a slot at certain angles of attack.

slave gyroscope. A gyroscope that is controlled by a magnetic force through a transmitter (e.g., as in a *gyrosyn,* an instrument employing such a device).

slave station. In a hyperbolic navigation system, that station of a given pair of stations that is controlled by the other station. *See* master station.

sled. *See* rocket sled.

slenderness ratio. Ratio of length to diameter of a missile; used in connection with aerodynamic studies. Sometimes termed *fineness natio.*

slip flow. An aerodynamic condition where the molecular mean free path is on the order of a fraction of the boundary layer thickness.

sliver loss or sliverage. (1) The portion of a solid propellant rocket charge which is undesirably unburned. Slivers result from the convergence of the burning surfaces toward a common point and either are discharged with the exhaust gases or left in the rocket case. (Slivers typically represent 1% to 2% of the propellant charge.) (2) Sliverage is sometimes defined as the propellant remaining at the end of *action time.*

SLOE. Special List Of Equipment (q.v.).

sloshing. The dynamic motion of a body of propellant (liquid or solid) in its tank or container.

slot. (1) An air gap between a wing and the length of a slat (q.v.) or other auxiliary airfoil, the gap providing space for airflow or room for the auxiliary airfoil to be depressed in such a manner as to make for smooth air passage on the upper surface. (2) Any of certain narrow apertures made through a wing to improve aerodynamic characteristics.

slot antenna. *See* notch antenna.

slow bending. The characteristic bending frequency of a missile associated with the interaction of the guidance system, the control system and the airframe (q.q.v.). The frequency is usually substantially less than the first free-free mode frequency.

slowing down kernel. In mathematics, the probability that a neutron will go from one position to another while slowing down through a specified energy range.

slug. A term frequently used by engineers as the unit of mass. The mass of a body in slugs is equal to its weight divided by the acceleration of gravity (32.2 fps²). One slug equals 32.2 lb. Also termed the *geepound* or *engineers unit of mass.*

SLV. Navy Bureau of Aeronautics designation for three-stage satellite launching vehicle termed VANGUARD (q.v.).

SM. Strategic Missile (q.v.).

SM-62. Air Force designation for the surface-to-surface intercontinental subsonic guided missile termed SNARK (q.v.).

SM-65. Air Force designation for surface-to-surface 1½ stage intercontinental ballistic missile (ICBM). Missile is termed ATLAS (q.v.) WS 107A-1.

SM-68. Air Force designation for surface-to-surface two-stage intercontinental ballistic missile (ICBM) termed TITAN (q.v.) WS 107A-2.

SM-73. Air Force designation for air-to-air and/or surface-to-surface missile termed GOOSE (q.v.) WS 123A.

SM-75. Air Force designation for surface-to-surface intermediate range ballistic missile (IRBM) termed THOR (q.v.) WS 315A.

SM-80. Air Force designation for second generation surface-to-surface three-stage intercontinental ballistic missile (ICBM) termed MINUTEMAN (q.v.) WS 133A.

small calorie. *See* gram-calorie.

SMART. *Supersonic Military Air Research Track*; Hurricane Mesa, Utah.

smog. City fog.

smoke puff. (1) Wind data can be obtained by tracking smoke puffs ejected from rockets or missiles by using either theodolites (q.v.) or cameras to record the azimuth (q.v.) and elevation angles. This method is used to obtain wind direction and velocity at any specified level. (2) Ordnance used in lieu of a warhead (q.v.) on practice rounds to give a visual indication of fuze and guidance performance.

S/N. (1) Serial Number. (2) Signal-to-Noise. *See* signal-to-noise ratio.

snaking. (Vernacular) The tendency of a high-speed vehicle to yaw from side to side with a certain frequency.

SNARK. Surface-to-surface intercontinental subsonic guided missile. Air Force designation: SM-62.

Body length (excluding probe): 69 ft; wing span: 42 ft; launching weight: over 48,000 lb; cruising speed: MACH 0.94; maximum range: 5000 miles. One J-57 turbojet sustainer engine and two solid propellant boosters (33,000-lb thrust). Inertial or celestial guidance. This air-breathing vehicle can deliver a thermonuclear warhead or deploy electronic countermeasures. Can be used as a reconnaissance missile for damage-assessment mission after intercontinental ballistic missile (ICBM) strikes.

Prime Contractor: Northrop Aircraft. Airframe: Northrop. Power plant: turbojet sustainer engine: Pratt & Whitney; solid propellant rocket boosters: Aerojet-General Corp. Guidance system: Northrop.

S-N curves. In materials testing, the curves obtained by plotting the number of cycles (N) as abscissa against the load per square inch (S) applied to the test specimen as ordinate. They graphically illustrate the effect of rapid reversals of stress of definite value on the life of the specimen.

SNAP. *Secondary Nuclear Auxiliary Power* (q.v.).

SNL. Standard Nomenclature List.

SNORT. *Supersonic Naval Ordnance Research Track*; Naval Ordnance Test Station, China Lake, Calif.

snow. (1) In radar, a type of interference resembling falling snow that appears on a radarscope. (2) Precipitation that consists of small columnar and tabular crystals of frozen water which fall separately or in loosely cohesive clusters.

S/N ratio. Signal-to-Noise ratio (q.v.).

snubber. A device to absorb energy at the end of the stroke of an actuator (q.v.) to avoid excessive inertial loading on the part being moved.

soak. The exposure of equipment to a given temperature for a period of time long enough for the temperature of the equipment to reach that of the environment in which it is to be operated.

sodium nitrate (NaNO₃). A solid rocket propellant inorganic *oxidizer* with 47% available oxygen.

sodium perchlorate (NaClO₄). A solid rocket propellant *oxidizer* with 52% available oxygen.

SOFAR. Sound *F*ixing *A*nd *R*anging (q.v.).

SOFAR net. A hydrophone system used to provide impact location of reentry bodies by measuring time of arrival of sound waves in the ocean and then triangulating.

soft base. A launching base that is not protected against atomic weapons attack. *See* hard base.

soft excitation. In a control system, the self-excitation which occurs in the presence of small signals.

soft stand. A stand used for hot firings of rocket engines (and/or complete missiles) in which the test article is mounted on a "low-frequency" support and provision is made to take out the thrust forces.

soft structure. (1) A structure relatively vulnerable to damage from nuclear explosion, usually located on the surface of the ground. *See* base hardness; hard structure. (2) A structure with a low natural frequency.

soft tooling. Synonymous with temporary tooling; used for short production runs and experimental articles.

soft tube. (1) A tube which has not been completely evacuated, or a vacuum tube which has lost part of its vacuum owing to gas released from the electrodes and envelope. (2) A tube which has been evacuated and recharged with an inert gas.

SOLAR. Research rocket. Air Force cognizance. Used for experiments at extremely high altitudes for eventual use of solar energy.

solar angle. The elevation angle of the Sun above the horizon expressed in degrees.

solar apex. The Sun, and the entire solar system with it, is moving relative to the neighboring stars with a speed of about 12 miles per second towards a point in the constellation Hercules. This point is the *solar apex,* and the point diametrically opposite to it from which the Sun is receding is the solar antapex. This motion is quite distinct from that which the Sun, together with the neighboring stars, performs about the center of our galaxy (at a speed of about 200 miles per second).

solar constant. The amount of energy arriving per unit area exposed to unobstructed solar rays at the mean radius of the Earth's orbit around the Sun. It is important when calculating the energy input to a space vehicle for cooling purposes or from the standpoint of using a solar

engine (q.v.). Its approximate value is 7.4 Btu/ sq ft/ min. The energy actually absorbed by the Earth's surface is about 5.3 Btu/sq ft/min at noon on a summer day. *See* albedo.

solar corona. The outer atmosphere shell of the Sun, divided into the F corona and the K corona.

solar corpuscles. Particles, usually protons, sprayed out into the solar system by disturbances on the Sun. If the Earth intercepts one of these sprays, the particles cross the Earth's magnetic field and produce ionospheric disturbances.

solar day. A day as measured by the interval of time between two successive transits of the center of the Sun over the same meridian.

solar engine. Any engine which transforms the energy of the Sun's radiation into work. Such an engine could be of use as a source of power in an artificial satellite or space vehicle.

solar flare. A catastrophic solar phenomenon which gives rise to intense ultraviolet and corpusclar emission from the associated region of the Sun. It affects the structure of the ionosphere (q.v.), interferes with communications, the control of space vehicles, etc.

solar flux. The energy from the Sun absorbed by a surface in terms of Btu/sq ft/hr. Typical values are:

Location	Solar Flux (Btu/sq ft/hr)	Distance from the Sun (astronautical units)	Inert Body Equilibrium Temp., °F
Earth	455	1.—	43
Venus	850	0.723	131
Mars	190	1.52	−53
Interstellar space	——	——	−454

solar heat. Heat received from the Sun which is the primary source of energy for the Earth. On a normal day solar radiation is about 105 Btu/sq ft/hr; maximum anticipated is 360 Btu/sq ft/hr.

solar motion. *See* physical units and constants.

solar noise. Electromagnetic radiation which radiates from the atmosphere of the Sun at radio frequencies.

solar radiation. The radiation from the Sun, comprising a very wide range of wavelengths from the long infrared to the short ultraviolet rays, with a maximum intensity in the visible green at about 5000 Ångstroms (q.v.). Since the air strongly absorbs the wavelengths toward either end of the spectrum, the solar radiation received on the surface of the Earth is confined largely to the visible and near infrared regions, with a very small proportion of the ultraviolet. The absorption of the ultraviolet radiation takes place largely in the higher stratosphere (q.v.), where it probably contributes to the atmospheric ionization (*see* ionosphere). The longer infrared is absorbed mainly by dust and water vapor at lower levels, which accounts for the low temperature of the air at high altitudes. (The estimated maximum at sea level is 360 Btu/sq ft/hr; the average is 105 Btu/sq ft/hr).

solar space. That part of space (q.v.) in which the solar planets are an important influence.

solar system. The solar system in which we live consists of one star (the Sun), nine planets possessing a total of 31 discovered satellites, and a great many smaller bodies: asteroids, comets, meteors, and those causing the zodiacal light.

solar system characteristics. Conspicuous regularities in the solar system: (a) The major *planets* all have nearly circular orbits lying in approximately the same plane, and all revolve around the Sun in the same direction, which is also the direction in which the Sun rotates on its own axis; (b) All the large *satellites*, with the exception of the Moon and Triton, revolve in nearly circular orbits in the equatorial planes of their respective primaries; (c) The distances of all except the two outermost major planets from the Sun are represented by Bode's law (q.v.); (d) The major planets fall into two groups. Mercury, Venus, the Earth, and Mars are relatively small and dense, and have few satellites and long rotation periods. Jupiter, Saturn, Uranus, and Neptune are relatively large and have low densities, many satellites, and short rotation periods.

solenoid. A coil of closely wound turns of wire, which, when electrified, acts as an electromagnet.

solid fuel. (1) Any fuel in a solid state. (2) A fuel in a solid or gelatinous state such as that used in certain rockets.

solid fuel (propellant) ramjet. A ducted solid propellant engine. In this type of missile propulsion system a solid reductant (fuel) contained in a duct is used, with air serving as the oxidant. This type of rocket is not a pure rocket system; i.e., it is an air-breathing engine.

solid-liquid rocket. Two types exist: (a) the motor employs a solid reductant (fuel), where the oxidizing agent is sprayed in as a liquid; (b) the other type has a solid oxidizing agent with the fuel being sprayed in.

solid propellant. A mixture of solid fuel and oxidizer cured into a shape which fits the combustion chamber (q.v.) of a rocket engine. When ignited, the mixture (termed the *grain*,

q.v.) burns at a nearly constant rate on all exposed surfaces. See Fig. 22.

solid propellant rocket engines. Rocket engines whose propellants are chemicals in the solid state prior to the initiation of combustion.

solid rocket. A rocket using solid fuel (q.v.).

solid rocket propellant characteristics. A solid rocket propellant desirably should have these properties: (a) high release of chemical energy (and therefore high combustion temperature and high specific impulse); (b) high density; (c) high physical strength; (d) low molecular weight of combustion products; (e) good storage characteristics (should not deteriorate); (f) auto-ignition should be difficult; (g) small coefficient of thermal expansion; (h) insensitive to processing variations; (i) low temperature sensitivity; (j) non-toxic exhaust; (k) chemically inert in storage.

solid-state physics. Generally speaking, that branch of physics which deals with the structure and properties of solids. It may be divided into: (a) *the anatomy of solids*—crystallography, theory of the structure of metals, alloys, ionic crystals, etc., cohesive forces, band structures, etc.; (b) *the physiology of solids*—specific heats, thermal vibrations, thermal and electrical conductivity, intrinsic semiconductivity, superconductivity, photoconductivity, magnetic and dielectric properties, etc.; (c) *the pathology of solids*—impurity semiconductivity, plasticity, lattice defects, color centers, dislocation theory, crystal growth, etc.

solution-ceramic. A non-brittle, inorganic ceramic coating containing no bonding agent and capable of application at low temperatures. (Typical solution-ceramics: zirconia, chromia, titania, ceria, etc.)

Sommerfeld formula. An approximate wave propagation relationship for distances short enough that the Earth's curvature may be neglected.

$$\varepsilon = \frac{K\sqrt{PA}}{d}$$

where ε = field strength; K = an antenna constant; P = radiated power; d = distance from the antenna; A = relationship involving frequency, distance and soil conductivity.

SONAR. *S*ound *N*avigation *A*nd *R*anging (q.v.).

SONCM. *So*nar *C*ounter*M*easures and deception.

sonde. (1) In telemetering, the complete airborne telemetering system (q.v.) in the vehicle. (2) Rocket or balloon carrying instruments to

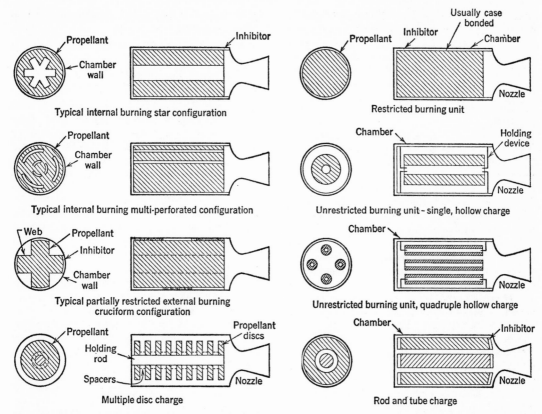

Fig. 22. Typical solid propellant rocket grain configurations. (G. P. Sutton, *Rocket Propulsion Elements*, John Wiley & Sons)

probe conditions in the upper atmosphere (q.v.). *See* planetary probes.

sonic. (1) Of or pertaining to sound; in missile contexts, to the speed of sound. (2) Velocity that is equal to the speed of sound. *See* hypersonic; subsonic; supersonic; transonic; ultrasonic.

sonic barrier. Common name for the transonic barrier (q.v.).

sonic boom. A loud report generated by a vehicle flying at sonic speed, and heard especially on the ground. This phenomenon appears to be caused by the buildup of vehicle and engine noise as the remote speed of the vehicle corresponds with that of sound, the sound waves continuously reinforcing one another and creating around the aircraft a pressure field, which when suddenly dissipated causes an explosive sound. The pilot of the vehicle does not hear the explosive sound because his speed outruns the speed of sound.

sonic nozzle. A nozzle converting a high pressure to a supersonic flow in which the velocity

of gas at the throat is equal to the velocity of sound.

sonic speed. The speed of sound. In ambient air, with ratio of specific heats assumed to be 1.4 and the air following the gas law, with temperature in degrees Rankine, the speed of sound is $33.42\sqrt{T}$ miles per hour, or $29.02\sqrt{T}$ knots; with temperature in degrees Kelvin, the speed of sound is $44.84\sqrt{T}$ miles per hour, or $38.94\sqrt{T}$ knots. *See* acoustic speed.

SOP. Standard Operating Procedure (q.v.).

sound barrier. Transonic barrier (q.v.).

sound fixing and ranging (SOFAR). In missile applications, the use of an explosive element to fix ocean impact location, which is determined from a sound measuring network.

sounding, air. *See* air sounding.

sounding rocket. A meteorological rocket used to gather atmospheric data at various altitudes.

sound navigation and ranging (SONAR). Equipment employed for underwater detection, ranging, and depth measurement. In a process analogous to that used in radar, sonic or supersonic pulses are transmitted, reflected from an object, and received at the point of transmission. The required time interval is used as a measure of the distance between the reflecting object and the transmitter. *Transducers* (q.v.), which are analogous to radar antennas, are used to propagate and receive the sound energy.

sound pressure (acoustomotive pressure). (1) The *instantaneous sound pressure* at a point is the total instantaneous pressure at the point minus the static pressure. The unit is the *dyne per square centimeter.* (2) The *effective sound pressure* at a point is the root mean square value of the instantaneous sound pressure over a complete cycle at the point. The unit is the *dyne per square centimeter.* (3) The *maximum sound pressure* for any given cycle is the maximum absolute value of the instantaneous sound pressure during that cycle. The unit is the *dyne per square centimeter.*

sound pressure level. In decibels, 20 times the logarithm to the base 10 of the ratio of the pressure of a sound to the reference pressure. The reference pressure should be explicitly stated. The following reference pressures are in common use: (a) 2×10^{-4} microbar; (b) 1 microbar. Reference pressure (a) has been in general use for measurements dealing with hearing and sound-level measurements in air and liquids, while (b) has gained widespread use for calibrations, and many types of sound-level measurements in liquids. It is to be noted that in many sound fields the sound pressure ratios are not proportional to the square root of corresponding power ratios and hence cannot be expressed in decibels in the strict sense; however, it is common practice to extend the use of the decibel to these cases. See Fig. 23.

sound pressure spectrum level. At a specified frequency, the effective sound pressure (q.v.) level for the sound energy contained within a band 1 cycle per second wide, centered at the specified frequency. Ordinarily this has significance only for sound having a continuous distribution of energy within the frequency range under consideration. The reference pressure should be explicitly stated. Since in practice it is necessary to employ filters having an effective bandwidth greater than 1 cps, the pressure spectrum level is, in general, a computed quantity. For a sound having a uniform distribution of energy, the computation can be made as follows:

$$L_{p_s} = 10 \log_{10} \left(\frac{p^2/\Delta f}{p_o^2/\Delta_o f} \right)$$

where L_{p_s} = desired pressure spectrum level; p = effective pressure measured through the filter system; p_o = reference sound pressure; Δf = effective bandwidth of the filter system; $\Delta_o f$ = reference bandwidth (1 cps). For computational purposes, if L_p is the band pressure level observed through the filter, the above relation reduces to:

$$L_{p_s} = L_p - 10 \log_{10} \frac{\Delta f}{\Delta_o f}$$

sound, speed of. See speed of sound.

soup. (1) (Vernacular) Fog or dense cloud through which a vehicle flies. (2) Nitroglycerin. (3) *To soup up:* to adjust or modify an engine or vehicle so as to increase its horsepower.

source impedance. The apparent impedance of the signal source. It may or may not be equal to the recommended load impedance. The lower the source impedance the better is the voltage regulation. (Inverse feedback in an audio power amplifier reduces source impedance, resulting in better speaker damping.)

source, neutron. See neutron source.

south magnetic pole. The magnetic pole (q.v.) located approximately at 73°S, 156°E, about 1020 nautical miles north of the South Pole.

space. As generally applicable to the Universe, the near-vacuum void beyond the Earth's atmospheric envelope in which the solar system, stars, and galaxies exist. *Outer space* pertains to the interplanetary region in which the Earth has no importance as the primary (q.v.). Sometimes considered to be the space between galaxies. *Deep space* usually is considered to exist from about 100 miles altitude to the distance beyond the Moon where the Earth still has importance as the primary.

space. *Types of, see* cislunar–; cisplanetary–; dead–; deep–; drift–; extra-planetary–; galactic–; inertial–; intergalactic–; interplanetary–; interstellar–; intraplanetary–; lunar–; outer–; planetary–; solar–; terrestrial–; translunar–; transplanetary–.

space attenuation. In electronics, space attenuation expressed in decibels is a relative measure which gives the relation between the signal level at the transmitting antenna and that at a given remote point. It is defined as a decibel comparison of the watts per square meter one meter away from an isotropic antenna (q.v.), to that at the remote range (distance = D) where the level is to be described. Thus attenuation (db) = $10 \log_{10}$ level one meter from antenna divided by the level at distance D.

If space attenuation is due only to spreading (free space propagation), it can be calculated

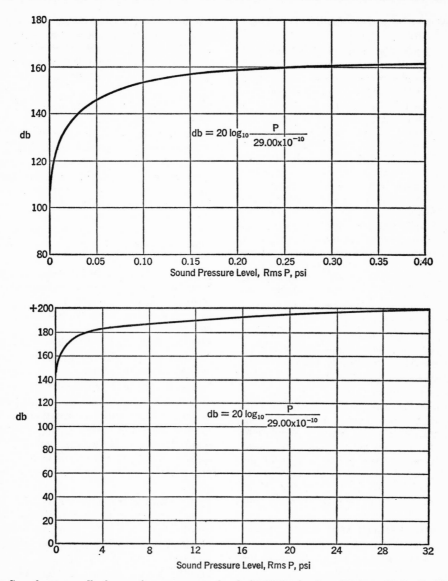

Fig. 23. Sound pressure db above reference pressure level of 0.0002 microbars (29.00 × 10⁻¹⁰ psi). (C. W. Besserer, *Missile Engineering Handbook*, D. Van Nostrand)

for any distance from the antenna by the following:

free space attenuation (db) =
$$10 \log_{10} (D^2 \times 16{,}090)$$

where D is the distance from the antenna measured in miles.

space charge. In electronics, a negative charge in a vacuum tube, resulting from electrons emitted from the cathode but not immediately drawn in to the anode, remaining in the space between the cathode and anode.

space classification. (proposed)

Patrol space equivalence —10 miles
Limit of space equivalence—120–140 miles
Terrestrial space —4000 miles
Outer space —greater than 4000 miles

space flight. The science of extraterrestrial flight of *unmanned vehicles*. Contrast with *space travel* (q.v.). *See also* astronautics; cosmonautics.

space gun. Early proposal to fire a vehicle at escape velocity (q.v.) from a monster gun; not technically feasible from the surface of the

Earth, but may be used one day from the Moon for orbital refueling.

space medicine. The new field of medical science which studies the human factors involved in space flight and which provides for the first time a link between medicine and those branches of science which deal with matters of an extraterrestrial nature. As the method of propulsion on which space flight is based is the rocket, space medicine is essentially the physiology of rocket flight. Medical problems in space flight stem, in the first place, from the environment of space *per se* and from the process of movement through this environment. Of special interest are the altitudes at which the characteristics of space flight begin and what protective measures must be taken; one of the most important is the climatization of the cabin. Other problems encountered are the state of weightlessness, high accelerations during launching and during reentry into the atmosphere, visual problems, the lack of day and night and the radiation belts.

space mirror. A large mirror in a satellite orbit, capable of focusing sunlight upon the Earth. A mirror very many miles in diameter would be needed to provide a source of appreciable power.

space platform. A large satellite, with both scientific and military applications, conceived as a habitable and safe base in space. The proposed space platforms would contain housing facilities, power supplies, gravity simulation, provisions for transferring personnel and cargo to and from other space vehicles, scientific instruments, weapon systems (?), controlled atmosphere, and communication systems. It is usually conceived as a giant wheel, assembled in space.

space probes. *See:* CENTAUR; DELTA; NOVA; PIONEER; SATURN; SCOUT; VEGA.

spaceship. A *manned* rocket to be used for interplanetary (q.v.) voyages.

space station. A *manned* artificial satellite (q.v.) built in orbit from materials and equipment ferried up by rockets.

spacesuit. Hermetically sealed enclosure for an individual, supplying him with a respirable atmosphere, suitable temperature, and permitting him mobility.

space travel. The science of extraterrestrial flight of *manned* vehicles. Contrast with *space flight* (q.v.). *See also* astronautics; cosmonautics.

space vehicle. An artificial body operating essentially or exclusively outside the Earth's atmosphere; technical requirements and mission are determined by space conditions. (a) *Instrumental space vehicle:* a pilotless space vehicle; (b) *Manned space vehicle:* occupied for a comparatively short time (also: piloted); (c) *Inhabited space vehicle:* occupied for days or longer.

space vehicle. *Types of, see* inhabited–; instrumental–; manned–.

space warfare. Warfare conducted by use of weapons brought to bear upon Earth targets from outer space.

space wave. In electronics, that component of a ground wave that travels more or less directly through space from the transmitting antenna to the receiving antenna. One part of the space wave goes directly from one antenna to the other; another part is reflected off the Earth between the antennas.

spacistor. A semiconductor amplifier for high-frequency operation. It is basically similar to transistor (q.v.), but has a different arrangement of injector, collector, and modulator connections.

SPAEROBEE. Research rocket. A SPAEROBEE is a second stage added to an AEROBEE (q.v.) to obtain additional altitude.

spallation. *See* nuclear fission.

SPARROW I. Air-to-air guided missile. Navy Bureau of Aeronautics designation: AAM-N-2. Length: 12 ft 6 in.; body diameter: 8 in.; wing span: 27 in.; firing weight: 295 lb; burnout speed: MACH 2.8; range: up to 5 miles. Solid propellant rocket engine. Radar beam rider guidance.

Prime Contractor: Sperry-Farragut Co. Airframe: Douglas Aircraft Co. Engine: Aerojet-General Corp. Guidance system: Sperry.

SPARROW II. Air-to-air guided missile. Military designation: AAM-N-3. Length: 4.2 ft; weight: 300 lb. Active radar homing.

Prime Contractor: Douglas Aircraft Co. Airframe: Douglas. Engine: Aerojet-General Corp. Guidance system: Bendix-Pacific Division, Bendix Aviation Corp.

SPARROW III. Air-to-air guided missile. Navy Bureau of Aeronautics designation: AAM-N-4. Length: 12 ft; wing span: 38.5 in.; firing weight: 350 lb; burnout speed: MACH 2.8. Solid propellant rocket engine; active radar all-weather type guidance.

Prime Contractor: Raytheon Manufacturing Co. Airframe: Douglas Aircraft Co. Engine: Aerojet-General Corp. Guidance system: Raytheon.

spatiography. Space geography. The science of mapping the relation between celestial bodies. Proposed by Dr. Hubertus Strughold.

SpecDevCen. Special Devices Center; Bureau of Aeronautics; Great Neck, Long Island, N.Y.

Special List of Equipment (SLOE). A military publication that establishes temporary equipment allowances. It also may be used to authorize nonstandard equipment on a continuing basis.

specification. A detailed statement, especially in a contract, that sets forth the requirements or standards for a piece of equipment, a material, a service to be performed, etc. *See* specification tree.

specification. *Types of, see* detail–; equipment (hardware)–; JAN–; military standard–; model–; performance–; weapon system–.

specification tree (or chart). A scheme for categorizing or tiering the specifications required for a weapon system to show their interrelation.

specific damping capacity. The ratio (in per cent) of the vibrational energy absorbed per cycle of vibration to the total energy of vibration at the maximum amplitude of the cycle.

$$\rho = 100(1 - e^{-2\delta})$$

where ρ = specific damping capacity; δ = logarithmic decrement; e = natural logarithm base. Typical values at 4000 psi bending stress: aluminum, 1%; magnesium, 3%.

specific fuel consumption. (1) In thermal engines, the mass of fuel used relative to an appropriate unit of output; jet engines usually are rated in pounds (fuel) per pounds (thrust) per hour, while reciprocating engines are rated in pounds (fuel) per horsepower-hour.

$$\text{SFC} = \frac{\text{fuel flow in lb/hr}}{\text{lb thrust}}$$

(2) The reciprocal of *specific impulse;* pounds per pound second. Sometimes termed the *performance index.*

specific gravity. The ratio between the density of a substance at a given temperature and the density of some substance assumed as standard. For liquids and solids the standard assumed is either the density of distilled water at 4°C or at 60°F. (This value is often used in calibrating industrial *hydrometers.*) For gases the standards are air, hydrogen, or oxygen at 0°C, and a pressure of 760 mm of mercury, or distilled water at 4°C. The specific gravity is a relative property that varies with the temperature.

specific heat. The number of calories required to raise the temperature of one gram of a substance through 1°C. Specific heats vary considerably according to the substance used (e.g., the specific heat of water = 1, that of lead = 0.03). The same amount of heat which will raise the temperature of water by 1°C will raise an equal weight of lead through approximately 33°C. Thus bodies of low specific heat may be at very high temperatures and yet contain relatively little heat.

specific impulse (I_{sp}). In rocketry, a parameter indicative of efficiency; a property of the propellant combination and the mixture ratio. Specific impulse in seconds is equal to pounds of thrust developed per pound of propellants consumed (fuel plus oxidizer) per second, or the ratio of thrust to propellant mass flow.

$$I_{sp} = \frac{F}{\dot{w}} = \frac{V_j}{g}$$

where F = thrust, lb; $\dot{w}$ = mass flow, lb/sec; V_j = velocity of exhaust, fps; g = acceleration of gravity, fps². *See* ideal specific impulse; total impulse.

specific impulse. *Types of, see* air–; delivered–; density–; fuel–; ideal or theoretical–; over-all–.

specific speed. A design parameter used in high-speed rotating pump calculations.

$$N_s = N \frac{Q^{1/2}}{h^{3/4}} \quad \text{rpm}$$

where N = speed, rpm; Q = pump output, rpm; h = rise in pump head, inlet to discharge, ft.

specific thrust (air specific impulse). The ratio between the thrust of a jet reaction motor and the total propellant flow rate producing the thrust.

$$I_{sp} = \frac{1}{g}(V_j - V)$$

where V_j = exhaust velocity; V = vehicle velocity; g = acceleration of gravity.

spectra. *See* absorption spectra.

spectral density. The relative distribution of radiant energy throughout the spectrum.

spectral density, power. *See* power spectral density.

spectroscopy. The science relating the nature of luminous sources to the characteristics of light they give out.

spectrum. *Types of, see* electromagnetic–; frequency–; microwave–; radio–; shock–.

spectrum level. *See* sound pressure spectrum level.

speed. *Types of, see* acoustic–; allowable flutter–; critical–; flutter–; ground–; sonic–;

specific–; subsonic–; suction–; suction specific–; transonic–.

speed of sound. The speed at which sound waves travel through a medium. Sound travels at different speeds through different mediums, and it travels at different speeds under different conditions of temperature, etc. In air under standard sea-level conditions, sound travels at approximately 1100 fps, or 33,220 cm per sec, or 750 mph. *See* MACH. Contrast with *acoustic velocity* (q.v.).

sphere. *See* celestial sphere.

SPHEREDOP. A DOVAP type measuring system employing a stable, airborne oscillator. In contrast to DOVAP, it eliminates the reference transmitter to the missile. *See* DOVAP.

spherical coordinates (Earth). The magnitude of the radius, and its angular displacement in azimuth and elevation from a line running east at the origin.

spherical-trigonometric computer. A computer (q.v.) capable of converting distance traveled into corresponding changes in latitude and longitude for the particular latitude of a missile.

spike diffuser. *See* Oswatitsch diffuser.

spillover. (1) That portion of the air in the stream tube which flows to the outside of a ramjet intake rather than through the intake. This takes place under conditions of detached shock (q.v.). Under conditions of *attached* or *swallowed* shock (q.q.v.), there is no spillover. See Fig. 5, page 73. (2) Interference received on a LORAN receiver from a station transmitting at a frequency near that to which the receiver is tuned.

spillover, diffuser. *See* diffuser spillover.

spinner rocket. A spin-stabilized rocket. *See* spin-stabilized projectile.

spinning axis. An axis about which an object rotates; used generally in reference to a gyroscope. See Fig. 21, page 254.

spinning gyroscope. The conventional gyroscope. Distinguish from a *vibrating gyroscope* (q.v.).

spin stabilization. A technique for stabilizing a missile during boost, midcourse, or terminal phases in which a slow spin is used to eliminate dispersion due to misalignments. Appropriate discrimination of guidance intelligence is required to insure proper control in each plane.

spin-stabilized projectile. A missile or rocket steadied in flight by a rotating motion about its longitudinal axis. On a rocket, a ring of nozzles may be used with each nozzle slanted sidewise,

so that the escape of the exhaust gases through them will impart spin to the rocket.

spiral antenna. A broadband, flush mounted antenna (impedance and radiation pattern essentially constant over 10:1 frequency range) which has the form of Archimedes' spiral.

spiral scan. A type of scan in which a point on the radar beam describes a spiral in space.

splash. (1) (Vernacular) The intentional destruction or impact of a missile that is deviating from the preselected safe range limits or is malfunctioning because of a fire or premature loss of propulsion. (2) Impact point of a booster or missile.

splasher beacon. A kind of nondirectional homing beacon.

splicing. (1) The process of physically uniting missile stages and any two or more of the major subsystems. *See* marriage. (2) The joining of any two subsystems.

split beam. In electronics, a radio beam or a light beam that is split.

spoiler. An aerodynamic device used to destroy negative lift. It is a projecting member on an aerodynamically designed body, used to break down the airflow around the body so as to slow down its movement or decrease its lift.

spoiler, thrust. *See* thrust spoiler.

spoking. In electronics, a malfunction in a radar set in which luminous spots continue on the screen for an abnormal length of time, interfering with the presentation.

spontaneous fission. *See* nuclear fission.

spoof. Equipment or procedures that cause the enemy to be misled. Examples are the continued use of a frequency after it has been effectively jammed, at the same time introducing new frequencies; and the establishment of decoy radio transmitters to lead the enemy into a considerable jamming effort in the belief that the transmitters are part of, say, a navigation system.

spot jamming. Jamming (q.v.) of a specific channel or frequency.

spot-size error. In electronics, an error in the presentation of a radarscope or in the interpretation of such a presentation, caused by the abnormally large size of the spot or blip, in which two or more objects appear as one, or in which range or azimuth presentation is distorted.

spray dome. The mound or column of broken water and spray thrown up over the point of burst of an underwater nuclear explosion by reflection of the blast wave at the surface.

spray injector. A liquid rocket engine injector in which the oxidizer and fuel are mixed by intersection of spray patterns.

spring loaded. Held or driven under spring pressure.

spurious signal. Any unwanted signal either generated in the equipment itself or having external origin (noise).

sputtering. The erosion of metal by impact of a high-velocity atom or molecule. The eroded material is in the form of single atoms.

squall. A sudden, strong wind which may or may not be accompanied by a wind shift. Rain and snow squalls are showers accompanied by strong winds.

squall line. A long line in which thunderstorms, rain showers or squalls, and snow showers or squalls often appear, sometimes reaching hundreds of miles but only one squall in depth. Such lines of squalls normally move perpendicular to their leading edge.

squall-line thunderstorm. A frontal thunderstorm (q.v.) occurring usually in advance of a cold front. Also termed a *prefrontal thunderstorm*.

square-law detector. A vacuum-tube circuit in which the output signal current strength is proportional to the square of the radio-frequency input voltage. The demodulation depends on curvature or nonlinearity of the characteristic, rather than on rectification, to produce the distortion or asymmetrical form of the modulated wave necessary for detection. The largest distortion term is the second power, or square term.

square wave. A wave which alternately assumes two fixed values for equal lengths of time, the time of transition being negligible in comparison with the duration of each fixed value. A square wave requires a considerable number of sine-function frequencies to express it in a Fourier series. These components are not mere mathematical fictions but are true electrical components in the case of an electrical wave. They may be separated and examined by means of proper filter circuits. Since a square wave will contain a long series of frequencies, it may be used for determining rapidly the frequency response of a piece of equipment by applying the wave to the input and noting the distortion of the output wave. The distortion is due to certain frequencies of the original wave being attenuated or amplified out of proportion in passing through the circuit. Thus the necessity of making a laborious series of tests at various frequencies using sine waves is avoided. When an operator is properly trained in interpreting the results of such testing, it offers a rapid means of checking amplifiers, networks, etc. These square waves may be generated by a variety of electronic circuits.

squib. An electrical-pyrotechnic device used to ignite an explosive material; a primer or igniter (q.q.v.).

squib switch. A type of switch with an explosive element for the actuating device.

squint angle. A geometrical characteristic of an antenna defined as the angle between the main lobe of the antenna pattern and the spin axis of the gyroscope used to stabilize the antenna.

squirt job. (Vernacular) A jet vehicle.

squitter. In electronics, accidental beacon replies generated without any remote interrogation.

SRA. Simultaneous Range Adcock antenna.

SRC. Sound Ranging Control.

SRI. Stanford Research Institute; Palo Alto, Calif.

SS. Standard frequency Station.

SSB. Single SideBand. Suppressed carrier.

SSIP. Sub-System Integration Plan.

SS LORAN. Skywave Synchronized LORAN.

SSM. Surface-to-Surface Missile (q.v.); a model designation (q.v.).

SSM-A-12. Army designation for surface-to-surface guided missile termed LACROSSE (q.v.).

SSM-A-14. Army designation for surface-to-surface ballistic missile termed REDSTONE (q.v.) and JUPITER A (q.v.).

SSM-A-17. Army designation for surface-to-surface ballistic guided missile termed CORPORAL (q.v.).

SSM-A-23. Army designation for surface-to-surface anti-tank and anti-emplacement missile termed DART (q.v.).

SSM-N-8A. Navy Bureau of Ordnance designation for surface-to-surface missile termed REGULUS I (q.v.).

SSM-N-9. Navy Bureau of Aeronautics designation for surface-to-surface guided missile termed REGULUS II (q.v.).

stabilator. A one-piece stabilizer mounted on the top of the vertical stabilizer.

stability. That attribute of a system which enables it to develop restoring forces between the elements thereof, equal to or greater than the disturbing forces so as to reestablish a state of equilibrium between the elements. Specifically,

(1) In aerodynamics, a characteristic of a vehicle in flight that causes it, if disturbed from its condition of equilibrium or steady flight, to return to that condition. (2) The tendency of a projectile to remain balanced in flight. (3) In meteorology, the condition that exists in a given space of the atmosphere when the air is quiet and resists vertical displacement, due to the lapse rate being less than the adiabatic rate. (4) In explosives, the property of an explosive against detonating under normal storage conditions.

stability. *Types of, see* automatic–; dead-beat–; directional–; discriminator output–; discriminator standby–; dynamic–; effective static–; inherent–; jet vane–; lateral–; longitudinal–; neutral–; static–; weathercock–.

stability (and control) coefficients. A set of coefficients which assume *linear aerodynamic coefficients* in the missile equations of motion in a plane of maneuver at a constant speed, and which are useful in defining certain characteristics of a missile (e.g., weathercock frequency, damping, stability and control, etc.).

stability derivatives. (1) Aerodynamic quantities expressing the variation of the forces and moments on missiles owing to disturbance of steady motion. They form the experimental basis of the theory of stability (q.v.), and from them the periods and damping factors of aircraft can be calculated. In the general case there are 18 translatory and 18 rotary derivatives. (2) Equations of motion for a missile associated with stability and control and based on linear aerodynamic coefficients. The *lateral stability derivatives* relate to: (a) directional stability-yawing motion due to yaw; (b) rolling moment due

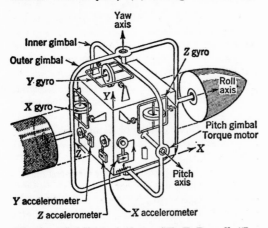

Fig. 24. Stabilized platform. (W. T. Russell, "Inertial Guidance for Rocket Propelled Missiles," *Jet Propulsion*, Jan. 1958)

to yaw; (c) damping in yaw; (d) damping in roll; (e) rolling moment due to yawing velocity; (f) yawing moment due to rolling velocity. Similar derivatives exist for the pitch plane.

stabilization. *See* tilt stabilization.

stabilized, gain. *See* gain stabilized.

stabilized platform. Major part of an all-inertial guidance system (q.v.), composed of an assembly of gimbal frames that hold three accelerometers (or similar measuring devices) in a fixed position in relation to inertial space. The accelerometers are mounted perpendicular to each other to measure accelerations along the three reference axes. These accelerations can be fed to a computer that will determine instantaneous velocity and position in space. *See* gyroscope-stabilized platform. See Fig. 24.

stabilizer. *See* horizontal stabilizer.

stable element (stable table; 3-axis table; stable platform). A gyroscope-stabilized platform or a stable free gyroscope used as a reference system for guidance and control purposes. The platform characteristics usually include: (a) minimum deadzone; (b) high gimbal frequency response; (c) good linearity; (d) high signal resolution; and (e) large angular range. *See* gyroscope-stabilized platform. See Fig. 24.

stable oscillation. An oscillation of constant amplitude and frequency.

stable servo. A servo system (q.v.) in which the output is always finite, or limited, for any finite input. Most servos are stable *only* if the open-loop transfer function gain is less than unity at any frequency at which the open-loop transfer function phase angle is 180 degrees.

stage. (1) In electronics, all the components in a circuit containing one or more vacuum tubes having one single input and one output, the input receiving power from a preceding stage or device, and the output feeding power to a succeeding stage or device. (2) In a missile consisting of several sections which are progressively jettisoned or staged during the flight, the independent sections, when containing a power plant, are termed *stages. Note:* an unpowered payload (e.g., reentry body) is not classified as a *stage.* (3) A step in the movement of fluid through a compressor that uses more than one impeller. *See* axial flow compressor.

stage. *Types of, see* buffer–; design–; main–; missile–.

staging. Transition from the booster phase to the sustainer phase. The act of jettisoning, at a predetermined flight time or trajectory point, certain missile components (engines, tanks, boosters, staging equipment, and associated equipment) that are no longer needed.

staging rocket. Auxiliary solid propellant units attached to a stage (q.v.) of a missile to provide adequate velocity or acceleration to one missile stage relative to a spent stage.

stagnation region. In high-speed missiles, a region at the front of the nose cone where there is negligible velocity of the airflow along the axis; the air is at *stagnation temperature.*

stagnation temperature. The temperature of air which has been brought to rest from a given velocity or MACH number.

$$T_s = T(1 + 0.2M^2)$$

where T = ambient temperature, °R; M = MACH number.

stall. The condition of an airfoil in which it is operating at an angle of attack greater than that which will support the flight of the vehicle.

stall fence. A barrier on the surface of a swept-wing that retards spanwise movement of the airflow.

stall, high-speed. *See* high-speed stall.

stalling angle of attack. *See* critical angle of attack.

stalo. In electronics, a *sta*bilized *lo*cal oscillator which is used as part of a moving target indication (MTI) device (q.v.), in conjunction with a radar.

stand. *Types of, see* dry–; soft–; test–; thrust–.

standard atmosphere. A model or standardized set of characteristics of a hypothetical Earth's atmosphere as a function of altitude. A number of *standard atmospheres* have been proposed and used (e.g., NACA, Rand Corporation, ICAO, etc.) but the *Abbreviated Tables of the ARDC Model Atmosphere* is the preferred model for current use. See Fig. 25.

standard day. A day whose temperature and pressure vs. altitude characteristics are standardized. A number of standard days are in use: NACA, Navy BuAer, ICAO, etc.

Polar Tropical }	Standard days used for design for history-dependent flight conditions.
Cold Hot }	Standard days used for design for non-time-dependent conditions. These characteristics represent statistical envelopes and cannot exist meteorologically.

See Fig. 25.

standard deviation (σ). A measure of dispersion. To obtain σ, the squares of the deviations (X) of the individual values from the average are added and divided by the number (N) of

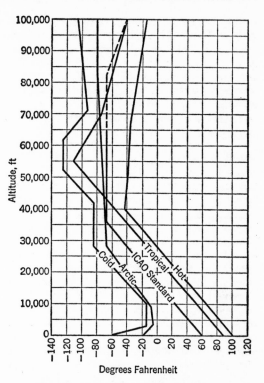

Fig. 25. Comparison of standard days.

data. Also termed *root mean square error; standard dispersion.*

$$\sigma = \sqrt{\frac{X^2}{N}}$$

$$1\sigma = 68.26\%$$
$$2\sigma = 95.46\%$$
$$3\sigma = 99.74\%$$
$$4\sigma = 99.994\%$$
$$5\sigma = 99.999578\%$$

standard international atmosphere. The atmosphere used as an international standard which presumes for mean sea level and a temperature of 15°C, a pressure of 1013.2 millibars, lapse rate of 6.5°C per kilometer from sea level to 11 km, and thereafter a constant temperature of −56.5°C.

standard operating procedure (SOP). A set of instructions covering those features of operations that lend themselves to a definite or standardized procedure without loss of effectiveness. The procedure is applicable unless prescribed otherwise in a particular case. Thus, the flexibility necessary in special situations is retained.

standard pound body (standard kilogram body). Refers to two material standards of mass, preserved at London and Paris, respectively (the U.S. pound is derived from the kilogram); the "standard locality" means sea level, 45 degrees latitude; or, more strictly, any locality in which the acceleration due to gravity has the value 980.665 cm/sec^2, which may also be termed the *standard acceleration*.

standard pressure lapse rate. The lapse rate in pressure in a standard atmosphere (q.v.). At zero altitude, the pressure is 29.92 in.; at 20 ft, 29.90 in.; at 66 ft, 29.85 in.; at 112 ft, 29.80 in.; etc.

standard time. The mean solar time, based upon the transit of the Sun over a certain specified meridian, termed the *time meridian,* and adopted for use over a considerable area (time zone). *Standard mean time,* with few exceptions, is based upon a time meridian which is an approximate multiple of 15° longitude from the meridian of Greenwich, England. The standard mean times of the United States are: *Eastern standard time (EST), Central standard time (CST), Mountain standard time (MST),* and *Pacific standard time (PST).*

Eastern standard time (EST) is effective in all territory between the Atlantic Coast and an irregular line drawn from the U.S.-Canadian boundary east of Port Huron, Mich., through Toledo, Ohio, Asheville, N.C., Atlanta, Ga., to the Gulf of Mexico at Apalachicola Bay, Fla. The time of this section is that of the 75° meridian, which is 5 hours slower than Greenwich time.

Central standard time (CST) is effective in all territory between the Eastern standard time zone and an irregular line drawn from the U.S.-Canadian boundary just west of Portal, N.D., through Phillipsburg, Kans., along the western boundary of Oklahoma and Texas to the Rio Grande River, and to the Mexican border. The time is that of the 90° meridian which is 6 hours slower than Greenwich time, and 1 hour slower than Eastern standard time.

Mountain standard time (MST) is effective in all territory between the Central standard time zone and an irregular line drawn from the U.S.-Canadian boundary at the northwest corner of Montana through western Idaho, Salt Lake City, Utah, and Arizona to the U.S.-Mexican boundary on the Colorado River. The time is that of the 105° meridian which is 7 hours slower than Greenwich time, 2 hours slower than EST, and 1 hour slower than CST.

Pacific standard time (PST) is effective in all territory west of the territory included in the Mountain standard time zone to the Pacific

Coast excluding Alaska. The time is that of the 120° meridian which is 8 hours slower than Greenwich time and 3 hours slower than Eastern standard time, 2 hours slower than CST, and 1 hour slower than MST.

Time for the state of Alaska, which includes Alaska only, is that of the 150° meridian.

standard time (labor cost). Refers to legal workday or workweek without premium rates, according to the geographical area. In the United States, this is eight (8) hours per day and/or forty (40) hours per week.

standard units of measurement—motion of particles.

	cgs	mks	Engi-neering System	British
Mass				
(M)	gram	kilogram	slug	pound
Length				
(L)	centimeter	meter	foot	foot
Time				
(T)	second	second	second	second
Force				
(F)	dyne	newton	pound	poundal

standard U.S. atmosphere. An arbitrary atmosphere which is used for numerous aeronautical purposes, but chiefly for comparing performance. The standard atmosphere recommended by NACA, and adopted in 1925 by all interested U.S. Government departments for official use, is based on the following assumptions: The air is a dry gas. Ground temperature $t = 15°C$ (59°F). Temperature gradient in the troposphere (below 35,332 ft) $a = 0.0065°C/m$ (0.003566°F/ft). Stratosphere temperature (35,332 ft up) isothermal $t = -55°C$ (−67°F). It was replaced by the ICAO standard atmosphere (q.v.).

standby. A condition or state of preparedness in which vehicles remain ready at all times for immediate launching.

standby storage. Storage for, or of, vehicles for withdrawal and use after ninety days, but within three years.

standing operating procedure (SOP). *See* standard operating procedure.

standing wave. (1) A wave disturbance which is not progressive; i.e., one in which any component of the field can be specified as a function of position multiplied by a sinusoidal function of time. Standing waves result from the superposition of two waves traveling in opposite directions, having identical amplitudes and frequencies. (2) The wave-like distribution of potential along a conductor, when electric waves are reflected from the end of the conductor to form stationary nodes and loops, a condition of equilibrium, or zero motion, at certain lines, points, or surfaces, termed *nodes* (q.v.), with regions of vibration between, produced by interference between similar wave trains travelling in opposite directions.

standing wave ratio. In a radio-frequency transmission line, the quantity describing the variation of the rms voltage.

$$SWR = \frac{E_{max}}{E_{min}}$$

When measurements are made which are proportional to the square of the voltage, the *power standing wave ratio* is obtained.

star. A glowing sphere of gas. Unlike the planets, the stars shine by their own light. Stellar energy is produced not by chemical but by *nuclear* reactions.

star, binary. *See* binary star.

star brightness. A *first magnitude star* gives about 100 times as much light as a *sixth magnitude star*. The fifth root of 100 is 2.512, and this is used as the *standard magnitude ratio*. A first magnitude star is 2.512 times as bright as a second magnitude star, and so on. Since a difference of 0.1 is the smallest change in magnitude that can be detected by the human eye, tabulated magnitudes are usually given to one decimal place. These magnitudes are apparent magnitudes of brightness in the optical wavelength portion of the spectrum.

star grain. A solid rocket propellant configuration with an internal star-shaped characteristic cross section. See Fig. 22, page 259.

start. *Types of, see* ground–; hot–.

star tracking (automatic celestial navigation). A celestial navigation technique used for guiding long-range surface-to-surface missiles. The system consists of a device to measure attitude of the stars, an accurate clock, and a storage device to include information on charts and star tables.

statampere. A unit of electric measurement.

$$1 \text{ statampere} = 3.336 \times 10^{-11} \text{ abampere}$$
$$= 3.336 \times 10^{-10} \text{ ampere}$$

statcoulomb. In electronics, that amount of charge which, placed one centimeter away from an identical charge, will be repelled by a force of one dyne.

$$1 \text{ statcoulomb} = 3.336 \times 10^{-11} \text{ abcoulomb}$$
$$= 9.259 \times 10^{-14} \text{ ampere-hour}$$
$$= 3.336 \times 10^{-10} \text{ coulomb}$$
$$= 2.0824 \times 10^{9} \text{ electronic charges}$$
$$= 3.457 \times 10^{-15} \text{ faraday}$$

state of the art. The level to which technology and science have, at any designated cutoff time, been developed in a given industry, group of industries, or activity.

statfarad. A unit of electric measurement.

$$1 \text{ statfarad} = 1.113 \times 10^{-21} \text{ abfarad} = 1.113 \times 10^{-12} \text{ farad} = 1.113 \times 10^{-6} \text{ micro-farad}$$

stathenry. A unit of electric measurement.

$$1 \text{ stathenry} = 8.988 \times 10^{20} \text{ abhenrys}$$
$$= 8.988 \times 10^{11} \text{ henrys}$$
$$= 8.988 \times 10^{17} \text{ microhenrys}$$
$$= 8.988 \times 10^{14} \text{ millihenrys}$$

static air pressure. Static pressure exerted by air upon an object, especially by the air of the atmosphere as in a pitot-static tube (q.v.). Distinguish from *dynamic air pressure.*

static balanced surface. A control surface (q.v.) that is in balance about its hinge axis when not subjected to aerodynamic forces.

static behavior. The behavior of a control system, or an individual unit, under *fixed* conditions (as contrasted to *dynamic behavior* which refers to behavior under changing conditions).

static electricity. A negative or positive charge of electricity that an object accumulates, which charge creates a spark when the object comes near another object to which it may transmit its charge, or from which it may receive a charge.

static equilibrium. A state of balance attained by a body acted upon by forces the resultant of which is zero.

static firing. A test of a rocket motor conducted on a stand on the ground instead of in flight. The preferred term is *captive firing.*

static missile. A test vehicle (basically the airframe) that is static loaded to simulate flight and ground handling environment loading to establish an evaluation of structural integrity.

static power supply. A nonrotating AC electrical power supply. Principle of operation: a stable, transistorized oscillator maintains proper frequency. Power transistors are driven by this oscillator in a push-pull (q.v.) switching circuit to produce high-power square waves which are impressed on a filter to give a sinusoidal voltage at the output.

static, precipitation. *See* precipitation static.

static pressure. The pressure exerted upon an object by air or other fluid by virtue solely of its own molecular activity resulting from its density and temperature, no gain being due to outside work. (Static pressure in a pitot-static tube is that exerted by the atmosphere.)

statics. The branch of mechanics (q.v.) which deals with particles or bodies in equilibrium under the action of forces or of torques. It treats of the composition and resolution of forces, the equilibrium of bodies under balanced forces, and such properties of bodies as center of gravity and moment of inertia (q.q.v.).

static stability. In aerodynamics, that property of a missile which causes it, when its state of steady flight is disturbed, to develop forces and moments tending to restore its original condition. The amount of static stability is usually measured in terms of missile body diameters; i.e., so many body diameters (distance) between the center of pressure and the center of gravity. *See* effective static stability.

static test. (1) A structural test used to establish degree of conformance to the design and the structural integrity of the article. (2) A test of a missile propulsion system while the engine or missile is restrained. This is more properly termed a *captive test.*

static thrust. The thrust produced by a jet engine, rocket motor, or the like, or by a propeller engine combination, when held stationary. Statically, 2.6 lb of thrust are equal to one hp.

static tube. In hydraulics and aeronautics, a cylindrical tube inserted in a fluid (e.g., air), with openings in the walls of the tube so that the direction of flow is across the openings, rather than into the tube; used in measuring the static pressure of the fluid. *See* pitot-static tube.

station. *Types of, see* augmented launch–; double pulsing–; alignment–; down range–; guidance–; launch–; master–; mobile–; slave–; space–.

stationary front. In meteorology, a front (q.v.) along which one air mass does not replace the other, thus tending toward unchangeable weather.

stationary orbit. A circular orbit (q.v.) around a planet in the equatorial plane and having a rotation period equal to that of the planet. A body moving in a stable stationary orbit appears fixed in the sky relative to an observer on the surface of the planet in the hemisphere facing the body. For Earth, the stationary orbit is about 26,000 miles in radius. Also, in reference to Earth, this is known as a *twenty-four-hour orbit* or *satellite.*

statistical quality control. A procedure based in part on the central limit theorem and the

theory of probability. In this sense the adjective "statistical" refers to a method of making decisions derived from mathematical laws.

statistical telemetry. An application of information theory based on generalized harmonic analysis. Wide-band data is statistically sampled, compressed, and transmitted on standard low-frequency Pulse Amplitude Modulation or Pulse Duration Modulation channels of a few cycles bandwidth with no loss of information. The data essentially are reduced "in the air" and thus little or no computation on the ground is required.

statmho. A unit of electric measurement.

$$1 \text{ statmho} = 1.113 \times 10^{-12} \text{ mho}$$

statoersted. A unit of electric measurement.

$$1 \text{ statoersted} = 3.336 \text{ EM cgs units of magnetizing force} = 1 \text{ ES cgs unit of magnetizing force} = 3.336 \times 10^{-11} \text{ oersted}$$

statohm. A unit of electric measurement.

$$1 \text{ statohm} = 8.988 \times 10^{20} \text{ abohms} = 8.988 \times 10^5 \text{ megohms} = 8.988 \times 10^{17} \text{ microhms} = 8.988 \times 10^{11} \text{ ohms}$$

statute mile. A measure of distance equal to 5280 ft.

statvolt. A unit of electric measurement.

$$1 \text{ statvolt} = 2.998 \times 10^{10} \text{ abvolts} = 2.998 \times 10^8 \text{ microvolts} = 2.998 \times 10^5 \text{ millivolts} = 299.8 \text{ volts}$$

statweber. A unit of electric measurement.

$$1 \text{ statweber} = 2.998 \times 10^{10} \text{ EM cgs units of magnetic flux} = 1 \text{ ES cgs unit of magnetic flux} = 2.998 \times 10^{10} \text{ maxwells} = 299.8 \text{ webers}$$

stay time. The average value of the time spent by each propellant gas molecule within the combustion chamber volume of a rocket:

$$t_s = \frac{V_c}{\dot{w}v}$$

where V_c = chamber volume, cu ft; $\dot{w}$ = weight flow, lb/sec; v = average specific volume of propellant gases in the chamber, cu ft/lb.

STC. Sensitivity Time Control (q.v.).

steady state. (1) A physical system is said to be in a steady state if the various quantities describing the system are either independent of time or are periodic functions of time. Thus an alternating-current circuit is in a steady state after all transient effects of a disturbance have disappeared. (2) A condition of dynamic balance in combustion, as in an equilibrium reaction, where the concentration of each of the reactants remains constant. In such cases the loss of reactants to form products just balances the formation of reactants from the products in the reverse reaction. (3) In aerodynamics, the state of *static stability* of the missile; no transients are present.

steady state oscillation. A condition in a dynamic system (q.v.) in which the energy input and damping are so in balance that the oscillation neither diverges nor damps out.

steady state vibration. Vibration in which the motion of every body in the system is periodic.

steam cloud. Fractonimbus (q.v.) that rises from a warm surface.

steam fog. A fog formed by cold air moving over warm water, causing the air to be saturated by evaporating water. Sometimes termed *frost smoke* or *sea smoke*. Steam fog may occur over open bodies of water or swamps.

steering. *Types of, see* jet–; vector–.

stellar atmosphere. The atmosphere about a star. The light from a star comes from near the surface, as the material of stars is quite opaque. The absorption lines seen in the star's spectrum are caused by the removal of certain wavelengths from the original light after it starts its journey to Earth; an investigation of the absorption lines can enable us only to decide what absorbing atoms exist *above* the opaque part of the star—in the star's atmosphere. The results of the analysis of stellar atmospheres reveal that nearly all stars have very similar atmospheres, and the differences between the classes of stellar spectra are caused almost wholly by differences of temperature and pressure. It is found that hydrogen and helium, in the ratio of about 5 to 1, vastly exceed all other elements. The following typical figures for the commonest of the other elements show that, so far as the atmospheres of the stars are concerned, they may all be considered as trace elements.

Element	Percentage
Oxygen	0.068
Neon	0.064
Nitrogen	0.020
Carbon	0.013
Iron	0.008
Magnesium	0.004

stellar constellation. Arbitrary groups into which stars are divided for reference and identification; in most constellations there is no relation between members, they seem close together merely as a result of perspective.

stellar guidance. *See* celestial navigation.

step rocket. A rocket made in multiple sections,

in such a way that, as part of the fuel is used up, the rocket sheds the fuel tanks and motor; a smaller, self-contained rocket—the second step —then takes off and starts afresh as an independent rocket but with an initial velocity imparted by the first stage. The net performance of a two-step or two-stage rocket is greater than if the original mass had all been used in a single step.

stereographic projection. In cartography, a technique for portraying the Earth's surfaces; the projecting plane is perpendicular to the axis of the Earth, and points on the Earth are projected by straight lines from the opposite pole.

stiction. *Static friction.*

stiffener. Any structural member in a missile the primary function of which is to stiffen or give rigidity to the craft or its elements.

stiffener, sheet. *See* sheet stiffener.

stiffness/weight ratio. In structural engineering, the ratio of the modulus of elasticity (q.v.) to weight.

still. (Vernacular) A heat exchanger.

stimulus. The motivating or exciting quantity which produces a response in a system.

stimulus, reference. *See* reference stimulus.

STL. Space Technology Laboratories; a subsidiary of Thompson-Ramo-Wooldridge Corporation; Los Angeles, Calif.

stochastic. The stochastic variable is dependent on the random variable (e.g., a random choice of ξ will define some value of X). The stochastic variable is usually the quantity measured experimentally.

Stokes theorem. The principle that if any closed curve is constructed and the tangential component of a vector around it is integrated, the result is equal to the surface integral of the normal component of the curl of that vector over an arbitrary surface bounded by the curve. Mathematically it may be stated:

$$\int F_s \, ds = \int \int \text{curl}_n F \, dS$$

stockpile. A reserve stock of material, equipment, raw material, or other supplies.

stoichiometric (mixture). The components involved in a burning process which are present in exactly the quantities needed for reaction without an excess of any component.

stopped accelerometer. In telemetering, an accelerometer with its diaphragm movement limited at one or both ends of its travel. The purpose of the stop is to restrict pad motion when overloads are applied, which consequently limits the frequency deviation of the associated oscillator and prevents it from interfering with adjacent channels.

stopped pickups. In telemetering, pickups (q.v.) provided with stops which limit the travel of the sensing element to prevent the pickup from producing excessive output with overloads. In an FM/FM telemetering system (q.v.) excessive output from a pickup may cause the associated oscillator to be driven into an adjacent channel, thereby causing interference.

storable propellant. A liquid rocket propellant capable of being stored in a flight ready condition for prolonged periods of time. Typical:

Oxidizers	Fuels
nitrogen tetroxide	hydrazine
chlorine trifluoride	UDMH
RFNA	RP-1

See Table 3, page 157.

storage. A missile environmental phase starting with delivery to a depot or other permanent storage area and ending with movement to a dock for transportation. Preventive maintenance is minimized during this period by protective design.

storage. *Types of, see* limited–; long-term–; ready–; standby–.

storm. An abnormal, and usually violent, disturbance of, or condition in, the atmosphere, accompanied by wind, rain, dust, hail, etc.; a wind force of 56-63 knots.

storm. *Types of, see* cyclone; hurricane; magnetic–; M storm; tornado; tropical–; typhoon.

stovepipe. (Vernacular) (1) A missile's tail pipe which is sometimes a part of the outside shell. (2) A term early applied to a ramjet (q.v.) (e.g., flying stovepipe).

stowage. A missile environmental phase covering its temporary storage phase, usually aboard a ship. Stowage is ordinarily and arbitrarily considered not to exceed a 6-month period.

strain. The deformation of a body resulting from a stress; measured by the ratio of the change to the total value of the dimension in which the change occurred.

strapping. *See* bootstrapping; magnetron–.

strategic information (SI). Unclassified scientific, technical, industrial, or economic (nonstatistical) information, the indiscriminate distribution of which may be inimical to the defense interests of the United States.

strategic missile (SM). A missile carrying a nuclear warhead used for long-range bombardment.

strategic missile squadron. The smallest Air Force strategic missile organization possessing an administrative capability. It consists of from three to six *flights* and appropriate command and administrative elements.

strategic missile support squadron. An Air Force organization assigned to a support base. It provides support for all missile units in the launch base area (q.v.).

strategic missile wing. An Air Force organization composed of one strategic missile support squadron (q.v.) and two or more strategic missile squadrons (q.v.).

strategic target. Any installation, network, group of buildings, or the like, considered vital to a country's war-making capability, and singled out for attack.

strategy. The art of utilizing national resources for best prosecution of a war; pertains to the preparations for battles or campaigns and the exploitation of their outcome.

strato. Abbreviation for stratosphere (q.v.).

stratocumulus cloud. A layer of broken or continuous cloud composed of globular masses or rolls and having water content. This cloud is usually turbulent.

stratosphere. That layer of the atmosphere beginning at the tropopause (q.v.) and extending from approximately 10 miles to 20 miles altitude. The stratosphere is between the troposphere (q.v.) and the mesosphere (q.v.). See Fig. 11, page 140.

stratus cloud. In meteorology, a uniform layer of broken or unbroken clouds characterized by a complete absence of structural detail, occurring at altitudes from near the surface to 6500 ft.

streamline flow. In a fluid flow, the path of particles originating at a common point. Except very near a body and in its wake, a flow streamline does not change direction with time.

stream thrust. The sum of the aerodynamic pressure forces transmitted across a specified cross section and the time rate of momentum flow across the same cross section.

$$F = \dot{m}V + pA$$

where $\dot{m}$ = mass flow, lb/sec; V = stream velocity, fps; A = difference in inlet and exhaust areas, sq ft; p = atmospheric pressure, lb/sq ft.

strength. *Types of, see* dielectric–; insulating–; offset yield–; signal–; yield–.

strength-weight criterion. A design criterion which gives the lightest weight member for a given geometry and loading condition (e.g., in high-temperature applications, a material based on a strength-weight-temperature criterion).

stress. The force producing or tending to produce deformation in a body; measured by the force applied per unit area.

stress. *Types of, see* allowable–; average unit–; bending–; component–; compressive–; crushing–; normal–; proof–; shearing–; tensile–; unit ultimate–; working–.

stress analysis report. A standard report used in missile design documentation. It includes shear and moment diagrams based on loading conditions presented in the loads report, design criteria, design allowables, margins of safety, detail stress analysis, and temperature corrections.

stress due to bending. The bending formula is:

$$s = \frac{Mc}{I} \quad \text{or} \quad s = \frac{M}{S}$$

where s = unit tensile or compressive stress in the extreme fiber; M = bending moment; c = distance between the extreme fiber and the neutral axis; I = moment of inertia of the section with respect to the neutral axis; S = section modulus = I/C.

stressed-skin construction. A type of airframe construction in which the skin bears all or part of the stresses. An airframe of this type is termed a monocoque or semimonocoque (q.v.).

stretcher. *See* pulse stretcher.

striking velocity. Impact velocity (q.v.).

string. (Vernacular) Any galvanometer (q.v.) used in an electromechanical oscillograph (q.v.).

stringer. Any one of a number of long, light, slender structural members used as longitudinal members in an airframe, rocket body, or similar structure, or as spanwise members in a wing. A stringer is lighter and more slender than a longeron (q.v.).

strip chart recorder. An instrumentation system element used for indicating and recording slowly varying functions in real time. Typical frequency response is less than 50 cps.

Strouhal number. A dimensionless parameter relating frequency of shedding of vortices to the wind velocity and characteristic dimension.

$$\text{Strouhal number} = \frac{\omega d}{2\pi V}$$

where d = diameter of missile or structure, ft; ω = frequency of vortex shedding, rad/sec; V = velocity of air flow, ft/sec.

structural damping (c). Damping caused by structural impedance in an oscillating mechanical system. The damping is independent of the frequency and proportional to twice the amplitude. Values vary from 0.001 to 0.08 for rigid structures.

structural density. The weight of a structural material relative to its enclosed volume.

structural drag. Parasitic drag (q.v.).

structural factor. A figure of merit ratio useful in rocket (missile) design. It is usually defined as the ratio of the empty mass of a rocket (stage) to the mass of the rocket (same stage) in its loaded condition.

structural feedback. A low-frequency oscillation of the airframe structure, caused by feedback (through the airframe or the air) of the structural and rigid body vibrations to servomechanisms located within the airframe, causing (usually) undesirable actuation of the aircraft controls in response to the vibrations.

structural feedback tests. Tests to determine the flight control system stability characteristics during structural feedback vibration.

structural filter. An electronic or mechanical device designed to filter a particular frequency (or frequencies) of a missile airframe or other structure. It is usually required to *notch out* the first free-free bending mode (*see* free-free mode) of the airframe to avoid coupling with the control system, sometimes in the form of a bandpass filter (q.v.) or a high cutoff filter. (Such filters seldom need to reduce the system gain by more than 12 db.)

structural integrity. The property of an airframe to withstand the loads for which it is designed.

structural loads. Aerodynamic loads, modified by the inertia loads of a missile's component parts during steady-state or dynamic conditions.

structural test report. A standard report used in missile design. It includes detail test procedures, loads and load distribution for the static and dynamic tests to be performed to confirm the basic design, and detail test results.

structural weight. The weight of the airframe of a missile; usually including primary and secondary structure.

structure. *Types of, see* hard–; indeterminate–; launcher and missile storage–; "make and buy"–; missile storage–; primary–; soft–; subcontract–; sub-surface launch–.

stub. A short circuited or open impedance path between the two conductors of a transmission line or in a waveguide. It is adjustable as to position so as to match the impedance of an antenna or transmitter to that of a transmission line.

stub tanks. Rocket propellant tanks which are shorter in length than a standard tank.

studies. *See* parametric studies.

stupalith. A ceramic material used in jet or rocket engines.

STV. Supersonic Test Vehicle (obsolete).

subassembly. A unit or element of a major assembly, consisting of two or more separate parts assembled together. It consists of parts which are individually replaceable, and may itself contain subassemblies. *See also* assembly.

subastral point. A substellar point (q.v.).

subcarrier. (1) In a multiplex system, a carrier of lower frequency than the carrier ultimately transmitted. Several subcarriers can be used simultaneously to modulate a carrier of higher frequency. Separate intelligence can be applied to the various subcarriers. (2) In telemetering, an intermediate frequency that is modulated by intelligence signals, and in turn is used to modulate the radio carrier, either along or in conjunction with subcarriers on other channels.

subcarrier amplifier. *See* filter amplifier.

subcarrier analyzer. A device which can be fed with a composite signal consisting of several subcarrier frequencies and used to check the characteristics (voltage, frequency) of any subcarrier signal.

subcarrier, audio. *See* audio subcarrier.

subcarrier discriminator. The component which demodulates a subcarrier frequency.

subcarrier frequency. In telemetering, an intermediate frequency that is modulated by intelligence signals and, in turn, is used to modulate the radio carrier either alone or in conjunction with subcarriers.

subcarrier oscillators. Those oscillators which translate the variations of electrical signals from end instruments (q.v.) into corresponding variations of a frequency-modulated signal at subcarrier frequencies (q.v.).

subcarrier wave. In electronics, a carrier wave (q.v.) which is applied as modulation on another carrier wave.

subcontract. Any purchase order or other contractual instrument or commitment entered into by a prime contractor or subcontractor with parties other than the Government.

subcontractor. A contractor who enters into a contract with a prime contractor (q.v.); may include a contractor to that subcontractor, etc.

subcontract structure. A composite listing of critical and/or major parts and/or assemblies made to a prime contractor's design which are to be subcontracted and manufactured off-site, plus the names of subcontractors the prime contractor proposes to use.

subcritical operation. A condition of ramjet operation; if the flight MACH number M_o decreases during subcritical operation, more air is "spilled over" the intake because of the decreased pressure rise achievable by the diffusion system. As a consequence, the gross thrust decreases still more, and if the decrease in MACH number cannot be halted, the ramjet engine finally becomes unable to overcome the drag of the missile it is propelling. See Fig. 5, page 73.

subharmonic. A sinusoidal quantity having a frequency which is an integral submultiple of the fundamental frequency (q.v.) of a periodic quantity to which it is related (e.g., a wave, the frequency of which is half the fundamental frequency of another wave, is termed the *second subharmonic* of that wave).

sublimation. (1) In meteorology, the act or process of changing from water vapor to ice, or ice to water vapor, without an intervening state of liquid. *See* condensation. (2) As applied to nose cones or reentry bodies, the process used to provide cooling to the warhead by sublimation of some part of the protective cover.

sublunar point. The geographical position of the Moon's center.

subminiaturization. Usually applied to airborne equipment; a technique of reducing size and weight. It is the next reduction after miniaturization (q.v.). Typical characteristics of subminiaturized packages are: (a) high density; (b) special heat dissipation provisions; (c) plug-in design; (d) modulized; (e) printed circuitry; (f) detail attention to layout.

sub-missile. One of several smaller missiles carried and released by a larger missile; especially in a warhead.

subpoint. A point on the Earth's surface directly beneath a celestial body or airborne object.

SUBROC. Submarine-to-submarine guided torpedo rocket.

subsidence. In meteorology, a sinking and spreading out of a body.

subsolar point. A point on the Earth directly beneath the Sun's center.

subsonic. Less than the speed of sound (q.v.) or less than a MACH number (q.v.) of one.

subsonic diffuser. The forward section of an air-breathing engine which reduces the MACH number of the supersonic stream to the low value required at the entrance to the combustion chamber. See Fig. 15, page 227.

subsonic leading edge. A condition of supersonic flow over an airfoil wherein the leading edge angle, as measured from the centerline, is less than that of the MACH angle μ, defined as:

$$\mu = \sin^{-1}\left(\frac{1}{M}\right)$$

The leading edge is said to lie within or behind the MACH angle. M = MACH number.

subsonic nozzle. A nozzle in which the velocity of gas at the throat is less than the velocity of sound. The velocity of gas at the exit is also subsonic.

subsonic region. A region in which the fluid flow is subsonic (q.v.) in contrast with supersonic (q.v.) (e.g., where the flow with respect to the surface of a nose cone is subsonic).

subsonic speed. A speed relative to surrounding fluid less than that of the speed of sound (q.v.) in the same fluid; incompressible flow (q.v.).

subsonic trailing edge. A condition of supersonic flow over an airfoil wherein the angle between the trailing edge and the centerline is less than that of the MACH angle (q.v.).

substellar point. A point on the surface of the Earth directly beneath a given star or planet. Also termed a *subastral point*.

substratosphere. A high-altitude region of the atmosphere, just below the stratosphere (q.v.). It has no fixed lower limit. The word is applied generally in the same manner as "high altitude" and usually refers to a region high enough to require special flying aids.

sub-surface launch structure. An underground launcher (q.v.).

subsystem. A major functional assembly within a system.

subsystem, major. *See* major subsystem.

suction head. *See* net positive suction head.

suction specific speed. A design parameter used in high-speed rotating pump calculations.

$$N_{sv} = N \frac{Q^{\frac{1}{2}}}{h_{sv}^{\frac{3}{4}}}$$

where N = speed, rpm; Q = pump output, gpm; h_{sv} = net positive suction head, ft.

suit. *Types of, see* g-suit; space–.

suitability. *See* operational suitability.

SUM. Surface-to-Underwater Missile (q.v.); a model designation (q.v.).

sump. (1) A pit or tank into which fluids drain.

(2) A storage tank. (3) A reservoir at a low point in a fuel or lubrication system where the liquid is collected to trap water or sediment.

sun, mean. *See* mean sun.

sunseeker. A photoelectric apparatus driving a two-axis device in the nose cone of a rocket which causes a section of the instruments to be directed constantly toward the Sun despite tumbling and rolling of the rocket in flight. It provides the stable platform necessary for long exposure photographs.

superaerodynamics. The study of the dynamics of gases at very high altitudes or extremely low densities; sometimes termed *rarefied gas dynamics*.

supercharger. A pump or compressor for forcing more air or fuel-air mixture into an internal-combustion, reciprocating engine, than would normally be indicated by the prevailing atmospheric pressure.

super-conductivity. The characteristic of a metal in which the resistance to electrical flow is reduced as the temperature approaches absolute zero (q.v). At present, 23 pure metals are known to have the property of superconductivity.

supercritical operation. A condition of ramjet engine operation wherein the heat released by the burner causes the back pressure on the exit section of the diffuser to become too small for maintaining the normal shock at the inlet. The excess pressure (or energy) in the air must be dissipated within the diffusion system by some form of discontinuous process, and such a process is possible only in a supersonic flow. Consequently, the air flows into the subsonic diffuser (q.v.) with supersonic velocities. Since the flow passage is diverging, the flow area is increasing, and the MACH number (q.v.) for the air likewise increases. The excess energy is finally dissipated by a strong shock wave (q.v.) forming in the diverging portion of the subsonic diffuser. See Fig. 5, page 73.

superheterodyne receiver. A radio receiver designed to obtain superior fidelity characteristics. The system includes: a radio-frequency amplifier, local oscillator, crystal mixer, intermediate-frequency amplifier, second detector, video amplifier, and cathode-follower output.

super-high frequency (SHF). In electronics, any frequency between 3000 and 30,000 mc/s. See Fig. 8, page 105.

superior planets. Those planets beyond the Earth with respect to distance from the Sun (e.g., Mars, Jupiter, Saturn, Uranus, Neptune, Pluto). Contrast with inferior planets (q.v.).

supernova. A star which explodes with the liberation of most of its energy into space.

superquick fuze. A type of impact fuze (q.v.) using a nose striker to cause the fuze to function almost instantaneously upon impact.

supersaturation. In meteorology, the condition of a body of air when it holds more moisture than it normally would under the prevailing temperature and pressure.

supersensitive fuze. An impact fuze (q.v.) designed to function upon a very light contact.

supersonic. Faster than the speed of sound (q.v.). When supersonic speed is attained by a moving object, no advance information in the form of pressure waves can be given to the oncoming air, as the body is moving faster than the pressure waves emanating from the body can propagate themselves forward. As a result, shock waves (q.v.) are formed which move with the body and are *attached* or *unattached* depending on the conditions.

supersonic compressor. A jet-engine centrifugal compressor that rotates at such a speed that a relative supersonic velocity is imparted to the air inside.

supersonic diffuser. The forward section of an air-breathing engine which is designed to reduce the supersonic airstream to practically a sonic stream. See Fig. 15, page 227.

supersonic nozzle. A nozzle in which the velocity of gas at the throat is equal to the velocity of sound. The velocity of gas at the exit is supersonic.

supersonic region. A region in which the fluid flow is supersonic as contrasted to subsonic (e.g., where the flow is supersonic with respect to a missile surface and remains that way downstream).

supersonics. (1) That branch of aerodynamics that treats of supersonic speeds or velocities; compressible flow. (2) Ultrasonics.

supply voltage error. The difference in output of a unit with changes of supply voltage when compared to the output with typical specified operating supply voltages. It is usually expressed as *per cent change from typical.*

support base. The place from which logistics (q.v.) support is provided for a group of missile launch complexes and their control center.

supporting facility. Any land, structure, apparatus, utility, or combination thereof that contributes primarily to the support and/or operation of a research and development establishment, a test or evaluation facility, an opera-

tional base, or other primary facility but which, in itself, is not used operationally in the pursuit of research, development, tests, evaluations, etc. (e.g., housing and administrative buildings, firehouses, roads, security installations, or distributive systems for water, fuel, electricity, air, steam, etc.).

supporting system. In logistics (q.v.), a total entity consisting of techniques, skills, and equipment, used to support a weapon system (q.v.).

supports. See missile stowage supports.

suppression. See carrier suppression.

suppressor grid. In electronics, an electrode between the screen grid (q.v.) and the anode of certain vacuum tubes for preventing the flow of secondary electrons from the anode to the screen grid, thus preventing the anode current from decreasing.

surface. *Types of,* see aerodynamic balanced–; aerodynamic lifting–; balanced–; constant pressure–; control–; fixed–; frontal–; main control–; static balanced–.

surface burst. A nuclear explosion at the surface of land or water or at a height above the surface less than the maximum fireball (q.v.) radius.

surface surveillance. Missile test range surveillance limited to that area between the firing area and the impact area.

surface-to-air missile (SAM). See ground-to-air missile; guided missile; model designation–.

surface-to-surface missile (SSM). See ground-to-ground missile; guided missile; model designation.

surface-to-underwater missile (SUM). See ground-to-ground missile; model designation.

surface wave. In radio, that component of a ground wave (q.v.) which travels along the surface of the Earth.

surge. A transient and abnormal rush in power or energy, such as occurs in an electrical or electronic apparatus or in an engine.

surge. (diffuser) See diffuser buzz.

surveillance. The close or continued observation, by any means, of an area, airspace, etc., in order to accrue information or to take action when the situation warrants.

surveillance. *Types of,* see air–; surface–.

survival probability. In operations research, the chance that a target will survive a given operation.

survival suit. An anti-exposure suit.

sustainer. A propulsion system that travels with, and does not separate from, a missile. The term usually is applied to a solid propellant rocket engine when used as the principal propulsion system as distinguished from an auxiliary engine, or booster. Sometimes it is applied to any missile stage except the booster.

swallowed shock. The condition in a supersonic diffuser (q.v.) when the shock wave (q.v.) has moved inside the intake lip. This is usually an *off-design* condition. The diffuser or internal drag is increased. See Fig. 5, page 73.

SWC. Special Weapons Command, Air Force; Kirtland Field; Albuquerque, N.M.

sweat (transpiration) cooling. A technique for cooling combustion chambers or aerodynamically heated surfaces by forcing a coolant (q.v.) through a porous wall. Film cooling by evaporation and/or conduction at the interface (q.v.) results.

sweepback. The acute angle between a line perpendicular to the plane of symmetry and the plan projection of a reference line on a missile wing.

sweep jamming. The action of jamming (q.v.) a radarscope by sweeping space with electronic impulses of the same frequency as those received by the radarscope.

sweep-through. A jamming transmitter that sweeps through a radio-frequency band and jams each frequency briefly, producing a sound like that of an aircraft engine.

SWEL. Special Weapons Equipment List.

switch. *Types of, see* commutator–; identification–; kill–; RT–; war-peace–.

switching. *Types of, see* channel–; lobe–.

swivel nozzle. The movable element of a thrust vector (steering) control system (q.v.) used on solid propellant rocket engines. The nozzle is hinged about the throat and motion is allowed in only one plane to provide thrust control (q.v.). Contrast with *rotatable nozzle* (q.v.) for solid propellant rockets and *movable thrust chamber* for liquid propellant engines.

SWR. Standing Wave Ratio (q.v.).

symbolic logic. A mode of developing and representing logical principles through the use of symbols for classes, propositions, etc., rather than a *theory* of logic. It provides an exact canon for deduction in general and usually is developed by rigorous deduction from postulates and definitions. It is sometimes termed *mathematical logic*.

symmetry. *See* plane of symmetry.

synchro. The universal term applied to any of the various synchronous devices such as the *Selsyn* (q.v.), *motor torque generator, mag-slip,* and *Siemans.* Theoretically, a synchro device is treated as a salient-pole, bipolar, alternating-current excited synchronous machine. The standard signal and control synchro has a two-pole, single-phase, rotor field and a Y-wound, single-phase, variable-voltage stator. The transmitter of the synchro, whose rotor is geared to, or otherwise linked with, mechanical equipment, is also termed a *generator, synchro generator,* or *Selsyn-motor,* has a motor that is free to rotate, and is damped to prevent excessive oscillation before coming into correspondence with the rotor of the transmitter.

synchroscope. (1) An instrument for indicating whether electrical machines, e.g., magnetos, are synchronized with one another. (2) An oscilloscope (q.v.) designed for the observation of short pulses, utilizing fast sweeps synchronized with the signal to be observed.

synergy. A term coined by Oberth to describe the compromise between the most efficient ascent of an escape vehicle when fired horizontally due east, and the avoidance of air resistance, etc. (e.g., the ideal velocity for a synergic ascent is between 37,800 fps and 39,400 fps, which would save 2300 to 6900 fps in energy requirements for escape from the atmosphere).

synodic satellite. A companion satellite to any more massive two-body system.

synoptic. A chart, such as the ordinary weather map, which shows the distribution of meteorological conditions over an area at a given moment.

synthesizer. *See* pulse synthesizer.

system. (1) A group of equipment or subassemblies especially integrated to perform a specific function or functions; e.g., a *fire control system* which includes the tracking radar, computer, and gun mount; a *weapon system* which includes the missile, GSE (ground support equipment), and ancillary guidance equipment. (2) A division of a missile such as a *propulsion system.*

system. *Types of, see* acoustical–; actuating–; air defense–; air warfare–; AN nomenclature–; armament–; arming–; assembly area cable–; automatic control–; auxiliary–; ballistic missile early warning–; blanket release–; central timing–; chirp–; circular–; closed–; control–; control force measuring–; cooperative–; damped aerodynamic righting attitude control–; data handling–; data reduction–; day–; deluge–; early warning–; electrical–; electrical mission–; electronic data processing–; fleet ballistic missile–; flight control–; FM data–; follow-up–;

frequency response–; ground antenna data link–; G-system; guidance–; guided missile–; gyroscope reference–; H-system; homing guidance–; ignition–; inertial–; K carrier–; launching–; low-tension ignition–; mechanical–; missile impact location–; missile safety–; mission–; non-cooperative–; phase coherent carrier–; pressure feed–; propellant utilization–; propulsion–; purging–; range safety–; Rebecca–Eureka–; reoperative–; self-destruction–; servo–; solar–; sub–; supporting–; telemetering–; three-phase three wire–; three wire–; vestigial sideband–; water deluge–; weapon–.

systematic error. A constant error or one that varies in a systematic manner throughout a missile test (e.g., instrument misalignment).

system calibration. Determination of the characteristics of a combination of components by measuring the output signal of the final component in the combination while an accurately known signal is applied to the input of the first component.

system phasing. Adjusting the acquisition of all components to the longest lead time item, and identifying and scheduling all action necessary to achieve development of a complete system by a programmed date.

system reliability. The probability that a system (q.v.) will perform its specified task under stated tactical and environmental conditions.

systems engineering. An engineering approach which organizes men, materials, and technologies for the purpose of developing an optimum device or system. Systems engineering covers two basic fields that are generally considered to be relatively independent: (a) *technical*—which deals with the compatibility of the physical components which go to make up a weapon system (q.v.); it is the effort which insures that each component fits physically, dynamically, and functionally with other components of the system; (b) *administrative coordination*—which deals with the problems of manpower utilization, procurement, scheduling, cost control, reporting, etc.

systems of measurement.

Name of unit:	Metric "gravitational" system, or "kilogram-meter-second" (mks) system	Metric "absolute" system, or cgs system	British "gravitational" system, or "foot-pound-second" (fps) system
Force	1 newton = 1 kg	10^5 dyne	7.015 poundal
Length	1 meter	100 cm	3.281 ft
Time	1 sec	1 sec	1 sec
Velocity	1 m/sec	100 cm/sec	3.281 fps
Acceleration	1 m/sec^2	100 cm/sec^2	3.281 fps^2
Pressure	1 kg/m^2	10^7 dyne/cm^2	0.205 lb/ft^2
Impulse (momentum)	1 kg-sec	10^7 dyne-sec	2.205 lb-sec
Work (energy)	1 joule	10^7 dyne-cm = 10^7 ergs	23.02 ft-poundal
Power	1 watt (1 kg-m/sec)	10^7 dyne-cm/sec = 10^7 ergs/sec	23.02 ft-poundal
Mass	1 kg/m/sec^2 = 1 metric slug	100 dyne/cm/sec^2 = 1 kg-mass	2.205 lb/fps^2 = 1 slug

T

T/A. Table of Allowance (q.v.).

tables. *Types of, see* damage assessment–; firing–; flight–; gyroscope transfer–; quantity-distance–; Scorsby–; servo–; sidereal–; tilt–.

table of allowance (T/A). A table or list that establishes the maximum amount of organic equipment for a base, organization, or activity.

tabulated altitude. The known angular altitude of a celestial body from a given point, as shown by a table.

TAC. Tactical Air Command.

TACAN. *Tactical air navigation* (q.v.).

tactical air navigation (TACAN). A system whereby the distance and bearing of an aircraft from a fixed point are indicated on dials, or other devices within the aircraft. Ultra-high-frequency signals pass between craft and ground station, the operator in the craft tuning to the station frequency. Because of the line-of-sight (q.v.) nature of these high-frequency waves, the effective range is limited by Earth curvature, and many ground stations are required in a complete system.

tactical doctrine. Standardized employment of weapons based on prior experience; doctrine is normally prescribed for field forces in suitable publications.

tactical missile (TM). A guided missile used in tactical operations.

tactics. The art of employing field forces and their materiel for best prosecution of a battle; pertains to military operations ensuing *after* contact with an enemy.

TAD. Target Area Designation.

TAF. Tactical Air Force.

tail assembly. The assembly of vanes and fins on a missile that provide directional stability or guidance (q.q.v.).

tail cone. (1) An exhaust cone. (2) A cone of fire from the tail of a vehicle.

tail control. A method of missile control using control surfaces at the rear of the body. Lateral forces are obtained from fixed lifting surfaces mounted on the body generally near the mid-

section, the entire configuration being deflected to an angle of attack (q.v.) by the tail control surfaces. A wingless tail control design may be achieved by omitting the wings and obtaining the desired lift from the angle of attack of the body.

tail grab. A device employed to secure a missile to its launcher by "grabbing" or holding the missile tail-section strong points to prevent missile motion until the desired thrust level is reached. Release is accomplished at the instant of launch. Also termed *missile retainer*.

tailless (elevon) control. A method of missile control using but one set of surfaces with control flaps located at the trailing edge, the fixed surface providing the lift and the movable surfaces the necessary lateral and longitudinal control.

tail-on wind. A tail wind that blows directly toward the tail. Contrast with *head-on wind*.

tailpipe. In a jet engine, the pipelike structure aft of the fuel injector; the combustion chamber. See Fig. 15, page 227.

tailpipe burner. An afterburner (q.v.); hence tailpipe burning.

tail wind. A wind blowing from such direction that the principal effect is to advance the ground speed of a given vehicle. Roughly, any wind coming in toward the tail from a direction within 45° either side of the longitudinal axis of a vehicle is considered a tail wind. *See* tail-on wind. Contrast with *head wind, cross wind* (q.q.v.).

TALOS. Surface ship-to-air guided missile. Navy Bureau of Ordnance designation: SAM-N-6. Air Force/Army designation: IM 70.

Over-all length of missile and booster: 31 ft 3 in.; length of basic missile: 20 ft 3 in.; wing span: 95 in.; body diameter: 29.5 in.; firing weight without boost: 3000 lb; maximum slant range: 38-40 miles; speed: MACH 3. Warhead is proximity fuzed. Ramjet cruise engine; solid propellant booster rocket. Beam rider, and interferometer homing for terminal phase guidance. Used on the nuclear cruiser Long Beach and the light cruiser Galveston for employment against supersonic and subsonic enemy aircraft and against enemy ships and shore targets. The missile has several versions including one with a nuclear warhead.

Technical Direction: Applied Physics Laboratory/The Johns Hopkins University. Prime Contractor: Bendix Aviation Corp. Airframe: McDonnell Aircraft Corp. Engine: McDonnell; engine controls: Bendix; booster rocket: Allegheny Ballistics Laboratory. Guidance system: Bendix.

tandem missile. A fore and aft configuration used in boosted missiles, long-range ballistic missiles, satellite vehicles, etc. Stages are stacked together in series and are discarded or staged at burnout of the propellant for each stage (e.g., TITAN, q.v.).

tangential ellipse. The most economical space-flight transfer ellipse from the energy standpoint; grazes the orbits of arrival and departure. Also known as a *Hohmann orbit*. The transfer ellipse from Earth to Mars carries a rocket vehicle halfway around the Sun and takes about eight months to traverse.

tank. *Types of, see* balloon–; battleship–; stub–.

tank circuit. A circuit capable of storing electrical energy over a band of frequencies continuously distributed about a single frequency at which the circuit is said to be resonant, or tuned. The selectivity of the circuit is proportional to the ratio of energy stored in the circuit to the energy dissipated. This ratio is often termed the Q of the circuit. An inductor and a capacitor in a parallel-connected resonant circuit make up a tank circuit. Since such a circuit has the ability to store energy for a short period of time, it acts as a reservoir or tank.

tape. *Types of, see* guidance–; magnetic–.

taper. An airfoil feature in which either the thickness or the chord length, or both, decrease from the root to the tip.

tape recorder. A device for storing information magnetically on tape. *See* recorder.

TARE. Telemetry Automatic Reduction Equipment.

target. An enemy vehicle, installation, facility, or other materiel or personnel against which attacks are to be made.

target. *Types of, see* point–; radar–; reflecting–; strategic–.

target acquisition. The first appearance in a radar or other search system of recognizable intelligence of a target. Also termed *detection*.

target area. *See* presented target area.

target complex. A group of targets having a common strategical or tactical interest. *See* horizontal target complex.

target cross section. The characteristic area of a target which, when placed perpendicular to the direction of the incident radar energy, is capable of intercepting just enough energy so that if this energy could be fed into a perfectly matched isentropic antenna (q.v.), radiation back toward the radar receiver would duplicate that actually obtained from the target.

target discrimination. That quality of a guidance system (q.v.) which enables it to distinguish a target from its background or between two or more targets in close proximity.

target drone. A pilotless aircraft used exclusively as a target for anti-aircraft weapons.

target elevation. In radar, the angular altitude of a radar target.

target fade. A decrease or loss of signal due to interference or other phenomena. (Tracking loops usually include *memory circuitry* to cause the radar to continue to track at the same rate during this period.)

target identification. The act of determining the nature of a target and whether it is friend or foe. *See* identification, friend or foe.

targeting. In missile warfare, the science of plotting the correct trajectory (q.v.) for a designated target.

target noise. Statistical reflections of a transmitted radar signal caused by the target having a number of reflecting elements randomly oriented in space.

target profile area. A sectional area of a target, as it affects detection, radar deflection, and vulnerability. *See* target cross section.

target scintillation. The apparent random movement of a target's center of radar energy reflectivity during the course of an operation.

target seeker. A missile designed as a seeker (q.v.); the device within such a missile that directs it to the target. *See* homing guidance.

target timing. A radar technique for determining wind velocity by correlating the distance that a radar target travels across a radar screen with other known speed data.

target vulnerability. The resistance to destruction which a target possesses with respect to a weapon which is intended to destroy it.

target weight. Synonymous with *bogey weight* (q.v.).

TARTAR. Surface ship-to-air guided missile to be launched from destroyers. Navy Bureau of Ordnance cognizance.

Maximum flight speed: 1500 mph; range: 20 miles. Solid propellant rocket booster and sustainer combined. Beam rider guidance with homing head. TARTAR is fitted to eight U.S. Navy destroyers where it replaces 5-inch dual-purpose guns.

Technical Direction: Applied Physics Laboratory/The Johns Hopkins University. Prime Contractor: Convair, Pomona. Airframe: Convair. Engines: Allegheny Ballistics Laboratory. Guidance system: Ford Instrument Co.

taunus. An antijamming device that differentiates the blip (q.v.) of a genuine target from that of window (q.v.).

T/BA. Table of Basic Allowance.

TBM. (1) Tactical Ballistic Missile. (2) Theater Ballistic Missile.

TCA. Thrust Chamber Assembly (q.v.).

TCO. Test Control Officer.

TD. Test Directive.

TEAL. Target drone. Navy Bureau of Aeronautics designation: XKDT-1.

Length: 12 ft; wing span: 58.8 in.; body diameter: 10 in.; design altitude: subsonic, 50,000 ft. Used as a target by Navy fighter aircraft, it is launched from the wing of a fighter aircraft.

technical. (1) Of persons, having knowledge, training, or skill to manipulate, use, inspect, appraise, or control mechanical apparatus, laboratory equipment, clerical procedures, manpower control, or the like; skilled or trained in a practical art. It is often used to distinguish persons trained in skills from persons with scientific or professional training. (2) Of abilities, belonging to a person skilled or trained in a practical art, as in engineering. (3) Of developments, marked by the use of new scientific or engineering discoveries or by the employment of new techniques or methods. (4) Of areas of activity, involving specialized knowledge or training; required persons with special skills. (5) Of standards, established by reference to special requirements serving exact and precise purposes. (6) Of publications, data, or information, concerned with the mechanical or practical arts, especially in reference to materiel, such as the engine or airframe of a missile. (7) Of an organization, established to maintain equipment, especially for the support of a tactical organization.

technical channel. A channel through which guidance and direction and sometimes control are exercised, or through which services are provided, but through which operational command is not exercised.

technical characteristics. Those characteristics of equipment which pertain primarily to the engineering principles involved in producing equipment possessing desired military characteristics; e.g., for electronic equipment, technical characteristics include such items as circuitry and types and arrangements of components.

technical control. Control exercised by virtue of technical jurisdiction.

technical direction (TD). The act of directing by a central agency of a weapon system development being done by a number of independent industrial/university groups. The concept is one of a *systems engineering* (q.v.) group giving broad *technical direction* to the program as a whole and detail direction where required to further the effort. *See* systems engineering.

technical evaluation. The study and investigation by a developing agency to determine the technical suitability of material, equipment, or a system, for use in the military services.

technical failure. An ambiguous or general term for materiel failure or mechanical failure.

technical manual (TM). A publication containing detailed information on technical procedures, including instructions on the operation, handling, maintenance, and repair of equipment.

technical objective. An objective towards which research and development (q.v.) are aimed in developing weapons or pieces of equipment or in developing techniques for the handling of such weapons or equipment.

technical test control. The specialized or professional guidance and direction exercised with respect to a missile test center aspect of tests. It includes the authority to schedule, alter, or stop individual tests in accordance with dictates of safety, undue interference to other tests, technical feasibility of the range to accept any test, and limitations imposed by available test resources.

technical test direction. The determination and execution of test programs in accordance with directives or contractual authority of the sponsoring service, including the determination of technical validity of test objectives, the formulation of general test programs and detailed test plans, the preparation of articles to be tested, and the prosecution of tests and evaluation of

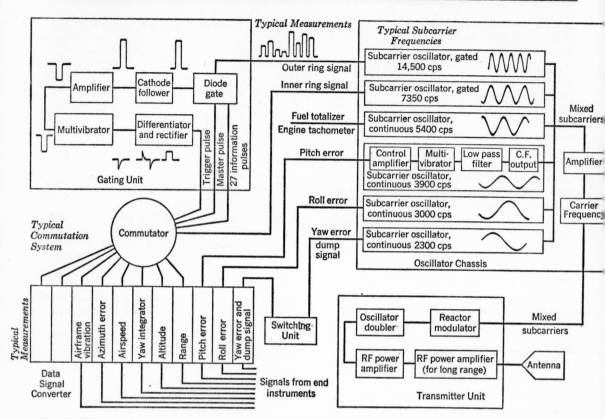

Fig. 26. Functional diagram of an FM/FM telemetering system. (U. S. Air Force, *Guided Missiles*, McGraw-Hill)

test data, the reporting of test results, and the reorientation of the test program and plans based on these data.

technician. One skilled or highly specialized in the method or practice of a particular trade, specialty, or the like, with special reference to mechanical details and the use of special techniques; one who has mastered the techniques of his art.

technological warfare. Warfare in which each contesting side strives to achieve an advantage by developments in technology (q.v.).

technology. The applied science by which improvements are made in the industrial arts and their products.

tee. (1) In electronics, a T-shaped joint or section in a waveguide. *See* magic tee. (2) Short for "wind-tee."

telemeter. (1) An electric or electronic instrument that measures a quantity (e.g., speed, angle of attack, temperature, atmospheric pressure), then transmits the measurements to a distant station. See Fig. 26. (2) An instrument

that measures the distance between an object and the observer (e.g., range finder).

telemeter band. A subcarrier band (there are 18 in the standard FM/FM telemetering system) which is used to modulate a carrier. The center frequencies of the 18 bands are separated by the ratio of 1.3:1 (except between 14.5 and 22 kc). Contrast with *telemeter channel* (q.v.).

telemeter channel. A term which designates the complete route for transmission of a telemetered function, including pickup, commutator, modulator, transmitter, receiver, demodulator, decoder, and recorder (q.q.v.); a single source or channel of information.

telemetering. Transmission of a measurement over long distances, usually by radio means. A receiving instrument converts the transmitted electrical signals into units of data which can be translated by data reduction into appropriate units. See Fig. 26.

telemetering. *Types of, see* FM/FM–; pulse amplitude modulation (PAM)–; pulse code modulation (PCM)–; pulse duration modulation (PDM)–; pulse width modulation (PWM)–.

telemetering pickup. A device used to measure and convert data to be telemetered into a form suitable for modulation of the telemetering link. Pickups are used to measure strain, pressure, voltage, vibration, acceleration, fuel flow, position, counters (cosmic ray), temperature, etc. Variable voltage, resistance, reluctance, capacitance, or inductance can be used. Sometimes termed *end organ, end instrument,* or *transducer.* See Fig. 26.

telemetering system. The complete measuring, transmitting, and receiving apparatus for remotely indicating, recording, and/or integrating information. See Fig. 26.

telemetry. The process of transferring information from one point to another remote point, usually electromagnetically. Telemetry is the science of telemetering (q.v.).

telemetry. *Types of, see* quick-look–; radio–; statistical–.

telemetry frequencies.

216–225 mc/s currently in use and available to Jan. 1, 1960; thereafter on a noninterference basis

225–260 mc/s available until Jan. 1, 1970, for missiles and upper-air research

2200–2300 mc/s probably available for missiles

telemetry playback. A graphic record made from telemetry data recorded on magnetic tape. It is not linearized.

telemetry-reduced. A graphic or tabular record of telemetry data which incorporates corrections for end instrument (q.v.) calibration and telemetry link calibrations.

telescope. *See* intermediate focal length tracking telescope.

telescopic photographic recorder (TPR). A transportable, single telescope, recording field instrument for tracking missiles. It provides velocity, acceleration, spin rate, attitude, and position. Angular data and correlated time are film-recorded.

television repeat-back guidance. A kind of command guidance (q.v.) for guided missiles in which a television camera and transmitter are mounted in the guided object to provide the operator with a picture to aid in guiding.

TE mode. Any mode of microwave propagation in a waveguide (q.v.) or between parallel plates, in which the electric field is wholly transverse to the direction of propagation. The $TE_{1,0}$ mode is commonly used in rectangular waveguide transmission lines.

TEM mode. A mode of microwave propagation between parallel plates (or in a coaxial transmission line), in which the electric field is everywhere perpendicular to the conductors and the wavelength is independent of the spacing between them.

$TEM_{0,1}$ mode. A mode of microwave propagation which has axial symmetry if excited in a circular waveguide.

temperature. *Types of, see* absolute–; ballistic–; critical–; design–; equilibrium (outer space)–; Joule-Thomson inversion–; potential–; reference–; stagnation–; virtual–.

temperature coefficient. One of a group of coefficients relating changes in reactivity of a nuclear reactor to changes in temperature of its components; the derivative of reactivity with respect to temperature. If the effect of these coefficients is negative so that a change in power level (hence in temperature) produces an opposite change in reactivity, the reactor may hold a nearly steady power level with very little further regulation.

temperature conversion formulas. The relation between the Fahenheit and Centigrade scales is:

$$\frac{°F - 32}{180} = \frac{°C}{100}$$

Degrees Fahrenheit   = 1.8(°C) + 32
Degrees Centigrade   = ⅝(°F − 32)
Degrees Fahrenheit absolute
  or Rankine   = °F + 459.58
Degrees Centigrade absolute
  or Kelvin   = °C + 273.1

temperature error. The difference in output of a unit with changes of temperature when compared to output at room temperature (70° approx.). It is usually expressed as total per cent change over a specified temperature range. It is sometimes expressed as *per cent change per °C or °F.*

temperature gradient. The rate of change in temperature between one point and another, especially in reference to increase in altitude.

temperature inversion. In meteorology, a condition existent when the temperature of air increases with altitude rather than decreases, as it does normally in the troposphere (q.v.).

temperature recovery factor (r). In aerodynamics, the ratio of actual temperature rise in the boundary layer (q.v) to the adiabatic temperature rise.

$$r = \frac{T_w - T}{T_o - T}$$

where T = ambient temperature, °R; T_o = adiabatic stagnation temperature, °R; T_w = missile skin or wall temperature, °R.

temperature sensitivity. In solid rocket usage, the percentage change of thrust per unit of temperature change. Typical values: 0.002 to 0.015 lb thrust/°F/lb of original thrust.

temperature sensitivity of pressure. In solid rocket usage, the percentage of chamber pressure change per degree of temperature change, π_K, at a particular value of K (the ratio of burning surface to the throat area). Typical values: 0.1 to 0.8%/°F/psi.

tensile stress. The normal amount of stress per unit area of a body subjected to a stretching or tension load.

tensor. A set of n^r components which are functions of the coordinates of any point in n-dimensional space. They transform linearly and homogeneously, according to certain rules, when a transformation of coordinates is made. Tensors are called *covariant, contravariant,* or *mixed,* according to the law of transformation. The number r is termed the *rank* or *order* of the tensor.

tentative table of equipment (TTE). A table or list prescribing equipment required to maintain newly developed or modified missiles until provided for by an appropriate master equipment or allowance list, equipment component list, or table of allowance (q.q.v.).

ten-tenths cloud. Cloud that covers the sky. *See* cloud cover.

term concept. In contracting, in a contract written on a "term" basis, a contractor agrees to make available facilities, material and personnel, and to furnish an estimated number of man-years (q.v.), man-months, or man-hours (q.v) of scientific effort for a stated period of time directed toward the accomplishment of the required research and development program (q.v.).

terminal ballistics. (1) A branch of ballistics (q.v) that deals with the modification or action of a missile at the target, or at the end of its trajectory. *See* penetration ballistics. (2) The study of the effects of missiles on their targets.

terminal guidance. The guidance applied to a missile between the termination of the midcourse guidance (q.v.) and the impact with or detonation in close proximity to the target. *See* homing.

terminal impedance (input impedance). In a microwave device (e.g., input impedance of an antenna), the impedance (q.v.) of the device as measured at the input connection.

terminal phase. (1) A guidance phase covering that portion of a missile's trajectory from the end of midcourse guidance to the impact with the target. (2) For ballistic missiles, the terminal phase is that part of the trajectory from reentry (q.v.) to impact. See Fig. 27, page 293.

terminal trajectory. The portion of the trajectory between reentry (q.v.) and impact. Reentry occurs at an altitude of approximately 250,000 ft. See Fig. 27, page 293.

terminal velocity (TV). (1) The hypothetical maximum speed a body could attain along a specified straight flight path under given conditions of weight and thrust. (2) The constant velocity of a falling body attained when the resistance of air or other ambient fluid has become equal to the force of gravity acting upon the body.

ternary fission. *See* nuclear fission.

TERRAPIN. Research missile. Navy cognizance.

Length: 15 ft; diameter: 6¼ in.; weight: 224 lb; speed: MACH 5.8; design altitude: 80 miles. Uses a two-stage solid propellant power plant. Used to gain information regarding temperatures, cosmic rays, etc.

Prime Contractor: Republic Aviation Corp. Airframe: Republic. Engine: Allegheny Ballistic Laboratory, Thiokol Chemical Corp.

terrestrial pole. Either of the Earth's poles, as distinguished from a celestial pole (q.v.).

terrestrial reference guidance. A technique of missile guidance wherein the predetermined path set into the control system of a missile can be followed by a device in the missile which reacts to some property of the Earth, e.g., magnetic or gravitational effects.

terrestrial space. The region roughly between 200 and 3500 miles (1 Earth radius) altitude dominated practically exclusively by terrestrial gravitational and geophysical phenomena.

TERRIER I. Surface ship-to-air guided missile. Navy Bureau of Ordnance designation: SAM-N-7.

Over-all length with booster: 26 ft 5 in.; length of basic missile: 14 ft 9 in.; firing boost: 1100 lb; maximum slant range: 20 miles; speed: MACH 2.5; altitude: 60,000 ft. Solid propellant rocket booster and sustainer. Beam rider guidance. Used on cruisers and destroyer-frigate type of vessels.

Technical Direction: Applied Physics Laboratory/The Johns Hopkins University. Prime Contractor: Convair. Airframe: Convair, Pomona. Engines: Aerojet-General Corp. Guidance system: Reeves Instrument Corp., Motorola.

TERRIER II. Surface ship-to-air guided missile. Navy Bureau of Ordnance cognizance.

Twice the size of TERRIER I (q.v.), has a nose of pyroceram to resist heat and thermal shock, yet to transmit radar waves. Solid propellant rocket engine. Beam rider and active homing guidance.

Technical Direction: Applied Physics Laboratory/The Johns Hopkins University. Prime Contractor: Convair, Pomona. Airframe: Convair, Pomona. Engines: Aerojet-General Corp., M. W. Kellogg Co. Guidance system: Motorola, Inc., Sperry Gyroscope Co.

test. The technique and methods employed to determine compliance of design and performance with requirements.

test. *Types of, see* acceptable environmental range–; acceptance–; captive (ground)–; climatic–; closed loop flight–; closed loop testing; cold tests, of resonant systems; corrosion–; design type–; drop–; employment and suitability–; evaluation–; field–; flight–; flight certification–; flight rating–; flight readiness firing–; functional–; interference compliance–; jolt and jumble–; material–; mock firing–; operational readiness–; preflight rating–; pre-launch–; production type–; proof–; qualification–; qualification flight–; radio noise interference–; reliability–; service–; shock–; static–; structural feedback–; type–; user–.

test chamber. *See* anechoic test chamber.

tester. *See* firing system tester.

test-failure load. For a structural member, the smallest load obtained by applying any of the following criteria to the results of static load tests: (a) The load which produces a permanent (strain) of X inches per inch at a critical point in a primary structural member. (The value for X is selected to suit the particular material, structure, and load situation); (b) The load which produces a total deformation (either permanent or elastic) established as a limit by performance requirements.

testing. *Types of, see* destructive–; go-no-go–; magnaflux–; magnetic–; marginal–; open-loop–; operational suitability–; production environmental–; random noise–.

test objective. The end result that is to be accomplished in testing. There are four classifications of test objectives: (a) *Primary objective:* one sufficiently important to warrant a hold or cancellation of the test if it becomes obvious that the objective cannot be accomplished; (b) *Secondary objective:* one that affords an optional hold of the test if it is obvious that the objective cannot be achieved. (A test will not

be held for secondary objectives if this will jeopardize the attainment of primary objectives); (c) *Tertiary objective:* one that does not warrant a hold of the test under any circumstances; (d) *Associated objective:* one that can be accomplished as a byproduct of the test.

test range coordinates. The coordinates used to define the position of a missile while in flight. These are: (a) *down range:* the great circle distance (q.v.) from the launch point to the projection of the position point onto the range plane; (b) *cross range:* the great circle distance from the position point to its perpendicular projection on the range plane. *See* great circle distance.

test ranges. *See* missile test ranges.

test report. *See* structural test report.

test stand. A device for holding a rocket engine or missile in position for captive or flight test (q.q.v.).

test vehicle. Any vehicle designed to achieve test data relating to a particular system, objective, parameter, etc. The term is usually applied to flight articles. *See* aerodynamic test vehicle.

tetranitro-methane. A liquid rocket propellant *oxidizer*. See Table 3, page 157.

tetryl. A crystalline explosive of high sensitivity and brisance, used especially as a detonator or booster, and sometimes as a bursting charge in small-caliber missiles.

theodolite. An optical instrument for measuring horizontal and/or vertical angles with precision.

theorem. *Types of, see* Bernoulli's–; reciprocity–; Stokes–.

theoretical exhaust velocity. The exhaust velocity (q.v.) a jet or rocket propellant would give if all the kinetic energy (q.v.) of the propellant were present as unidirectional motion of translation.

theory. *Types of, see* perturbation–; quantum–.

thermal. (1) An ascending air current caused by heat. (2) Of, or pertaining to, heat.

thermal battery. A series of electrochemical cells that are activated by applying heat to melt a solidified electrolyte.

thermal diffusivity. A ratio relating to heat conduction.

$$\frac{\text{thermal}}{\text{diffusivity}} = \frac{\text{thermal conductivity}}{\text{specific heat} \times \text{specific gravity}}$$

Thermal diffusivity for steel, 0.56; for titanium, 0.07; for aluminum, 0.07.

thermal efficiency. The efficiency with which a rocket engine, jet engine, or any other engine employing heat converts the total heat energy of its fuel into energy available for propulsion. *See* over-all efficiency; propulsive efficiency.

thermal heating. (1) Aerodynamic heating produced by supersonic and hypersonic (q.q.v.) travel through the atmosphere. (2) Transfer of heat from laminar or turbulent flow (q.q.v.) to a body as it loses kinetic energy (q.v.).

thermal inertia. The reciprocal of thermal response (q.v.).

thermal instability. In meteorology, the instability of a body of air with respect to its temperature distribution. *See* convective instability.

thermal jet engine (air-breathing engine). A jet propulsion engine which uses air to support combustion and for the creation of a high-speed *jet stream* (q.v.). *See also* jet engine; jet propulsion.

thermal jet engine. *Types of, see* pulsejet; ramjet; turbojet.

thermal radiation. Radiation emitted by a body as a result of its high temperature.

thermal reactor. A nuclear reactor in which fission is induced primarily by neutrons of such energy that they are in substantial thermal equilibrium with the material of the core. Energy of 0.025 electron volts (2200 meters per second), which corresponds to the mean energy of neutrons in a Maxwellian distribution at 293°K, is often taken as representative for thermal neutrons, although most thermal reactors actually operate at a higher temperature. A *moderator* is an essential element of a thermal reactor.

thermal response. The rate of temperature rise in a body if no heat is withdrawn by cooling. The reciprocal of this rate is termed *thermal inertia.*

thermal thicket. An artificial, loosely defined flight regime in which aerodynamic heating (q.v.) becomes sufficiently high to require new materials, cooling techniques, or reduced allowables on conventional materials. It is said to be the next major *barrier* (after the *sonic barrier*) to the design of high supersonic missiles and aircraft.

thermal wind. A wind caused by differences in horizontal temperature.

thermion. An electrically charged particle emitted by an incandescent material or substance. A thermion is either negatively or positively charged.

thermionic converter. A device for the conversion of thermal energy (q.v.) directly into electrical energy.

thermionic emission. The evaporation of elec-

trons from a heated surface. Energy of from 0.7 to 6.0 electron volts (depending on the surface) is necessary for the escape of an electron. Increase in temperature gives more and more electrons the energy to escape from the surface. Increase in temperature also accelerates evaporation of the cathode surface material, thus shortening cathode life.

thermistor. *Therma*l re*sistor.* A partial conductor or resistor whose value varies with temperature in a definite desired manner. It is used in circuits to compensate for temperature variations in other parts, or to measure temperature, or as a nonlinear circuit element.

thermocouple. A junction of two dissimilar metals which exhibit voltage generating characteristics when subjected to changes of temperature. A thermocouple is used to measure temperature by monitoring the voltage generated.

thermodynamic barrier. A hypothetical *barrier* to high-velocity flight in the atmosphere, reached when friction heat caused by air particles striking or rubbing against the vehicle is sufficient to melt or weaken the surface of the vehicle.

thermodynamic probability. The number of *a priori* equally probable states of statistical assembly, usually denoted by Ω. It is a measure of the disorder of the assembly, and is connected with the entropy, *S*, by the relation:

$$S = K \log \Omega$$

where *K* is the Boltzmann constant.

thermodynamics. The science that treats of the mechanical action of heat, or the relationship of heat and mechanical energy, and the conversion of one into the other.

thermodynamics, first law of. One of the many forms of statement of this law is that *energy cannot be created or destroyed, but can only be converted from one form to an equivalent quantity of another form.* The discovery of the equivalence of mass and energy, based on the relativity theory, and its application in the conversion of mass into energy in nuclear reactions, has become the basis for a broader generalization, combining the first law of thermodynamics with the law of conservation of matter (q.v.), in the statement that *the total mass and energy of a system, whether expressed in terms of equivalent total mass or equivalent total energy, is constant.*

thermodynamics, second law of. One of the many forms of statement of this law is that *heat cannot pass from a colder to a hotter body* *without the intervention of some external force, medium, or agency.* It follows from this law that all natural or isolated processes which occur spontaneously are irreversible.

thermodynamics, third law of. *Every substance has a finite positive entropy which may become zero at a temperature of absolute zero,* as it does in the case of crystalline substances. (Methods of quantum statistics, however, show that entropies at absolute zero, while small, are not necessarily zero, there being, for example, a finite entropy due to nuclear spin.)

thermojet. Thermal jet engine. An air-duct type engine in which thrust is obtained by scooping air from the surrounding atmosphere, compressing, heating by combustion, and discharging the exhaust gases at high velocity. *See* jet propulsion.

thermonuclear. (1) Of or pertaining to nuclear reactions or processes caused by heat, especially to nuclear fusion caused by the intense heat of an atomic bomb explosion. (2) A generic term applied to fission-fusion processes (e.g., hydrogen bomb or warhead).

thermonuclear reaction. A nuclear reaction in which the energy necessary to overcome the potential barrier and maintain the reaction is derived from purely thermal energy.

thermonuclear rocket. A propulsion system using a controlled fusion (q.v.) process. Typical process is to heat a fuel such as deuterium-tritium to extremely high temperatures. Escape of the orbital atoms accelerates the ions with the result that the fuel is converted into a high-speed plasma. The reaction must be contained within magnetic lines of force because of the high temperatures. In theory, specific impulses of 3 million seconds can be obtained but the thrust is very low. The addition of a coolant, such as lithium, reduces the temperature, increases the thrust, and still gives a specific impulse over 3000 seconds.

thermopile. A series of thermocouples (q.v.) joined together so as to increase the current when heated.

thermoplastic. A plastic which softens upon the application of heat and rehardens upon cooling. It can be softened and hardened repeatedly.

thermoset plastic. A plastic which undergoes a chemical change upon the application of heat and which does not appreciably soften or deform if later reheated.

thermosphere. A layer of the upper atmosphere, so named for the range of temperatures that prevail in it. This is coextensive with the iono-sphere extending from the stratosphere at 80 km (50 miles) to the upper limits. Temperatures range from the temperature minimum at 80 km (50 miles) to several thousand degrees at around 400 km (250 miles). *See* ionosphere. See Fig. 11, page 140.

THOR. Surface-to-surface intermediate range ballistic missile (IRBM). Air Force designation: for weapon system: WS315A; for the missile: SM-75.

Length: about 65 ft; maximum body diameter: 8 ft; launching weight: just under 100,000 lb; burnout speed: MACH 10; maximum range: 1500 miles. Uses a single liquid propellant motor with gimbal-mounted chamber. Propellants are LOX/RP1. Engine: one 135,000-lb thrust and two 1000-lb thrust verniers. Inertial guidance; thermonuclear warhead. Used as the first stage for early lunar probes.

Systems Engineering Contractor: Space Technology Laboratories. Prime Contractor: Douglas Aircraft Co. Engine: Rocketdyne Division, North American Aviation. Guidance system: AC Spark Plug Division, General Motors Corp. Nose cone: General Electric Co.

THOR-ABLE. An Air Force/National Aeronautics and Space Administration (NASA) satellite and space probe launching rocket originally used for the initial PIONEER (q.v.) Moon shots.

    1st stage—THOR (q.v.)
    2nd stage—VANGUARD (q.v.) 2nd stage using an Aerojet engine
    3rd stage—Allegheny Ballistics Laboratory solid propellant rocket

Payload about 25 lb.

THOR-HUSTLER. A 2-stage satellite launching vehicle sponsored by Advanced Research Projects Agency (ARPA) (q.v.).

    1st stage—THOR (q.v.)
    2nd stage—Bell Hustler liquid rocket engine using JPA (q.v.) and RFNA (q.v.).

The payload can vary up to 150 lb. The 2nd stage, which orbits, weighs 7,000 lbs. Used to launch the DISCOVERER (q.v.) satellite. See Table 6, page 245.

thp. Thrust horsepower.

three-phase three-wire system. An alternating-current supply system comprising three conductors over which three-phase power is transmitted. A *four-wire system,* which includes a ground, is sometimes used in local installations.

three-way valve. A type of transfer valve-actuator combination in which only one valve port is used and the actuator output is achieved by metering the working fluid into or out of only one actuator chamber. The system pressure always acts on the small area of the actuator. Thus if A_2 is twice the area of A_1, the available control pressure, P_c, is one-half the supply pressure, P_s, under no-load conditions. The load induced pressure is:

$$P_L = P_c - \frac{P_s}{2}; \quad \text{if } P_E = 0 \text{ (exhaust pressure)}$$

three-wire system. A direct-current or single-phase alternating-current system comprising three conductors, one of which (the neutral wire) is maintained at a potential midway between the potential of the other two.

threshold. *See* improvement threshold.

throat. The most constricted area or section of a duct, passage, or the like, as of a jet nozzle.

throat velocity (critical velocity). The velocity of flow in a nozzle throat. The local acoustic velocity is equal to the critical velocity and $M = 1$.

$$V_t = \sqrt{gkRT_t}$$

where g = acceleration of gravity, ft/sec.^{2}; k = ratio of specific heats; R = universal gas constant; T_t = absolute temperature of gases at the throat, °R.

thrust. (1) The driving force exerted on any vehicle, rocket, guided missile, or other object by its jet or rocket engine or engines, or other propulsive force. In this sense thrust is a component of the total aerodynamic forces acting on a vehicle or winged missile parallel to and opposed to the relative wind, and results from engine power or from energy external to the body exerted in that direction. (2) Jet thrust (q.v.). Thrust, in this sense, is measured in terms of the fluid mass flow in pounds per second multiplied by jet velocity (relative to the body) in feet per second divided by gravity acceleration of 32.18 feet per second per second. (3) In jet propulsion, the resultant force in the direction of motion, owing to the components of the pressure forces in excess of ambient atmospheric pressure, acting on all inner surfaces of the vehicle parallel to the direction of motion. Thrust less drag equals accelerating force.

For a rocket: $\text{thrust} = \dfrac{V_e \dot{w}}{g} + (p_e - p_o)A_e$

where V_e = velocity at nozzle exit, ft/sec; p_e = pressure at nozzle exit, lb/sq ft; p_o = ambient pressure, lb/sq ft; A_e = nozzle exit area, sq ft; g = acceleration of gravity, ft/sec^2; $\dot{w}$ = mass flow, lb/sec.

For a turbojet or ramjet:

$$\text{thrust} = \frac{\dot{w}}{g}(V_j - V)$$

where V_j = exhaust jet velocity, ft/sec; V = vehicle velocity, ft/sec.

thrust. *Types of, see* effective vehicle–; gross–; jet–; net jet–; pressure–; specific–; static–; stream–; velocity–.

thrust augmentation. The increasing of the thrust of a jet engine or of a rocket by any of various means. Thrust augmentation for jet engines is accomplished by afterburning, reheating, water injection (q.q.v.), etc. *See also* augmentation.

thrust buildup. The sequence of events at the start of a large rocket power plant that begins with the ignition phase, progresses through prestage (q.v.), and is completed when full thrust is obtained at main stage (q.v.).

thrust chamber. In a liquid rocket, the assembly (consisting of the injector, nozzle, and combustion chamber, q.q.v.) in which mixing of liquid propellants takes place to form hot gases which are then ejected through a nozzle at high velocity to give momentum to the system. See Fig. 20, page 240.

thrust chamber assembly (TCA). In liquid rocket engines, the assembly composed of the thrust chamber, propellant control valves, valve actuators, igniter, and other associated parts. See Fig. 20, page 240.

thrust coefficient. In rocket applications, a coefficient useful in determining the thrust amplification due to gas expansion in the nozzle as compared to the thrust exerted if the chamber pressure acted over the throat area ideally.

$$C_f = \frac{F}{p_c A_t}$$

where F = thrust; p_c = chamber pressure; A_t = throat area.

thrust control. A means of controlling velocity, M, or burnout velocity in order to provide proper performance. Control may be obtained by throttling, termination at a specified time, reduced thrust by controlled burning (e.g., in a solid rocket). Differentiate from *thrust vector control* (q.v.).

thrust equalizer. A device used to prevent motion of a solid propellant rocket in the event of inadvertent ignition by permitting discharge of exhaust gases from both ends to result in a zero net thrust. The device is closed off or otherwise inactivated when the rocket is readied for use. A typical design would provide a blow-out disc in the head end approximately equal to the nozzle exit area.

thrust horsepower. (1) The actual horsepower delivered by the engine-propeller unit of a vehicle. In this instance thrust horsepower is derived from the formula, thp equals bhp multiplied by the percentage of propeller efficiency. Thrust horsepower is less than brake horsepower because the propeller is not 100% efficient. (2) The thrust of a jet engine or rocket expressed in terms of horsepower. In this sense, thrust is converted into horsepower by the formula, thp equals thrust pounds times vehicle speed in miles per hour divided by 375.

thrust misalignment. The difference between the actual and desired direction of thrust in a propulsion system. It adversely affects dispersion, the greatest effect occurring early in the flight when the flight velocity is low.

thrust mount. A portion of the test or launch stand that supports a complete missile or its separate stages during captive or flight tests (q.q.v.). Missile support is provided at, usually, four points by the thrust mount.

thrust output. The net thrust delivered by a jet engine or rocket engine (q.q.v.).

thrust-pound. A unit of measurement for the thrust produced by a jet or rocket engine (q.q.v.).

thrust programming. The control of a trajectory (q.v.) by means of thrust variations in accordance with a predetermined or computed program (q.v.).

thrust specific fuel consumption. A measure of the performance of a turbojet engine.

$$\text{TSFC} = 3600 \frac{\dot{w}}{F} \text{ lb of fuel/hr/lb of thrust}$$

where $\dot{w}$ = weight flow of fuel, lb/sec; F = thrust, lb.

thrust spoiler. As applied to a jet engine, a system of shutters over the end of the jet tailpipe to destroy most of the positive thrust at idling speeds, and thus reduce the landing run. (Not in general use.)

thrust stand. A test stand (q.v.) used to measure the thrust (frequently in several planes) of engines.

thrust termination device. The scheme used to cut off thrust (q.v.) of an engine on command from the guidance system (q.v.). It is usually applied to solid propellant rocket engines; implemented by blowing off end closures or opening vents.

thrust termination equipment. A component of the propulsion system (q.v.) uniquely used to terminate thrust (and thus acceleration) at a predetermined cutoff (q.v.) time to achieve proper positioning of the point of impact of the missile or payload.

thrust-to-weight ratio. A parameter useful in comparing the performance of rocket engines and vehicles. The ratio is that of thrust to loaded weight.

thrust vector control. A means of controlling a missile by use of *jet deflection* devices which, in response to appropriate signals from the autopilot, maintain proper attitude and path control. Typical schemes used in rocket engines: (a) swivelling or gimballing nozzles; (b) jetavators (q.v.); (c) jet vanes (q.v.). *See* vector steering.

thunderstorm. Cumulonimbus clouds (q.v.) accompanied by lightning and thunder. Normally thunderstorms are accompanied by torrential rain for brief moments during the passage of the storm, but occasionally no precipitation reaches the ground. Often they cause hail and gusty surface winds of considerable velocity. They are sometimes attended by tornadoes which cause great damage. Vertical velocities inside thunderstorms are extremely erratic and as high as 120 mph.

thunderstorm. *Types of, see* air-mass–; cold front–; frontal–; prefrontal–; squall-line–; warm front–.

thunderstorm cell. Any one of a number of discrete regions of convective activity making up a thunderstorm.

thyratron. A gas-filled grid-controlled soft tube which operates characteristically in such a way that, starting from a high negative grid potential, current flow occurs suddenly at some more positive grid potential, after which the anode current is independent of the grid, and must be stopped by reducing the anode potential. (Thyratrons are used in radars mainly for *switching* or *triggering* in modulator circuits. Lower power versions are used in control circuits.)

Thyristor. Trade name for a modified germanium transistor (q.v.). It is characterized by fast action and low power requirements.

tilt angle. A mathematical artifice used to program (q.v.) the trajectory (q.v.) of ballistic missiles (q.v.) from the vertical ascent toward the horizontal to get "on-target." In practice, the tilt is not a discrete angle but is slowly changed.

tilt stabilization. The stabilization (q.v.) of something against tilting (e.g., the stabilization of a radar antenna by means of a gyroscope).

tilt table. A table of accurate orientation with respect to the local gravity vector; used to test accelerometers.

time. (1) The mode of grouping sense impressions by the order in which events are observed. *Abstract time,* as used in mechanics and physics generally, is a parameter serving as the fundamental independent variable in terms of which the relative dynamic behavior of all physical systems may be compared. As a parameter it may take all the succession of values of the real number continuum. (2) Time (as commonly used) is an artificially developed reference, based on the daily rotation of the Earth with respect to the Sun. The speed of the Earth in its orbit about the Sun varies, and the length of the day, based on the rotation of the Earth relative to the Sun varies. The mean sun moves eastward in the celestial equator at a uniform rate equal to the average rate of the true Sun in the ecliptic, thus removing the irregularities of apparent time. Time as measured by this means is termed *civil time.* The difference between civil time and apparent time reaches a maximum value of nearly 16½ minutes in November. To avoid confusion, the Earth is divided into time zones, each 15 degrees wide in longitude, starting at the zero zone, extending 7½ degrees each side of the zero meridian at Greenwich. (3) Time measured by the Earth's rotation in a star reference system is termed *sidereal time.*

time. *Types of, see* action–; apparent–; available–; burning–; dead–; delay–; down–; equation of–; Greenwich apparent–; Greenwich civil–; Greenwich mean–; Greenwich sidereal–; inverse recovery–; local apparent–; local civil–; local mean–; local sidereal–; LOXing–; procurement lead–; pulse decay–; range–; readiness–; real–; relaxation–; repair–; response–; rise–; safe–; settling–; sidereal–; standard–; stay–; trouble shooting–; t-time, T-time; up time; usable–; web–; x-time, X-time; zebra–.

time base. In a radar set, a bright line on the cathode-ray screen, traced by the electron beam in synchronization with the transmitted pulses, by which range to an object is determined as a function of time, as indicated by the distance of the echo signal along the line.

time constant. The time required for a varying quantity to reach $(1 - 1/e)$ of its total change (approximately 63.2 per cent of its total change). (1) In electronics, in a capacitor-re-

sistor circuit, the time in seconds for the capacitor to reach approximately 63.2 per cent of its full charge after a steady voltage is applied; in an inductor-resistor circuit the time in seconds required for the current to reach approximately 63.2 per cent of its final value, after a steady voltage is applied. (2) In structural dynamics, the response time characteristic of a structure to a transient load.

time-delay relay. A relay in which the energizing or de-energizing of the coil precedes movement of the armature by an appreciable and generally determinable interval.

time dilation. Relativity effect experienced within bodies moving at very high speeds in which time measured by a clock travelling within the body seems slower than time measured by a clock at rest in the initial frame of reference (such as Earth). In nature, time dilation seems to slow the decay of mesons (q.v.) passing through the atmosphere. In interstellar flight, it is suggested that time dilation might make it possible for interstellar voyagers to make their trip in a few years of their "time" while many more years pass back on Earth.

time-division multiplex. In electronics, pulse modulation is commonly used in time-division multiplex systems. Because of the time space available between the modulated pulses, other pulses corresponding to other signal channels can be inserted if they are in frequency synchronism.

time function graph. A plot of quantity vs. time (e.g., altitude, pressure, acceleration, etc., vs. time).

time fuze. A fuze used on a delayed action explosive; a delay fuze.

time limit failure. A failure (q.v.) that judgment and experience indicate could become a critical or an abortive failure (q.v.), but which has been averted by replacement within a specified time. Time limit failures can be classified only by actual weapon system experience.

timer. In radar, a device in a radar set that establishes the pulse rate and controls the timing of other elements in the set.

timer, calibration. *See* calibration timer.

time response. Of a system or element, the output as a function of time, following the application of a prescribed input under specified operating conditions.

time sharing. *See* multiplexing.

timing. *See* target timing.

tin bender. (Vernacular) A company or individual that makes missile airframes or sheet metal parts.

TING-A-LING. *See* GENIE.

tinsel. A type of confusion reflector (q.v.).

TINY TIM. A code name for a type of large (11.75 in.) aircraft rocket.

tip-loss factor. A mathematical factor used in correcting for the loss of lift in the tip region of an airfoil.

tip-off. The angular momentum, due to the action of gravity, acquired by a missile if its forward supports leave the launcher before the aft supports.

tip rake. A geometrical characteristic of aerodynamic surfaces; the trailing edge tip is cut such that its angle with the missile centerline is less than the MACH angle.

TIROS Project. A National Aeronautics and Space Administration (NASA) program to orbit twenty-four hour meteorological satellites carrying television cameras. Air Force booster THOR (q.v.) is used.

TITAN. Surface-to-surface two-stage intercontinental ballistic missile (ICBM) (q.v.). Air Force designation: for the weapon system: WS-107A-2; for the missile: SM-68.

Over-all length: about 90 ft; body diameter of first stage: 10 ft; launching weight: over 200,000 lb; burnout speed: about MACH 15. TITAN is a two-stage, liquid propellant (LOX/RPI) rocket with a 5,500 mile range. Booster consists of two 150,000 lb thrust engines; one 60,000 lb sustainer. Radar guidance or inertial guidance. Thermonuclear warhead. It can be broken down into several parts for easier ground or air-cargo transportation.

Systems Engineering contractor: Space Technology Laboratories. Prime Contractor: Martin Co. Airframe: Martin. Engines: Aerojet-General Corp. Radar guidance system: Bell Telephone Laboratories/Western Electric Co. and Remington-Rand Univac Division. Inertial guidance system: AC Spark Plug Division of General Motors. Nose cone: AVCO Manufacturing Corp.

TM. (1) Tactical Missile (q.v.). (2) Technical Manual (q.v.).

TM-61A, TM-61B, and TM-61C. Air Force designation for surface-to-surface winged bomber termed MATADOR (q.v.).

TM-76A and TM-76B. Air Force designation for surface-to-surface winged bomber termed MACE (q.v.).

T/O. Table of organization.

tolerance. *Types of, see* aerodynamic–; frequency–; tuning–.

tone. *See* complex tone.

tonitro-cirrus cloud. Tendrils of cloud combed by the wind from the top of a cumulus (q.v.) or cumulonimbus (q.v.). Sometimes termed *false cirrus.*

tooling. *Types of, see* coordinated–; hard–; soft–.

tool-made samples. Articles manufactured on and with production tooling. Qualification tests are usually performed on tool-made samples.

top. (Vernacular) A gyroscope (q.v.).

topping. Replacing propellants, lost through vaporization and initial consumption, from *ground supply.*

TOPSEC. TOP SECRET (q.v.).

TOP SECRET. Of classified material, having such status that its unauthorized disclosure would cause exceptionally grave damage to the United States. The highest level of security classification (q.v.) outside the AEC system. *See* security classification.

tornadoes. Some thunderstorms, particularly the line-squall type, occasionally develop a violent whirl of air (or tornado) which extends down from the base of the cloud and touches the Earth. It often draws up into the cloud again and may strike some distance away or never reappear. Very low pressure prevails inside a tornado because of its great vorticity. Velocities of 200 to 300 mph are suspected in tornadoes.

torque. A moment that produces, or tends to produce, rotation, twisting or torsion. The product of a force and the perpendicular distance from the axis of rotation to the line of action of the force. Often represented as a vector drawn along the axis of rotation with a length equal to the magnitude and a direction that is the same as that in which a right-hand screw would advance if the torque caused the rotation of such a screw.

torquing. *See* gyroscope torquing.

torsion. The internal moment of a body subjected to twisting or wrenching, e.g., by the application of torque to one end of a shaft while the other is held fast or turned in the opposite direction; the act of turning so as to create this moment.

total frequency deviation. In electronics, the sum of the positive and negative deviation from band center. This also applies to a unit tuned to a band edge and deviated in one direction only.

total impulse. In jet propulsion usage, the product of the average thrust (in pounds), developed by the engine, times the burning time (in seconds).

$$I = F \, \Delta t = W_p I_{sp}$$

where F = thrust, lb; Δt = burning time, sec; W_p = propellant weight, lb; I_{sp} = specific impulse, sec.

total stress. The total internal force acting on a section taken through a body. The component of the internal force perpendicular to the area of the section is termed *normal stress*, and the component parallel to the area is termed *shearing stress*. If the body is being elongated, the normal stress is a *tensile stress*, and if the body is being shortened, the normal stress is a *compressive stress*. The units are: pound, kips, etc.

touchdown. The landing of a manned or unmanned space vehicle on the surface of a body by any method except gliding. Reverse jets would be the probable method of touchdown for spacecraft.

tower. *Types of, see* boresight–; ivory–; missile servicing–; umbilical–.

tower launcher. A missile launcher that is vertical (or nearly so) and high enough to give directional stability (q.v.) to the missile. Also termed a *vertical tower launcher*.

TPR. Telescopic Photographic Recorder (q.v.).

trace. In radar, the line on a radar screen made by the time base.

track-command guidance. A method of missile guidance wherein both target and missile are tracked by separate radars. Corrective commands are sent to the missile via the coded beam. The two beams are programmed in coincidence on the target. See Fig. 4, page 51.

tracker. *See* horizon tracker.

tracking. *Types of, see* aided–; automatic–; celestial radio–; star–.

tracking beacon. An electronic device installed on a missile that transmits pulses which can be received by tracking equipment (e.g., AZUSA system).

tracking radar. A high-powered radar designed for tracking targets usually in two axes (azimuth and elevation) and equipped with pickoffs (q.v.) to permit accurate readout (q.v.) of antenna position. Range and range rate are obtained by measuring the time required for a pulse to be transmitted and received. *See* radar.

track Mercator. In cartography, a transverse Mercator projection tangent to a great circle between any two selected points.

track-while-scan (TWS). A radar technique used to detect a target, to compute its velocity, and to predict its future position without interfering with continuous radar screening.

trade inversion. In meteorology, a temperature inversion between the trade winds and the dry air aloft.

trade wind. A drying wind that blows almost continually from an easterly direction from a sub-tropical high-pressure region to the region of lower pressure near the equator. There are two belts of trade winds, one on each side of the equator. Those winds north of the equator come from the northeast, those south of the equator from the southeast. They are produced, in part, by Coriolis forces (q.v.).

traffic-handling capacity. The ability of a guidance or weapon system (q.q.v.) simultaneously to control multiple missiles against one or more targets; for example: (1) the active air-to-air homing guidance system is limited only by the number of missiles carried by the interceptor aircraft and the time available for launching the missiles. It is theoretically possible for the interceptor aircraft to launch more than one missile against the same target. In addition, it is possible for the interceptor aircraft to launch one missile against a target, break away, and launch another missile against a different target. (2) In the TERRIER (q.v.) weapon system, several missiles may be salvoed and made to ride the same radar beam. The traffic capacity, thus, is greater than if each missile required a separate radar beam.

trail. *See* vapor trail.

trailing-edge pulse time. The time at which the instantaneous amplitude of a pulse of electrical energy last reaches a stated fraction of the peak pulse amplitude (q.v.).

trailing edge, subsonic. *See* subsonic trailing edge.

train. *See* pulse train.

training. *See* on-the-job training.

trajectory. The path of a missile from launch to impact or destruct. *Design trajectories* have restraints imposed by mission, velocity, altitude, dynamic pressure, temperature, etc. See Fig. 27. *See also* reference trajectory.

trajectory. *Types of, see* ballistic–; electron–; glide–; hyperbolic–; parabolic–; powered flight–; skip–; terminal–; vacuum–; zero lift–.

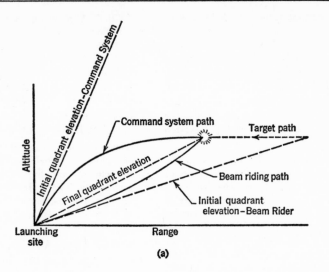

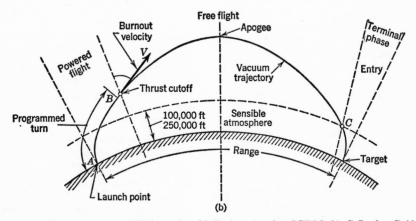

Fig. 27. (a) Beam rider and command flight paths. (b) Trajectory of an ICBM. (A. S. Locke, *Guidance*, D. Van Nostrand; U. S. Air Force, *Air University Quarterly Review*, Vol. IX, No. 3, Summer 1957)

trajectory-controlled. In missilery, guided or directed so that the trajectory will follow a predetermined curve.

trajectory phases. (1) *Launch phase:* normally that portion of the flight path from launch to booster burnout, in the case of aerodynamic missiles; or from launch to motor burnout in the case of ballistic missiles. (*Note:* this definition may vary from missile to missile and must be defined for each missile.) (2) *Mid-course phase:* from end of launch to beginning of terminal phase. (3) *Terminal phase:* that portion of the path from initiation of terminal dive or recovery, in the case of aerodynamic missiles, or from reentry (approx. 100,000 ft altitude), in the case of ballistic missiles to termination of flight. See Fig. 27.

tranceiver. A unit combining the radio or radar transmitter and receiver, such as is used in a transponder.

tranquilizers. (Vernacular) Instruments needed to stabilize a missile's "brains."

transcendental. A term for *numbers, equations,* or *functions* which are not algebraic.

transconductance (mutual conductance). A conductance (I/R or I/E) relating input and output. Also it denotes the small change in plate current in an electronic tube which results from a small change in grid voltage. Transconductance is equal to the amplification factor of a tube divided by the plate resistance.

transcriber. A device for converting coded information back to its original state.

transducer. (1) A device actuated by power from one system and supplying power in the same or any other form to a second system. These systems may be *electrical, mechanical,* or *acoustical.* (2) A *pickup* or *end organ* in a telemetering system. *See* beacon. See Fig. 26, page 282.

transducer. *Types of, see* digital–; harmonic conversion–; insertion power gain–; insertion voltage–.

transducer gain. The ratio of the power that a transducer delivers to its specified load under specific operating conditions to the available power of the specified source. If the input and/or output power consists of more than one component, e.g., multifrequency signal or noise, then the particular components used and their weighting should be specified. This gain is usually expressed in decibels.

transducer insertion gain. The gain resulting from the insertion of a transducer into a transmission system; the ratio of the power delivered to that part of the system following the transducer, to the power delivered to that same part before insertion of the transducer. If the input and/or output power consists of more than one component, e.q., multifrequency signal or noise, then the particular components used and their weighting must be specified. This gain is usually expressed in decibels. The "insertion of a transducer" includes bridging of an impedance across the transmission system.

transducer insertion loss. The loss resulting from the insertion of a transducer into a transmission system; the ratio of the power delivered to that part of the system following the transducer (before insertion of the transducer) to the power delivered to that same part of the system *after* insertion of the transducer. This ratio is usually expressed in decibels. If the input power, or the output power, or both consist of more than one component, the particular components used must be specified.

transfer ellipse. The path followed by a body moving from one elliptical orbit (q.v.) to another. Transfer ellipses which intersect departure and arrival orbits at large angles are most expensive in energy requirements. *See* tangential ellipse.

transference. *See* heat transference.

transfer function. A mathematical expression which expresses the relationship between the outgoing and incoming signals of a process, control element, system, device, etc. Shaping, restraints, band-pass, and other characteristics are defined. A common expression for the transfer function is the Laplace transform of the network input, with all initial conditions set equal to zero. The expression *transfer characteristic* can be used to refer either to the transfer function or the frequency response when the initial conditions are all equal to zero.

transfer orbit. Line of motion characterized by initial and final constraints.

transfer room. A room below the erection area of a missile launching stand and connected to the control building (usually) by an underground cableway. It houses the relay racks, terminal boards, and other equipment necessary to route cables from the test stand to the control building.

transfer valve. An electrohydraulic or electromechanical device used to control the power circuit of a servo (q.v.) by means of an electrical signal. *See* four-way valve; three-way valve.

transfer velocity. In orbit mechanics, the escape velocity (q.v.) less the orbit velocity (q.v.). It is the net escape velocity from the solar system.

transformer. *See* push-pull transformer.

transient. (1) A waveform which does not have a basic or periodic function (e.g., nonrepeating). (2) An adjective applied to describe a waveform or event which is not periodic (e.g., random pulses of pressure, voltage, etc.).

transient motion. A motion that exists when a mechanical system or apparatus passes from one steady state to another.

transient state. A condition in a dynamic system which implies a temporary abnormal or erratic behavior of a variable such as speed, temperature, pressure, etc. Contrast with *steady state* in which the variable is either held at a constant value or else changes uniformly with time.

transistor. A nonlinear semiconductor with three or more electrodes. Best known of the solid-state, semiconductor devices that "put to work our ability to control the flow of electrons in solids." An electronic device for amplification and control which consists of a semiconducting material to which contact is made by three or more electrodes. It controls the flow of electrons by means of selective crystal properties of certain materials, e.g., germanium. Within limits, a transistor can replace a vacuum tube.

Developed by Bell Telephone Laboratories, the transistor is produced commercially by more than a dozen companies. *See* spacistor; thyristor; trisistor.

transistor. *Types of, see* junction–; point contact–.

transit. *See* upper transit.

TRANSIT Project. An Advanced Research Projects Agency (ARPA) program for navigational satellites. Air Force provides the THOR (q.v.) booster and launcher.

transition engineering. That phase of engineering effort encompassing the movement of a project from research and development into detail design and production.

transition flow. A flow of fluid about an airfoil that is changing from laminar flow to turbulent flow (q.q.v.).

transition piece. In a turbojet engine, a part or section leading from an inner liner to a nozzle diaphragm. Sometimes termed a *fishtail*.

transition point. In aerodynamics, a point or line on an airfoil where the laminar flow (q.v.) becomes turbulent usually under circumstances where the airfoil travels at a speed in excess of that for which designed.

translunar space. The space between the distance of the lunar orbit (q.v.) and the limit of the Earth's activity sphere with respect to the Sun.

transmissibility. The ratio of transmitted force to the applied force in a mechanical system. When damping is negligible:

$$\text{TR} = \frac{1}{(\omega/\omega_{nd})^2 - 1} \quad \text{and} \quad \frac{\omega}{\omega_{nd}} \geqslant \sqrt{2}$$

where ω = natural frequency, rad/sec; ω_{nd} = damped natural frequency, rad/sec.

transmission. *Types of, see* double sideband–; single sideband–.

transmission line. Any conductor or system of conductors used to carry electrical energy or radio-frequency energy from a source to a point of expenditure. Applied to: (a) a cable or wire; (b) a set of conductors from a radio conductor to an antenna; (c) a waveguide.

transmission loss (or gain). The transmission loss of a system joining a *load* having a given electrical, mechanical, or acoustical impedance, and a *source* having a given electrical, mechanical, or acoustical impedance, and which impresses a given electromotive force, force, torque, or pressure, is expressed by the logarithm of the ratio of the power actually delivered to the load to the power delivered to the load under some *reference* condition. For a *loss* the reference power is greater. For a *gain* the reference power is smaller.

transmission security. That aspect of communication security concerned with the transmission of electrical and radio communications.

transmissometer. An electronic apparatus for ascertaining the degree of visibility by measuring the amount of light that comes through the atmosphere to a fixed point from a fixed transmitting point.

transmitter. Any mechanism or device that converts one form or measure of energy or movement into a suitable form for transmission and then transmits it (e.g., a potentiometer, synchro, or the like that converts voltage or current into new measures of voltage or current for transmittal; a radio apparatus transmits frequency energy into the transmission line; also, the whole apparatus of a radio sending station, including the antenna).

transmitter. *Types of, see* amplitude-modulated–; crystal-controlled–; crystal-stabilized–; double sideband–; fixed frequency–; frequency-modulated–.

transmutation. The process whereby an atomic nucleus of one species changes into one of a different species, often accomplished by bombardment with nuclear particles, as in a cyclotron or nuclear reactor.

transonic. The intermediate speed in which the flow patterns change from subsonic flow to supersonic; i.e., from MACH numbers of about 0.8 to 1.2 or vice versa.

transonic "barrier." A so-called "barrier" to flight encountered by a vehicle designed for subsonic (q.v.) speeds when it reaches transonic (q.v.) speed and meets the turbulence incident to diverse degrees of compressibility. Like other obstacles to flight (e.g., drag or gravity) the sonic "barrier" is overcome by aerodynamic application. It is usually termed the *sonic barrier*. *See* MACH line.

transonic range. The range of speeds between the speed at which *one* point on a vehicle reaches supersonic (q.v.) speed, and the speed at which *all* points reach supersonic speed. The transonic range for a particular vehicle depends upon its design, but it may spread for some vehicles between approximately MACH 0.8 and MACH 1.2. *See* speed of sound.

transonic speed. A speed at which a vehicle moves relative to surrounding fluid when one or more local points on the body are moving at subsonic (q.v.) speed at the same time that one or more other points on the body move at sonic or supersonic (q.q.v.) speeds; any one of the several speeds within the transonic range (q.v.)

of a particular vehicle. Since transonic speed is relative to the surrounding fluid, the particles in the fluid pass over or across different parts of the vehicle at different speeds, depending upon the contours or shapes of the component parts. Thus, for example, one point on a vehicle may be moving at only 600 mph, yet several other points may at the same time be moving at 750 mph; likewise, when several points on the vehicle achieve a speed of 900 mph, several other points may have a speed of less than 750 mph. *See* critical speed; remote velocity.

transpiration cooling. *See* sweat (transpiration) cooling.

transplanetary space. Space beyond the orbit of the particular planetary orbit as seen from the Earth (e.g., Mercury's orbit lies in the trans-Venusian space).

transpolar. Across the north polar region.

transponder. Usually a beacon containing a receiver and transmitter. The purpose is to *increase the energy level of the target or missile signal* in order that the surveillance range can be extended. The transponded signal may be at the same frequency as the surveillance radar or it may be preset at some value which is different (e.g., 50 mcs). Under these conditions the surveillance radar transmits at one frequency and the transponder transmits back at another frequency.

transverse (antenna) fuze. An electronic fuze in which the antenna is set at right angles to the longitudinal axis of a missile, the sensitivity pattern being ahead of the nose.

transverse Mercator projection. In cartography, a map projection like the Mercator projection (q.v.) but with the base line at some great circle other than the equator.

trap. In rocketry, that part of a solid rocket engine that keeps the grain (q.v.) in place.

trapped propellant. In a liquid rocket engine, the residual propellant in the feed lines which cannot be used because of inadequate suction head. *Trapped propellant* plus *engine dry weight* equals *engine wet weight*.

traveling-wave tube. A broadband microwave tube which depends for its characteristics upon the interaction between the field of a wave propagated along a waveguide and a beam of electrons traveling with the wave. In this tube, the electrons in the beam travel with velocities slightly greater than that of the wave, and on the average are slowed down and bunched by the field of the wave. (It is used as a microwave amplifier.)

tree aircraft rocket launcher. An aircraft rocket launcher (q.v.) having a central stem with rocket-bearing branches.

triangle. *See* wind triangle.

tridop. An elliptical instrumentation or measuring system using the Doppler frequency shift resulting from missile velocity as intelligence.

triethylamine. A liquid rocket propellant *fuel.*

triethylborane $[(C_2H_5)_3B]$. A liquid, high-energy rocket or ramjet *fuel*, spontaneously flammable in air and miscible with hydrocarbons (and therefore may be used as an additive); a boron derivative; heat of combustion: 20,230 Btu/lb.

triethyl-trithiophospite. A liquid rocket propellant *fuel.* See Table 3, page 157.

trigger circuit. A multivibrator circuit in which either of the two tubes can operate stably, but the firing of either tube extinguishes the other. The "flip-flop" action is produced by a trigger pulse in the grid of both tubes. Modifications make possible the use of positive or negative triggering, a double flip-flop, or one-shot operation. (It is used in radar and counting circuits.)

trim. In aerodynamics, a steady-state (static) condition wherein the wing or other control surface of a missile is deflected to provide the necessary lifting or normal force; it is required that the over-all moments acting on the full configuration missile must be zero. The missile is said to be *trimmed* when it is at its equilibrium (total moments equal zero) angle of attack for a given control surface setting.

trimetrogon camera. An assembly of three aerial cameras arranged and hooked up so as to take one vertical and two oblique photographs simultaneously, giving a horizon-to-horizon coverage. Also termed the *horizon-to-horizon camera.*

trim ratio. The ratio of angle of attack to angle of trim at steady-state conditions; a measure of the maneuverability as a function of control surface deflection (the aerodynamic *gain* in the control loop).

tri-*n*-butylborane $[(C_4H_9)_3B]$. An organic boron compound suitable for use as ramjet fuel or as a fuel additive. Heat of combustion is 19,500 Btu/lb.

triode. A three-electrode vacuum tube, containing a cathode, control grid, and anode.

triple diversity. *See* diversity radar.

triple point. In supersonic aerodynamics, the

point of intersection of the incident front, the reflected front, and the MACH front.

triplet. *See* LORAN triplet.

trisistor. Trade name for a modified alloyed junction transistor (q.v.) with thyratron—(q.v.) like characteristics, designed for use as a trigger in switching circuits.

trisonic wind tunnel. A test facility capable of subsonic, transonic, and supersonic (q.q.v.) operations.

TRITON. Surface-to-surface ramjet missile. Navy Bureau of Ordnance designation: XSSM-N-2.

Weight with fuel: 20,000 lb; range: 1500 miles cruising at 80,000 ft; cruising speed: MACH 3.5. Two ramjet cruise engines, two solid propellant rocket boosters. Map-matching (ATRAN) guidance system. Submarine-launched; can use REGULUS (q.v.) launching equipment. Described as a long-range, supersonic, air-breathing bombardment missile falling midway in capability between REGULUS II and POLARIS (q.q.v.).

Technical Direction: Applied Physics Laboratory/The Johns Hopkins University. Prime Contractor: McDonnell Aircraft Corp. Airframe: McDonnell. Engines: cruise: McDonnell; boosters: Hercules Powder Co. Guidance system: Goodyear Aircraft Corp.

Project cancelled.

Trojan points. In planetary orbits, those satellites whose positions are stable fore and aft of a planet. The points are located at such distances that lines drawn through the centers of the satellite, planet, and Sun would form an equilateral triangle.

tropical air mass. *See* air mass.

tropical cyclone. A cyclonic storm originating in the tropics. *See* hurricane; typhoon.

tropical day. A synthetic temperature vs. altitude profile used for performance calculations. Characteristics are shown in Fig. 25, page 267.

tropical storm. A general term sometimes applied to a tropical cyclone in which the surface wind speed is 34 to 63 knots, below that of a hurricane (q.v.).

tropopause. The boundary or zone of transition between the troposphere and the stratosphere (q.q.v.). It varies in height from about 55,000 ft at the equator to 25,000 ft over the poles. The height also changes with the seasons and with the passage of cyclones and anticyclones. The temperature at the tropopause ranges from approximately $-67°$F above the poles to about $-100°$F over the equator. See Fig. 11, page 140.

tropopause, multiple. *See* multiple tropopause.

troposphere. The region of the atmosphere extending from the surface of the Earth up to the tropopause (approximately 10 miles); characterized by convective air movements and a pronounced vertical temperature gradient decreasing with altitude, in contrast to the convectionless and almost vertically isothermal stratosphere above the tropopause. It contains about 75% of the total weight of the atmosphere. The thickness of the troposphere varies from approximately 60,000 ft at the equator to approximately 30,000 ft at the poles. Its thickness also varies with the seasons and with different meteorological conditions. See Fig. 11, page 140.

tropospheric wave. A radio wave that is propagated by reflection from a place of abrupt change in the dielectric constant or its gradient in the troposphere (q.v.). In some cases the ground wave may be so altered that new components appear to arise from reflections in regions of rapidly changing dielectric constants; when these components are distinguishable from the other components, they are called *tropospheric waves*.

trouble shooting. The location of a malfunction by making a series of checks based on symptoms or indications.

trouble shooting time. The time required to determine or to isolate the cause of a system malfunction. It does not include the time required to replace or to repair the units in which the fault occurred.

trough. In meteorology, an elongated extent of relatively low atmospheric pressure.

trough, polar. *See* polar trough.

true altitude. The altitude above mean sea level. Since the pressure altimeter registers the altitude above whatever setting is set into the altimeter according to the standard pressure lapse rate, true altitude is ascertained at any given point by a setting determined by local ground-level pressure reduced to sea-level pressure. Contrast with *pressure altitude* (q.v.).

true azimuth. Azimuth measured by an angle from true north (q.v.); abbreviated Zn or Z_n.

true north. The direction of the North Pole from the observer; a line showing this direction.

true precession. Actual precession, as distinquished from apparent precession. *See* precession.

true range. The distance along a great circle on the Earth's surface (sea level) connecting the launching and impact points.

TTAF. Technical Training, Air Force; Gulf-port, Miss.

TTE. Tentative Table of Equipment.

t-time, *T*-time. Time measured from the first motion, or lift-off, of a missile when it is being launched. Only (+) *t*-times are used. Prior events are timed in (−) *x*-time. (+) *x*-time is used alternatively with *t*-time.

Tuba. A code name for a type of jamming transmitter operating in the range of 480 mcs to 500 mcs. *See* electronic jamming.

tube. *Types of, see* ballast–; cathode-ray–; crossover–; electron–; gassy–; hard–; local oscillator–; photoelectron-multiplier–; pitot-static–; shock–; soft–; static–; traveling-wave–; vacuum–; venturi–.

tubular aircraft rocket launcher. An aircraft rocket launcher (q.v.) carrying the rocket in, and launching it through, a tube.

tubular grain. A solid propellant grain cast in the form of a tube which burns with a constant value of K_n. The thickness of the propellant grain, termed the *web thickness*, determines the duration of the burning. See Fig. 22, page 259.

tumble counter. A form of counter in which individual stages, in response to successive stimuli, consecutively complete missing or incomplete cycles.

tumbling. (1) The act performed by a two-frame free gyroscope when both frames become co-planar. Under these circumstances, the gyroscope wheel rotates about a diameter as well as about its polar axis, resulting in loss in control. (2) Concerning missiles and projectiles in flight, the uncontrolled turning end-over-end about the transverse axis.

tuning tolerance. The precision with which it is possible to set a frequency to a desired value.

tuning unit. The frequency determining elements of a discriminator.

tunnel. *Types of, see* molecular beam–; shock–; wind–.

turbine. *Types of, see* aerodynamic–; closed-cycle–; full emission–; gas–; impulse–; impulse reaction–; open-cycle–; reaction–; single-stage–.

turbofan. The fan used in a ducted-fan jet engine (q.v.).

turbojet. A thermal jet engine (q.v.) whose air is supplied by a turbine-driven compressor, the turbine being activated by exhaust gases from the combustion chamber. *See* jet engines.

turboprop. A gas-turbine engine designed to drive a propeller for use at intermediate air-craft speeds. Also termed *propeller-turbine engine; prop jet.*

turbulence. (1) A condition in the airflow about a wing or other airfoil in which different velocities and pressures are laterally mixed between layers of the airflow. (2) In the atmosphere, a local condition characterized by updrafts, downdrafts, and gusts.

turbulent boundary layer. A condition in the boundary layer (q.v.) when the laminar flow (q.v.) breaks down or when random lateral movement is superimposed on the laminar flow.

turbulent flow. (1) Any part of a fluid flow in which the velocity at a given point varies more or less rapidly in magnitude and direction with time. (2) In aerodynamics, a condition wherein the air close to the surface is of a turbulent nature; that is, contains unpredictable eddies and generally *rough* flow. The opposite of *laminar flow* (q.v.).

turbulent separation. Separation of the flow of air in a turbulent boundary layer.

turpentine ($C_{10}H_{16}$). A liquid rocket propellant *fuel*. See Table 3, page 157.

TV. (1) Test Vehicle (guided missile). (2) Terminal Velocity (q.v.).

twenty-four-hour orbit. *See* stationary orbit.

twenty-four-hour satellite. An Earth satellite with an orbiting period of 24 hours. It would appear to hang motionless in the sky if it were in a west to east circular orbit at a height of 5.7 Earth radii (22,600 miles).

twilight. The sunlight that is diffused or reflected in the sky before sunrise and after sunset by the atmosphere and its dust; the period of time during which this light is diffused. Twilight is considered to be divided into four overlapping twilights: *civil, observational, nautical,* and *astronomical* (q.q.v.), each characterized by the amount of light afforded at its darker limits.

twilight. *Types of, see* astronomical–; nautical–; observational–.

twilight band. In RF transmission, a band or zone lying between a bisignal zone and the equisignal zone. *See* Adcock radio range.

twilight zone. A bisignal zone.

twisted pair. A cable composed of two insulated conductors twisted together either with or without a common covering.

twister. (Vernacular) A tornado.

two-dimensional flow. In aerodynamics, a flow in which two cartesian coordinates are sufficient to specify conditions. The fluid undergoes a significant change of direction in one plane only; i.e., at right angles to the direction of the flow, as in the case of flow over a wing of infinite span. Wind tunnel tests are facilitated by two-dimensional observations, assuming uniform conditions along any line perpendicular to the walls of the tunnel.

two-stage compressor. Normally, a compressor of the centrifugal type in which the compressed air from the low-pressure or first stage is passed into the second stage and recompressed. This affords higher compression ratios than the theoretical maximum of approximately 4:1 available from a single-stage centrifugal compressor.

two-stage missile. (1) Any missile consisting of two stages or phases of powered flight using *two* distinct power plants. (2) A missile consisting of a booster stage and a second or sustainer stage. At staging the booster or first stage (consisting of propulsion system, tankage, structure, and autopilot) is discarded. The second-stage engine may be required to start at altitude or it may be ground-started, giving thrust during the boost phase. *See* tandem missile.

TWS. Track-While-Scan (q.v.).

type test. A test made on a typical or sample article to demonstrate that the particular design is adequate and qualified for its intended use. A *type test* is usually "one of a kind" and the test input may be to design extremes (e.g., structural test to failure).

typhoon. A violent tropical cyclonic storm, especially in the Pacific. Often termed a *hurricane* in the West Indies.

U

UAL. Unit Authorization List (q.v.).

UAM. Underwater-to-Air Missile. *See* ground-to-air missile; model designation.

U-coil. A variable inductor consisting of an open-face stack of U-shaped laminations with a coil wound on one or both of the legs.

U-DETA. A storable liquid rocket *fuel* consisting of a mixture of 65% UDMH (q.v.) and 40% DETA (q.v.).

UDMH. A liquid rocket propellant *fuel*. See Table 3, page 157.

UE. Unit Equipment (q.v.).

UEE. Unit Essential Equipment (q.v.).

UFO. Unidentified Flying Object.

UHF. Ultra-High Frequency (300-3000 mc/sec). See Fig. 8, page 105.

ullage. The volume of a propellant tank in excess of the propellant. It is provided to allow for thermal expansion of the propellant and for accumulation of gaseous products evolved from the propellant.

ultimate factor of safety. The ratio of the ultimate strength of a structure to the limit load.

ultimate load. In stress analysis, the maximum load a structure will support without failure. The ratio of ultimate and limits loads is the *factor of safety* (q.v.).

ultimate operational capability (UOC). That phase of a weapon system's use which follows initial operating capability (IOC) (q.v.) and which utilizes unit equipment.

ultimate strength load factor. The load factor (q.v.) which will cause the ultimate strength to be reached.

ultimate stress. The maximum stress that can be produced in a body per unit of original cross-sectional area.

ultrasonic. (1) Speeds between sonic and hypersonic (q.q.v.). (2) In acoustics, of or pertaining to frequencies above those that affect the human ear; i.e., above 20,000 vibrations per second.

ultrasonic frequency. Any frequency above the limits of 20,000 vibrations per second.

ultrasonic relief map. A special map made of various sound-reflecting materials, used with the ultrasonic trainer (q.v.) so as to simulate the radar reflection that would occur from that part of the Earth represented.

ultrasonics. That branch of acoustics (q.v.) dealing with ultrasonic (q.v.) frequencies.

ultrasonic trainer. A ground trainer for using radar equipment in which ultrasonic waves are directed against an ultrasonic relief map to simulate responses occurring in actual radar operation during flight.

umbilical cord. A cable fitted with a quick-disconnect plug on a missile, through which missile equipment is controlled and tested while the missile is still attached to launching equipment or parent plane.

umbilical plugs. Plugs used for missile external power, for checkout circuits, etc. Umbilical plugs are usually of three general types: (a) multiple pin-in-sheath type; (b) button type; (c) frangible type.

umbilical tower. A simple structure provided to support service lines and cables that must remain attached to a missile after the erector has been removed.

UME. Unit Mission Equipment (q.v.).

unbalanced gyroscope. A gyroscope (q.v.) which is unbalanced to make it sensitive to acceleration. Any acceleration about the sensitive axis produces gyroscope precession (displacement) at a rate proportional to the integral of acceleration, hence proportional to vehicle velocity. *See* integrating (pendulous) accelerometer gyroscope.

uncage. To disconnect the erection device in a displacement gyroscope (q.v.) system.

undercast. A layer of cloud beneath an aircraft. Distinguished from an *overcast* (q.v.) by the point of view.

undercooled. Of a liquid, supercooled.

underexpanded nozzle. A nozzle in which the working fluid is discharged at a pressure greater than the external pressure (i.e., the exit area is too small and expansion continues outside the nozzle).

underground burst. A nuclear explosion with its center of detonation beneath the surface of the ground.

underground launcher. A launching complex capable of *launching* a missile from underground. Contrast with *underground storage*. *See* launcher and missile storage structure, surface or underground.

underwater burst. A nuclear explosion with its center of detonation beneath the surface of the water.

underwater-to-air missile (UAM). *See* ground-to-air missile; model designation.

underwater-to-surface missile (USM). *See* ground-to-ground missile; model designation.

unguided. Of a missile or other object sent through the air, not subject to guidance or control during flight; aimed only in launching (e.g., HONEST JOHN, q.v.).

unidirectional antenna. An antenna which radiates or receives radio waves most effectively in or from one direction only.

unit (equipment). A group of components (q.v.) which, when operating together, accomplish a specified task (e.g., missile, radar, Doppler, launching and ground-handling equipment).

unit. *Types of, see* Ångstrom–; arithmetic–; astronomical–; British thermal–; complexity–; discriminator tuning–; electromagnetic–; electrostatic–; inertial measurement–; memory–; milli-earth rate unit; nautical–; Rato–; tuning–.

unit authorization list (UAL). An allowance list of equipment for each operational unit.

United States grid. A military grid (q.v.) superimposed upon a polyconic projection (q.v.) of the United States and its possessions. *See* world polyconic grid.

unit essential equipment (UEE). That portion of the unit mission equipment (q.v.) for T/O units which is air-transportable and required to perform the mission.

unitization (unitized design). In design, the grouping together of functional components into an assembly, often subminiaturized.

unit mission equipment (UME). Those items of equipment authorized in the master equipment allowance list (MEAL) (q.v.) or special lists of equipment for specific T/O units as authorized by headquarters United States Air Force. This equipment will normally be moved with the unit from location to location.

unit of measurement. *See* standard units of measurement.

unit property record and equipment authorization list (UPREAL). Consists of a list of items authorized as standard unit as prescribed by a master equipment allowance list (MEAL) (q.v.). Equipment formerly listed in the UPREAL is now listed under unit mission equipment (q.v.) in the unit authorization list (q.v.).

unit strain. Unit deformation.

unit stress. The intensity of stress; the stress per unit of area. The unit stress may be a normal or shearing stress (*see* total stress), measured at a point on the section being considered. *Average unit stress* is obtained by dividing the total stress by the total area:

$$s = \frac{P}{A}$$

where s = average unit stress in compression, shear or tension; P = total force in the direction of the stress; A = total area of the section. Units are: pound per square inch; kips per square inch.

unit support equipment (USE). Equipment other than unit mission equipment (UME) (q.v.) required by a unit to perform its mission at a specified base. Unit support equipment is normally retained by the base upon movement of the unit.

universal transverse Mercator grid. A military grid system in which a grid network is applied to a transverse Mercator projection (q.v.) of certain zones, each zone extending to 80 degrees north and south latitude, 6 degrees of longitude wide, with one-half degree of overlap on each side.

unrestricted propellant. A rocket propellant grain wherein combustion takes place on more than one planar surface. Unrestricted burning.

unsatisfactory report (UR). A report used by Air Force activities to report a field failure or malfunction.

unstable oscillation. An oscillation (q.v.) whose amplitude increases continuously until a catastrophe occurs or stabilizing forces are brought to bear (e.g., in aerodynamics, an oscillation which increases continuously until an attitude is reached from which there is no tendency to return towards the original attitude, the motion becoming a steady divergence).

unstable servo. A servo (q.v.) in which the output drifts away from the input without limit.

unsymmetrical dimethyl-hydrazine (UDMH) [(CH$_3$)$_2$N$_2$H$_2$]. A liquid rocket propellant *fuel*. See Table 3, page 157.

UOC. Ultimate Operational Capability (q.v.).

upper atmosphere. (1) In geophysics, the atmosphere of the ionosphere (q.v.), near and above 62 miles. (2) In meteorology: (a) the atmosphere above the troposphere (q.v.); (b) the atmosphere above the stratosphere (q.v.); (c) the atmosphere above the limits to be reached by sounding balloons. See Fig. 1, page 21.

upper front. In an occluded front situation, the upper line of intersection between the cold air masses.

upper transit. The transit of a given celestial body across the upper branch of a celestial meridian (q.v.).

UPREAL. Unit Property Record and Equipment Authorization List (q.v.).

upslope fog. A fog caused by dynamic cooling in air flowing uphill. Upslope fog will form only in air that is convectively stable; never in air that is unstable, because instability permits the formation of cumulus clouds and vertical currents.

up-time. The calendar time in which a system is considered in condition to perform its required function.

up-wash. The slight upward flow of air just prior to its reaching the immediate vicinity of the leading edge (q.v.) of a rapidly moving airfoil or wing; a damming up of the air under the airfoil, and this condensed mass of air forces the newly arrived mass to flow upward.

upwind. Into the wind.

UR. Unsatisfactory Report (q.v.).

usable time. Time during which equipments are capable of doing useful work. A part of this time may be used for preventive maintenance.

USAF. United States Air Force.

USE. Unit Support Equipment (q.v.).

useful range. The effective range of equipment, components, instrumentation, etc.

user test. A missile or weapon system test conducted by the ultimate using activity instead of the development or evaluation agency.

USM. Underwater-to-Surface Missile. *See* ground-to-ground missile; model designation.

USNMTC. United States Naval Missile Test Center; Point Mugu, Calif.

USSTAF. United States Strategic Air Force.

utilization. *See* factor of utilization.

UTM. Universal Transverse Mercator grid (q.v.).

V

V. (1) V-band frequency (46,000-56,000 mc/sec). See Fig. 8, page 105. (2) Velocity, as used in mathematical formulas. (3) Volt.

vacuum trajectory. The elliptical curve of any ballistic trajectory (q.v.) neglecting air friction. See Fig. 27, page 293.

vacuum tube. A sealed tube in which the air or other gas has been exhausted to such a low pressure that electric discharges may pass between electrodes inserted into the tube; an electron tube.

vacuum-tube amplifier. (1) A device consisting of components used to increase power, voltage, or current of a signal. (2) A device employing one or more electronic tubes to amplify an electrical signal. *Class A:* The grid potential always remains between two potentials and the grid flow never goes positive. (Characteristics: good linearity, good power and voltage amplification, poor efficiency.) *Class B (push-pull):* Two tubes used in parallel with a negative grid bias. (Characteristics: good linearity and power efficiency.) *Class A-B:* The grid bias and alternating grid voltages are such that the plate current in a specific tube flows for appreciably more than half but less than the entire electrical cycle. *Class C:* An amplifier in which the grid bias is appreciably beyond the cutoff so that the plate current in each tube is zero when no alternating grid voltage is applied, and so that plate current flows in a specific tube for appreciably less than one-half of each cycle when an alternating grid voltage is applied.

valley breeze. On hot days, uneven terrain gives rise to uphill breezes; i.e., from the valley up mountain or hill slopes. This breeze is known as a valley breeze; it is an *anabatic wind* (q.v.). With sunset, the breeze dies.

value engineering (VE). A concept of engineering evaluation early in the design phase aimed at reduced cost and complexity. A Navy BuShips concept.

value, Q. See Q-value.

valve. *Types of, see* acceleration switching–; check–; four-way–; relief–; sequence–; three-way–; transfer–; vent–.

valve man. (Vernacular) The operator who actually fires a liquid-fuel rocket.

valve overlap. A situation in which two valves synchronized to open and shut oppositely are momentarily open or shut at the same time.

Van Allen Belt (Radiation Layer). Two layers or belts of particles spiraling along the magnetic lines of force which surround the Earth. Named for Dr. J. A. Van Allen who obtained experimental data from the EXPLORER (q.v.) satellite program and the Lunar Probes. The charged particles in the outer belt are believed to originate from the Sun. The inner layer appears to be protons.

Vandenberg Air Force Base. Dedicated October, 1958. Formerly Camp Cooke and Cooke Air Force Base; Lompoc, Calif. Site of the first training base for intermediate range ballistic missiles (IRBM) and intercontinental ballistic missiles (ICBM) (THOR, ATLAS and TITAN, q.q.v.). A launching site for the Pacific Missile Range (q.v.).

vane. (1) Any plate, blade, or strip of metal, wood, or other material, so placed that it either (a) trails free in a fluid flow; (b) imparts a reaction to a fluid flow that passes about its side, as it may in the exhaust stream of certain rocket engines or as it does in the airflow of a diffuser. (2) A blade on a rotating part that catches a fluid and impels it in a given direction, as on a compressor. In the exhaust of a rocket engine, the vanes serve as a rudder or elevator (*see* jet vane); on a diffuser, the vanes, being fixed, give direction to the airflow; on a compressor, the vanes serve to build up compression.

vane, jet. *See* jet vane.

VANGUARD. Three-stage satellite launching vehicle. Navy Bureau of Aeronautics designation: SLV.

Length: 72 ft; weight: 22,000 lb; maximum payload: 18 lb. Missile guidance uses a pitch programmer with gyroscope reference system. First and second stages are liquid rocket; third stage is solid rocket. See Earth satellite summary, Table 6, page 245.

Technical Direction: Naval Research Laboratory. Prime Contractor: The Martin Co., Baltimore. First stage: General Electric Co. Second stage: Aerojet-General Corp. Third stage: Grand Central Rocket Co. Payload: Naval Research Laboratory.

vapor. (1) Any substance in its gaseous state, especially a vaporized liquid that is visible. (2) Fuel vapor. (3) The water vapor in a condensation trail (q.v.).

vapor lock. A stoppage or diminution in the liquid fuel flow of an engine caused by fuel vapor accumulating in the fuel lines.

vapor trail. A condensation trail (q.v.).

VAR. Visual-Aural VHF radio Range (q.v.).

variable. *Types of, see* cepheid–; method of–.

variable-area exhaust nozzle. An exhaust nozzle on a jet engine, the opening of which is of a variable size, being varied by a control system to provide thrust control or operating efficiency over a wide range. Contrast with *fixed area exhaust nozzle* (q.v.).

variable elevation beam (VEB). A height-finding beam, used in radars.

variable focus lens. A lens system, part of which is movable, so designed as to have correction for lens aberrations, continual sharp focusing of the image on the receiving film, and constant *f*-value as the focal length is changed. Such a lens gives the effect of moving the camera toward or away from the object. Variable lenses are used in motion picture and television cameras; commonly termed *zoomar lenses*.

variable inductance oscillator. An oscillator (q.v.) which has been specifically designed for use with variable inductors to provide frequency changes (e.g., frequency modulation produced by varying the tank inductor).

variable reluctance pickups. A telemetering term used synonymously with variable inductance pickups (q.v.). The inductance of the pickup varies because the reluctance of the magnetic path is changed.

variable resistor. In electricity, a resistor (q.v.) having a sliding contact to change its value of resistance.

variable-time fuze. A type of proximity fuze (q.v.) that detonates within varying distance of the target after it comes under the influence of the target. Often termed *VT fuze*.

variation. *Types of, see* pressure altitude–; magnetic–.

Variplotter. A trade name for a device which automatically plots or reads a graph by means of a photocell system.

varistor. A two-electrode semiconductor device having a voltage-dependent, nonlinear resistance. The resistance is markedly reduced when the applied voltage is increased. (It is used for voltage surge protection.)

V-beam radar. A radar that uses two planes of radiation, one vertical, the other slanted at an angle of 45°, each receiving separate signals, which are coordinated with the range of the target to secure an accurate measure of height.

VE. Value Engineering (q.v.).

VEB. Variable Elevation Beam (q.v.).

vector. (1) An entity which has both magnitude and direction, such as a force or velocity; a line segment that represents this entity. *See* air vector; ground vector; wind vector. (2) The translation of an object (e.g., missile) from one point to another point usually in a given interval of space. (3) The line segment or direction followed into space, or to be followed, to achieve this translation. (4) A line on a chart, or a voice communication, that indicates speed and direction to achieve this translation. (5) The positioning of an interceptor with respect to its target through commands issued from a separate control station.

vector. *Types of, see* air–; collision–; *E*-vector; ground–; *H*-vector; velocity–; wind–.

vectoring error. The radial distance between desired and actual tracks of an interceptor vectored to a target by a separate control station.

vectoring requirement. The boundary loci of tracks within which a given interceptor must pass in order to acquire a given target with its weapon control system and thereafter launch its missiles to obtain the desired probability of kill.

vector problem. A problem in interception in which the speed and direction of the object to be intercepted are first determined, followed by a calculation that determines the direction and speed that the intercepting object must pursue starting from a given point at a given instant in time. Vector problems are subject to solution by electronic devices built into the intercepting object.

vector steering. (Vernacular) A steering method where one or more thrust chambers are gimbal-mounted so that the direction of the thrust force (thrust vector) may be tilted in relation to the center of gravity of the missile to produce a turning moment. Two servo actuators, one on the pitch axis and one on the yaw axis, tilt the thrust direction according to signals from the flight-control system. *See* thrust vector control.

VEGA. An Advanced Research Projects Agency (ARPA) (q.v.) sponsored advanced satellite and Space Probe program.

1st stage—ATLAS (q.v.) first stage

2nd stage—VANGUARD (q.v.) first stage with G. E. engine

3rd stage—a 6,000 lb storable liquid rocket engine developed by Jet Propulsion Laboratory.

Capable of orbiting at 300 miles a 6,000 to 7,500 lb payload or of sending about 1,000 lb to Mars. *See* CENTAUR; NOVA; SATURN.

vehicle. *Types of, see* aerodynamic test–; glide–; hypersonic test–; inhabited space–; instrumental space–; manned space–; reentry–; satellite–; skip–; space–.

veering wind. Any clockwise change in wind direction is known as *veering of the wind*. It is the opposite of a *backing wind*.

velocity. (1) Speed. In many contexts, no distinction in meaning is made between "speed" and "velocity," the choice between the words being governed by a sense of association. However, "velocity" is not normally used in reference to movements of a person or animal; instead "speed" is used. This restriction tends to carry over to inanimate objects when they are associated with man (e.g., the *speed* of an aircraft). On the other hand, "velocity" appears to be preferred in reference to other inanimate objects (e.g., *velocity* of the wind; *velocity* of electrons). (2) Speed, or rate of motion, in a given direction and in a given frame of reference. In this sense, "velocity" is used in scientific or technical contexts. In these contexts, "speed" denotes a scalar quantity equal only to that part of velocity that comprises its magnitude; whereas "velocity" denotes a vector quantity that includes both magnitude and direction.

velocity. *Types of, see* absolute–; acoustic–; angular–; burnout–; characteristic–; circular–; circular orbital–; cutoff–; Doppler–; effective exhaust–; escape–; exhaust–; group–; initial–; jet–; linear–; orbital–; parabolic–; phase–; radial–; reduced–; relative–; remote–; satellite–; striking–; terminal–; throat–; transfer–; vertical flight cutoff–.

velocity (at burnout). The velocity of a missile when propulsion ceases; especially important in ballistic and boost-glide vehicles (q.q.v.). *See* burnout velocity. See Fig. 27, page 293.

velocity limiting servo. A servomechanism (q.v.) in which the performance is limited by the velocity (or rate) attainable by the servo.

velocity meter (velocimeter). A device used in inertial guidance systems (q.v.) to provide information regarding small changes in velocity (q.v.). The output is conditioned to provide acceleration and position data used to establish missile position in inertial space (q.v.). *See* accelerometer.

velocity modulation. A type of modulation in which the velocity of electrons in an electron beam is varied in cyclic fashion, causing the electrons to bunch together, each bunch of electrons causing a cycle of current as it passes an output electrode.

velocity of radio/radar propagation. Within the accuracy demanded of radar equipment, usually taken as the velocity of light: 2.998×10^8 m/sec; 299.8 m/microsec; 186,296 miles/sec.

velocity of sound. Speed of sound (q.v.).

velocity pickup. A telemetering end instrument (q.v.) used to measure vibrations; usually designed with a low natural frequency.

velocity resonance. The resonance that exists between a body, or system, and an applied sinusoidal force if any small change in the frequency of the applied force causes a decrease in velocity at the driving point; or if the frequency of the applied force is such that the absolute value of the driving-point impedance is a minimum.

velocity shock. The shock condition occurring in equipment when a sudden change occurs in the linear velocity, or in the direction of motion, of the equipment or its mount. *See* shock; shock motion.

velocity thrust. That part of the thrust of a rocket due to the weight flow of the exhaust gases. This part of the thrust is influenced by the nozzle exit configuration.

$$\text{velocity thrust} = \frac{\dot{w}}{g} \lambda V_j$$

where $\dot{w}$ = weight flow, lb/sec; λ = exit correction, see Fig. 6, page 76; V_j = exhaust velocity, ft/sec; g = acceleration of gravity, ft/sec².

velocity-to-be-gained. The increment of velocity which, if added to or subtracted from the actual velocity of a missile, will result in the desired ballistic trajectory (q.v.) to impact on the target. In ballistic missile applications, vernier engines may be used to adjust the velocity.

velocity vector. The combination of two ballistic missile trajectory values; the velocity of the missile's center of gravity at a designated point on the trajectory and the angle between the local vertical and the direction of the velocity.

vendor. In supply usage, any contractor, manufacturer, jobber, or commercial agency that sells something to an armed service.

vented pressure pickup. A telemetering pickup with a vent in the reference pressure chamber to allow reestablishment of a reference pressure just before use.

venturi tube. A short tube with a constricted throat which, when placed in a fluid parallel to the flow, brings about an increase in flow velocity at the throat with a consequent diminished pressure within the fluid at the throat. The principle of the venturi tube was first applied in hydraulics, especially to provide a means of metering liquid through a pipe by inserting a venturi tube in the pipe. In aeronautics, the tube has been combined with the pitot tube for measuring airspeed, and advantage has been taken of the diminished pressure at the throat to operate a gyroscope or other device. *See* Bernoulli's law.

vent-valve. A valve used in a hydraulic/pneumatic system to provide a means for bleeding or venting the container.

Venus Probe. A test vehicle designed to orbit, pass, or impact planet Venus with the objective of gaining certain scientific knowledge.

vernal equinox. (1) The point where the Sun appears to cross the celestial equator from south to north. Also termed the *first point of Aries*. (2) The time of this crossing, when day and night are everywhere of equal length. The vernal equinox occurs about March 21. Contrast with *autumnal equinox* (q.v.). *See also* equinox.

vernier engines. Low-thrust, long-duration (usually) rocket engines used to adjust the final velocity and to correct heading errors of a long-range ballistic missile.

versitron. *See* microwave amplification by stimulated emission of radiation.

vertical and horizontal polarization. With less ambiguity, vertical and horizontal polarization should be described as parallel and perpendicular polarization with respect to the plane of incidence (the plane containing the incident and reflected rays).

vertical attitude. The attitude of a vehicle with respect to its position about its lateral axis. The vertical attitude changes when the vehicle pitches.

vertical axis. (1) The axis of a vehicle in the plane of symmetry, about which the vehicle revolves in yawing. (2) In a gyroscope or gyroscopic body, an axis of precession (q.v.) that lies more or less vertical.

vertical circle. A circle on the celestial sphere (q.v.) passing through the zenith and nadir (q.q.v.) of an observer.

vertical drop. The drop of an object in trajectory or along a plumb line, measured vertically from its line of departure to the object. Also termed *drop*.

vertical flight cutoff velocity. The velocity of a vertically ascending single-stage rocket from a nonrotating earth:

$$V = \bar{c} \log \lambda - \bar{g}t_b$$

where $\bar{c}$ = average effective exhaust velocity, ft/sec; λ = mass ratio, W_o/W_e; $\bar{g}$ = average value of gravity, ft/sec^2; t_b = burning time, sec; W_o = overall gross weight, lb; W_e = empty weight, lb.

vertical interval. A contour interval (q.v.).

vertical (normal) acceleration. Angular acceleration about the pitch axis. From the left side of a vehicle, positive acceleration is clockwise. *See also* acceleration.

vertical plane. (1) Any plane extending outward from the Earth that passes through a vertical line, e.g., the plane of a vertical circle. (2) The projection into a single plane of all the vertical planes in which a particular object moves, or in which several objects may be at rest.

very high frequency (VHF). Any radio frequency between 30 and 300 mc/sec. See Fig. 8, page 105.

very low frequency (VLF). Any radio frequency below 30 kc/sec. See Fig. 8, page 105.

very stable oscillator (VSO). An oscillator with a frequency deviation of about 1 part in 10^{10} or better.

vestigial sideband. The transmitted portion of a sideband which has been largely suppressed by a transducer (q.v.) having a gradual cutoff in the neighborhood of the carrier frequency, the other sideband being transmitted without much suppression.

vestigial sideband system. In RF communication applications, an amplitude modulation (q.v.) technique in which the two sidebands (q.v.) are not completely suppressed. The modulating wave is recovered without wave distortion with a product demodulator (q.v.).

VG. Velocity Gravity; i.e., g force due to acceleration.

VG recorder. An instrument for recording g force due to acceleration.

VHF. Very High Frequency (30-300 mc/sec). See Fig. 8, page 105.

VHF/DF. Very High Frequency Direction Finding.

VHF homing adapter. A homing adapter operating in the very high frequency range.

VHF/UHF direction finder. A ground-based direction finder capable of use alone or in conjunction with surveillance radar.

vibration. A periodic motion of the particles in an elastic body in alternately opposite directions. Contrast with *oscillation* (q.v.).

vibration. *Types of, see* forced–; free–; natural mode of–; normal modes of–; steady-state–.

vibration error. Variations in accuracy due to vibration effects. It is usually expressed in *per cent peak-peak noise* or output compared to full range of maximum usable output.

vibration pickup. A sensitive device for detecting vibration. Both velocity pickups and accelerometers are used for telemetering the vibration environment.

vibratory gyroscope. An instrument that utilizes a vibrating rod or tuning fork to perform certain equilibrium or directional functions of the spinning gyroscope.

video amplifier. An electronic device which provides wide-band operation in the frequency range from approximately 15 cycles per second to 5 megacycles per second. It is used to give a signal of sufficient intensity to modulate a cathode-ray tube (either by intensity modulation or deflection modulation, according to the type of display used), or to operate some auto-following, or other, special circuit.

video frequencies. Frequencies existing in the demodulated output of a television camera as a result of scanning the image being transmitted. The range is from almost zero to well over 4 mc/sec. Also termed *visual frequencies*.

VIKING. Research rocket. Navy cognizance. Formerly NEPTUNE.

Early research rocket used to replace the limited supply of captured German V-2's which were used after World War II for experiments. Used a liquid propellant engine; the largest version of the VIKING was 48¾ ft in length. Fourteen were built and tested. Two of these were used for VANGUARD (q.v.) tests.

Prime Contractor: The Martin Company. Engine: Reaction Motors, Inc.

virga. In meteorology, a trail of rain or snow from clouds, which evaporates before reaching the ground.

virtual temperature. In meteorology, the temperature at which dry air would have the same pressure and density as the air under consideration.

viscosity. (1) In a liquid, the property of internal resistance, caused by molecular attraction, that makes the liquid resist flow. (2) In a solid, the property of yielding steadily under stress.

viscous damping. The damping in a mechanical system in which the force varies in proportion to the velocity. The viscous-damping coefficient is equal to the ratio of the viscous-damping force to the velocity.

visibility. *See* zero visibility.

visible horizon. The apparent meeting of the Earth and sky as observed from any place on the Earth or in the atmosphere. *See* horizon.

visual-aural radio range (VAR). Any radio range that sends out signals for both visual and aural reception; applied especially to certain types of VHF radio ranges.

visual-aural VHF radio range (VAR). A VHF radio range in which two separate signals are beamed in opposite directions for visual reception, and two additional signals beamed at right angles for aural reception and identification.

visual inspection. Inspection (q.v.) by the use of the eyes only; it does not include use of any measuring devices, tools, or equipment.

visual omnirange. An omnidirectional radio range (q.v.) that transmits signals for visual reception.

VLF. Very Low Frequency (3-30 kc/sec).

volatile (volatility). (1) Easily passing away by evaporation; the quality or property of a liquid for evaporating (e.g., liquid fuels). (2) In computer terminology, the attribute of a memory device that information is lost in the event of a power interruption.

volt. The unit of electromotive force. An electromotive force of one volt, when steadily applied to a conductor, the resistance of which is one ohm (q.v.), will produce a current of one ampere. The electromotive force between the poles or electrodes of a voltaic cell, known as the *Weston normal cell*, at a temperature of 20°C, which is 1.0183 volts, is used as a reference standard.

1 volt = 10^8 abvolts = 10^6 microvolts = 1000 millivolts = 0.003336 statvolt

1 volt-electronic charge-second = 2.4186×10^{14} Planck's constants

1 volt-faraday-second = 1.4566×10^{38} Planck's constants

1 volt-second = 10^8 maxwells

1 volt/centimeter = 10^8 abvolts/cm = 2.540×10^8 abvolts/in. = 0.001 kv/cm = 10^8 microvolts/meter = 2.54 volts/in.

voltage. *Types of, see* breakdown–; composite modulation–; inverse peak–; peak inverse–; reference–; Zener–.

voltage-controlled oscillator (VCO). An oscillator which converts static DC or dynamic (time-varying) input voltages to a frequency-modulated carrier with good accuracy and stability.

voltage divider. A network used for the purpose of tapping off a fractional part of the electrical potential difference existing between the input terminals.

volume, grain. *See* grain volume.

volume impulse. In solid rocket propellant usage, the total impulse per unit volume of propellant grain. It is used for comparing propellant characteristics.

VOR. VHF Omnidirectional Range (q.v.).

vortex. A mass of fluid (air or water) having such circular or whirling motion that a cavity is formed in the center toward which things caught in its influence tend to move; the motion of such a fluid.

vortex, bound. *See* bound vortex.

vortex generator. A movable surface on an aerodynamic body that may be used as a spoiler (q.v.) to break down the airflow.

vortex thermometer. A thermometer used to measure free-air temperature around a vehicle, mounted in a special housing that creates a vortex around the thermometer to eliminate errors caused by frictional and adiabatic heating.

vortices. *See* Karman street of vortices.

vorticity. The vector obtained by taking the curl of the flow velocity. It is also the anti-symmetric part of the velocity gradient tensor u_i/x_j (u_i is the component of the velocity parallel to OX_i). It measures the rate of rotation of the fluid (e.g., in a uniformly rotating fluid the vorticity is twice the angular velocity).

VSO. Very Stable Oscillator (q.v.).

VT fuze. A proximity or variable time fuze (q.v.). The principle of operation is based on receipt of RF energy radiated from a transmitter in the fuze and returned by the target. Such fuzes are used to optimize the time delay prior to burst.

vulnerability. The susceptibility of a target to a damage agent. *See* target vulnerability.

W

WAC-CORPORAL. Research rocket. An early research vehicle used for experiments (before the firing of the first captured German V-2). It was replaced by the AEROBEE (q.v.).

WADC. Wright Air Development Center; Wright-Patterson Air Force Base; Dayton, Ohio. Conceives and monitors research and development in aircraft, missiles, power plants, propellers, armament, airborne and ground equipment, and other aeronautical material carried on by industry, universities, and research institutions.

waffle construction. A fabrication technique in which a thin sheet with reinforcing ribs in a waffle pattern is used to provide a structure equivalent to sheet-stiffener (stringer) (q.v.) construction. Usually formed by chemical milling (q.v.).

WAG TAIL. Air-to-surface missile. Air Force cognizance.

Prime contractor: Minneapolis-Honeywell, Missile Control Center.

waiver. A contractual agreement to permit acceptance by the procuring agency of a piece of hardware even though the part or equipment does not conform to the applicable specification and/or drawing. Contrast with *deviation* (q.v.).

wake. (1) The turbulent volume of gas enclosed by the boundary layer (q.v.) and originating from the base of a missile. (2) The trail marked by disturbed air or other fluid created by a body passing through the fluid. (A wake differs from a wash in that the latter denotes the surge of air or other fluid rather than the air itself, or rather than the trail made by disturbed air.)

wake efficiency. The efficiency with which the air or other fluid thrust backward by a vehicle's jet power plant propels the vehicle forward, expressed by the ratio of thrust power to jet power. *See* jet power; jet thrust.

Wallops Island. A test facility in Virginia established by the National Advisory Committee for Aeronautics (NACA) and planned to be an important test center for the National Aeronautics and Space Administration (NASA). Installations include: (a) minitrack system; (b) optical tracking equipment; (c) portable launching equipment; (d) conventional instrumentation.

wamoscope. *Wave modulated oscilloscope.* A cathode-ray tube system including detection and display of a microwave signal in a single envelope amplification, thus eliminating the local oscillator, mixer, IF amplifier, detector, video amplifier, and associated circuitry in a conventional radar receiver. Tubes are available for the range of 2000 to 4000 mc/sec.

wander. The drift of a gyroscope. *See* drift.

warfare. *Types of, see* electronics–; space–; technological–.

warhead. That portion of the armament system (q.v.) of a guided missile or projectile which consists of the explosive, chemical incendiary, or other contents that inflict the intended damage on the target; includes the charge or filler and its container or casing, but not the fuze.

warhead. *Types of, see* blast cluster–; blast–; fragmenting–; isotropic–.

warhead booster. The end element of an explosive train (q.v.) whose detonation initiates the warhead detonation.

warhead gain. The increase in damage effectiveness of a *non-isotropic warhead* achieved by enhancing the effects in particular directions at the expense of other directions.

warhead pattern. A description of the relative angular variation of the damage parameter of a *non-isotropic warhead*. The warhead pattern is the spatial distribution of some significant warhead damage or emission parameter in a particular set of coordinates and in a particular environment.

warhead yield. The energy release of a nuclear weapon, usually expressed in kilotons (1000 tons) of TNT equivalent.

warm front. The front (q.v.) or frontal surface of an air mass that is displacing a receding colder air mass. The passage of a warm front is followed by a rise in temperature, shifting winds, and generally clearing weather.

warm front thunderstorm. A frontal thunderstorm (q.v.) caused by warm, moist, unstable air being forced aloft over a colder layer of retreating air.

warm-up. The period between the instant that power is applied to a device until the equipment has reached a steady-state condition. Some equipments reach equilibrium almost immediately, while others require several minutes or even hours.

warning. *See* distant early warning.

war-peace switch. A category of devices such as switches, safety keys, interlocks, and similar elements used to permit peacetime exercising of equipment which has a capability of wartime use. Also used for training of personnel.

washboard course. A generic term applied to roads and test areas used to evaluate equipment when subjected to a rough and irregular but known road characteristic. *See* Belgium block road.

WASP. Research rocket. Navy cognizance.

Used for gathering scientific data at altitudes of 20-30 miles. Uses a solid propellant power plant, can be launched from shipboard or land.

Prime Contractor: Cooper Development Corp.

water. *Types of, see* heavy–; process–.

water calorimeter. In radio, a type of calorimeter (q.v.) incorporating a water chamber, that measures the power of radio frequencies by the change in temperature of water heated by the frequencies.

water deluge system. A high-capacity, high-pressure water system at missile test and launch stands for washdown, fire prevention, and fire fighting.

water line (WL). A longitudinal reference plane which is parallel to the top and bottom of a missile. The water line number (inches) decreases as the reference plane approaches the bottom of the missile and increases as the top is approached.

watt. (1) The practical unit of electric power; in a direct-current circuit, equal to volts multiplied by amperes. In an alternating-current circuit, true watts are equal to effective volts multiplied by effective amperes, then multiplied by the circuit power factor. (2) The unit of electric power. A watt is equivalent to the work done at the rate of one joule (q.v.) per second. It is also equal to the power expended by an electric current of one ampere flowing through a resistance of one ohm. One kilowatt is equal to one thousand watts.

1 watt = 3.413 Btu/hr = 0.05688 Btu/min = 0.00094799 Btu/sec = 0.23889 cal, gram/sec = 10^7 ergs/sec = 44.254 ft-lb/min = 0.0013405 hp (elec) = 1 joule/sec = 0.001 kw

1 watt-hour = 3.413 Btu = 860 cal, gram = 2655.3 ft-lb = 0.00134 hphr = 0.001 kwhr

1 watt-second = 0.00094799 Btu = 0.73756 ft-lb = 3.72506 × 10^7 hphr = 1 joule = 2.778 × 10^{-7} kwhr = 0.00027778 watt-hr

wave. *Types of, see* ballistic–; blast–; carrier–; centimeter–; compressive–; detonating–; electromagnetic–; expansion–; ground–; interrupted continuous–; long–; MACH–; rarefaction–; reflected–; shock–; sky–; space–; square–; standing–; subcarrier–; surface–; tropospheric–.

wave cloud. A billow cloud (q.v.).

wave drag. Drag which occurs at supersonic (q.v.) speeds. The air in front of a body moving faster than sound cannot get out of the way quickly enough, and is suddenly compressed when the object arrives; shock waves (q.v.) are formed at the front and back of the object. The compression of air in shock waves leads to adiabatic (q.v.) heating, and friction in the air layers near a moving surface also generates heat. *See* double wedge–; modified double wedge–; biconvex–.

wave filter. (1) A transducer (q.v.) or network for separating waves on the basis of their frequency. It introduces a relatively small insertion loss to waves in one or more frequency bands, and relatively large insertion loss to waves of other frequencies. (2) A filter which acts primarily upon the mode (q.v.) rather than the frequency of the wave (also termed wave-type filter).

waveguide. A device consisting either of a metal tube or dielectric cylinder, capable of propagating electromagnetic waves through its interior. The widths or diameters of such guides are determined by the frequency to be propagated. *Metal guides* may be evacuated, air-filled, or gas-filled, and are generally rectangular or circular in cross section. *Dielectric guides* consist of solid dielectric cylinders surrounded by air.

waveguide phase shifter. A device for adjusting the phase of a particular field component (or current or voltage) at the output of the device relative to the phase of that field component (or current or voltage) at the input. It may consist, in its simplest form, of merely a variable-length section so that the traveled path may be modified. Another method of obtaining a variable phase shift is to insert a slab of low-loss dielectric into the waveguide. The electrical length of the guide appears longer as the strip is moved toward the center, because of the decreased phase velocity which accompanies such a move.

wavelength. The distance in meters travelled by an electromagnetic wave during the time interval covered by a cycle.

WDD. Western Development Division; Air Research and Development Command; Inglewood, Calif. Changed to BMD, Ballistic Missile Division, in 1957.

weapon. *Types of, see* absolute–; aircraft–.

weapon effectiveness. The degree to which a weapon system (q.v.) can perform its mission with minimum drain on national resources.

weapon evaluation (analysis). The science of determining weapon effectiveness through techniques of operations research (q.v.).

weaponization. The application of techniques and changes to convert a research and development (q.v.) weapon into the operational version.

weapon specification. A top tier specification expanding on the requirements set forth in the weapon system specification (q.v.). It usually includes the design and test requirements for the airborne and support unit equipment, but does not include facilities and the personnel subsystem. Field maintenance equipment requirements should be included.

weapon system. A group of tactical devices which together perform a *mission;* i.e., detect a target, identify it as friend or foe, deliver a payload upon it, and assess the resulting damage. The complete weapon system includes the equipment, skills, techniques, and personnel required for providing the desired role or mission in the operational environment.

Weapon System Project Office (WSPO). A central point for management (q.v.) control of one or more weapon system programs. The office is used at Wright Air Development Center (WADC) to achieve proper phasing of actions in development, procurement, maintenance, and supply, thereby insuring timely delivery and support of weapon systems (q.v.). An important function of this office is that of providing a central contact point for industry and Air Force relations.

weapon system specification. A top tier specification (q.v.) developed in accordance with military requirements, which outlines the design criteria and performance requirements for a weapon, the support equipment, facilities, and manpower.

wearout failures. Those failures (q.v.) which occur late in the life of an equipment and ultimately are cause for failure of all equipment remaining in the population (used in its statistical sense); failure due to weaknesses created in the equipment by its use.

weather abort. An abort (q.v.) of a test or mission caused by weather conditions.

weathercock. The tendency of a rocket or missile to align, or attempt to align, its longitudinal axis with the direction of the wind.

weathercock frequency. The frequency of the characteristic motion of a missile airframe as it returns to its steady-state condition after a disturbance has produced an unbalanced moment.

weathercock stability. An aerodynamic characteristic of a body which points it into the relative wind. The partial derivatives of yawing and pitching moments with respect to angles of attack in yaw and pitch establish the stability characteristics. *See* stability derivatives.

weather front. A frontal surface.

weather type. Any set of large-scale meteorological conditions identifiable by prominent characteristics, which occurs frequently enough to be recognized as a particular type and which allows future developments to be anticipated.

weathervane. To weathercock (q.v.).

weather, zero-zero. *See* zero-zero weather.

web. In rocketry: (1) the wall of tubular solid propellant grain (q.v.) with holes cut through it to suggest webbing; (2) the thickness of the powder charge in either a tubular or perforated grain, measured at its thickest point; (3) in unrestricted burning solid rocket grains, the minimum distance which can burn through, as measured perpendicular to the burning surface.

web fraction. That part of the diameter of a solid propellant rocket grain (q.v.) representing the minimum dimension of propellant, or the propellant burned during web time (q.v.).

web time. In solid propellant rocket usage, the burning time from ignition to the first point of burnout of the grain; i.e., time for the shortest burning distance.

weight. Force exerted by a mass under local gravitational acceleration conditions.

weight. *Types of, see* atomic–; basic–; bogey–; burnout–; construction–; design–; *g*-weight; jettison–; structural–; target–.

weight bogey. A system or functional group design weight established as a target or objective at the start of a design. It is usually fixed by the Weight Group and is periodically adjusted as a program progresses. Also termed *target weight*.

weight flow coefficient. An arbitrary relation useful in rocket calculations involving only those variables which can be measured accurately.

$$C_w = \frac{\dot{w}}{P_c A_t}$$

where $\dot{w}$ = weight flow, lb/sec; P_c = chamber pressure, lb/sq in.; A_t = throat area, sq in.

weightlessness. A condition in free fall (q.v.). It may be physiologically unimportant but psychologically dangerous in space flight. It can be avoided by spinning the space vehicle and simulating the effects of gravity by providing a weight feeling with centripetal force (q.v.).

weights report. A report commonly used in missile design which includes detail weights (estimated, calculated, or actual weights), mass distribution, moments, location of center of gravity of each component, weight distribution by station for inertial calculations, weight and center of gravity variation as function of time and/or velocity or MACH number for boost and flight phases. Usually *three* weight reports are used: *estimated, calculated,* and *actual*.

well. *See* gravity well.

wet fog. A fog having a high water content. Contrast with *dry fog*.

white fuming nitric acid (HNO₃). A liquid rocket propellant *oxidizer*. See Table 3, page 157.

WHITE LANCE. The Air Force designation for the Navy Bureau of Aeronautics developed air-to-surface missile BULL PUP (q.v.).

white noise. (1) Random noise, such as *shot* noise and *thermal* noise, which has a constant energy per unit bandwidth that is independent of the central frequency of the band. The name is drawn from the analogous definition of white light. (2) The electrical disturbance caused by the random movement of free electrons in a conductor or semiconductor (q.q.v.). Since the electrical energy in this type of noise is evenly distributed throughout the entire frequency spectrum, it lends itself to use in testing frequency response of amplifiers, speakers, etc.

"white room." A sterile, dust-free room maintained at a positive air pressure, used for final assembly of precision parts and equipment (e.g., gyroscopes). Dust particles larger than 1 millionth inch diameter usually are eliminated by the filtering system.

White Sands Missile Range. Cognizance of the Army. Formerly White Sands Proving Ground, WSPG (q.v.).

White Sands Proving Ground. *See* WSPG.

williwaw. A violent wind sweeping down the leeward side of a mountain and outward from the mountain, resulting from a buildup of air on the windward side.

Wilson cloud. A misty cloud of short duration, caused by the condensation of water vapor in the air due to the drop in temperature that accompanies the passage of the refraction in a shock wave.

wind. *Types of, see* anabatic–; ballistic–; cross–; cyclostrophic–; effective–; fall–; foehn–; geostrophic–; gradient–; head–; head-on–; helping–; katabatic–; prevailing westerlies–; relative–; radar–; squall–; tail-on–; thermal–; trade–; veering–; williwaw.

windage. (1) The deflection of a projectile due to wind. (2) The correction made for such deflection.

wind flow pattern. The pattern made by the flow of the prevailing winds, particularly in the upper atmosphere (q.v.).

wind load. The load or pressure exerted on a surface by wind, usually expressed in pounds per square foot.

window. Strips of frequency-cut metal foil, wire, or bars which may be dropped from aircraft or missiles or expelled from shells or rockets as a radar countermeasure. *See* confusion reflector.

wind profile. A graphical distribution of the steady wind speed over a large altitude range.

wind rose. A diagram showing the relative frequency and average strength of the winds blowing from different directions in a given area, and sometimes showing the average relation between wind direction and the occurrence of other meteorological phenomena.

windrow cloud. A billow cloud (q.v.).

winds. In meteorology winds can be divided into categories: (1) *Gradient winds* blow in accordance with the existing pressure gradient, centrifugal force and Coriolis force. There are two sub-types: (a) *cyclonic winds* blow counterclockwise about regions of relatively low pressure in the Northern Hemisphere and clockwise in the Southern Hemisphere; (b) *anticyclonic winds* blow clockwise about regions of relatively high pressure in the Northern Hemisphere and counterclockwise in the Southern Hemisphere. (2) *Geostrophic winds* blow in accordance with the pressure gradient, but only where the pressure gradient is balanced by the Coriolis force.

They are, therefore, winds which blow in straight or nearly straight lines over the Earth. Geostrophic winds are not possible at the equator because there is no Coriolis force present. (3) *Cyclostrophic winds* blow cyclonically in both hemispheres in wind systems where the pressure gradient is balanced by centrifugal force in the absence of the Coriolis force. Cyclostrophic winds occur near the equator as hurricanes and other local less intense vortices. (4) *Antitriptic winds* are small-scale, short-duration winds which blow, in general, along the pressure gradient. Land and sea breezes are of this type.

In general, winds are mainly gradient winds. Many strictly local winds blow over relatively small regions. Most of these occur where there is sharp contrast in surface temperature over a relatively small distance or where terrain is highly irregular. Sea breezes blow from cool water to heated land during the heat of day. Land breezes blow from cooled land to warmer water during the cool of the night. Valley breezes blow upslope in valley-hill terrain during sunny days, and mountain breezes blow downhill in a reverse manner during darkness. Mountain breezes often become very strong and extremely variable as a result of large-scale eddies and venturi effects in mountain passes. *See* Beaufort wind scale.

winds aloft. (1) Winds at high altitudes, unaffected by surface features. (2) The direction and speed of such winds.

wind scale. *See* Beaufort wind scale.

wind shear. The average wind gradient; the difference in the wind velocity at two altitudes divided by the altitude increment. The units are ft per sec/1000 ft.

windstream. (1) The flow of air in a wind tunnel. (2) The flow of wind in a given direction.

wind triangle. A triangle used in finding the effect of wind on the flight of a vehicle. The sides of the wind triangle consist of the air vector, the ground vector, and the wind vector (q.q.v.). Calculations may be made by trigonometry, but they are normally calculated on the vector face of a computer.

wind tunnel. A test device for producing a controlled wind or airstream in which objects can be placed for investigating the airflow about them and the aerodynamic forces exerted on them.

wind tunnel. *Types of, see* helium–; trisonic–.

wind vector. In air navigation, a vector representing the direction and velocity of the wind, and forming part of the wind triangle (q.v.).

wing control. A method of aerodynamically controlling a missile wherein the control surfaces (q.v.) are located near the center of the body and also become the main lifting surface; tail surfaces are mounted at the rear of the missile mainly for stabilizing purposes.

wing-control-during-boost. A technique used for boost phase attitude stabilization wherein winged missiles are controlled as a canard configuration (q.v.). After the booster rocket is jettisoned or staged (q.q.v.) the wings may be used for midcourse control.

wing drag. (1) The sum of the induced drag (q.v.) and the profile drag (q.v.) upon a wing. (2) This drag plus the parasite drag (q.v.) of objects attached to the wing.

winged missile. A missile that has wings, particularly a wing that provides lift. Distinguish from a *wingless missile*.

wing, isoclinic. *See* isoclinic wing.

wing loading. For a missile in level flight, the ratio of load on its wing to the wing area.

winterization. Preparation of material to permit storage and operation in frigid regions by such means as insulation against cold, addition of heating elements, changes in lubricants, and changes in dimensional clearances of parts to a point where operation at extremely low temperature is reasonably efficient.

wiresonde. An apparatus for gathering meteorological data at low altitudes, in which meteorological data such as temperature and humidity are transmitted over wire to ground-recording devices from a sensing and sending apparatus carried aloft by a captive balloon. Contrast with *radiosonde* (q.v.).

wiring diagram. A drawing that indicates the actual make-up of a unit or component. All parts, wiring, and connections are shown.

wiring, point-to-point. *See* point-to-point wiring.

WIZARD and WIZARD II. Anti-missile missiles.

Range is 1000 miles; has solid-fuel propulsion and is designed to be effective against all types of enemy vehicles, including MACH 2 bombers, air-to-ground missiles, and long-range ballistic missiles. The WIZARD II is intended to search out an incoming intercontinental ballistic missile (ICBM) and explode it high in the atmosphere.

Prime Contractor: Convair, San Diego. Missile warheads: General Electric Co. Electronic steering devices: AVCO Manufacturing Co. Antenna system: Sanders Associates. Guidance and computer: Radio Corporation of America.

WL. Water Line (q.v.).

WLO. Water Line Zero.

WMO. World Meteorological Organization (q.v.).

wobbulation. (1) Similar to gyro nutations (q.v.); a source of drift in single-axis gyroscopes. (2) A variation of a steady-state frequency for test purposes.

wobbulator. A device, usually mechanical, used to frequency-modulate an oscillator (q.v.) for test purposes (e.g., a small trimmer capacitor rotating at constant velocity across the frequency-determining network of the oscillator).

word. In digital computer applications, an instruction, a number, or an arbitrarily coded quantity.

work. In mechanics, the transference of energy by a process of applying force to a point so as to displace the point, measured as the product of force exerted times the distance of displacement.

working load. In stress analysis, the load at which a structure works; usually, but not always, the *design load* (q.v.).

working pressure. The maximum pressure to which a component is subjected under steady-state conditions in *service* operations.

working stress. A stress (q.v.) to which a structure or machine is subjected under actual working or operating conditions.

World Meteorological Organization (WMO). A specialized agency of the United Nations, made up of the meteorological services of many states and territories of the world. It was established in 1950, taking the place of the International Meteorological Organization. The WMO facilitates world-wide cooperation in the establishment of networks of stations for meteorological and related observation, promotes the establishment and maintenance of systems for rapid exchange of meteorological information, encourages research and training in meteorology, promotes standardization of meteorological observations, etc.

world polyconic gril. A military grid (q.v.) superimposed on polyconic projections (q.v.) of the Earth's surface, each segment of the grid covering 9 degrees of longitude with 1 degree of overlap between segments, and extending to 72 degrees north and south latitude.

wow. (Vernacular) Speed variation in reproduced sound; i.e., a low-frequency flutter.

WPAFB. Wright-Patterson Air Force Base; Dayton, Ohio.

WR. War Reserve.

WS. Weapon System (q.v.).

WS 104A. Surface-to-surface intercontinental weapon system. Missile was designated NAVAHO (q.v.). Cancelled in 1958.

WS 107A. Intercontinental ballistic missile (ICBM) weapon system. See WS 107A-1 and WS 107A-2.

WS 107A-1. Surface-to-surface intercontinental ballistic missile (ICBM). Missile is designated ATLAS (q.v.) SM-65.

WS 107A-2. Surface-to-surface two-stage intercontinental ballistic missile (ICBM). Missile is designated TITAN (q.v.) SM-68.

WS 117L. Reconnaissance satellite system. Missile is designated SENTRY (q.v.) and PIED PIPER.

WS 122A. Air-to-air decoy weapon system. Missile is designated QUAIL (q.v.) GAM-72.

WS 123A. Air-to-air and/or surface-to-surface; missile is designated GOOSE (q.v.) SM-73.

WS 131B. Air-to-surface; missile is designated HOUNDDOG (q.v.) GAM-77.

WS 132A. Bomber-defense missile. General Electric Co., McDonnell Aircraft Corp., Republic Aviation Corp., and Westinghouse Corp. have studied this problem.

WS 133A. ICBM weapon system; second generation. Missile is designated MINUTEMAN (q.v.) SM-80.

WS 138A. Air launched ballistic missile (ALBM). Was originally WS 199B (q.v.).

WS 199B and WS 199C. Air launched ballistic missile (ALBM). Initial tests by the Martin Company (WS 199B) were from a B-47. Initial tests by Lockheed (WS 199C) were from a B-58. See BOLD ORION. Designation was later changed to WS 138A.

WS 315A. Intermediate range ballistic missile (IRBM) weapon system. Missile is designated THOR. (q.v.) SM-75.

WSEG. Weapon Systems Evaluation Group (q.v.).

WSM. Weapon System Manager.

WSPG. (1) White Sands Proving Ground (U.S. Army); located in the Tularosa Basin, 25 miles east of Las Cruces, N. M., and 60 miles north of Fort Bliss, Texas. Changed to White Sands Missile Range in 1958. (2) Weapon System Phasing Group.

WSPO. Weapon System Project Office (q.v.).

WSR. Weapon System Review.

WSSM. Weapon System Supply Manager.

WWV. Call letters for the Naval Observatory Radio Station transmitting accurate timing signals; National Bureau of Standards; Washington, D.C.

WXD. Meteorological radar station, as authorized for usage among NATO nations.

WXR. Radiosonde station, authorized for usage among NATO nations.

X

X. The letter "X," when used as a prefix in the designation of a guided missile, indicates that the missile is an experimental model (e.g., XSM-65).

X-2. A research rocket aircraft which in July, 1956, set a speed record of 1900 mph. It is released in mid-air from a larger plane to conserve the propellants for the high-speed run. In September, 1956, it ascended to a record altitude for manned flight of 126,000 ft (approx. 24 miles).

Prime Contractor: Bell Aircraft Corp.

X-7. A recoverable ramjet vehicle. The Air Force is the cognizant service.

Used for evaluation of ramjet engines such as those used for the BOMARC (q.v.). One version is a target drone.

Prime Contractor: Lockheed Missile Systems Division.

X-10. Test missile. Air Force cognizance.

Test vehicle for the NAVAHO (q.v.) which was phased out of production.

Prime Contractor: North American Aviation Corp.

X-15. High-altitude ("space") manned vehicle with reentry provisions.

Length: 50 ft; wing span: 22 ft; gross weight: 31,275 lb. Liquid propellant rocket engines use liquid oxygen and liquid ammonia (see Table 3, page 157) to provide 50,000-lb thrust for 90 sec. A B-52 is used to launch the vehicle at 40,000 to 50,000 ft. Reentry is by skip-glide techniques. Reentry speed: approximately 4000 mph.

Prime contractor: North American Aviation Corp.

X-17. 3-stage reentry test missile. Air Force cognizance. Used for reentry experiments for ballistic missile nose cones and as a test vehicle for the POLARIS (q.v.) program and ARGUS project (q.v.). Weight: 12,000 lbs; length: 40 ft.

Prime Contractor: Lockheed Aircraft Corp.

XAAM-A-1. Military designation for the air-to-air rocket termed FIREBIRD (q.v.).

XAAM-N-1. Military designation for the air-to-air rocket termed FIREBIRD (q.v.).

XAAM-N-4. Navy Bureau of Aeronautics designation for the air-to-air missile termed ORIOLE (q.v.).

XASM-N-4. Navy designation for the air-to-ground missile termed DOVE (q.v.).

XASR-SC-2. Army Signal Corps designation for the research atmospheric sounding rocket termed AEROBEE (q.v.).

XAUM-N-4. Navy designation for the air-to-underwater missile termed DOVE (q.v.).

X-band. A radio-frequency band of 5200 to 11,000 mc/sec with wavelengths of 5.77 to 2.73 cm, respectively. See Fig. 8, page 105.

XKDT-1. Navy Bureau of Aeronautics designation for the target drone termed TEAL (q.v.).

XM-21. Army designation for the target and tactical missile termed FIREBEE (q.v.).

XM-47. Army designation for the surface-to-surface "free" unguided rocket termed LITTLE JOHN (q.v.).

XPM. Experimental prototype missile (obsolete).

XQ-4A. Target drone. Air Force cognizance.

Designed to evaluate weapon systems. Missile is supersonic.

Prime Contractor: Radioplane, Division of Northrup.

XRV-N-13. Navy designation for the research atmospheric sounding rocket termed AEROBEE HI (q.v.).

XSAM-N-5. Military designation for the air-to-surface missile termed GORGON (q.v.).

XSM. Experimental (or developmental) strategic missile.

XSM-64. Air Force designation for the air-breathing surface-to-surface missile termed NAVAHO (q.v.) WS 104A. Phased out.

XSSM-N-2. Navy Bureau of Ordnance designation for surface-to-surface ramjet missile termed TRITON (q.v.). Phased out.

x-time, X+ time. The time remaining before launching of a missile, according to a schedule established by launch control personnel. *x*-time is used for timing events prior to missile liftoff. *X*+ time is used for timing events after missile liftoff.

Y

Y. The letter "Y," when used as a prefix in the designation of a guided missile, indicates that the missile is a prototype (q.v.) model which is produced in limited numbers for operations tests (e.g., YTM-61).

y_k. Propellant loading ratio (q.v.).

yard. A unit of length.

    1 yard = 91.44018 cm = 3 ft = 36 in. = 0.91440 meter

yaw. (1) An angular displacement about the normal axis of a missile from its prelaunch attitude. Looking forward, clockwise yaw is positive. (2) The movement of a vehicle about its vertical axis; the extent of this movement, measured in degrees.

yaw, angle of. *See* angle of yaw.

yaw damper. A control system (q.v.) or device that reduces the yaw of a vehicle.

yawmeter. An instrument that measures the yaw of a vehicle.

y-axis. (1) The lateral axis in a coordinate system of axes about which a vehicle pitches. (2) The vertical axis in a system of rectangular coordinates on a map, chart, or graph, on which distances above and below, or north and south of a reference line are measured.

year. *Types of, see* anomalistic–; International Geophysical–; light–; man-year; tropical–.

yield factor of safety. The ratio of the yield strength of a structure to the limit load.

yield load. The limit load (q.v.) multiplied by the yield factor of safety.

yield point. The load per unit of original cross section at which (e.g., in soft steel), a marked increase in deformation occurs without increase in load. In other steels and in non-ferrous metals, *yield point* is the stress corresponding to some definite and arbitrary total deformation, a permanent deformation of slope of the stress deformation curve; this is more properly termed the *yield strength* (q.v.).

yield strength. Stress corresponding to some fixed permanent deformation such as 0.1% or 0.2% offset from the modulus slope. *See* offset yield strength.

yield strength load factor. The load factor (q.v.) which will cause the yield strength (q.v.) to be reached.

yield, warhead. *See* warhead yield.

yogi. In electronics, a code or popular name for a type of endfire antenna array.

Young's modulus. *See* modulus of elasticity.

YQ-1B. Target drone. Air Force cognizance.

Prime contractor: Radioplane.

Yukawa kernel. *See* diffusion kernel.

Z

Z. In communications practice, the symbol used to designate Greenwich mean time (GMT) (q.v.). *See also* zebra time.

z-axis. The vertical axis in a coordinate system of axes about which a vehicle yaws.

zebra time. Time measured from Greenwich mean time (q.v.). The hour 2400 zebra time is 1900 EST, 1800 CST, 1700 MST, 1600 PST, 1400 Hawaiian standard time, 1000 Sydney standard time, 0900 Tokyo standard time, 0800 Manila standard time, 0300 Moscow standard time, 0100 Berlin standard time. It is used in communications and for synchronized reckonings.

Zener voltage. (1) The field required to excite the Zener current, of the order of 1 volt per unit cell or 10^7 volts/cm. (2) The voltage associated with that portion of the reverse volt-ampere characteristic of a semiconductor wherein the voltage remains substantially constant over an appreciable range of current values.

zenith. The point in the celestial sphere (q.v.) directly overhead.

zenith distance. In celestial navigation, the shorter angular distance of a celestial body from the zenith (q.v.) measured along the vertical circle that passes through the body. Also termed *co-altitude*. This is equivalent to the angular distance between the observer and the subpoint of the body, and may be expressed in nautical miles (q.v.). When so expressed, it is not called co-altitude.

zenith-nadir axis. A line connecting the zenith and nadir (q.q.v.) of an observer.

zero. *Types of, see* absolute–; ceiling–; ground–; recommended ground–.

zero azimuth. (1) The azimuth (q.v.) of an object lying along a grid north, magnetic north, or true north line (q.q.v.). (2) The direction ahead of a vehicle, along the line of flight.

zero beat. The condition in which a given circuit is oscillating at the exact frequency of an external radio wave so that no beat tone is produced or heard when the combined waves are demodulated.

zero ceiling. The term applied when the ceiling is at, or near, the ground. Also termed *ceiling zero*.

zero gravity. *See* weightlessness.

zero hour. The hour or time at which something is scheduled to be done or at which something takes place.

zero-length launcher. A launcher which supports a missile in the desired attitude prior to motion, but which exercises negligible control on the direction of the missile's travel after first motion.

zero-length launching. A technique in which first motion of the missile removes it from the launcher (q.v.). A zero-length launcher (q.v.) orients the missile initially but has no significant effect on the missile flight path.

zero-lift angle of attack. An angle of attack (q.v.) of an airfoil at which it delivers no lift.

zero-lift drag. The total drag (q.v.) upon a missile experiencing no lift; the integral of all axial components of forces acting on the outside of a body with attached flow conditions at the lip of the inlet, or of a cylindrical body. The forces are caused by viscous phenomena (skin friction) only.

zero-lift trajectory. A trajectory in which the control system (q.v.) acts to maintain a condition of no aerodynamic lift on a missile.

zero reader. A gyroscopic instrument that combines the functions of gyro horizon, directional gyro, magnetic compass, sensitive altimeter, and cross-pointer indicator.

zero'th law of thermodynamics. The principle that, when two bodies are in thermal equilibrium, no heat flows from one to the other and both are at the same temperature.

zero velocity error servo. *See* servo order.

zero visibility. Visibility on the ground considered limited to a few feet.

zero-zero weather. Weather conditions in which the ceiling and visibility are nil.

Zeta 58. International Geophysical Year (IGY) designation for the ATLAS satellite (q.v.). *See also* Table 6, page 245.

Z.I. Zone of Interior (q.v.).

zip fuels. (1) A popular term for high-energy fuels (q.v.). (2) An Air Force project (formerly BuAer) with the objective of developing high-performance, non-hydrocarbon fuels (e.g., boron compound based fuels).

Z marker beacon. Zone marker beacon. A transmitter installed at certain radio-range stations to aid in identifying the cone of silence directly above the station. Also termed *cone marker beacon*.

Zn. True azimuth (q.v.). Also written Z_n.

Z_o. Characteristic impedance (q.v.).

zodiac. The belt in the sky through which the planets appear to move as viewed from the Earth. It extends 8° on each side of the ecliptic.

zodiacal band. Faintly luminous band of light appearing on the celestial sphere (q.v.), connecting the zodiacal light with the gegenschein (q.v.). It is caused by an extension of the solar corona out and beyond the Earth. It could indicate the presence of interplanetary matter in space which might be hazardous to space vehicles moving in the plane of the ecliptic (q.v.).

zodiacal light. "Wings" of hazy light extending on either side of the Sun approximately in the plane of the ecliptic (q.v.). Only visible after sunset or before sunrise, it is believed to be part of the outer atmosphere of the Sun.

zone. *Types of, see* equiphase–; equisignal–; intertropical convergence–; skip–; twilight–.

zone of interior (Z.I.). (1) That part of a national territory held intact against the enemy, in which the main manpower, weapons, and equipment are generated for use of the armed forces. (2) By inference, the continental United States.

zoomar. *See* variable focus lens.

z-score. A sigma score (q.v.).

Z-score. A standard score that has been modified.

ZUNI. Air-to-air and air-to-surface rocket. Navy cognizance.

Length: just under 10 ft; speed: MACH 3; weight: 107 lb; diameter: 5 in. Used on naval fighter aircraft under the wings. Fired in maximum salvo of 24 to a plane.